YEARBOOK OF SCIENCE
AND THE FUTURE
2000

YEARBOOK OF SCIENCE AND THE FUTURE
2000

Encyclopædia Britannica, Inc.

Chicago • London • New Delhi • Paris • Rome • Seoul • Sydney • Taiwan • Tokyo

2000
YEARBOOK OF SCIENCE AND THE FUTURE

Editor
Charles Cegielski

Associate Editor
Dan Blaustein

Assistant Editor
Sherman Hollar

Contributing Editors
David Calhoun,
Melinda C. Shepherd,
Karen Sparks

Guest Editor,
Millennium Section
Edward Tenner

Product Operations
Barbra A. Vogel

Creative Director, Art
Bob Ciano

Art Staff
Kimberly L. Cleary,
Ethan Persoff, Carla M.
Whittington

Coordinator, Composition
Danette Wetterer

Composition Staff
Carol A. Gaines

Cartography
John E. Nelson

Cartography Staff
Amelia Gintautas,
David A.R. Herubin

Manager, Production Control
Mary C. Srodon

Senior Coordinator,
Production Control
Marilyn L. Barton

Director, Manufacturing
Dennis M. Flaherty

Librarian
Shanta Uddin

Assistant Librarian
Robert Lewis

Curator, Geography
Kenneth Leivers

Administrative Staff
Heather Blackmore,
Julie Stevens

Publishing Technology Group
Steven Bosco, Ray
Goldberger, Jeff Hostetler,
Vincent Star, Bruce Walters,
Mark Wiechec

FOREWORD: 2000.*

When does the third millennium begin?

If we choose to believe the countdown clocks that seem to be flashing their digital message everywhere these days—or the throngs of people making various plans to celebrate, pray, hide, or wait for the mother ship—the new millennium will commence the first instant of the year 2000. If we are precisionists, however, we will be trying (likely to no avail) to convince our less mathematically concerned friends that, because the first year of the first millennium is AD 1, a full 2,000 years will not have passed until the first instant of 2001. Now, wait a minute, some of us ultraprecisionists may say. The beginning of the first millennium traditionally marks the birth of Jesus Christ. If we accept the prevailing scholarly view that the historical Jesus was born around 6–4 BC—certainly no later than 1 BC—then we must conclude that the third millennium has already begun.

We have become accustomed to believe that the end of 100 or 1,000 years—both nice round numbers—denotes a particularly proper time to reflect on the past and the future, to assess the road we have traveled and to imagine where we might be going next. Nevertheless, if we cannot even agree on when to start or stop counting, when do we start reflecting? How can we know when that "proper time" has arrived?

The answer, at least for the present and past editors of Encyclopædia Britannica's *Yearbook of Science and the Future,* is that it hardly matters. The time is always appropriate for thinking about the ways that science has affected our history and about the possible futures toward which our technological accomplishments might point us. For more than three decades the yearbook has pursued this approach. Since 1969 it has featured major articles on topics ranging from the unrivaled construction methods of the ancient Greeks and Romans and the practice of science in colonial America to our boldest proposals for building ocean-crossing mass-transit systems and our most ambitious plans to colonize the solar system and reach the stars.

This, the year 2000 edition—the yearbook's 32nd—is not unusual in that respect. One feature, for example, recounts the history of our ideas to build a permanent orbital habitat, using it as a prelude to a detailed discussion of tomorrow's reality, the International Space Station. This half-century-old dream at last has begun to take form above Earth and promises to dominate human activity in space for decades to come. Past and future are also represented, respectively, in an authoritative photo essay that reveals exactly what awed the earliest microscopists as they peered at the natural world with their single-lensed instruments and in an account of the ways that navigation satellites will become our indispensable aids in the 21st century. As always, in addition to the yearbook's in-depth features, the significant events and achievements of our more immediate history are comprehensively reported in dozens of illustrated annual review articles written by experts in their respective fields.

Nevertheless, in this edition the editors also have included something quite different—a special millennium-inspired collection of speculative essays prepared with the advice and editorial help of writer and scholar Edward Tenner, who has also contributed the collection's keynote piece. During his work with the yearbook's editors, Mr. Tenner used the expression *2000.** as a metaphor for the guiding philosophy of the project. Those familiar with search functions on a computer know that an asterisk symbol in a search request represents one or more "wild card" characters, a place in the request where literally "anything goes." In Mr. Tenner's metaphor, we would be wise not to expect the world beyond the second millennium to bow to the opinions of the assembled authorities who think they know what will happen. On the contrary, as history has demonstrated, the future will deal us a few wild cards of its own—unforeseen developments in science and technology and equally unforeseen ways that we will choose to apply them. Thus, our contributors to the special section were encouraged to consider the unlikely, the heretical, and the novel as well as the consensus scenarios in imagining our technological future and its cultural correlates. The result, the editors believe, is a unique body of speculation that sidesteps a common pitfall of this genre of writing.

On behalf of everyone who has been involved with the production of this volume, I express our hope that you discover the year 2000 edition of the yearbook to be exceptionally informative, provocative, and entertaining. Please feel free to share, by mail or in electronic form, your impressions. Our E-mail address is <yearbook@eb.com>.

Finally, although it will be premature for some and belated for others, a happy and healthy third millennium to all.

—Charles Cegielski, Editor

41

404

214

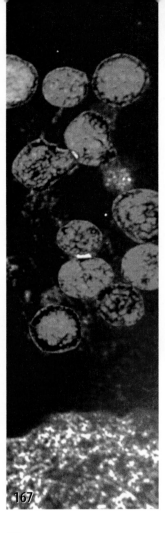

167

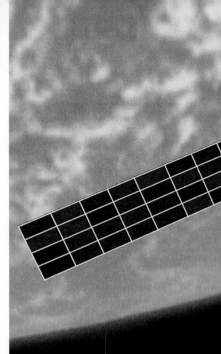

Today the celestial objects that are guiding people from place to place are artificial stars— sophisticated navigation satellites that, under the right conditions, can pinpoint any location on Earth within millimeters.

CONTENTS

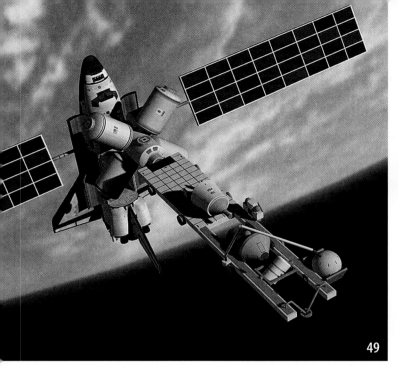

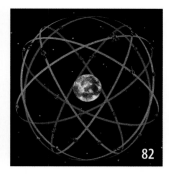

century economist Irving Fisher nonetheless made a fatally wrong assumption and a consequent prediction from which his reputation never recovered. In examining the life and times of Fisher, writer and lecturer Edward Tenner shows how various assumptions can hobble our capacity to imagine the future and suggests ways for us to recognize and question them.

More than a millennium ago, the ancient Maya were a flourishing culture in the rain forests of Mesoamerica. Then, within 100 years, much of their society mysteriously collapsed. Today, archaeologists are using new tools and developing new theories to understand what happened.

Unlocking the Mysteries of the Maya

by Michael Woods

Hidden by jungle for hundreds of years, the great cities of the Maya are being reclaimed. The archaeologists shown at left are planning to excavate a residential structure at La Milpa.

Mention an expedition to a "lost kingdom" in the Central American rain forest, and people often visualize archaeologists excavating treasure-laden tombs and ornate temples where colorfully dressed priests once celebrated bloody ceremonies. La Milpa, an ancient Maya city in the lowland rain forests of northern Belize, is just such a place. About 1,200 years ago, at its zenith, La Milpa was a booming metropolis with elaborate temples, palaces, open plazas, ball courts, roadways, a 24-meter (80-foot)-tall Great Pyramid, and a population in the tens of thousands. On market days and at festivals, thousands gathered to shop, trade, worship, and celebrate in La Milpa's Great Plaza, one of the largest public spaces ever built by the Maya.

Michael Woods is Science Editor in the Washington Bureau for the Toledo *(Ohio)* Blade *and the* Pittsburgh *(Pennsylvania)* Post Gazette. *He has made several trips into the rain forest to view ancient Maya ruins.*

Today, however, La Milpa is a city in jungle-clad ruins. The once majestic buildings are collapsed and crumbling and entirely overgrown with gumbo-limbo, palm trees, and other tropical vegetation. Roots of the strangler fig entwine ancient ceibas, the sacred trees of the Maya, while troops of spider monkeys patrol the dense forest canopy overhead, screeching at tourists, archaeologists, and other visitors. La Milpa today is quite literally a lost kingdom. What happened to the people who built and inhabited this ancient metropolis?

Archaeologists have long known that the ancient Maya endured for more than 2,000 years, from before the time of Christ until the Spanish conquest of Mexico in the early 16th century. Without the advantage of metal tools, beasts of burden, or even the wheel, these Stone Age people managed to carve magnificent cities out of the rain forest. The Maya perfected the most advanced writing system in pre-Columbian America, mastered mathematical concepts before their European counterparts, kept a calendar more accurate than the Gregorian calendar, and made highly precise astronomical observations. They were accomplished artists and skilled craftspeople, and they followed a religion that included more than 160 gods and goddesses. Then, around AD 900, this successful culture began to collapse. Construction of buildings and monuments slowed, existing structures fell

into disrepair, and entire cities were depopulated. The elaborate civilization of the Maya was in the midst of coming apart at the seams.

Questions about the collapse of the Maya empire have interested scientists ever since the early 19th century, when traveler John Lloyd Stephens hacked his way through the Honduran jungle and announced his discovery of the ruined city of Copán. The mysterious hieroglyphics—the writing system of the Maya—and spectacular architecture found at Copán sparked enormous interest among archaeologists worldwide, who subsequently spent their time excavating the palaces, temples, pyramids, and monuments in the largest ancient Maya cities. Today, however, scientists are taking a much different tack in fathoming the mysteries of the Maya. Realizing that the old approach might have presented a somewhat biased picture of these ancient peoples, archaeologists are no longer focusing solely on the obvious structures in the major Maya settlements. Instead, efforts are now being directed toward remains that earlier researchers might have dismissed as unimportant, including humble dwellings of ordinary people like farmers and laborers who made up much of the population.

The ancient Maya developed a sophisticated artistic tradition, producing painted murals and ceramics, clay figurines, and sculpted stone monuments, or stelae. Stela H from the site of Copán in Honduras (left), dated to AD 782, depicts "18-Rabbit," the 13th ruler of Copán, who transformed the ancient city into one of the Maya's most cosmopolitan centers.

"Imagine archaeologists a thousand years from now trying to develop a true portrait of 20th-century American civilization by excavating the remains of high-rise office buildings in downtown New York, Los Angeles, Chicago," said archaeologist Fred Valdez of the University of Texas at Austin, commenting on the old approach. To Valdez and many other modern scientists, the work of the early archaeologists was much too limited. In an attempt to paint a more accurate portrait, modern archaeologists are paying closer attention to the subtle, perhaps less spectacular, aspects of ancient Maya civilization. At a site near La Milpa in the Belizean rain forest, for instance, archaeologists Vernon L. Scarborough and Nicholas P. Dunning of the University of Cincinnati, Ohio, have been studying relationships between the use of critical natural resources like land and water and the development of the Maya socioeconomic system over time. The scientists hypothesize that in an agricultural society like the Maya, which faced a long dry season each year, water-control and agricultural technology must have been critical for survival. This kind of research exemplifies the new archaeology. By studying how the Maya utilized natural resources, archaeologists may be able to say with more certainty how and why this empire so suddenly and mysteriously collapsed.

Hundreds of other scientists, working at scores of sites, are also involved in the effort at a deeper, broader, and more accurate understanding of the Maya. They are using new methods for mapping and excavating Maya ruins; new research tools, such as sophisticated airborne and space-based remote-sensing devices, which can spot ancient ruins through dense jungle undergrowth; and new strategies for deciphering the Mayan hieroglyphics system. The reorientation and refocusing of Maya research have kindled a revolution in the scientific understanding of who the Maya were, how they lived, and why the center of their world collapsed after many centuries of successful adaptation. Far from being knowledge for the sake of knowledge, the findings may hold timely lessons for people today, according to some researchers. "There are secrets of the ancient Maya that may be important for modern society," said Peter S. Dunham of Cleveland (Ohio) State University, who has studied the extraction and processing of commercially important mineral resources in the ancient Maya world, including hematite for pigments, granite for grinding stones, and pyrite for mirrors. "Something went wrong in the social and economic structure of their civilization," Dunham said. "By learning from their mistakes, their history, we might avoid repeating it."

Modern archaeologists, such as those shown below working among ruins at the site of Xunantunich in Belize, are using new techniques and research tools for mapping and excavating Maya city-centers.

Chris Sharp/South American Pictures

The volcanoes Atitlán and Tolimán rise above Lake Atitlán in the Guatemalan highlands (left). The mountainous and thickly forested highlands of present-day Guatemala made up only one portion of the ancient Maya's landscape. Much flatter terrain and drought-tolerant vegetation characterized the central and northern parts of the Yucatán Peninsula, whereas the southern lowlands were covered by dense rain forest.

A GLIMPSE OF THE ANCIENT MAYA WORLD

At its peak the Maya civilization encompassed a region of roughly 310,000 square kilometers (120,000 square miles) that spread through what are now Guatemala, Belize, El Salvador, Honduras, and the five Mexican states of Yucatán, Quintana Roo, Tabasco, Campeche, and Chiapas. The topography of the area varies greatly, from volcanic mountains and thick forests making up the highlands to the south, to the much flatter landscape known as the lowlands in the central and northern regions of the Yucatán Peninsula. The southern lowlands, as they were at the time of the Maya, are covered by a dense rain forest that is sporadically interrupted by swamps and savannas, while the northern lowlands are drier and mainly covered with scrub vegetation and small thorny trees.

The climate is as varied as the landscape. In general it is hot and humid, as the area lies within the tropics about 2,000 kilometers (1,240 miles) north of the Equator. The rainy season lasts from May to December, with a relative humidity above 80% for the entire Maya area. January to April is the dry season, characterized by air that is intensely hot and uncomfortable,

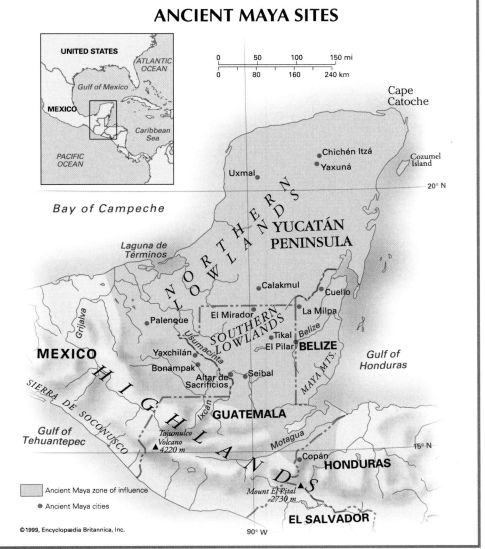

ANCIENT MAYA SITES

UNITED STATES

ATLANTIC OCEAN

Gulf of Mexico

MEXICO

Caribbean Sea

PACIFIC OCEAN

0   50   100   150 mi
0   80   160   240 km

Cape Catoche

Chichén Itzá

Yaxuná

Cozumel Island

Uxmal

20° N

Bay of Campeche

NORTHERN LOWLANDS

YUCATÁN PENINSULA

Laguna de Términos

Calakmul

Cuello

Grijalva

Palenque

El Mirador

La Milpa

SOUTHERN LOWLANDS

Usumacinta

Tikal

Belize

El Pilar

BELIZE

MEXICO

Yaxchilán

Bonampak

Altar de Sacrificios

Seibal

MAYA MTS.

Gulf of Honduras

Pasión

GUATEMALA

SIERRA DE SOCONUSCO

Gulf of Tehuantepec

Tajumulco Volcano 4220 m

HIGHLANDS

Motagua

15° N

Copán

HONDURAS

Ancient Maya zone of influence

Ancient Maya cities

Mount El Pital 2730 m

EL SALVADOR

© 1999, Encyclopædia Britannica, Inc.

90° W

particularly in the lowlands. Rainfall in the Yucatán region is strongly influenced by the presence of mountains near the Pacific coast, which create significant differences in rainfall amounts across the region. Northern Yucatán is the hottest and driest area, where the absence of mountains to intercept moisture-bearing clouds from the Atlantic gives it limited rainfall.

Archaeologists believe that the people now known as the ancient Maya first migrated into the region around 2600 BC, where they gathered foods from the forest and hunted for small game such as peccary, rabbit, monkey, and tapir. Around 2000 BC, at the start of what archaeologists refer to as the Pre-Classic Period (2000 BC–AD 250), the Maya abandoned their hunter-gatherer existence and began to form small farming hamlets in the lowland rain forests of the southern Yucatán Peninsula. They raised maize (corn), beans, and other crops, and as those first farming villages expanded, Maya society evolved. They began to develop new agricultural techniques to help feed their growing populations, and they adopted royal rule as the mechanism for governing their expanding cities. By the late Pre-Classic Period, they had built magnificent cities

Maya Civilization Chronology	
Early Pre-Classic	2000 BC – 1000 BC
Middle Pre-Classic	1000 BC – 300 BC
Late Pre-Classic	300 BC – AD 250
Early Classic	AD 250 – AD 600
Late Classic	AD 600 – AD 900
Post-Classic	AD 900 – AD 1521

such as Tikal and El Pilar in the southern lowlands. The Classic Period (AD 250–900) was the height of ancient Maya civilization with the biggest cities, most elaborate architecture, and peak population. After 900, in the Post-Classic Period, the death knell began to sound for the lowland Maya civilizations. The majority of the large cities and capitals of the southern region suddenly collapsed. Some Maya cities in the Yucatán to the north, however, continued to flourish to about 1250. Eventually those cities, too, were abandoned, and by the end of the Post-Classic, around 1520, more than a dozen rival rulers were competing for control of the Yucatán.

EARLY DISCOVERIES

The modern world's view of the ancient Maya began to form in the early 16th century when Hernán Cortés began his conquest of the Aztec empire in Mexico. After capturing the Aztec capital of Tenochtitlán in 1521, the Spanish gradually subdued Maya settlements in the Yucatán Peninsula and other areas. Missionaries followed the conquistadors, including Diego de Landa, a Spanish priest who visited some of the demolished cities and questioned the Maya about their history, customs, and religious practices. De Landa's famous book, *Relación de las cosas de Yucatán* (1556; *On the Things of Yucatán*, 1941), contains the

first published descriptions of temple-pyramids, carved stone monuments, hieroglyphics, and other Maya remains.

Although de Landa provided scholars with important information, he also, ironically, created one of the biggest obstacles to modern understanding of the Maya. De Landa was very sympathetic to the Maya people, but because they practiced human sacrifice as part of their religion he feared that the devil had inspired them. In a reprehensible act, he ordered the burning of hundreds of ancient Maya books, or codices. Only three codices and scraps of a fourth survive to this day. Much of current scientific knowledge about the Maya calendar, timekeeping methods, and astronomy has come from these books.

Among the first modern Westerners to explore and document the ancient Maya world were American traveler John Lloyd Stephens and British artist Frederick Catherwood who, between 1839 and 1842, studied the ruins of more than 40 Maya settlements, including Copán in Honduras and Palenque, Chichén Itzá, and Uxmal in Mexico. They published two books, *Incidents of Travel in Central America, Chiapas, and Yucatán* (1841) and *Incidents of Travel in Yucatán* (1843), both of which

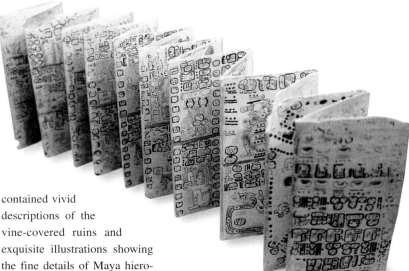

Photri

In their eagerness to Christianize the New World, Spanish missionaries destroyed almost all of the Maya's books, or codices. The Dresden codex (left), today housed in Dresden, Germany, is one of four survivors. The codices, which contain information about Maya mathematics, astronomy, and medicine, are made from tree bark that has been flattened, covered with a lime paste, and folded accordion-style.

contained vivid descriptions of the vine-covered ruins and exquisite illustrations showing the fine details of Maya hieroglyphics and architecture. The books were enormously popular and they interested many others in the mysterious Maya culture. Over the next half century, archaeologists discovered, among other things, a copy of de Landa's book, which had been lost to the world for 300 years; copies of the three ancient codices that escaped de Landa's fires; and the *Popol Vuh,* the sacred text of the Maya that describes the creation of human beings, the journeys of mythological heroes, and the spiritual worlds of the Maya gods.

Without the advantage of modern dating techniques and other archaeological tools, however, speculation among scholars and laypersons about who the Maya were and where they came from tended to run rampant. Some people argued that the Maya were survivors of a disaster that supposedly destroyed the mythical lost continent of Atlantis. Others, noting

An engraving from one of the beautifully illustrated 19th-century books by John Lloyd Stephens and Frederick Catherwood shows Stela D and its altar from the site of Copán.

Drawing by Frederick Catherwood/South American Pictures

some similarities between the pyramids, suggested that the Maya were descendants of ancient Egyptians who brought their wisdom and technology to the New World.

THE TRADITIONAL VIEW

By the 1880s archaeology as a science was becoming much more serious. Rather than indulge in fanciful interpretation, scientists were more concerned with discovery and careful description. Led by British archaeologist Alfred Perceval Maudslay, they were now taking photographs, making plaster casts of sculptures, and compiling comprehensive catalogs of Maya buildings, monuments, and hieroglyphics. Provided with a wealth of data, late-19th- and early-20th-century scholars began studying the collections.

Large-scale excavations of Maya settlements in the 1930s-1950s by J. Eric Thompson and Sylvanus Morley of the Carnegie Institution of Washington, D.C., set the tone for Maya archaeology. Their research projects, like Maudslay's, were very data oriented, designed more to catalog the greatest achievements of the Maya than to answer specific questions about them. The palaces, temples, pyramids, and monuments that dominated the major Maya centers were carefully described, whereas answers to questions about the rise and fall of the Maya were secondary goals. Largely as a

A Maya temple at the site of Hochob in Campeche, Mexico, exemplifies the distinctive Chenes architectural style of the Late Classic Period, characterized by elaborate mosaic facades and doorways framed by intricate monster-mouth masks.

result of their work, many scientists held the view that Maya culture was fundamentally and significantly different from other ancient societies. The Maya were thought of as a mystical people, a population of peaceful, stargazing intellectuals cut off from the world's evils in their pristine rain forest environment.

Morley and Thompson made important contributions to the modern understanding of the Maya, but today many of their ideas have been overturned by new evidence. In his 1990 book *The New Archaeology and the Ancient Maya,* archaeologist Jeremy A. Sabloff of the University of Pennsylvania mounted a challenge to the tra-

ditional view of the Maya, pointing out key errors made by earlier researchers. One of the most widely held beliefs was that, even during the peak of civilization in the Classic Period, the Maya never became a truly urban society. Although they built huge cities, these were only ceremonial centers that were empty much of the time, archaeologists argued. Rulers, priests, scribes, and their attendants were the only permanent city dwellers. Farmers and other peasant workers, who lived in the surrounding villages, only poured into town on market days, festivals, and religious holidays. The peasant farm-

ers, it was believed, built the urban palaces, temples, and other structures and provided priests and rulers with food and other necessities of life. In return the rulers provided authority that kept the society together, while the priests convinced the gods to provide ample rain and good growing conditions for crops.

Another popular misconception about the Maya involved their form of agriculture. Because early archaeologists had found no evidence of irri-

Carved stone hieroglyphs (above) are from the Temple of the Inscriptions at Palenque. In the Maya's mathematics system (right), dots had a value of one, bars had a value of five, and shells had a value of zero. Combinations of bars and dots represented the numbers 1 to 19; numbers above 19 were indicated on the basis of position. The Caracol observatory at Chichén Itzá is shown below. Several of the building's windows fix astronomically important lines of sight; one line of sight through the west wall bisects the setting Sun on March 21, the vernal equinox; other lines coincide with the moonset on this same date.

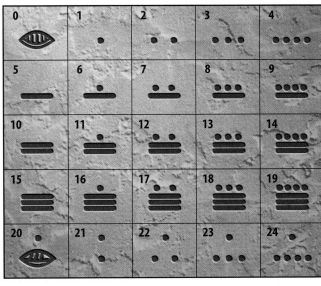

gation or other water-control systems, they assumed that the Maya practiced slash-and-burn agriculture, a type of farming technique still used in the South American rain forests. In the slash-and-burn method, farmers begin working a plot of land by felling trees and allowing them to dry on the ground. The trees are then burned, clearing the field for planting and enriching it with nutrients from the ash. The plots are typically worked for several years until the soil becomes depleted of nutrients, and then new patches of forest are cleared.

Archaeologists also believed that the Maya were a very mystical people. Colossal observatories were built in cities such as Copán and Chichén Itzá, but many scholars thought that Maya priests used them only for spotting good and bad omens in the sky and for setting dates for the planting and harvesting of crops. Whereas the Maya recorded astronomical observations and mathematical calculations on paper and stone using an ornate system of hieroglyphics, scholars thought that the content of the Maya records was somehow different from the writings of ancient Egypt and other Old World civilizations. According to many scientists, the Maya never kept records of financial transactions, wrote about contemporary or historical events, or celebrated the lives or deeds of great rulers or heroes. Rather, most archaeologists believed that the glyphs represented nothing more than religious inscriptions or astrological information.

The traditional model also depicted the Maya as a peaceloving people who lived in harmony with one another. According to many workers, the Maya somehow escaped the tendency, common throughout the ancient world, to engage in civil conflicts and in wars with neighboring settlements. Warfare, it was argued, had nothing to do with the eventual demise of the lowland Maya cities around AD 900. Many scientists began favoring single-cause theories for the collapse of the Maya empire, including epidemic diseases and environmental devastation by earthquakes, climatic change, or hurricanes. There was fierce debate over each, and no agreement ever seemed possible.

NEW TECHNIQUES, NEW IDEAS

Beginning in the 1970s new ideas about ancient Maya civilization began to surface. Some of them came, in part, from the

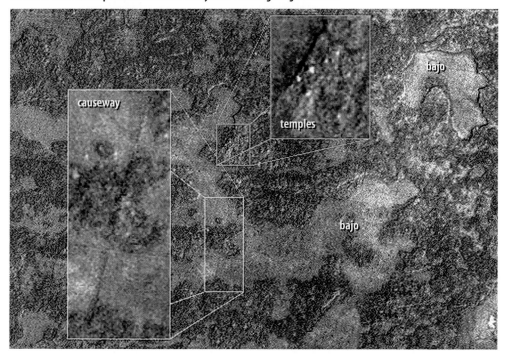

This Thematic Mapper image taken by an orbiting Landsat satellite reveals archaeological structures previously shrouded beneath the forest canopy. The white spots represent Maya temples at the site of El Mirador in Guatemala, while the dark lines represent ancient causeways and natural geologic features.

wide use of new archaeological tools that were becoming available to scientists. Side-looking airborne radar (SLAR) technology, for example, which is employed by the military to obtain high-resolution images of ground activities during periods of darkness or cloud cover, was now being used to detect canals, agricultural fields, dwellings, and other surface features that lay hidden under thick jungle vegetation. Improved aerial photography techniques and images from or-

biting Earth-resources satellites also enabled researchers to spot things that were invisible to earlier workers.

The new imaging techniques were especially valuable to archaeologists studying settlement patterns. In the past archaeologists only mapped the big structures in the central area of a site, which were regarded as the most important features. The surrounding areas, where much of the population must have lived, were typically ignored because workers were

unable to detect any obvious stone structures. Equipped with new imaging tools, archaeologists for the first time were able to map, excavate, and analyze all of the components of an ancient settlement, including the ruins of peasant dwellings, roads, dams, reservoirs, agricultural fields, and other structures. The lives of the common people, who were the backbone of ancient Maya society, were now getting much more attention.

Settlement pattern research conducted by the University of

Pennsylvania between the 1950s and the 1970s at the ancient site of Tikal was also important in the new model of the Maya. Located in northern Guatemala, Tikal is often regarded as the largest and most important ancient Maya center. Maps reveal more than 3,000 separate constructions. Tikal provided clear evidence that Maya cities were not empty ceremonial centers occupied only by rulers, nobles, and stargazing priests. They were true cities. Mapping and excavating an area of 16 square kilometers (6 square miles) surrounding the central core of Tikal, archaeologists discovered the remains of thousands of wood and thatch dwellings that had apparently been occupied for centuries. Based on this and other evidence, it has been estimated that Tikal's peak population during the Classic Period could have been as high as 50,000 people.

Research at Tikal also helped dispel the notion that ancient Maya society was a simple two-class system. Some dwellings at Tikal, for example, were single-room huts probably occupied by poor peasant farmers. Other residences consisted of several rooms, including a kitchen, that may have been occupied for generations by the same family groups. Artifacts found near some of these dwellings suggested that the inhabitants were skilled craftspeople engaged in the manufacture of stone tools, pottery, jewelry, and other products. Maya society was apparently far more complex than previously believed.

Tikal (top), the largest Maya site, has been subjected to the most comprehensive archaeological investigation of any site to date. At its peak Tikal was a bustling city with temples, palaces, shrines, residences, ball courts, terraces, causeways, and plazas. Huge reservoirs for storing rainwater are evident in the scale model of Tikal (bottom). There were no natural springs, cenotes (naturally occurring wells), or rivers near Tikal. Maya engineers designed the city's plazas to tilt slightly so that rainwater collected in a plaza would drain directly into a reservoir. One such plaza at Tikal tilts about 5°, hardly noticeable when standing in the plaza, but effective nonetheless.

The Maya had an advanced culture, but also a brutal one. Their cities engaged in constant battle with one another—sometimes for the sole purpose of gaining sacrificial victims. At the site of Bonampak, colorful murals depicting warfare and sacrifice (opposite page) cover the three vaulted chambers of a single small building. One painting shows the taking of captives and their "judgment" before their captors. A sculpture from the nearby site of Yaxchilan (below) depicts a ritualistic bloodletting ceremony.

A REVISED IMAGE EMERGES

The new conception of Tikal and other ancient Maya centers as densely populated cities forced archaeologists to reexamine other key elements in the traditional model, in particular the Maya's system of agriculture. Tikal's population density, it was calculated, may have exceeded 600 people per square kilometer (1,550 per square mile). Research had shown, however, that slash-and-burn farming could not have sustained a population of this size. It was becoming clear to many archaeologists that the Maya must have used more advanced agricultural production techniques.

Again, remote-sensing technology provided an answer. Using satellite images, SLAR, and other techniques archaeologists were able to identify irrigation canals and rectangular raised-bed fields at La Milpa and other cities, hinting that the Maya used a more intensive form of agriculture. Raised-bed agriculture, familiar to many backyard gardeners, involves piling rich soil into mounds that rise above ground level. Evidence indicates that the beds were arranged in a checkerboard pattern with irrigation ditches running between them, assuring adequate water

supply to the roots. In ancient times the Maya may have used nutrient-rich muck scooped from swamps or the bottoms of irrigation canals to enhance the fertility of their soil.

That the Maya made use of water-management technology to supply water to themselves and their crops is understandable when one considers the extreme climate of the area in which they lived. The lush forests of Central America are often, and mistakenly, thought to be wet year-round. In reality, 90% of annual precipitation in the southern Maya lowlands falls during the eight-month rainy season. Droughtlike conditions typically prevail from January to April and sometimes beyond. With little precipitation and few permanent streams and springs, how did the ancient Maya supply water for tens of thousands of city residents and crop fields during the dry season?

Evidence from the ruins at Tikal, La Milpa, and other major settlements suggests that the Maya were great hydraulic engineers. It is now clear that they built huge water reservoirs

to help sustain themselves through dry spells. In 1991 scientists discovered six large reservoirs in and around the central portion of Tikal, each with a volume great enough to cover a football field meters deep in water. Smaller reservoirs, some constructed by modifying natural swampy depressions in the ground, were discovered in the residential areas surrounding the city. Archaeologists also believe that open, paved areas such as the plazas at Tikal and La Milpa were specifically designed to allow gravity to divert rainwater into the reservoirs. Some scientists, including Valdez, believe that discoveries of this kind have potential implications for modern residents of the area, many of whom are farmers that have

great difficulty growing enough food. "Reintroducing raised-bed agriculture and other ancient Maya approaches to boost productivity may be possible," he said. Preliminary experiments recreating ancient Maya farming on a small scale have shown promise.

Perhaps the most dramatic difference between early and modern views of the Maya is the new emphasis on warfare and violence. Experts no longer view the Maya as a culture of gentle priests and nobles. Numerous examples of Maya iconography—their murals, stone carvings, vase paintings, and the like—show that torture and human sacrifice existed in many aspects of their culture, from religious celebrations to sporting events.

(Opposite page) Robert & Linda Mitchell/Robert & Linda Mitchell Photography;
(below) D. Donne Bryant/D. D. Bryant Stock Photo; (bottom) Robert Frerck/Odyssey Productions

Many artifacts indicate that the Maya tortured captives taken in battle, and that priests and rulers engaged in blood-spilling rituals to appease their gods, including horrible forms of self-mutilation such as piercing the penis and tongue with thorns and sharp rods. One beautiful, full-color mural at the Mexican site of Bonampak in the western lowlands, for instance, portrays captives cowering before a powerful-looking ruler dressed in a jaguar skin. One of the captives has been decapitated, and the others appear to be awaiting similar fates. In addition, Maya ball games, in which players attempted to throw a rubber ball through a wall-mounted hoop, were not sporting events

in the modern sense. Some archaeologists, including Linda Schele of the University of Texas at Austin, have argued that the ball games were in reality ceremonial reenactments of past battles won. Often the losing players were decapitated. Other times they were tortured or rolled into human spheres and pushed down the steps of a towering pyramid.

21

Most researchers also now agree that warfare between neighboring cities was common and played a key role in Maya civilization. Schele, through pioneering deciphering work at Palenque, was able to show that Maya hieroglyphics provided detailed accounts of actual historical events, such as wars between cities, the taking and sacrificing of captives, and military alliances between kingdoms. Aerial photographs and excavations have also confirmed that some Maya cities were surrounded by high walls, parapets, and ditches that may have been fortifications. More recently, in 1996, archaeologists working at the site of Yaxuná in northern Yucatán discovered a sealed royal tomb containing the skeletal remains of a royal family who may have been sacrificed when their kingdom was overthrown by neighboring Chichén Itzá.

Many carved monuments, clay figurines, and murals also depict Maya warfare. In the past such scenes were dismissed as recordings of isolated raids or other rare instances of conflict in the Maya's otherwise peaceful existence. It is not entirely clear to archaeologists why bloody conflict between cities was so common, but many suggest that Maya wars were religious in nature. Other scientists have argued that competition for scarce natural resources, such as water and arable land, was an influential factor. Conflict over trade routes may have also played a role, as it did in Old World civilizations.

THE COLLAPSE

Sabloff has argued that the collapse of Maya civilization represents a special case in archaeology. Many civilizations, he points out, have collapsed throughout history, but almost invariably new civilizations spring up in the ashes of the old. The lowland Maya civilizations, however, never recovered. Even today the few people who do live in the region are mostly poor farmers, laborers, and craftspeople. The collapse of the Maya empire remains a mystery, but most archaeologists today reject the

A funerary urn depicts a Maya warrior. Basic questions remain about why the Maya went to war. For instance, were sacrifices the chief reason, or were these only the ceremonial trappings of campaigns mounted to gain territory?

single-cause theories proposed by their predecessors. Many factors probably contributed to the collapse of cities in the southern lowlands. Uncontrolled warfare was probably a main one. Evidence indicates that warfare became much more common in the late Classic Period as cities engaged in intense competition for water supplies, food, and other resources to supply growing populations. In earlier wars the victors took and sacrificed captives. In the late Classic Period, however, they began sacrificing defeated soldiers as well. As a result, there may have been a gradual depopulation of peasant farmers and other workers who served both as warriors and as food producers.

Few archaeologists, however, feel that warfare explains it all. Water shortages, overpopulation, and environmental degradation, perhaps from soil erosion caused by intensive agricultural production, have also emerged as factors. One inevitable consequence of overpopulation and an unproductive agricultural system is malnutrition and, in fact, scientists have documented evidence of undernourishment in skeletal remains found at several Pre-Classic and Classic Maya sites, including Altar de Sacrificios and Seibal in the Guatemalan highlands, Cuello

in Belize, as well as La Milpa. "These conditions might have served to sap the strength of the Maya, both as individuals and as a population," explained physical anthropologists Frank

Michael Woods

Analyses of skeletal remains are helping archaeologists learn about the health of the Maya population at the time of the collapse. Evidence of malnutrition and disease may be a sign that Maya cities were overpopulated.

and Julie Saul of the Medical College of Ohio in Toledo. "Their weakened state may have made them more susceptible to infectious diseases."

Evidence also indicates that the Maya peasant population as a whole may have been overworked and undermanned. Studies have shown that some Maya rulers ordered an increase in pyramid building during the late Classic Period, perhaps in an effort to gain

the good favor of their gods in overcoming enemies and food shortages. The formidable work of cutting limestone from quarries, hauling it to construction sites, and the building process itself took workers away from agriculture. With an increasing amount of warfare and a faltering food supply, almost any unusual event, such as a single crop failure due to bad weather, could have pushed Maya civilization over the brink.

Experts agree that the issue is far from settled. Some scientists suggest that the collapse of the Maya should be investigated on a region-by-region basis. While warfare may have been an important factor in the demise of some Maya centers, environmental factors might have been more influential at other sites. Archaeologist Richard Hansen of the University of California, Los Angeles, has also suggested that the failure of some Maya settlements may have been the result of multiple, interrelated factors that were not necessarily duplicated in all locations. Hansen has studied the ruins of El Mirador, a Pre-Classic site located in northwestern Guatemala. There he found clues in remains from plants buried in lake-bottom muds that a prolonged drought followed by catastrophic rains

may have ruined that city's productive agricultural system and eventually caused the collapse of the settlement in AD 150. Hansen suggested in 1995 that the local people may have also contributed to their own environmental problems by cutting down too many trees to make stucco for their buildings. When the heavy rains came, the dried-up, powdery soils were easily eroded and depleted of nutrients. Hansen has argued that the demise of El Mirador was unique and in some ways self-created, but he believes that similar circumstances could have been at work in the later collapse of other Maya settlements.

In the end, it may be that unless scientists excavate every demolished Maya temple, interpret every elaborate monument and mural, and decipher every hieroglyphic inscription, the world may never know the complete story of the mysterious Maya of Central America. As noted archaeologist David Freidel of Southern Methodist University, Dallas, Texas, has pointed out, however, there are lessons the world can derive from Maya history. "Environmental problems were most likely driven by governmental decisions in Maya antiquity, just as they are in our own time," Freidel said. "Parts of the Yucatán Peninsula are being abused now. Rampant overcutting of the forest is destroying the agricultural potential of delicate soils. People are not using the painstaking techniques of the ancient Maya, but it would be a big mistake to ignore it by thinking that the ancient Maya collapsed because they didn't know how to survive in that tropical forest. The Maya lived and prospered in this area for thousands of years. They were an advanced and flourishing society that supported millions of people. We would do best by learning from their successes as well as their mistakes."

THE MODERN MAYA

The Maya people did not disappear with the decline of their ancient civilization. About six

Although subdivided by many related dialects and languages, the modern Maya people (right and below) live in the same land that belonged to their ancestors. Despite political and economic oppression, they have preserved many cultural traditions and have creatively adapted other practices to the modern world.

million Maya still live throughout Central America, representing the single largest group of indigenous people outside Peru. An estimated 1.2 million people live in the southern Mexican state of Chiapas, and nearly 5 million more are spread throughout the Yucatán Peninsula, Honduras, Belize, Guatemala, and El Salvador. Many of these modern peoples live like their ancestors, as small-scale farmers who raise corn, beans, chili, squash, and other foods. Others have taken advantage of the region's ancient heritage by selling fabrics, pottery, jewelry, and other

crafts to the millions of tourists who visit the ancient ruins each year. Yet despite centuries of intermarriage and the pressures of modernization, Maya people today still manage to preserve their own distinctive cultural traditions.

Civil wars, poverty, repressive governments, racial discrimination, and other social injustices, however, pose a threat to the modern Maya. In the 1980s the Maya were the primary victims of the military's antiguerrilla campaign in Guatemala's civil war, which left almost 200,000 people dead or missing. In 1992 Rigoberta Menchú, a Quiche Maya from Guatemala, won the Nobel Prize for Peace for raising public awareness about the situation in Guatemala and other repressive activities against the Maya. Conflict between the Maya and governments in Mexico and other countries continues.

Indiscriminate cutting of the rain forest for timber and agriculture poses another threat to the modern Maya's homelands and their way of life. Deforestation in this region has left the already nutrient-poor

soils exposed to erosion. Some farmers have even contributed to the problem by continuing to embrace ancient agricultural practices, such as slash-and-burn farming. Yet the population of many Maya cultural groups is growing. The Maya people are drawing strength, cohesiveness, and determination to persist by celebrating their civilization's glorious past.

AP/Wide World Photos

In 1992 Rigoberta Menchú was awarded the Nobel Prize for Peace for bringing international attention to the conflict between the indigenous Maya and the military government of Guatemala. Due to her effort, the United Nations declared 1993 the International Year for Indigenous Populations.

FOR ADDITIONAL READING

Ancient Maya Civilization, Norman Hammond (Rutgers University Press, 1982).

"The Earliest Maya," Norman Hammond, *Scientific American* (March 1977, pp. 116–133).

A Forest of Kings: The Untold Story of the Ancient Maya, Linda Schele and David A. Freidel (William Morrow and Co., 1992).

Lost Cities of the Maya, Claude Baudez and Sydney Picasso (Harry N. Abrams, Inc., 1992).

Lost Kingdoms of the Maya, Gene S. Stuart and George E. Stuart (National Geographic Society, 1993).

Maya Civilization, Patrick T. Culbert and Jeremy A. Sabloff (Smithsonian Books, 1995).

The Maya World, Elizabeth P. Benson (Thomas Y. Crowell Co., 1977).

The New Archaeology and the Ancient Maya, Jeremy A. Sabloff (W.H. Freeman and Co., 1990).

The Rise and Fall of Maya Civilization, John Eric Sidney Thompson (University of Oklahoma Press, 1966).

INTERNET RESOURCES

The Maya
http://criscenzo.com/jaguar/maya.html

Maya Adventure
http://www.sci.mus.mn.us/sln/ma/

Maya Civilization
http://www.indians.org/welker/maya

Mystery of the Maya
http://www.civilization.ca/membrs/civiliz/maya/mminteng.html

Scientific misinformation and distortion
abound in the news, the classroom, television
and movie fare, and the body of lore we call
common knowledge. Recognizing instances of
"bad science" can be difficult, but science
itself comes equipped with a highly effective
tool for sharpening our perception.

Bad Science

by Philip Plait

Science has been getting a bad rap lately.

Perhaps that should not be surprising, since science often has been the target of negative criticism. Science has a way of making people look at things in a different manner, and throughout history change has been frowned upon by the establishment. In ancient Greece, for example, arguing that the Sun was actually larger than Greece itself could get a person charged with impiety and ban-ished, as was the philosopher Anaxagoras. In the early 1600s, declaring, as Galileo did, that the Sun had blemishes and that Venus underwent phases like the Moon could get one sentenced by the Roman Catholic Church as a heretic. Not that these were the worst of fates. For saying that stars were just like the Sun, only very far away and possibly circled by planets with life on them, the Italian philosopher and astronomer Giordano Bruno was burned at the stake just a few decades before Galileo was sentenced. Unfortunately, each of those men found himself in trouble for saying things that were actually correct.

Today, most people who challenge the received ideas of

Philip Plait is a professional astronomer who works with the Hubble Space Telescope and is a programmer for Advanced Computer Concepts, Inc., Potomac, Maryland. He also maintains the Bad Astronomy Internet site at <http://www.badastronomy.com>.

In the early 1600s Galileo was made to stand trial by the Roman Catholic Church for challenging the received ideas of the way the universe worked. Science often lets people see things in a different light, and throughout history change has been met with disapproval by the establishment.

the way things work are usually not in imminent danger of death or exile. In fact, there exists a kind of establishment—a group of people who think they know how things work—that actually enjoys being told that it is wrong. Not only do these people appreciate it, but their professional lives depend on it as well. These people are scientists.

Of course, scientists' ultimate goal is to be right, but being wrong is an essential step along the way. When a theory is wrong, those who support it need to rethink it and adjust it to better fit the facts. They then reapply it, noting whether, after the alterations, it predicts things more accurately.

A METHOD FOR THINKING CRITICALLY

The hallmark of a good theory is its predictive power. If a theory cannot correctly predict events, it is modified or dis-

carded. Even if it does make a correct prediction, it might be wrong the next time. It is fundamental to science that theories be tested vigorously. In such a stringent environment, the weak theories die out and the strong survive. Scientific theories also evolve, from primitive to more complex, from being able to make gross conclusions to predicting fine details. A theory must be able to make testable predictions so that scientists can check up on its health. As scientists say, for a theory to be scientific, it must be falsifiable—that is, it must make predictions that might turn out to be wrong. If a theory made no predictions that could be tested, scientists could never be sure if the theory had the correct idea.

In his book *The Demon-Haunted World: Science as a Candle in the Dark* (1995), the American astronomer and science popularizer Carl Sagan

uses an example of someone who says that there is a dragon in his garage. In a sense this statement is a scientific theory because it makes a prediction: if I go into the theorist's garage, I will see the dragon. When I ask to see the dragon, however, the theorist says that the dragon is invisible. I then ask to touch it, to discern its shape and its characteristics. The theorist replies that the dragon is not made of matter and cannot be touched, tasted, heard, or sensed in any manner. Does he have a dragon in his garage or not? He may, but there is no way to know if he is wrong. His theory is no longer scientific; because it cannot be tested in any way, it has no practical value.

Do scientists delight in proving theories to be true? It seems only common knowledge that they do, but in this case—and in other questions of science to be discussed—common knowl-

edge is quite wrong. Scientists can never prove that a theory is true; they can only prove that it is false. At best, they can show that the theory does a good job of explaining and predicting events. Even so, it may be proved false in the future.

Over the centuries this method has been developed into a wonderfully effective tool for learning. It is a scientific method of looking at the world—observe an event, make a theory, use the theory to predict another event, observe again, alter the theory if needed to fit the additional facts, and then start over. This method has the tremendously powerful characteristic of being self-correcting. Theories tend to get better with time, or else they get discarded.

We could greatly benefit from using the scientific method more often in our daily lives. If we applied it in voting for political candidates, for example, we might cast a somewhat more jaundiced eye on political spin. Politicians in some ways resemble theories. They make promises during campaigns that are much like predictions. Does their "prediction" of no new taxes or better schools come about? If not, perhaps it is time to discard the theory. If the promise is kept, what about the next one and the one after that? Product ad-

Some of us are lucky enough to receive our introduction to science and critical thinking from our parents (right). For the majority, however, the first real contacts with science come from school (below) and television.

vertisements, too, make prediction-like promises, depending heavily on consumers' believing them unquestioningly. This shampoo, claim its makers, will make your hair shinier than the competitors' products. Is the product really better, however, or just different? An ad's hyperbole would lose much of its ability to distract if consumers determined whether its predictions fit the facts.

We make numerous important decisions in our lives. We vote, we invest money, and we purchase not only shampoo but also homes, cars, and educations for our children. It is safe to say that many of us fail to think critically about these decisions. We accept a "theory" without knowing whether it is good or bad—whether it will predict events correctly. In other words, we lack a firm idea of the consequences of our choices. Without analyzing what we choose to accept, we are doomed to repeat the same mistakes.

THE GOOD, THE BAD, AND THE BORING

It is particularly ironic that the knowledge on which science itself is based—good information hard-won through the scientific method—is being adulterated by all sorts of bad information purporting to be scientific fact.

Collectively this misinformation might be called "bad science," and like those other bad "theories" encountered in daily life, bad science escapes being recognized and discarded because too few of us have been taught how to think critically, to apply the scientific method as a tool for learning. Accepting bad science unquestioningly only allows it to spread, leading inevitably to a general misunderstanding of science and scientists in the mind of the public. Exploring the ways that the method and knowledge of science can be disregarded or distorted is enlightening, after which it may be easier to understand just how extreme the situation can get and how dire the consequences can be.

Some of us are fortunate enough to receive our first introductions to science and critical thinking in everyday life from our parents. It is not necessary that parents be actual scientists. They need only be interested in providing an environment that fosters a questioning attitude, a love of nature, and a fascination with the way the physical world works. For the majority of us, however, the first real contacts with science

usually come from teachers at school and television in the home.

Too often, science is not taught well in school. Although it is true that some teachers and textbooks perpetuate errors, misconceptions, and outdated information, the much more serious problem is that they rarely teach the scientific method as a tool for learning. Course work in most scientific disciplines is heavy on fact, rote memorization, and the logic of cause and effect, but it usually conveys little of the insights, clever deduction, coincidence, and sheer hard work that go into the process of advancing knowl-

edge. Even laboratory assignments often fail to teach critical thinking, opting instead to lead students by narrow steps through the work—more like painting by numbers than honing drawing skills. This trend is being reversed; many introductory astronomy texts, for example, now include material about individual scientists and stress the important roles of women and minority scientists in research. Nevertheless, many students still take away from their classrooms the idea that science is a dull database of facts rather than an exciting, evolving process of questioning and learning.

TV and movie science fiction abounds with spaceships that swish past the stars and space battles that rumble with the sound of weapons, although sound cannot travel in a vacuum. Also quite common are aliens having distinctly humanoid features, even though creatures that have evolved on other planets would likely look much different.

SCIENCE ON TELEVISION

Even with the best teachers and the most loving and nurturing parents, however, the overwhelming source of information about science is television. TV is, arguably, also the largest font of misleading, poorly explained, or just outrageously wrong science. Furthermore, TV can hardly be accused of teaching us—as children or adults—to think for ourselves and act accordingly. Rather, it tells us to watch, absorb, and believe.

Bad science on TV comes in two main categories: science in fictional contexts such as science-fiction series and movies, and "real" science presented in the news and documentaries. The bad science in TV science fiction—and this applies to theatrical movies as well (*see*

Sidebar: *The Asteroid That Destroyed Science*)—can be quite silly. Spaceships roar or swish across a background of stars, although sound cannot travel through a vacuum, and bank like aircraft when making turns, although there is no air against which to bank. Aliens almost always speak human language and have two arms, two legs, a head with eyes and a mouth, and other humanoid anatomical features, even though patterns of evolution would likely be very different on other planets. Much of these inaccuracies, nevertheless, can be forgiven. Noisy spaceships have been depicted for so long that viewers might find it disconcerting if Star Trek's *Enterprise* sailed past without the familiar rumbling of engines. Extremely "alien" aliens are difficult and expensive propositions for the makeup

and special-effects departments, although modern computer graphics are making it more

common to see truly unearthly beings leaping, rolling, flying, or slithering around the set.

In defense of science-fiction fare on the screen it should be said that, although the science in it can be weak, it does get people, especially children, interested in science. From personal experience I can attest that growing up on a TV diet of "Lost in Space" and black-and-white 1950s monster flicks fed my appetite for rockets and alien worlds, yet they left me wanting more. I read books on real science and watched science documentaries on public television. Through a small, cheap department-store telescope that my father bought for my family, I got my first glimpse of Saturn's rings and became hooked on astronomy forever. Today I do research using the Hubble Space Telescope. The connections seem clear.

Television commercials, many of which are essentially 30-second fictional mini-shows, are another source of science misinformation. Of course, no one expects commercials to be scientifically accurate; usually they exaggerate reality in a cartoonlike manner to make a point. Nevertheless, these images can reinforce inaccuracies that may already exist in the viewer's mind. One of my favorites is a recent chewing gum ad in which a scientist who has waited his entire career for a certain comet to pass Earth is poised to make his once-in-a-

lifetime observation. Suddenly the gum in his mouth loses its flavor. As he hunts distractedly through his pockets for another stick, he looks down the instant the comet whizzes by. Too late, he stares at the sky in dejection, his flavorless gum, obviously not the sponsor's brand, seen clearly as his jaw slumps.

The bad science in this ad is the speeding comet. Indeed, a meteor flashes across the sky in seconds, but to a casual stargazer a comet hangs essentially motionless all night. It generally takes days of observation for a comet to show perceptible movement against the stars. In 1998 Comet Hale-Bopp was seen for months by hundreds of millions of people, all of whom had time to change their gum as often as they wished. The ad reinforces the common confusion between comets and meteors.

Ironically, it is not TV fiction but news reports and so-called science-fact shows that serve up the most damaging distortions of science. Certainly, many reporters and more than one network do a consistently excellent job of delivering accurate and interesting science news to their audience. MSNBC falls in this category (and their Web site gets high marks from me for its astronomy reporting), and CNN can be counted on for the latest news about the space program.

The Discovery Channel and the Learning Channel also provide fine science shows; as of 1998 the former even had a weekly half-hour news program dedicated to reviewing the week in science. Nevertheless, it is common to see local newscasts making mistakes in their science coverage—using incorrect terminology, misunderstanding the conclusions of the study being highlighted, or simply not giving enough information for the viewer to make sense of the reportage. Many national newscasts are guilty of this as well.

The news-gathering and -reporting process itself may be the most to blame for these kinds of errors. For example, a reporter contacts a scientist who has made a newsworthy discovery. The reporter conducts an interview, recording what was said, and then translates the information into copy ultimately intended for a TV news spot. Along the way the copy gets edited by one or more people for content, size, and interest and finally is reviewed by a news producer or senior editor. It is not hard to imagine that some or all of the people involved in this process have little in-depth understanding of the particular topic or of science in general, and each of those points of contact is a potential source of distortion. The final version of the story may be quite different from the (continued on page 34)

Some networks do a consistently excellent job of presenting accurate science news to their audience. MSNBC and CNN fall in this category. The Discovery Channel and the Learning Channel also provide good shows on science.

MSNBC

The Asteroid That Destroyed Science

In the movie *Armageddon,* fragments from an exploded asteroid caused only minor damage to Earth, contrary to what would be expected from our knowledge of physics.

Like TV, theatrical motion pictures are a major media outlet for bad science. Hollywood pushes comic-book-level science to the limit of believability and then blithely shoves it even further. An excellent showcase for this over-the-top approach is the 1998 movie *Armageddon.* The premise: a giant asteroid "the size of Texas" is rammed by a comet, which knocks it out of the asteroid belt and into a collision course with Earth. The impact will wipe out all life on the planet unless a team of macho oil drillers led by Bruce Willis can plant a bomb inside the asteroid and blow it to bits.

It must be conceded that *Armageddon* has at least one item of accurate science—it features an asteroid, and asteroids in fact do exist. Beyond this, the scientific inaccuracies loom as large as the asteroid itself. The following are among the worst examples.

The movie opens with a recounting of the theory that a giant asteroid impact wiped out the dinosaurs at the end of the Cretaceous Period, about 66 million years ago. Whereas many scientists do think that this event happened, the impact energy is described in the movie as having the equivalent of 10,000 nuclear bombs. That number, which may have sounded huge to the scriptwrit-

ers, falls woefully short of the actual estimate. The dinosaur-killer asteroid would have had the energy of about 800,000 nuclear weapons—nearly 100 times larger than the fictional figure.

The problem with an asteroid "as big as Texas" is that there is none that big in the solar system. The largest, Ceres, is about 900 kilometers (560 miles) across; Texas is about 1,300 kilometers (800 miles) across. Although in the movie an amateur astronomer discovers the asteroid only 18 days before impact, any asteroid larger than Ceres actually would have attracted our attention long ago. Ceres, which resides in the asteroid belt between Mars and Jupiter, was discovered on the first day of the 19th century. Just 18 days away from Earth, a rock the size of the fictional asteroid would easily be visible to the naked eye; it would be second only to the Sun and Moon in brightness.

The collision of a comet with an asteroid of that size would barely make a crater in it, let alone knock it into an orbit toward Earth. That kind of acute deflection would require an improbably high velocity for the comet, whose impact then would shatter the asteroid rather than move it much. Furthermore, outer space is

quite empty, even within the asteroid belt. Although movies like *The Empire Strikes Back* (1980) create a picture of the asteroid belt as being jammed with tumbling rocks, the average distance between asteroids is actually millions of kilometers. The odds of the comet-asteroid collision depicted in the movie are extremely low, essentially zero.

Blowing up a Texas-sized asteroid is completely beyond human capability. Detonating every single nuclear weapon we have on the asteroid would hardly make a dent. Even if we did manage to shatter it shortly before impact, we would be making the situation worse. In the movie the exploded asteroid created little else than a tremendous fireworks display. In reality, all those rock fragments hitting Earth's atmosphere would deposit the same amount of energy as the intact body. Moreover, broken into numerous small pieces, the asteroid would burn up more completely, and more of its en-

ergy would go into heating the atmosphere than vaporizing rock in surface impacts. The total explosion would dwarf the one thought to have killed the dinosaurs, and the temperature rise over the planet would make our worst global warming fears seem a joke.

Not all of *Armageddon*'s competition at the box office was as scientifically bad. *Deep Impact,* which was released just weeks before *Armageddon,* is a thoughtful movie about the consequences of an impending comet impact. The movie producers actually sought advice from astronomers and space scientists on technical issues and then implemented most of the recommendations. For example, because a comet has very little gravity, astronauts sent to rendezvous with the comet and leave a bomb under its surface would have a difficult time landing their spacecraft. The solution, given by one of the scientist advisers, was to tether the craft. Thus, the spacecraft in the movie

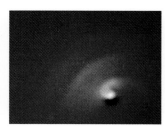
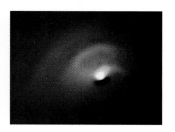

The movie _Deep Impact_ deliberately gave its comet an unscientifically bright surface (below) to make visiting astronauts visible. The movie comet's gas-emitting vents are accurate, however. Comets do vent gas and dust, as revealed in sequential photos of Comet Hale-Bopp (right) showing waves of dust jetting from vents in the comet's spinning nucleus as the vents are exposed repeatedly to the Sun.

fires harpoons into the ice, mooring it.

The movie also adheres to scientific accuracy in giving the comet vents—deep fissures in the surface that expel gas when the area is heated by sunlight. From ground-based observations and images made during space probe flybys of comets, astronomers know that comets really do vent gases in this way and that they can be spectacular sights.

Nevertheless, _Deep Impact_ has its slipups. For instance, it makes the same mistake as _Armageddon_ in having a large chunk of the impacting body blown up moments before it is to hit, with no ill effects. Some errors were made not out of ignorance but out of necessity.

For example, a comet's head, or nucleus, is surrounded by so much gas and dust that reflected sunlight makes it look big and bright. In reality, its surface is actually very dark. Because filming astronauts on a black surface with the black sky of space as a backdrop would have made everything hard to see, the moviemakers chose to bend the truth and make the comet surface white.

Surprisingly, a satirical thrashing of the same topic on the Fox Network's animated TV show "The Simpsons" turned out to be a champion of good science. In that episode a comet threatens to hit the town of Springfield. Bart Simpson, the show's young antihero, discovers the comet (in fact, most comets are discovered by amateur astronomers), reports it to the local observatory (also good form), and even uses the correct type of coordinates. Scientific accuracy accedes to humor when Springfield is saved after the comet's nucleus burns up in the town's thick polluted air, but it hits the ground reduced to a chunk of rock "no bigger than a Chihuahua's head." Bart then picks up the warm rock and puts it in his pocket. In fact, most small meteorites—rocks from space that make it to the ground—are only warm when they hit, not flaming hot. The initial passage through the upper atmosphere slows the object so much that it falls much more slowly for the rest of its descent, giving it time to cool. Any outer parts heated enough to melt will get blown off, or ablated, by the rush of air.

Laughing at Ignorance

One day in September 1995, I watched a broadcast-network morning show do a short wrap-up of the daily news events, and on that particular day it reported on a space shuttle mission. Reading from the teleprompter, one of the show's three cohosts attempted to describe the wake shield experiment being carried aboard the shuttle. The wake shield is a large piece of metal that creates a very high-grade vacuum behind it as it moves through space, similar to someone wiping dust off a tabletop and leaving a clean path behind. The vacuum created in this way can be used to make improved computer parts. After the man finished, he and his colleagues all laughed at how hard the copy had been to read and how all of them—three of the national network's high-profile journalists—had no idea what had just been said.

Should we find it strange, if not shocking, that journalists would actually joke over their lack of comprehension of a subject? Imagine that the report had been about elections in Chechnya and that the broadcasters had bantered about not knowing where Chechnya was. Would we tolerate journalists who not only fail to understand the political events that they report on but also make light of the situation on the air? Nevertheless, this morning show's staff apparently felt secure in their public display of ignorance when the topic was science.

(continued from page 31)

reporter's original version and may actually come to a conclusion opposite to that of the researcher. At the very end of the information pipeline, even TV news readers may contribute to the problem, for example, when they stumble over scientific terms and concepts while delivering stories in front of the camera (*see* Sidebar: *Laughing at Ignorance*).

Science journalists, too, are responsible for some of the misrepresentation, error, and oversensationalism that can get into science stories. Although they bring a seemingly innocent agenda to their work—to popularize science and inform the public of its value—their goal of getting the public's attention is occasionally achieved at the expense of balance, fairness, and accuracy. In seeking that high-profile segment on the nightly news, a reporter's story may exaggerate and dramatize, focusing on the "newsy" aspects of a discovery or the ambitiously optimistic expectations for it without giving due consideration to whether the discovery even merits such attention.

On the whole, journalists do the best they can, but they cannot be experts in every field of science. Sometimes when they approach scientists to clear up an issue, things get worse. Most scientists have a narrow

focus on their research and are not used to speaking about it in terms that are easy for reporters and the public to understand. Furthermore, sensing that they may be "burned" by journalists, some scientists may be ill at ease during interviews and communicate poorly.

Quite apart from honest scientific news reportage are the so-called scientific documentaries that actually thrive on promulgating bad science. Some, like the Sci-Fi Channel's series "Sightings," fall clearly in the realm of pseudoscience. "Sightings" uncritically accepts every paranormal claim, UFO sighting, and psychic that it features. When it does report on "real" science, it evidently spends little time or resources double-checking for accuracy.

For example, one report thoroughly confused astronomical distance scales when it described molecules in space as traveling from "galaxy to galaxy" rather than "star to star."

On the other hand, there are TV documentaries that set out with good intentions but fall short of the mark. An episode of the world-travel series "Pole to Pole," produced in the early 1990s and hosted by former Monty Python member Michael Palin, apparently became the inadvertent vehicle for a fraudulent demonstration of the Coriolis effect when the film crew crossed the Equator in Kenya. A man giving a tourist lecture at the burnt-out remains of a hotel claimed that a line that had been marked on the ground precisely demarcated

the Equator, which, to be fair, it may well have. Using a pan with a small hole in the bottom, he then showed how water drained from it in a clockwise swirl when he stood on one side of the line, in a counterclockwise swirl when on the other side, and straight down when he placed the pan directly on the line. Palin offered no comment other than a wry expression and a bit of humor, and because the episode carried no disclaimer, some viewers might well have taken it as proof for what they had long thought to be true, rather than a simple trick. (For discussions of the Coriolis effect and astronomical sizes and distances, *see* Sidebar: *Spot the Bad Science: A Quiz.*)

THE EGG AND THE EQUINOX

In addition to TV, a particularly powerful medium through which bad science is spread is so-called common knowledge. A classic example is the widely held notion that on the day of the vernal equinox—the first day of spring in the Northern Hemisphere—an egg can be stood on end. If an explanation is given at all, it is usually that at the equinox the gravity of the Sun and Earth balance, creating an equilibrium so delicate that even the squat, ungainly

Rotolo/Gamma Liaison International

Standing apart from honest scientific news reportage are the so-called scientific documentary shows that thrive on promulgating bad science such as UFO sightings, paranormal events, and psychic experiences.

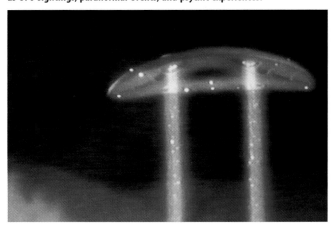

(Left and below) Phil Plait

With patience, it is easy to demonstrate that on any day of the year at least one or two eggs out of every dozen—eight in the photo below—will balance on end. The most important factor is not the time of year but the tiny bumps scattered on the eggshell surface (left). If the bumps are arranged just right on the balancing end, they will act like little legs to prop up the egg.

egg shape acquires additional stability. To those people who have only a fuzzy idea of what the vernal equinox is, it sounds like an important time. If an egg can balance on end at all, then it will surely do it at this time of year. Thus, each year newspapers and TV news shows run local human-interest stories showing students—in science class, no less—standing an egg on end on the first day of spring, thereby proving the story and reinforcing its "correctness" for countless readers and viewers.

Are the students really proving it, however? At most, they are showing that it is possible to balance an egg on end at the vernal equinox. They have not applied the scientific method to check out their theory further, to see if it can make other correct predictions. The theory, in fact, is very simple to disprove. Just for the effort of trying, an egg can be made to balance on

end at any time of the year. With patience, at least one or two eggs out of every dozen will balance. The most important factor is not the time of year or any kind of "cosmic equilibrium" but the tiny grit-like bumps scattered about the eggshell surface. If they happen to be arranged just so on the tip of the balancing end, they will act like little legs, propping up the egg.

As for the vernal equinox, it is not a special time of the year in a gravitational sense. It and its half-year-distant counterpart, the autumnal equinox, occur because Earth's axis is tilted with respect to the plane on which it orbits the Sun. Twice a year, on the equinoxes, the Sun's annual pathway appears to cross the celestial equator, the projection of Earth's Equator on the sky. Geometrically the two equinoxes are equivalent, but no one appears to make a fuss

about balancing eggs on the first day of fall.

Some people who hear the story may believe it unreservedly. Others may try it for themselves and demonstrate that, indeed, an egg will balance on end on the day of the vernal equinox. In the process, they may go through several eggs before finding one that works. They then point to that success as proof that the story is correct.

Ignoring the failures and acknowledging only the successes, often called selective memory, is yet another power-

ful process for perpetuating bad science. When the egg story is covered by the media, what journalist will mention all the eggs that fell over, and what editor will run a picture of them? Selective memory makes other "theories" easy to prove as well. Astrology works for those who remember the one prediction that comes true rather than the 99 that do not. Unfortunately, remembering only the successes severely biases what one learns in life. As the 16th-century English cleric and statesman Thomas Wolsey said (often quoted by

Sun's Path on the Celestial Sphere

north celestial pole

Sun

summer solstice

ecliptic

vernal equinox

Earth

celestial equator

23.5°

autumnal equinox

winter solstice

south celestial pole

Seasonal references are for Northern Hemisphere.

Earth's axis is tilted with respect to the plane on which it orbits the Sun. Twice a year, on the vernal and autumnal equinoxes, the Sun's annual pathway appears to cross the celestial equator. Geometrically the two equinoxes are equivalent, but the vernal equinox gets all the attention.

bad-science adversary and webmaster, Alistair Fraser of Pennsylvania State University): "Be very, very careful what you put into that head, because you will never, ever get it out."

CUMULATIVE DAMAGE

It is reasonable to ask if any great harm is being done. After all, each individual bit of misinformation may have only a tiny effect on our ability to think critically. The cumulative effect, nevertheless, can be enormous. If 10,000 people buy a book claiming Earth will be destroyed in the year 2000, the author—whether knowingly wrong or not—makes a living and each buyer is out the price of a good dinner. If each of those same people buy a used car on the word of a salesperson, without a test drive or an inspection by a mechanic,

they are investing a lot of money in a machine that may kill them. Even worse, if a U.S. president makes vastly important decisions—life and death decisions affecting millions of people—based on advice from a self-proclaimed astrologer who is doing little more than guessing, then the harm is tragically clear.

The scientific method may well be our most formidable weapon against bad information. It forces us to think about why we believe something, and if we are good at using it, it makes us skeptical as well. People who apply the word *skeptic* as a derogatory term are likely those who stand to profit from an audience not prepared to question what it is hearing.

Unfamiliarity with the scientific method may leave us open to bad decision making,

but it has another, less obvious consequence as well. In watching scientists apply the method, some people see only the contention in it and fail to discern its powerful property of self-correction in action. For example, in March 1998, astronomers reported orbital calculations indicating that an asteroid discovered the previous December would make a very close pass to Earth in 2028—so close, in fact, that they could not rule out an impact. Naturally this was headline material, and many TV news shows put it first in their lineup. The very next day, however, other astronomers reported that the asteroid would actually pass more than twice as far away as the Moon and that Earth was safe. Many newspapers played up the idea that the second group of astronomers was slighting and

contradicting the results of the first. People interviewed on the street asked why scientists can never agree on anything, and commentators joked about astronomers making math mistakes. Some writers even called publishing of the first report irresponsible.

Who was right, the first group or the second? As it happens, both were. The first group announced the results based on calculations using the best data that it had—about three months of observations. The results were then delivered to astronomers all over the world, with a request that astronomers check their photographic records for older, "prediscovery" images of the asteroid, which could be used to make a more accurate prediction of its orbit. Within a day, observations from 1990 were found in image archives and a better calculation was made, which resulted in the shifting of the predicted orbit out to about a million kilometers (600,000 miles) from Earth at closest approach. Note that this was good science—when better data became available, it resulted in a better conclusion, with which both groups of astronomers agreed. The public, however, was shown scientists in discord.

Even when scientists do disagree, over time the scientific

In 1989 engineers on Earth brought Voyager 2 to Neptune, the culmination of a complex 12-year journey that involved gravitational assists from Jupiter, Saturn, and Uranus. Their achievement is a telling demonstration of what science can accomplish.

Seth Shostak/Science Photo Library/Photo Researchers, Inc.

method typically reveals who has the superior theory. Nevertheless, what the public hears often creates the impression that scientists simply do not know what they are talking about. This sets up an unfounded mistrust of scientists and the body of knowledge that they have accumulated. If the voting public mistrusts science, it is less likely to fund research. Furthermore, the vacuum left by the mistrust of science will likely be filled by charlatans and scam artists.

Being skeptical of a scientific result is healthy, but a blanket disbelief in any scientific result at all is an extraordinarily dangerous path to follow. As Sagan wrote in *The Demon-Haunted World,* the countries that fund research in the sciences will inevitably have a better standard of living (and have a better chance of surviving) than those that do not. The prospect of improved medical technology alone should be reason enough to press on, but other important beneficiaries of science such as

communication, transportation, and food production also come easily to mind. Even basic research with no obvious applications may produce life-changing results. The 19th-century Scottish physicist James Clerk Maxwell was not funded to produce television and radio when he worked out the basic laws of electromagnetism, but they were an inevitable outcome just the same.

Despite thousands of years of sometimes vicious attacks, science and its method have

accomplished an incredible amount. Science works. Lights come on at the flip of a switch. Cars, fantastically complicated machines, travel our roads with ease and reliability. In the 1970s and '80s, engineers sent the Voyager 2 spacecraft all the way to Neptune, using the gravitational influence of Jupiter, Saturn, and Uranus to help guide it along an amazingly complex path. In the end, their aim was accurate to a few kilometers after billions of kilometers of flight—not unlike shooting a rifle in New York City and hitting a nickel in Miami, Florida, ricocheting off a few trees on the way. Because of innovations in medicine and fundamental advances in our understanding of disease, the average human life span has lengthened dramatically in industrialized nations in just the past century. All of this was accomplished because people questioned their surroundings, poked and prodded them, learned and relearned until the physical principles that underlie nature were better understood.

(continued on page 41)

Spot the Bad Science: A Quiz

Those who would deny that they are victims of bad science have an opportunity to put their knowledge to the test. Astronomy and planetary science deal with physical events that affect our lives literally every day, yet just how well do we understand them? On a clear night we see points of light in the sky, but do we know what we are really seeing? In the following quiz, decide which of the statements are true and which are bad science.

1. The year is defined as the length of time that it takes for Earth to turn once on its axis.
2. The Coriolis effect, which causes hurricanes to spin counterclockwise in the Northern Hemisphere and clockwise in the Southern Hemisphere, also makes water drain from bathtubs and toilets in opposite directions on opposite sides of the Equator.
3. Almost none of the stars we see in night sky are actually white.
4. Polaris, the North Star, is the brightest star in the night sky of the Northern Hemisphere.
5. A star is larger than a galaxy. (For a more challenging test, put these objects in order of size from smallest to largest: galaxy, solar system, star, universe, planet.)
6. An alignment of planets has almost no physical effect on Earth; it does not, for example, contribute to earthquakes, unusually high tides, or other natural disasters.

1—false. A year is the time that it takes Earth to go once around the Sun. In addition to this yearly orbital revolution, Earth is also spinning on its axis like a ball, moving from west to east and making one complete rotation every day. Because Earth is so large compared with us humans, who ride on its surface, we cannot feel that daily turning; the Earth seems fixed while the Sun rises and sets every day. In the time that Earth travels once around the Sun, it turns roughly 365 times. If all this seems like fare for a child's textbook, the results of a survey conducted by the U.S. National Science Foundation and published in 1997 may be surprising—27% of adults polled did not know that Earth went around the Sun, and 52% did not know how long it took.

2—false. The Coriolis effect indeed does make hurricanes spin in opposite directions in opposite hemispheres. A hurricane is a low-pressure weather system. Air tends to move in toward its center, where the pressure is lowest, from outlying areas of comparatively high pressure. As the air flows in-

NASA

ward, however, Earth's rotation complicates its motion.

As stated above, Earth is rotating from west to east. Consequently, even calm patches of air—calm with respect to the surface beneath them—are being carried along as part of this motion. Calm air at the Equator travels the entire distance of Earth's circumference, about 40,000 kilometers (24,000 miles), in a 24-hour period. This translates to a speed of 1,600 kilometers (1,000 miles) per hour. As our reference point moves north or south from the Equator, however, the west-to-east circular paths around Earth—the circles of latitude—get smaller and smaller, meaning that the distance that the air travels in a 24-hour circuit, and thus its speed, gradually decreases. Above either pole a calm air patch is barely moving at all.

This ever-present north-south gradation in speed affects any movement of air—actually

Tony Cordoza/Gamma Liaison International

The Coriolis effect causes Southern Hemisphere hurricanes, or cyclones, to spin clockwise. Does it do the same thing to a draining bathtub in Brazil?

any fluid motion—including the air flowing into a hurricane. In the Northern Hemisphere, air moving north, away from the Equator, has a higher eastward speed than the surface beneath it, and so it races ahead eastward relative to that surface. By contrast, air moving south, away from the North Pole, has a lower eastward speed than the surface, and so slips back westward. The total effect is a counterclockwise rotation of the air around the hurricane as it flows into the storm. In the Southern Hemisphere, the process is the same: air moving south from the Equator races east, and air moving north from the South

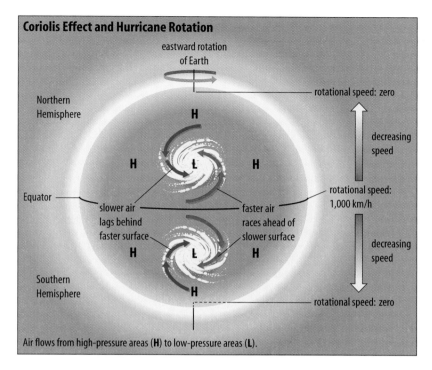

Coriolis Effect and Hurricane Rotation

eastward rotation of Earth

rotational speed: zero

Northern Hemisphere

H

H L H

Equator

slower air lags behind faster surface

faster air races ahead of slower surface

H H

Southern Hemisphere

H

rotational speed: zero

decreasing speed

rotational speed: 1,000 km/h

decreasing speed

Air flows from high-pressure areas (**H**) to low-pressure areas (**L**).

The Coriolis effect on hurricanes results from Earth's west-to-east rotation. In either hemisphere, air traveling away from the Equator has a higher eastward speed than the surface beneath it and so races ahead relative to that surface. Air traveling toward the Equator has a lower eastward speed than the surface and so slips back westward. If the air movement is into a storm, a low-pressure area, the total effect appears as a counterclockwise rotation in the Northern Hemisphere and a clockwise rotation in the Southern Hemisphere.

Pole slips west. The result is a clockwise rotation of the air around the hurricane. Just as it does for air movements, the Coriolis effect influences the movement of water currents in the ocean.

Nevertheless, it is important to note that hurricanes and ocean currents dwarf the drains of even the most decadent bathtubs. The Coriolis effect is manifested only over very large distances, where Earth's spin makes a difference. Bathtubs, sinks, and toilets are simply too small to be noticeably affected. Although they do experience a tiny effect, it is vastly overwhelmed by currents in the water created by filling or washing or from irregularities in the drain as the water flows out. According to one study, the water in a typical sink would need to rest for three days, to let the eddies die out, before the

Coriolis effect would have a chance to appear. (Incidentally, a toilet typically has water jets under the rim, permanently angled in a way that sends the water spinning down the drain in the same direction, irrespective of hemisphere, each time the toilet is flushed.)

3—true. Almost all the stars in the night sky have color. This answer surprises many people, because most stars look white. The stars that stand out most brightly in the sky tend to be either very hot, which makes their light blue, or extremely large, old, and cool, which makes their light red. Although the very brightest of these, if carefully observed, do indeed look blue or red, the remainder appear white.

The answer to this mystery lies with human physiology. Our eyes have two different kinds of light detectors, rods

and cones. Rods are very sensitive to faint light but cannot differentiate colors. Cones distinguish colors, but they need brighter light to work. Most stars, which are relatively faint to the unaided eye, activate our rods but not our cones, causing the stars to appear white. A small telescope, however, or even a pair of binoculars will collect enough light from dimmer stars to activate the cones and reveal the stars' true colors. One particular star, Albireo, which appears high in the summer sky in the Northern Hemisphere, is actually a double star, composed of a deep blue star and an orange-yellow one. People inevitably gasp in surprise when they see it through a telescope for the first time.

4—false. To the eye, Polaris is actually a rather dim star. Earth's spin causes the starry

sky to appear to revolve around the planet. At the North Pole, where Earth's axis points directly upward, the stars seem to be spinning about a point overhead at the center of the sky. As it happens, there is a star very near that position. Its official name is Alpha Ursae Minoris, but the common name is Polaris. It is not a particularly bright star; from most cities and many suburbs, with their glare of artificial lights, it is difficult or impossible to see. Most people have heard of Polaris, however, and may know that, as the North Star, it has aided seafarers in navigation for hundreds of years. Because of its importance, people sometimes assume that it must be the brightest in the sky.

5—false. A galaxy is much larger than an individual star and, in fact, is composed of many stars that on average are trillions of kilometers apart. The correct order of astronomical objects, smallest to largest, is planet, star, solar system, galaxy, universe.

The size of astronomical objects is difficult to grasp. As big as Earth seems, it is a minuscule object compared with the rest of the universe. The Sun, nearly 1.4 million kilometers (860,000 miles) across, is itself dwarfed by the extent of the solar system, which is perhaps 10 billion kilometers (six billion miles) across Pluto's orbit alone (and thousands of times larger if one includes all the icy debris extending beyond the known planets).

The next giant step upward is to a galaxy, which is a collection of billions or even trillions of stars. Our own Milky Way Galaxy is roughly 100,000 light-years across. A light-year, the distance a beam of light travels in space in the course of a year, is more than nine trillion kilometers (nearly six trillion miles). A light beam takes a few hours to cross the whole solar system and a few years to reach the stars nearest the Sun, but it takes 100 millennia to cross our galaxy. Our galaxy, in turn, is but one of hundreds of billions in the universe, which may itself be 20 billion light-years across. A light beam from Earth would

have to travel 2,000 millennia just to reach the Andromeda Galaxy, one of our nearer neighbor galaxies.

6—true. On May 5, 2000, there will be a grand conjunction, or alignment, of planets. Six of the eight other major planets will be in a relatively small patch of sky rather than spread out across it. If that was all scientists knew, it would be easy to assume that the combined gravity of the planets could stress or deform Earth enough to cause massive earthquakes, floods, or volcanic eruptions. After all, Jupiter alone has 300 times Earth's mass.

Fortunately, much more is known about gravitational effects. For all their combined mass, the planets are extremely far away. Gravity does depend on mass, but it weakens with the square of the distance. Move an object to twice its original distance, and it has one-fourth the gravitational effect. Move it ten times the original distance, and its force drops to $1/100$ the original value. Even at their absolute closest to Earth, the planets produce a combined gravitational force that is only about 2% of the Moon's force. In addition, the Moon orbits Earth in an ellipse—its distance from Earth varies, which means that its gravitational force on Earth

Can the combined gravitational effect of a gathering of planets in the same part of the sky cause earthquakes and other natural disasters? We can gain insight into the answer by examining the gravitational influence of Earth's nearest neighbor in space, the Moon.

NASA

changes as well. This change alone is 10 times the size of the effect of the other planets combined. It is safe to say that, whatever a planetary conjunction could possibly do to Earth, the Moon far exceeds it every two weeks, without disastrous consequences.

Yet another problem in expecting disaster from the May 2000 conjunction is that it will occur on the far side of the Sun. If the planets at their closest produce no measurable ef-

fect, the addition of hundreds of millions of kilometers to the distance of every planet reduces their combined effect to the vanishing point. In 1982 a similar conjunction took place. It was actually a much better one than the 2000 event for those writing doomsday books and selling survival gear, because the planets were in a tighter formation and closer to Earth. Nevertheless, 1982 is notable as a year in which the Earth was not destroyed.

(continued from page 37)

PETER PAN AS ROLE MODEL

There is nothing magic about the scientific method. All young children apply it innately. They question everything; they want to learn, to give things names, to figure out why things happen. They delight in such examples of nature as butterflies, rainbows, or even Jupiter shining in the night sky. Many parents learn science for the second time when their children are old enough to ask "why?"

If there is nothing magic about the method, there is certainly magic about the results. Even as we mature, most of us retain something of that childlike sense of wonder and awe. Astronomy in particular provides an excellent avenue for these qualities to emerge. The gasps of amazement from the audience at a planetarium show when the lights go low and the "stars" come out is a wonder to behold. People who may have never given the sky a moment's notice will cry out loud during a total solar eclipse when the corona, the Sun's tenuous and ethereal upper atmosphere, springs magnificently into view. Scientists maintain an especially strong and lasting link with this childhood wonder. They delight in learning new things, or even better, seeing

Eric Futran/Gamma Liaison International

There is nothing magic about the scientific method. Young children apply it every time they delight in a butterfly, a rainbow, or a starry gleam in the night sky. The real magic lies in its results.

old things in a new way. "I think physicists are the Peter Pans of the human race," said Nobel laureate I.I. Rabi. "They never grow up, and they keep their curiosity."

By keeping a curious and skeptical attitude we question the world around us; by questioning it we learn more about it and appreciate it all the more. The other side of the coin is that, by not encouraging this attitude, we risk falling into the trap of believing everything that we are told. This is the exact opposite of science—

a society that fails to think critically will become one that will be directed what to think and then never get the chance to think critically again. In this sense the scientific method and freedom of thought go hand in hand. Without one, the other will quickly disappear.

Luckily, the problem has a solution, and it rests in our ability to think. We need to remain ever critical and skeptical. We must always consider options, look for loopholes, peer around corners, try unusual approaches, push theories into new territory,

predict outcomes. Moreover, we must ensure that our children are taught how to do the same. Above all, we must be prepared to change our minds when better evidence reveals itself.

Think of the possibilities.

FOR ADDITIONAL READING

Worlds Apart: How the Distance Between Science and Journalism Threatens America's Future, Jim Hartz and Rick Chappell (First Amendment Center, 1997).
The Demon-Haunted World: Science as a Candle in the Dark, Carl Sagan (Random House, 1995).
Cranks, Quarks and the Cosmos, Jeremy Bernstein (Oxford University Press, 1997).

INTERNET RESOURCES

Bad Astronomy site
http://www.badastronomy.com
Bad Science site
http://www.ems.psu.edu/~fraser/
BadScience.html
National Science Foundation
http://www.nsf.gov

In December 1998 spacesuited shuttle astronauts connected Zarya and Unity, the first Russian and American components of a permanently inhabited international outpost in orbit around Earth. Assembly and operation of the station, the culmination of a 50-year-old vision, will dominate human activity in space well into the 21st century.

The International Space Station

by David M. Harland

Wernher von Braun (bottom) published his sweeping plan for the colonization of space in a series of *Collier's* magazine articles beginning in 1952. His visions of winged space planes, rotating, doughnut-shaped space stations, and in-orbit construction activity were brought to life in inspiring illustrations, such as the one at right, by space artist Chesley Bonestell.

(Right) Space Art International/Black Cat Studios; (below) Corbis

Chesley Bonestell

In 1952 the popular magazine *Collier's* started a series of articles in which the renowned rocket scientist Wernher von Braun advanced his vision of the human colonization of space. His lucid prose was accompanied by space artist Chesley Bonestell's magnificent paintings of winged space planes, enormous rotating space stations, and ungainly interplanetary ships. Although spaceships were widely considered science fiction, the furious pace of aircraft research, which was developing ever-faster and higher-flying vehicles, held out a real promise of orbital space planes. Braun's logic at the time seemed impeccable: using winged shuttles, humans would build a space station, which would serve as the way station to the Moon and planets.

Five years later, the launch of Sputnik dealt that logic a serious blow. Humans soon reached space, but they rode in tiny capsules in which they were essen-

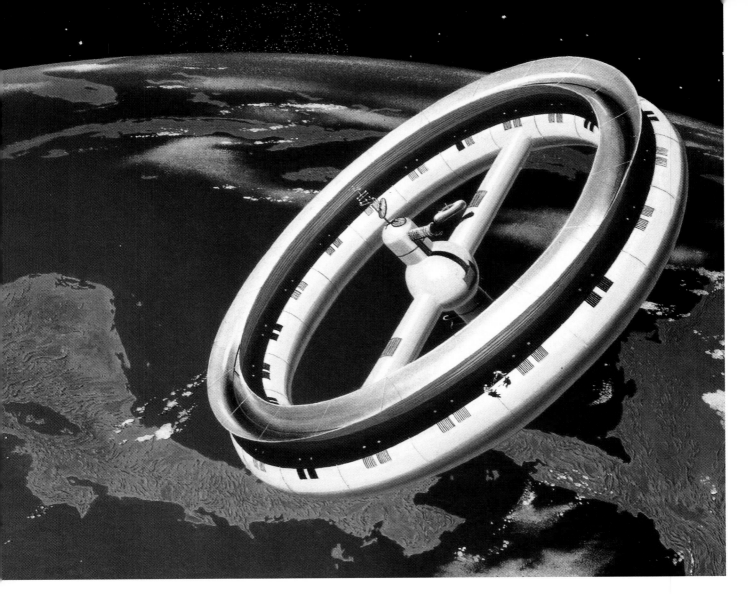

tially passive components. Three decades would pass before they were piloting aircraftlike shuttles high above Earth. In fact, it would be almost a half century before a fuller version of Braun's grand conception began to unfold. Only in late 1998 did astronauts from the space shuttle *Endeavour* unite the first two pieces of a space platform worthy of Braun's vision—the International Space Station (ISS).

Involving the participation of at least 16 nations and costing tens of billions of dollars, the ISS is one of the most ambitious engineering projects ever mounted. Over a period of sev-

eral years, dozens of shuttle flights and unmanned rocket launches will ferry into orbit several hundred tons of equipment, which will gradually be assembled by spacewalking astronauts into a complex of trusses, habitats, laboratories, and solar arrays covering an area larger than that of a football field. If all goes as expected, a crew of three will begin permanent occupancy of the partially finished ISS sometime in the year 2000. A few years after that, the permanent crew will be expanded to six. By then, scientific work aboard the station, focusing initially

on life-sciences and materials-sciences research in the weightless environment, will be well under way. At last, shortly into the new millennium, humankind will be poised on that threshold to space conceived by Braun so long ago.

A VISION ON HOLD

In October 1957 the Soviet Union startled the U.S. out of its technological complacency with the launch of Sputnik, Earth's first artificial satellite. The following year, reacting to the shock, the newly established U.S. National Aero-

nautics and Space Administration (NASA) set out to put an American in space as quickly as possible. Riding in a capsule atop a rocket, he would make a ballistic reentry through the atmosphere, descend by parachute, and splash down in the

David M. Harland is a freelance writer on space topics. His recent books include The Mir Space Station: A Precursor to Space Colonization *(1997),* The Space Shuttle: Roles, Missions and Accomplishments *(1998), and* Exploring the Moon: The Apollo Expeditions *(1999).*

(Below) AP/Wide World; (right) NASA

A capsule atop a rocket proved to be a successful expedient for putting Americans into space as quickly as possible, beginning with Alan Shepard, Jr. (above), in 1961. The strategy was pursued with the development of the powerful Saturn V rocket (right), which took the Apollo 11 astronauts and their successors by direct route to the Moon.

(Below) NASA; (opposite page) Kobal Collection

Skylab (below), the first U.S. space station, was an application of the Project Apollo Moon program. Consisting of the converted third stage of a Saturn V rocket, it was designed as a manned orbital workshop to support a variety of space and terrestrial studies. Although Skylab was a gesture toward Braun's and NASA's original station concept, it fell far short of the popular portrait of mankind's future in space advanced in Stanley Kubrick's *2001: A Space Odyssey* (opposite page, top).

ocean. This Project Mercury would serve as an expedient way to achieve parity in the "space race" until a space plane could be developed.

When the Soviets beat Mercury into orbit in 1961 and U.S. Pres. John F. Kennedy challenged Soviet Premier Nikita S. Khrushchev to reach the Moon within the decade, it became clear that not only the reusable space plane but also the orbital way station would have to be bypassed. The combination of a truly enormous rocket and a ballistic capsule was the only viable

option. The direct route to the Moon, it seemed, had rendered Braun's master plan redundant.

Nevertheless, even as NASA worked flat out to reach the Moon with Project Apollo, it also embarked on a program, dubbed Apollo Applications, of converting the third stage of a surplus Saturn V rocket into a manned orbital workshop that would support a program of astronomical, solar, and terrestrial studies. This effort resulted in the first U.S. space station, Skylab, which hosted three successive teams of astronauts in 1973 and '74. Thus, although it

had been obliged to revise Braun's master plan, NASA had every intention of reintroducing the station just as soon as the pressure was off. Still, a workshop made from a rocket stage was a far cry from the spinning space wheel, serviced by a commercial Pan Am space plane, that was depicted in Stanley Kubrick's 1968 film *2001: A Space Odyssey*. Furthermore, now that NASA had developed the Saturn V and the Apollo spacecraft, a winged space plane seemed unnecessary.

STARTING OVER

No sooner had Neil Armstrong's "small step" onto the lunar surface in 1969 eased the strain on NASA than Pres. Richard Nixon drastically cut spending on all of the Apollo applications that NASA had intended to follow Skylab. The cost-conscious Nixon administration had its own strategy for space. In energy terms, the costliest part of a space flight is attaining low orbit. Most of the Saturn V's energy was used climbing out of Earth's deep gravity well. All

the subsequent maneuvers were relatively inexpensive. Cutting the cost of achieving low orbit was, in the long term, Nixon ruled, the key to a sustainable space program.

In 1969 the Space Task Group, chaired by Vice Pres. Spiro Agnew, acknowledged Nixon's case that expendable rockets were too wasteful and suggested a reusable space plane for routine access to low orbit. In keeping with its long-term objective, NASA said that this shuttle would be used to assemble and service a 12-person space station. Unfortunately, the innovative shuttle's projected development cost was so high that NASA once again had to shelve the station.

It was not until 1972, when NASA finalized the shuttle's configuration, that Nixon gave the go-ahead to build it. At the time, it was hoped that the shuttle would be in service in the late 1970s and that a fleet of them would soon begin flying weekly missions. In reality, the space shuttle took far longer to develop than expected, but its debut in April 1981 was spec-

tacular. No sooner was it declared operational than NASA dusted off its station proposal and started lobbying for support. To its surprise, the agency found key members of Pres. Ronald Reagan's administration to be receptive. Reagan was taken with the idea and particularly appreciated the suggestion that international participation be sought. In January 1984 he directed NASA to build a space station that would be permanently occupied by eight astronauts. It would cost $8 billion. In an echo of Kennedy's historic call to arms, Reagan ordered that the station be made operational within 10 years. Furthermore, in response to NASA's overtures, the Canadian, European, and Japanese space agencies promised to build laboratory modules that shuttles would ferry into orbit to expand the station.

THE SOVIET EFFORT

NASA had so humiliated the Soviet Union in the race to the Moon that the Soviets denied ever having taken part. In fact, by the time Armstrong stepped on the lunar surface, they had turned to the development of orbital stations, and in 1971 they launched the first in a series of craft named Salyut ("Salute").

Unlike NASA's still-unfinished Skylab, Salyut 1 was no converted rocket stage. It was actually part of a project designed to develop a military reconnaissance platform, although in its inaugural form, it was fitted for scientific research. The Soyuz spacecraft, developed for the lunar program, had been adapted for use as a crew ferry.

The designers of the first generation of Salyut stations, which had only a single docking port for the Soyuz craft, had been obliged to fit everything needed for the mission into the station prior to its launch. Consequently, to maximize the scientific program, the crew's facilities were basic and their tenancy limited by the station's consumables. Whereas Skylab had the same problem, it had the advantage of being much bigger.

The operational life of these early space stations was limited not only by the available food and water but also by the propellant supply, which was consumed overcoming orbital decay and altering the station's orien-

tation to perform experiments and optimize the output of the solar panels. It was also limited by the ability of its environmental system to regulate the temperature and maintain a breathable atmosphere. If, therefore, the crew ran out of air, food, or water; if the station ran out of propellant; if its thermal control system broke down; or if too many toxins accumulated, it would have to be abandoned.

Salyut 6, the first second-generation Salyut, had two docking ports. It was capable not only of being replenished in orbit but also of hosting additional visitors. During a total of 684 days of occupancy between 1977 and 1981, it was used by 7 resident and 9 visiting crews. Salyut 7, which went into space in 1982, was rather less reliable. During 815 days of occupancy, its crews often were called upon to push back the frontiers of in-space repair, although this came to be seen in retrospect as a valuable learning exercise.

By the time Reagan finally ordered NASA into the space-station business in 1984, the Soviets were making excellent progress toward developing a modular station from Salyut-sized blocks, which would be permanently occupied. It was evident, therefore, that NASA would have to move fast if it was to catch up.

CHOOSING A CONFIGURATION

Five years before Reagan's directive, NASA had initiated conceptual studies of a modular space station that could be carried into orbit in pieces by shuttle. This Space Operations Center would serve as a laboratory, a satellite-servicing shop, and a base for assembling vehicles for manned missions beyond Earth. In 1983, realizing that it was unlikely to secure funding for a return to the Moon, NASA shifted the emphasis away from a stepping-stone role and toward the idea of a laboratory for research, as a preliminary to manufacturing-in-space applications. Once Reagan gave the go-ahead, NASA requested proposals from industry for station concepts. To constrain the scope of the submissions, it specified what it called a Power Tower concept, which had emerged from preliminary studies by the agency's Johnson Space Center in Houston.

The Power Tower was centered on a long keel, a 120-meter (400-foot) open-lattice-work truss that was to be aligned with its axis aimed straight down, an orientation that would allow it to exploit the planet's gravity gradient. Because gravity is inversely proportional to altitude, Earth

would pull the lower end of the keel a little more strongly than it would the upper end, thus stabilizing the station without the need for attitude-control thrusters. For further stability, most of the inhabited modules were to be mounted at the lower end. Instruments for observing Earth could conveniently be mounted at the base of the keel, whereas astronomical instruments could be mounted at the top end. Electrical power would come from solar panels mounted on either end of another lattice-work truss, set perpendicularly as a boom, halfway up the keel. With the prospect of a large number of users beating on its door to put their apparatus on the station, NASA later decided to add a short T-piece at either end of the keel to accommodate more instruments.

In 1985, once it realized that a single keel would be too flimsy, NASA discarded the Power Tower for a more rigid structure. Known as the Dual Keel, this rectangular arrangement had two main trusses linked at the top and bottom by crosspieces that could support a large number of instruments. All the instruments would be remotely operated from a single cluster of crew modules, now located with the solar panels on a long central cross truss. In March 1986 this design was

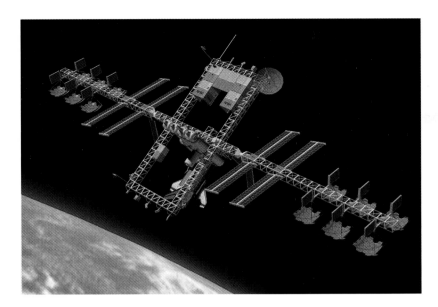

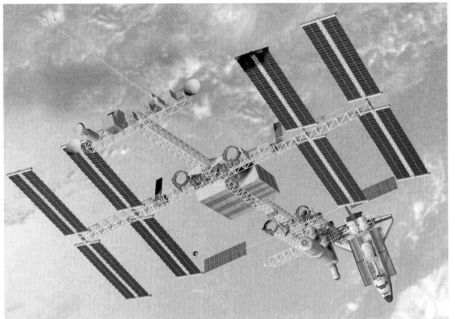

POTW Animations

NASA's design for the space station had several incarnations in the 1980s: the small cluster first presented to Pres. Ronald Reagan and his administration (bottom); the subsequent Power Tower, with its long keel pointed toward Earth (center); and the Dual Keel (top).

formally accepted as being suitable.

Although the catastrophic explosion of the space shuttle *Challenger* just two months earlier was causing serious setbacks for NASA's overall space program, long-term planning for the space station went ahead. In 1987 NASA acknowledged that its shuttles would not achieve the initially planned flight rate and so not be able to ferry sufficient hardware to build the enormous dual keel. Consequently, the agency deleted this structure and, with it, the dedicated observational sites. This left only the long cross truss with its solar panels and cluster of modules. In 1988, with the design seemingly finalized, the project got a sense of identity in the name Space Station Freedom, a moniker in keeping with Reagan's hostility toward the Soviet Union, which he had recently called the "Evil Empire." Just as Apollo had been two decades earlier, the space station became a symbol of the Cold War.

COST CUTTING

Although Congress had authorized the space station, it ordered a succession of reviews in an effort to cut the cost, and in 1990 it sent NASA back to the drawing board. NASA proposed

a delay in the installation of the habitat module, the station's living quarters, which would push the key milestone of permanent occupancy downstream in the schedule. Although this strategy would reduce early operating costs, the station would be less effective overall because it could be used only while a shuttle was attached. In NASA's terminology, in the five years that would elapse before the habitat was installed, the station would be "tended" rather than "inhabited."

By mid-1990 NASA also had come to terms with the fact that it could fly shuttles no more often than about eight times a year. To further reduce the missions required to ferry the station's components into orbit, the agency shortened the truss by 30% and scaled down the pressurized modules by 40% so that a shuttle could deliver them fully outfitted rather than having to make additional flights to fit them with racks of apparatus once in orbit. Reducing the size of the habitat, however, cut the crew. NASA's original plans had called for 12 astronauts, Reagan had specified 8, and the latest configuration limited the number to 4. For the European and Japanese space agencies, already frustrated by the delays and repeated configuration changes, this came as very bad news—they would not be able

to maintain an astronaut aboard to operate their own laboratories. As a result, morale was low when Daniel Goldin, NASA's current administrator, took over in April 1992. This mood did not improve when he ordered yet another redesign of Freedom to further cut costs.

COMPETITION BECOMES COLLABORATION

In February 1986, just weeks after the *Challenger* explosion, the Soviet Union launched the first piece of an advanced,

third-generation space station called *Mir* ("New World"), which incorporated all the lessons learned from operating the Salyuts. It would be assembled from modules launched over a period of years. The first element, or base block, was the habitat. The following year, an astrophysics module of X-ray telescopes was added at one end. Its name, Kvant ("Quantum"), reflected the plan to assemble the station from specialized modules. In late 1989 a module to augment the life-support system was mounted perpendicularly on the other end, making the station L-shaped, and six months later the addition of a materials-processing facility transformed it into a T-shape. By this point not only was *Mir* permanently inhabited but it also was hosting fee-paying researchers from other nations.

With the collapse of the Soviet Union in 1991 and the overnight obsolescence of the Cold War, the political scene became transformed. At their first summit, in June 1992, U.S. Pres. George Bush and Boris Yeltsin, the new Russian president, defined the basis for the Human Spaceflight Cooperation protocol, which was signed in October. Specifically, the agreement called for flying a cosmonaut on a shuttle, having an astronaut visit *Mir*, and having the shuttle dock with *Mir* to exchange the station's crew. NASA also decided to explore the possibility of buying a Soyuz spacecraft, which a shuttle would ferry up to Freedom once the station was operational, to serve as a lifeboat for returning the crew to Earth in an emergency.

The *Mir* space station incorporated all the lessons learned by the Soviet Union in operating its two earlier generations of Salyut stations. It was assembled from modules launched over a period of years beginning in 1986.

NASA

After Bill Clinton succeeded Bush in January 1993, the provocative name Freedom was quietly dropped. Clinton's priority was to cut the budget deficit that had accumulated during the Reagan and Bush years. Consequently, in March NASA was ordered once again to come up with a more cost-effective space station plan. Three months later it submitted three options, neutrally labelled A, B, and C.

Option A proposed cutting costs by replacing the propulsion, guidance, and navigational systems designed for Freedom with systems already in use in military satellites. Option B was essentially the Freedom configuration but with its assembly phased over a longer period to reduce the annual spending. It was, nevertheless, the most expensive of the options. Option C was a radical rethink that called for retiring *Columbia*, the first shuttle orbiter, and using its engines to place a fully outfitted Skylab-style station in orbit.

In June the White House chose Option A, and Congress quickly voted the necessary funding—$2.1 billion per annum for five years—although by the narrowest of margins. The Boeing Co. was nominated as prime contractor in August, and the project definition for the station, which had acquired the name Alpha, was sent to the White House on September 7. Meanwhile, and essentially independently, the U.S. had expanded the scope of its earlier agreement with Russia, and on September 2 the two countries signed an accord that called for their respective space-station developments to be merged into a single orbital structure. As competition in space had symbolized the Cold War, collaboration in space perfectly expressed the new spirit of cooperation. It was ironic that spaceflight, the technology that had been so vigorously developed by the two nations primarily as a means of illustrating the superiority of their individual ideologies, should become the symbol of the end of that competition.

With the political commitment for its space station finally in place, NASA moved fast. In November 1993 NASA and Russia signed an implementation plan, which involved three phases. In Phase 1 NASA, in effect, signed up as one of Russia's fee-paying clients. By paying $400 million, NASA would be able to place a succession of astronauts on *Mir*, allowing the agency an early start on its experiment program. In addition, NASA argued, the dockings would provide experience in operating shuttles in conjunction with a space sta-

tion. Phase 2 required sufficient elements of the new station to be in orbit to enable the first crew to take up residence by the end of 1998. Phase 3 was to complete the assembly process by 2001. The White House endorsed this International Space Station Alpha plan in late November, and the next month Russia joined Europe, Japan, and Canada as a partner in the project.

UNIFICATION

NASA's starting point for developing the joint station was the Option A configuration. A key early decision was to incorporate a Russian maneuvering unit, or tug module, which would be carried into orbit by a Russian Proton rocket from the Baikonur Cosmodrome in Kazakstan. Not only would this unit provide the propulsion, guidance, and navigation capabilities that NASA had intended to borrow from military satellites, but it also could be replenished in space, which would greatly reduce operating costs.

The Soviet Union's space program had called for replacing *Mir* in the early 1990s with a sprawling Freedom-style structure—*Mir 2*—assembled and serviced by Buran, its version of the space shuttle. The economic climate following

the Soviet collapse, however, prompted Russia to cancel Buran, prolong *Mir*'s useful life, and freeze the development of *Mir*'s replacement. Subsequently, on deciding to work with NASA to develop a single structure, Russia dusted off components of its *Mir 2* design for use on the ISS.

One problem with the plan for NASA was that Russia prefers to launch its station components from Baikonur at a fairly high inclination of 51° to the Equator to avoid sending its rockets over China. On the other hand, the most efficient shuttle trajectory from Cape Canaveral is east out over the North Atlantic at 28°. NASA switched the space station's orbit to the higher inclination to accommodate Russia, but in so doing it sacrificed some altitude to which heavy shuttle payloads could be lifted.

On the plus side, Russia's *Mir 2* elements and its approach to station building advanced a critical milestone in NASA's assembly sequence for the station: the point at which a shuttle could leave a crew on board. In NASA's independent plan, that status would not have been attained until its habitat module was added, toward the end of the assembly. Russia's own assembly strategy, in contrast, had been to start with a habitat. When Russia and the U.S.

joined forces, the habitat for the *Mir 2* was already fairly well along in development. Docking this habitat to the tug early in the assembly sequence would enable the nascent station to be inhabited immediately. Even though the full station would take just as long to assemble, it would be far more productive. The plan was a striking unification of politics and space technology. Acknowledging the crucial role of the Russian tug and habitat, NASA called them the core modules.

For once, NASA was confident that it would not be held back. As Goldin put it in 1994, it was "no longer just a design . . .we are building hardware." This was just as well, because the decade thought by Reagan to have been sufficient to assemble the space station had already expired, some $11 billion had been spent, and absolutely nothing had been placed in orbit. In September 1995, in an unprecedented move, Congress approved a multiyear continuation of the budget and thereby guaranteed the funding needed to build and launch what, by now, was simply being called the International Space Station.

ASSEMBLY

Phase 2, the initial assembly of the ISS, began in November

1998 when a Proton rocket placed the tug, now named Zarya ("Dawn"), in orbit. Manufactured by Khrunichev, the Russian space-industry center that had built *Mir* and its Salyut predecessors, Zarya comprises a large cylindrical compartment carrying rows of externally mounted propellant tanks. It has a docking connector, or port, on one end and a small spherical compartment on the other. The spherical compartment, in turn, possesses three docking ports, one axial (on the end) and two radial (on the top and bottom).

A few weeks later, a shuttle delivered NASA's first element, a pressurized module called Unity. Because this 5.5-meter (18-foot)-long cylinder is to serve as a six-way

(Above) The first two joined modules of the ISS, Zarya (left) and Unity (right), fly free after release from the space shuttle *Endeavour*. During their linkup, shuttle astronauts conducted external and internal sojourns to integrate the modules' systems. At left, American and Russian crew members work near an internal hatch on Zarya. At bottom, a spacewalking astronaut checks the linked modules in the shuttle's cargo bay.

node, or connection point, it has four radial connectors in addition to two axial ones. Spacewalking shuttle astronauts attached Unity by one of its axial ports to the axial port of Zarya's spherical compartment and made internal connections for powering and activating the node. Being self-sufficient, the Russian vehicle was able to support Unity once the shuttle had departed.

In 1999 the Russian habitat, which NASA prosaically dubbed the Service Module, is scheduled to be brought up by Proton rocket and mounted on the free end of Zarya. Like Zarya, it comprises a large cylinder terminating at one end in a small spherical compartment fitted with axial and radial docking ports. In addition to

(Top, middle and bottom) NASA

53

With plans and resources in flux, NASA's conception of the full configuration of the ISS has been put forth in a number of versions. In this one, from 1998, the main truss, solar-panel units, and European and Japanese laboratories are featured prominently.

providing living quarters and life support, the Service Module is designed to assume the station's guidance and propulsion functions initially provided by Zarya. NASA then plans to send its 8.8-meter (29-foot)-long Laboratory Module, called Destiny, by shuttle and mount it on the free end of Unity. At that stage of assembly, the complex will be essentially a linear chain of pressurized modules, oriented with its primary axis in the direction of flight and the habitat trailing. This orientation will allow arriving shuttles to position themselves directly ahead of the station, with the docking unit in the shuttle's payload bay facing the Laboratory Module's free axial port, and employ NASA's standard mode of approach. It also will allow Russian resupply tankers to dock at the rear of the Service Module, using the Russian method of closing from behind. After the habitat is in place, the first resident three-person crew will arrive in a Soyuz and dock at a radial port on Zarya.

During Phase 2 NASA also plans to ferry up racks of apparatus, to be installed within the station, in a 6.3-meter (22-foot)-long pressurized Multipurpose Logistics Module. Supplied by the aerospace firm Alenia Aerospazio of Italy, it was named Leonardo. When mounted in a shuttle's payload bay for flights to and from the station, the module will function as a reuseable cargo carrier. Between flights, it will be connected to the station. Equipment that does not require a pressurized environment will be carried by shuttle on open-frame pallets in the payload bay.

Another critical event in Phase 2 will be the installation of a large solar-panel unit on an 11.8-meter (39-foot)-long truss mounted on top of Unity. This array will provide the power required to operate the Laboratory Module. There is no overriding imperative for achieving the milestone of an operational laboratory by mid-2000, but as of early 1999, there was every chance that it would be accomplished.

Nevertheless, even the rosiest expectations could wither quickly. In the past, NASA had learned that, because its complex shuttles could not always be readied for new flights as rapidly as expected, a strict mission schedule was unrealistic. The agency often found it feasible to advance one mission while allowing another to slip. In committing to the highly integrated schedule of the ISS project, however, NASA denied itself that option, and because its flight rate was already high, delays would propagate strongly through the timeline.

Building the rest of the station, as Phase 3, will take a few more years. One theme will be the assembly of the primary truss. On the Laboratory Module, astronauts will mount a 13-meter (43-foot)-long spur with a hexagonal cross-section and then extend this out to either side with truss segments

to create the full span. Rails will be installed within the truss so that spacewalking astronauts can transport equipment along its length on handcarts. A 17.3-meter (57-foot)-long remote manipulator arm supplied by Canada will ride on external rails fitted to one side of the truss, and a pair of 23-meter (75.5-foot)-long thermal radiators will be fixed on the other side. Once solar-panel units have been mounted at either end of the truss—the one initially mounted on Unity will be relocated so that there will be two units at either end—the truss will span 94 meters (308 feet).

The second theme of Phase 3 will be the installation of the Japanese and European laboratories. A new node, this one supplied by Alenia, will be fitted to the leading end of NASA's laboratory. The European Space Agency's Columbus Orbital Facility then will be attached to one side of the node, and an Italian life-sciences facility with a large U.S.-supplied centrifuge will be mounted on top, pointing away from Earth. Japan's Experiment Module, mounted opposite Columbus, will be a more elaborate facility having an unpressurized experiment pallet on its end (a pair of miniature remote manipulator arms will provide access to the apparatus on the pallet) and a connector for a pressurized resupply

module. Although these international modules will be delivered by shuttle, both Europe and Japan will use their own rockets and automated vehicles to replenish the laboratories.

Having decided to continue to operate *Mir* as long as possible, Russia postponed further contributions to the ISS until late in the assembly; but it plans to affix a solar-panel truss and a cluster of modules to the Service Module's spherical docking compartment.

The completion of Phase 3 will be marked by the addition of NASA's own habitat. Mounted on Unity, it will enable the resident crew to be increased. This milestone is unlikely to be achieved before 2004.

In all, some three dozen shuttle flights will be needed to commission the ISS. Nevertheless, NASA has proven that it can sustain the required flight rate. What will be unprecedented will be the number of spacewalks: several hundred hours per year. Even after the station is fully assembled, astronauts will have to venture out for routine maintenance, such as the replacement of the batteries linked to the solar-panel units. Assembly of the ISS will involve about three times NASA's previous accumulated experience of spacewalking, but *Mir*'s crews have shown that construction in orbit is feasible—

their achievements are evident in pictures of *Mir* taken at various times during its long life.

OPERATIONS

Flight operations will be managed by the Space Station Control Center at the Johnson Space Center. The Tracking and Data Relay System, a network of relay satellites in geostationary orbit, will provide continuous high-capacity communications. Satellites of the Global Positioning System will enable the ISS to monitor its position on an ongoing basis, eliminating reliance on costly-to-operate tracking stations. (*See* Feature Article: YOU ARE HERE: NAVIGATION IN THE 21ST CENTURY.)

The ISS will run on a 24-hour basis. Not only will the crew work in shifts, but much of the apparatus also will be operated via telescience—scientists on the ground will monitor experiments by video transmissions and conduct them with remote manipulators. A six-person permanent crew will allow the resident scientists to work in the laboratories while the commander and the engineer focus on station operations. *Mir*'s full-time crew of three (at most) forced maintenance to be performed at the expense of the science program. By contrast, when both a shuttle and a Soyuz

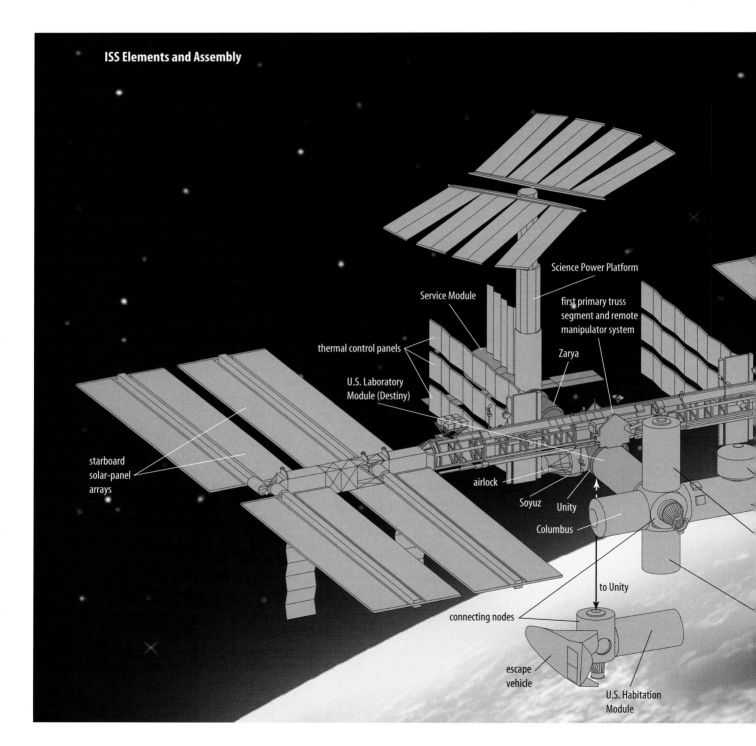

Science Power Platform

Service Module

first primary truss segment and remote manipulator system

thermal control panels

Zarya

U.S. Laboratory Module (Destiny)

starboard solar-panel arrays

airlock

Soyuz

Unity

Columbus

to Unity

connecting nodes

escape vehicle

U.S. Habitation Module

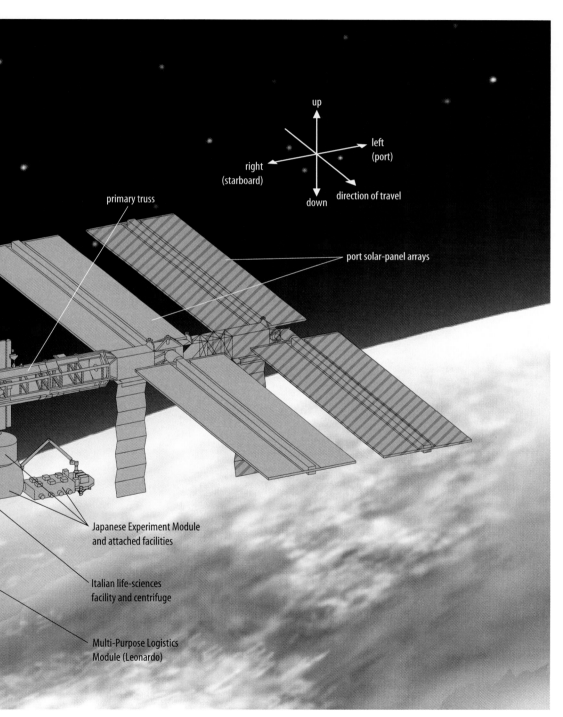

up

left
(port)

right
(starboard)

down

direction of travel

primary truss

port solar-panel arrays

Japanese Experiment Module
and attached facilities

Italian life-sciences
facility and centrifuge

Multi-Purpose Logistics
Module (Leonardo)

Zarya-Unity

addition of Service Module

addition of U.S. Laboratory
Module (Destiny), airlock, first
primary truss segment, and
remote manipulator system

solar-panel array to be mounted
first atop Unity, then moved to
port end of primary truss

addition of later-stage
components including complete
primary truss, solar-panel arrays,
and European and Japanese
laboratories

**Major stages in the construction
of the ISS are depicted in the
schematic diagram. Critical early
events in the assembly are the
additions of the Service Module
habitat supplied by Russia, the U.S.
Laboratory Module, and a solar
panel unit on Unity that will provide
power for the laboratory. The solar
array will be relocated later to the
port end of the primary truss.
Because plans for the station will
continue to evolve even as it is built,
the configuration of some elements
in the last stage of construction—
for example, the U.S. Habitation
Module—may change. Also
scheduled for late-stage installation,
the Russian modules to be attached
under the Service Module are not
depicted.**

Long-term studies in microgravity may shed light on the nature of the bone-mass loss seen in both astronauts and osteoporosis victims. The 10-day shuttle flight of John Glenn (above) in 1998 was part of this research, but only a space platform like the ISS can provide the necessary time and laboratory facilities.

are docked with the ISS for crew replacements, as many as a dozen people may be aboard for periods of several weeks. The ISS will operate on a 90-day service cycle, providing 30 days of high-quality microgravity for research and materials processing, 10 days of maintenance, another 30 days of microgravity, then a period of resupply and reboost of the station to reverse the effects of orbital decay.

MICROGRAVITY SCIENCE

The early cost-cutting downscaling of its Freedom design obliged NASA to delete dedicated sites for instruments for making solar, astronomical, and terrestrial observations. Conse-

quently, ISS research will focus on life and materials sciences in the space environment. To ensure that this work got off to a running start, NASA funded a number of Centers for Commercial Development of Space, each dedicated to a different discipline. These centers tested apparatus on pre-ISS shuttle flights.

The key feature of the space environment that scientists wish to study is the weightless state called zero gravity, or more correctly, microgravity. In principle, an orbiting satellite is in zero gravity; the effect of Earth's gravity is canceled by the inertial force resulting from orbital flight. If the satellite contains moving parts, however, the inevitable vibrations will impart tiny accelerations,

which correspond to a few millionths (hence, *micro*) of the gravitational acceleration experienced on Earth. On a particularly "noisy" satellite, where the environment may correspond to milligravity, or thousandths of Earth's gravity, it is impossible to undertake highly sensitive experiments. The presence of the crew on the ISS will render the station fairly noisy, but specially stabilized mounts will be available to accommodate particularly sensitive experiments. The great advantage of the ISS as a microgravity laboratory is that it will be possible to conduct long-term experiments. A shuttle, with its limited consumable supplies, can spend no more than two weeks in orbit.

For studies of the way in which living organisms are affected by the lack of gravity, the length of time spent in space can be crucial. About a third of astronauts suffer space sickness, a kind of motion sickness resulting from a disturbance of the body's orientation and balance system. Because symptoms usually subside after the first few days in orbit, space sickness and the body's adapation process can be studied on shuttle flights. Other biological processes, however, take much longer to react to the lack of gravity. Many processes—for example, the rate at which new bone cells

are created—gradually slow down when gravity is removed. Although the loss of bone mass can take several months to become serious, the loss rate is an order of magnitude faster than that of an osteoporosis sufferer. The close similiarity of osteoporosis and bone-mass loss in astronauts suggests to researchers that the former is induced by a change in the way the aging body copes with gravity. U.S. Sen. John Glenn's shuttle flight, made in late 1998 when Glenn was 77, was part of microgravity research into bone-mass loss, although the 10-day flight time limited what could be learned. With more time and more sophisticated facilities, scientists aboard the ISS will be able to study this process and other long-term effects of weightlessness in much finer detail than before.

Time is also important to the study of protein crystals, another line of research with down-to-Earth relevance. Proteins are complex organic molecules essential to life processes in all organisms. They include enzymes, hormones, antibodies, molecules that regulate gene expression, respiratory molecules like hemoglobin, and structural molecules like collagen and various muscle proteins. Understanding their molecular structure and function is essential to developing new pharmaceuticals, which can be proteins themselves or substances that interact in specific ways with natural proteins. A well-established method for studying a protein is to crystallize it and then determine its three-dimensional structure by means of X-ray crystallography. Earth's gravity, however, makes it difficult to crystallize large organic molecules, and a flawed crystal not only is difficult to analyze but also does not necessarily yield information representative of the molecule's true structure. In microgravity, away from normal gravity's distorting effects, crystallization runs more slowly and precisely, allowing large representative crystals to be grown more readily. Shuttle flights have demonstrated that not all protein crystals grow at the same rate, and the ISS will allow enough time for even slow-growing ones to be made.

In a similar way, the ISS will enable scientists to expand research in other areas of materials research. Over thousands of years, humans have become conditioned to observing physical and chemical processes in a gravity field and only recently have begun to realize that, outside gravity's influence, some of those processes—among them combustion, fluid flow, and melting and freezing—possess surprising subtleties. On the ISS, scientists will have the time to subject all manner of familiar processes to tests to see what happens. Combustion research in microgravity, for example, may lead to more efficient, less-polluting fuel-burner designs and advances in fire safety aboard spacecraft.

ORBITAL ECONOMICS

As an ongoing, round-the-clock facility, the ISS will transform the way in which space experiments are undertaken. In a terrestrial laboratory, scientists have the time to repeat an experiment, adjusting and fine-tuning it to hone a crucial measurement or observe how results vary with conditions. By contrast, on a limited-duration shuttle flight, time is a resource that must be shared among the many payloads carried in order to justify the cost of a launch. For an experiment on the ISS, the economics will be different. Once the experiment is on the station, it will be decoupled from the shuttle's launch costs and can be operated for prolonged periods or rerun for only the cost of the science itself. Working together, the shuttle program and the station will slash the cost of operating in space.

From previous in-space experiments, researchers know that a microgravity enviroment allows the manufacture of met-

Processes such as combustion and crystallization proceed differently outside gravity's influence than they do on Earth's surface. Burning flames in space (below, left) and on Earth (below, right) show strikingly distinct behavior. Zeolite crystals grown in orbit (bottom left) are larger than those formed in normal gravity (bottom right).

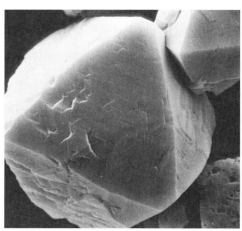 

(Top left, bottom left, and bottom right) NASA; (top right) Thomas Brase/Tony Stone Images

Shuttle astronauts took this photo of Cyclone Daniella in 1996. Future research aboard the ISS may be directed toward Earth, allowing scientists to make use of the unique vantage point of a permanent space platform to better understand Earth's weather systems.

als, semiconductors, and other materials with improved properties—for example, higher purity, more uniform physical characteristics, and near-perfect crystalline structures. Nevertheless, the in-orbit processing of materials on a commercial scale has been deterred by more than launch costs. So far, NASA has

been able to offer only infrequent flights on a very indeterminate schedule. It is difficult to justify commercial investment in an innovative process that can be achieved for at most two weeks twice a year.

Ongoing ISS operations will obviate these obstacles and make it possible to run commercial processes on a semicontinuous basis. If raw material can be ferried up in bulk, the desired material can be massproduced and returned to Earth when convenient, free from the vagaries of flight operations. If necessary, processes can be run on parasitic satellites released

from the ISS to operate alongside the station, with their products benefiting from optimum microgravity, and then retrieved for servicing. For little overhead, the ISS will be able to service an entire flotilla of such free flyers.

As NASA's proposal to Nixon had explained three decades earlier, the shuttle and the station form an integrated system. Either craft without the other is deficient. As an orbital outpost, the station will facilitate year-round operations that minimize the overhead of scientific and commercial activities, and the shuttle's prodi-

gious cargo capacity will sustain that outpost by exchanging crew, supplying consumables and new apparatus, and off-loading its products and unneeded equipment.

When all the costs that NASA calls space station related are totaled, from Reagan's initiation of the program in 1984, through assembly, and for a decade of operations, the U.S. contribution to the ISS will have been $75 billion, expressed in mid-1990s terms. Less-conservative critics have argued that $100 billion would be a more realistic figure. Nevertheless, viewed from one perspective, the ISS represents a mere 0.015% of the federal budget. By contrast, the Department of Defense can spend $250 billion in a single year. In this light, the ISS seems a small-change item for a nation as economically strong as the U.S.

THE FUTURE

Despite the initially limited focus of the scientific program, sooner or later microgravity research aboard the ISS will be joined by observational work in astronomy and Earth sciences. One important part of NASA's activity has been its Earth Sciences Enterprise, an international effort making use of the unique vantage point of space to discover climate patterns that will allow scientists to predict events such as floods and severe winters far enough in advance for nations and local populations to mount adequate responses. Technologists have been extremely inventive in devising sensors to observe Earth from space at different wavelengths. Such remote sensing is vastly enhanced if the data from different sensors can be integrated, a task that will be made easier when the sensors are all on the ISS rather than separate satellites.

As those most critical of the cost of the ISS have argued, many of the tasks being planned for the ISS could be done more cheaply by automated satellites. A major drawback of satellites, however, is that they have to operate completely autonomously. In the case of larger satellites, which usually carry a number of instruments, the higher development cost is offset by expectations of a longer lifetime. If one instrument fails, the satellite can continue operating in its degraded state, but if a key utility fails, the satellite has to be abandoned. What is needed is a platform that combines long life with reliability and flexibility. The most reliable and flexible element that can be built into a system is a human operator. Thus, once an inhabited station is running, it makes sense to load it with all the automated instruments that it can support.

The ISS will present an infrastructure for operating, servicing, and upgrading automated instruments and experiments that would otherwise have to have been designed for autonomous satellites. It will free scientific programs from the operational lifetimes of the technologies that support them and from the pace of technological advance. Moreover, it will allow the participating scientists, for the first time, to design instruments free of the mass, size, power, and communications limits of individual satellites. With shuttles for transportation and the ISS for support, the appallingly long time that is currently required to conceive, develop, and fly an instrument will be reduced.

The ISS should not be seen as a short-term venture. It is actually only the core of a complex that will be progressively expanded. By designing its modules with more connectivity than required in the basic configuration, NASA has expressed its confidence that the end of Phase 3 will be just the start of humankind's expansion into space. Once the ISS is up and running, the incentive to expand it will be strong because the overhead of each new facility will be small. As facilities are added, however, the workload, even with telescience, will exceed the capacity of the crew; another habitat will be needed to support more people. If free flyers are used for materials processing and maintained by the ISS crew, it will be necessary to add a large airlock that can act as a berthing facility and garage with a shirtsleeve environment.

Humans may not return to the Moon until far into the 21st century, and they may not follow their automated probes into deep space for many more years after that. As these events unfold, however, the ISS—or what it has become by then—will be serving, as Braun clearly envisaged, as the way station to destinations beyond.

FOR ADDITIONAL READING

Dragonfly: NASA and the Crisis Aboard the Mir, Bryan Burrough (HarperCollins Publishers, 1998).

Island in the Sky: Building the International Space Station, Piers Bizony (Aurum Press, 1996).

Living and Working in Space: A History of Skylab, David Compton and Charles Benson (NASA publication SP-4208, 1983).

The Mir Space Station: A Precursor to Space Colonization, David M. Harland (Wiley-Praxis, 1997).

The Space Shuttle: Roles, Missions and Accomplishments, David M. Harland (Wiley-Praxis, 1998).

INTERNET RESOURCES

Bill Harwood's CBS Space Page
   http://cbs.com/network/news/space
Boeing's ISS Home Page
   http://www.boeing.com/defense-space/space/spacestation/index.html
Florida Today's Space Page
   http://www.flatoday.com/space
Johnson Space Center Mission Status Reports http://www.jsc.nasa.gov/pao/media/mstat
NASA Human Spaceflight (ISS and shuttle information) http://spaceflight.nasa.gov
Today@nasa.gov
   http://www.nasa.gov/today/index.html

For centuries forensic scientists have helped police put criminals behind bars by producing scientific evidence in courts. Now, driven by an ever-growing national and international trade in endangered wildlife, scientists are helping conservationists by perfecting forensic techniques that protect the furred and feathered.

Forensics on the Wild Side

by Patricia J. West

Nearly one-third of the wildlife trade is estimated to involve illegal transactions. In Indonesia, orangutans (below), an endangered primate species, are being captured from the rain forest and sold as pets for as much as $50,000. (Opposite page, bottom) The desiccated remains of a male elephant, slaughtered for its ivory tusks, lie on the African savanna. The 1989 worldwide ban on the sale of elephant ivory has led to increases in some elephant populations, but poaching continues. To discourage trade, stockpiles of ivory confiscated from poachers are burned (opposite page, top).

The case started with a simple anonymous phone call identifying the site of the carcasses. Arriving at the scene, officials from the Wyoming Fish and Game Department found six headless pronghorn antelopes carelessly discarded near a city dump, a clear violation of the state's laws governing the disposal of game animal meat. As detectives would do in a human homicide case, the wildlife wardens collected the bodies and searched the entire area for clues. Weeks later an antelope head registered to a Wyoming hunter turned up at a local taxidermy shop. Was there any way of confirming that the head belonged to one of the carcasses?

Tissue samples from the head and carcasses were sent to a forensics laboratory in Edmonton, Alberta. Using a highly sophisticated technique known as DNA profiling, scientists were able to genetically link the head with one of the

Patricia J. West is a freelance writer based in Tuscaloosa, Alabama.

discarded antelope remains. The hunter was charged with six counts of wanton destruction and received jail time, six years of probation, a $12,000 fine, and revocation of his hunting license for 36 years.

The antelope case represents a new twist on an age-old activity, applying forensic techniques to track down criminals using the clues they leave behind. Forensic science, which includes forensic pathology, toxicology, and serology, has long been used to pursue crimes perpetrated against humans. Today scientists are using these same techniques and developing some unique solutions to identify those who breach laws protecting wildlife.

A NEED FOR WILDLIFE FORENSICS

The need for a scientific approach to solving crimes against wildlife has been obvious for as long as people have poached, unlawfully traded in the body parts of wildlife, and violated other laws protecting animal species. Every day thousands of wild animals are illegally captured for medical research, zoos, and the pet trade or killed for their meat, hides, fur, ivory, antlers, or other parts. The potential for profit, especially among poverty-stricken people, makes the hunting and collecting of wildlife worth the risk to poachers. According to current

estimates, wildlife trafficking generates from $6 billion to $10 billion annually worldwide, with about one-third of this total coming from illegal transactions.

Today around 30% of the world's wildlife is in danger of extinction, and a major cause, second only to habitat loss, is the illegal trade of exotic wildlife and wildlife products. Today, for instance, North American black, grizzly, and polar bears are being killed in record numbers as a result of a flourishing black market for bear gallbladders in Korea. There, dealers in traditional Chinese medicines are willing to pay more than $250 for a single gallbladder, which is be-

(Above) Frans Lanting/Tony Stone Images; (opposite page, top) Wendy Stone/Gamma Liaison International; (opposite page, bottom) Mark N. Boulton/Photo Researchers, Inc.

lieved by some people to be an aphrodisiac and a potential anticancer agent. Poachers have already decimated Asian bear populations and are now turning to North American bears as a fresh source. Estimates suggest that more than 40,000 bears are killed in North America each year for their gallbladders.

Other animals have suffered greatly from this multibillion-dollar market as well, including some that are much more in danger of extinction than American bears. According to the World Wildlife Fund, for example, more than 90% of the world's rhinoceroses have vanished since 1970, killed by the thousands for their precious horns, which are ground into powder and sold on the open market as a remedy for headaches, fatigue, and convul-sions. Similarly, wild tiger populations have shrunk considerably since the start of the 20th century, from 100,000 to fewer than 6,000 left in the wild by the late 1990s, due to a growing demand for powdered tiger bone, a traditional Chinese treatment for arthritis and rheumatism. Although only 5% of all the ingredients used in Chinese folk medicines originates from endangered species like rhinos and tigers, poaching to support this market still represents one of the most urgent threats to these animals today.

Most developed nations have laws in place to protect rare and endangered species and to regulate the commercial and recreational hunting and collecting of animals. In the U.S. the Endangered Species Act of 1973 authorizes the government to protect plants and animals that have been classified as endangered as well as those listed as threatened, meaning that they are likely to become endangered in the foreseeable future. Additionally, individual states have their own laws regarding commercial and recreational hunting and fishing. On an international scale, wildlife are protected by a number of significant laws, including the Convention on International Trade in Endangered Species (CITES). Established in 1975 in response to concerns about the impact of the illegal wildlife trade, CITES protects

(Below) Steve Hillebrand/US Dept. Interior, Fish & Wildlife Service; (Bottom) Bill Fitzpatrick/US Dept. Interior, Fish & Wildlife Service

Rhinoceros horn is in great demand for use in traditional Asian medicines (above). Below are examples of worked ivory products seized by Fish and Wildlife Service inspectors at U.S. international airports, ports, and border crossings.

H. Donnezan/Explorer/Photo Researchers, Inc.

Many of the animal derivatives used in Chinese folk medicines come from endangered species, yet black marketers are able to circumvent laws and reach markets around the world, such as these medicinal shops in China (center, this page and opposite) and Singapore (bottom left). Tiger parts (left), especially the bones, are ground into powder and made into pills and plasters. Other animal parts, such as this elephant foot (bottom right), are crafted into decorative items and sold to wealthy collectors.

(Above, top) Dan Habib/Impact Visuals; (above, left) W&D McIntyre/Photo Researchers, Inc.; (above, right) Bill Fitzpatrick/US Dept. Interior, Fish & Wildlife Service

animal species by banning international trade in an agreed-upon list of endangered species and regulating the trade of others that might become endangered.

Violators of the Endangered Species Act are subject to fines as high as $100,000 and one year's imprisonment. Organizations found in violation may be fined as much as $200,000. Even with such strict laws in place, however, enforcement is difficult both nationally and internationally. Execution of wildlife laws requires the employment of specialized personnel, preferably trained wildlife or fisheries wardens who are familiar with animals and the tendencies of hunters, anglers, and would-be poachers. While many governments strive to manage native wildlife populations, protecting and managing species is much more difficult for some countries, especially where illiteracy and poverty are high. In such nations protective laws are hard to enforce because of a dearth of trained wardens and a fundamental lack of understanding and acceptance of the laws that are in place.

Until recently, even when serious violations of wildlife laws were noted, most government agencies did not have the means to uncover the evidence necessary to bring the cases to court. Without proof many cases have had to be abandoned. Change is afoot, however, as countries are now searching for ways to minimize wildlife losses. They understand that solving wildlife crimes may serve as a powerful deterrent to other potential abusers of wildlife laws. Fortunately, with the help of a new breed of forensic scientists, the odds for solving and prosecuting wildlife crimes are improving.

FORENSICS AS A SCIENCE

Forensics, in the broadest sense, is defined as the application of science to legal issues. Most people view the field in terms of forensic medicine; that is, the application of medical knowledge to civil and criminal proceedings. Although the forensic sciences form a vital part of the entire justice and regulatory system, some of their many disciplines have become identified primarily with law enforcement, an image enhanced by crime fiction, television, and movies. A forensic pathologist, for example, may be asked to determine the cause of an unexplained death, the time of death, and similar information. A forensic molecular biologist might analyze the DNA in a biological sample, such as semen or blood associated with a victim of sexual assault or murder. Other experts in the field of forensic science include odontologists, who specialize in teeth and related dental evidence; toxicologists, who are trained to identify poisons and other chemicals in the body; entomologists, who utilize insect evidence to solve crimes; and psychiatrists, who help law enforcement by studying the motives and tendencies of criminals and predicting their behavior.

Modern forensic science developed only as recently as the middle of the 19th century. Prior to this period, police investigations of suspicious deaths or analyses of trace evidence found at a crime scene were extremely difficult and highly subjective. One of the first celebrated cases in forensic science involved the Spanish-born French chemist Matthieu Orfila, who worked in Paris and testified in an arsenic poisoning criminal trial in 1840. Orfila developed a chemical test to detect arsenic, the poison of choice at the time because the symptoms, which included violent stomach pains and vomiting, were very similar to those of cholera and therefore often mistaken for them. Paris police official Alphonse Bertillon's anthropometry system, using a series of body and facial measurements for individual identification introduced in 1882, and English scientist Francis Galton's fingerprint classification work in the 1890s were other important contributions to the emerging field of forensic science.

Several developments spurred the advancement of forensic science in the 20th century, paving the way for more detailed and reliable criminal investigations. These included the evolution of biochemistry as a science and its application to the analysis of evidence, including poisons in body fluids and tissues. A second development was the refinement and application of the microscope to the study of trace evidence— hairs, spores, seeds, fibers, and other microscopic bits—from a crime scene. A third milestone was the development of photography, which provided a mobile way to document evidence. Lastly, advances in pathology enabled doctors to make definitive statements about medical evidence in cases of unnatural death.

Some of the newest techniques being applied to forensic science involve molecular genetics. In the past fairly large amounts of blood or tissue were necessary for investigative work, and often all that could be determined was blood type. Today scientists use DNA profiling, or fingerprinting, which makes use of the fact that, except for identical twins, every individual has a unique genetic makeup. Developed in England in the mid-1980s for paternity testing, DNA profiling allows investigators to test for an exact match between a suspect and biological material from the scene of a crime. Using another modern laboratory technique, the

British scientist Alec Jeffries developed DNA profiling in 1984. DNA profile comparisons, like fingerprint comparisons, produce a unique pattern that can identify an individual or a species.

David Parker/Science Photo Library/Photo Researchers, Inc.

polymerase chain reaction (PCR), scientists can now take DNA from a single strand of hair or a drop of dried blood and amplify it into a sample large enough for testing.

APPLYING FORENSICS TO WILDLIFE CRIMES

Although the application of forensic techniques to wildlife crimes began as early as the 1960s, wildlife forensics as a branch of forensic science is still in its infancy. Authoritative textbooks on the subject are lacking, as are professional societies that specialize in the field. Professionals who work in wildlife forensic science come from a wide variety of backgrounds, including law enforcement, wildlife management, zoology, ecology, and veterinary medicine. Indeed, many individuals who become involved in wildlife forensics do so opportunistically because their particular expertise is applicable to a specific case.

Until recently very few government agencies routinely applied forensic techniques to solve wildlife crimes. Even now only a handful of U.S. state governments have the capabilities to do so, according to Bob McClymont of the Northwest Association of Forensic Scientists. For example, the Wyoming Game and Fish Department has operated a small wildlife forensics laboratory for almost 20 years. There, officials deal mostly with crimes involving the illegal hunting of deer, antelope, and elk. With a small staff, the lab is able to make species and gender identifications using DNA analyses on hair, bone, blood, and other biological materials. Only four other states had labs dedicated to wildlife forensics as of late 1998: California, Idaho, Nebraska, and Texas. Many states rely on police labs to do their wildlife-related work, whereas others enlist university scientists or museum personnel to analyze wildlife evidence.

The U.S. government took a significant step in 1989 when it established the National Fish and Wildlife Forensics Laboratory (NFWFL) in Ashland, Oregon. Devoted to combating the illegal trafficking in wildlife, the full-service laboratory is the only facility of its kind in the world. The lab's team of more than 30 scientists and staff provides an investigative service for law enforcement in many types of wildlife crimes, from the shooting of game birds and mammals out of season to the killing of endangered or threatened animals. Casework is submitted to the lab from state and federal agencies all over the U.S. and from the more than

The National Fish and Wildlife Forensics Laboratory, which opened in 1989, offers an investigative service for wildlife crimes ranging from the shooting of game out of season to the killing of endangered animal species.

Stephen Ferry/Gamma Liaison International

140 foreign governments that participate in CITES. Much like their counterparts in a police crime lab, the lab's forensic specialists conduct crime scene investigations, examine submitted items of evidence, and provide expert witness testimony in court.

The state-of-the-art laboratory has a wide scope of analytical capabilities in four areas: pathology, morphology, criminalistics, and serology. The lab is arranged in a linear fashion with one end of the building dedicated to receiving and cataloging evidence. The evidence could be anything that suggests that an animal was killed: a piece of jewelry fashioned from a tiger's claw, a pufferfish lamp, scrimshawed whale teeth, zebra pelts, tiger-skin rugs, or boots made from crocodile hide. Even pieces of artwork built from animal parts have been submitted as evidence. Housed in a 650-square-meter (7,000-square-foot) warehouse, the lab's evidence collection is a grim reminder of the enormity of the problem.

The process of linking evidence in a wildlife crime to potential suspects often requires expertise in a number of disciplines. Consequently, the nature of an evidence sample determines its passage through the lab. If, for example, a whole carcass is received, it might first be studied by members of the pathology unit. A pathologist trained in veterinary medicine would typically conduct a full autopsy on the carcass and collect other evidence, such as bullets, arrow tips, and stomach contents, in order to figure out how the animal died. On the other hand, if the evidence is more fragmentary, such as a single feather, a bone, or an animal pelt, it might first go to an expert in the morphology lab, who will attempt to identify the family, genus, and species of the animal victim. To aid scientists in this work, the lab is stocked with numerous cabinets and drawers filled with bones, teeth, animal furs, fish scales, feathers, and hundreds of preserved specimens against which evidence samples can be compared.

Scientists in the criminalistics unit use chemical and microscopic techniques to identify, compare, and interpret a

Bill Fitzpatrick/US Dept. Interior, Fish & Wildlife Service

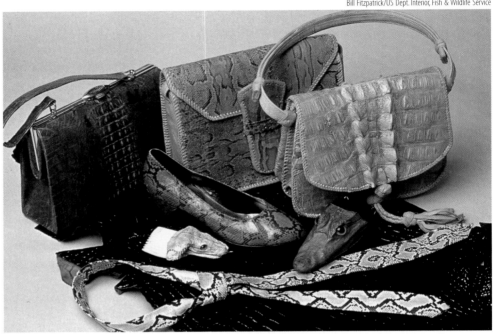

Evidence submitted to the NFWFL rarely comes in the form of an intact body. Rather, the lab typically receives products made from animal parts, such as this collection of reptile-themed garments, purses, and other items.

wide range of evidence, including wildlife parts and products, poisons and pesticides, bullets and cartridge cases, paint, soil, and synthetic fibers. Experts in this section must deal with a suite of questions that might be asked by law enforcement agents: Is it real elephant ivory (which is banned in international trade owing to elephant poaching) or just an imitation? Was the animal killed with a gun or an arrow? Was the animal poisoned intentionally, and if so, with what chemicals? The answers to these kinds of questions can produce the type of solid evi-

dence needed for prosecution in a courtroom.

The smaller an evidence sample, the harder it is to identify the species. Should the evidence be nothing more than a packet of powder supposedly containing rhino horn or blood scrapings from a suspect's hunting knife, it would be sent to the lab's serology unit where scientists would conduct protein and DNA analyses on the tissues to identify the species in question. Serologists can tell law enforcement officials a great deal about the animal evidence; for example, how many animals may have been in-

volved in a poaching incident or whether animal remains found in the field match meat seized from a suspect's freezer.

With wildlife crimes and their economic impact on the rise, other countries have recently established forensic laboratories on their own turf. One of the newest facilities, opened in 1998, is located in Shanghai. Built in response to new Chinese laws that require the tightening of international wildlife trade regulations, the laboratory is associated with East China Normal University and is staffed by about 20 faculty members. To date, the lab has focused mostly on species identification and has handled cases involving deer, Arctic foxes, sparrows, and other animals. Canada now has two small wildlife forensic laboratories as well, in Ontario and Alberta. Both facilities have small staffs and focus primarily on game animals such as moose, deer, bear, and elk. Other countries, including India, are also attempting to set

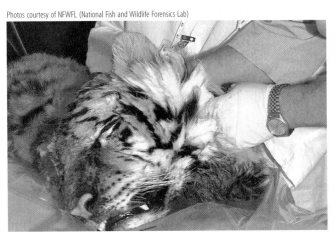

When the NFWFL receives a full carcass, it is often first studied by the laboratory's pathologists (above), who determine the cause of death. When evidence consists of a partial animal—for example, skeletal remains, hides, claws, teeth, fur, feathers, or wings—it may be directed to the morphology department (right and below) for species identification.

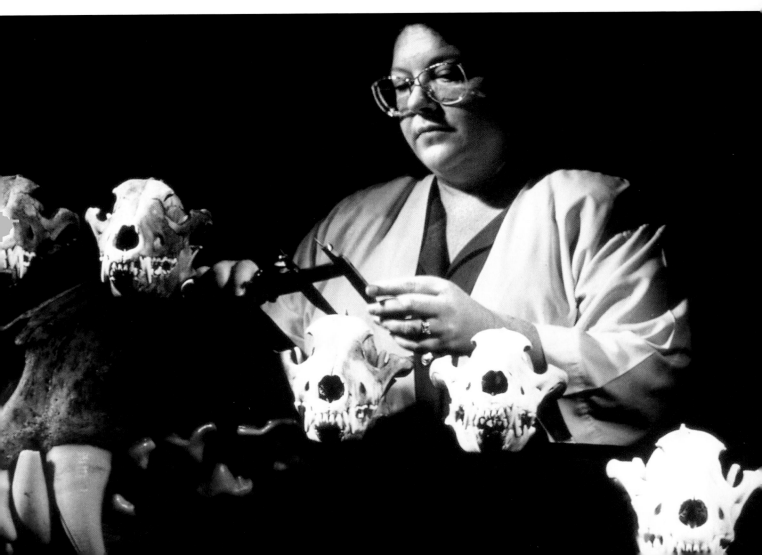

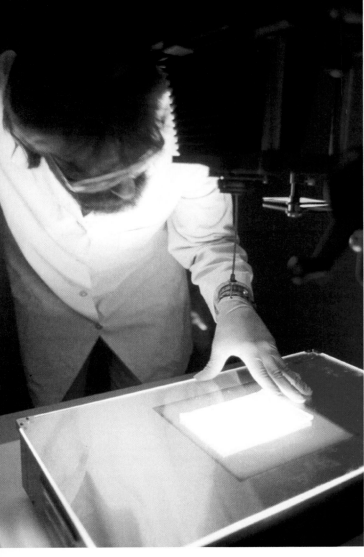

Photos courtesy of NFWFL

Scientists in the NFWFL's serology laboratory use protein and DNA analysis techniques to link poachers to their victims. A pool of blood in a field, for instance, could be matched to bloodstains on a suspect's knife, or the head of a trophy buck might be linked to a gut pile found in the woods. The lab's serologists can even determine the gender of the source of blood or tissue evidence, which can be important if a suspect is licensed only to hunt male deer and the seized meat comes from a doe.

up wildlife laboratories, but such facilities have proven difficult to establish and even harder to fund.

CHALLENGES OF WILDLIFE FORENSICS

Although forensic techniques for solving human and wildlife crimes have much in common, there are also a host of differences. Ken Goddard, director of the NFWFL, has stated that the greatest challenge faced by wildlife forensic scientists comes from dealing with thousands of species of animals from all over the world. Police crime labs are geared toward

investigating crimes involving just one species, *Homo sapiens*. Wildlife specialists, on the other hand, must contend with evidence from about 30,000 different vertebrate species and

Ken Goddard, director of the NFWFL, began his career as a police criminalist. In addition to his work at the Oregon forensics laboratory, Goddard is a best-selling author of crime novels that typically involve forensics and wildlife law enforcement.

the occasional case involving invertebrates.

In addition, because evidence samples are frequently nothing more than a spot of blood, a piece of feather, or a scrap of fur, one important task of scientists working at the Oregon lab is to identify new species-defining characteristics. In this way, they can establish that an animal piece, part, or product came from a specific species of animal and not from any other possible species around the world. The illegal trade in elephant ivory, in fact, has been virtually wiped out in the U.S., in part because the lab's scientists worked out a way to identify the source of a given piece of ivory. Most of the ivory tested today comes from wild boars and extinct mammoths, which are legal sources.

Another challenge associated with the work comes from the fact that wildlife laws sometimes

differ from region to region. In Ontario, for instance, it is legal to possess bear gallbladders, but it is illegal to sell gallbladders that came out of Ontario bears. To get around the law, people often sell Ontario bear gallbladders under the guise of their having come from bears in Canadian provinces where it is legal to kill bears and collect their gallbladders. As a result, Canadian wildlife officials often have difficulty prosecuting those obtaining Ontario bear gallbladders and those involved in selling them. Scientists at Trent University's Wildlife Forensic DNA Laboratory in Peterborough, Ontario, have begun work on an extensive DNA database that they believe will allow them to identify the population, and thus the geographic area, from which a particular bear gallbladder originated.

Cost is another factor when investigating wildlife crimes. A typical investigation can cost thousands of dollars, especially when DNA analyses are involved. Even when a suspect is

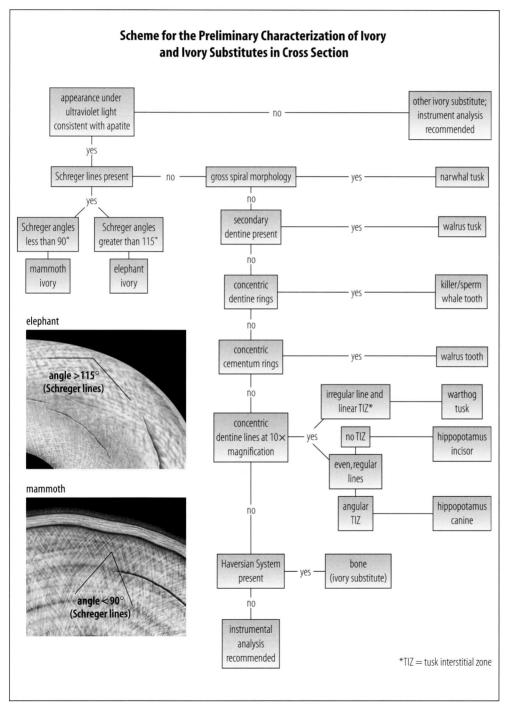

Scheme for the Preliminary Characterization of Ivory and Ivory Substitutes in Cross Section

To help distinguish between legal and illegal sources of ivory, NFWFL scientists worked out an identification scheme. Cross sections of dentine in elephant and mammoth ivory reveal uniquely characteristic Schreger lines. In mammoths Schreger angles (formed between Schreger lines) average less than 90°; Schreger angles in elephant ivory average greater than 115°.

appearance under ultraviolet light consistent with apatite
— no → other ivory substitute; instrument analysis recommended

yes

Schreger lines present — no → gross spiral morphology — yes → narwhal tusk

yes

Schreger angles less than 90° → mammoth ivory

Schreger angles greater than 115° → elephant ivory

gross spiral morphology — no → secondary dentine present — yes → walrus tusk

no

concentric dentine rings — yes → killer/sperm whale tooth

no

concentric cementum rings — yes → walrus tooth

no

concentric dentine lines at 10× magnification — yes →
- irregular line and linear TIZ* → warthog tusk
- no TIZ → hippopotamus incisor
- even, regular lines
- angular TIZ → hippopotamus canine

no

Haversian System present — yes → bone (ivory substitute)

no

instrumental analysis recommended

*TIZ = tusk interstitial zone

elephant

angle >115° (Schreger lines)

mammoth

angle <90° (Schreger lines)

tried and convicted of a wildlife crime, such as illegal possession and sale of deer meat, the law only allows for a relatively small fine, often just a few hundred dollars. Thus, pursuing such crimes is not always cost-effective. Wildlife officials and conservationists hope, however, that this will change as wildlife laws are strengthened.

CASE STUDIES IN WILDLIFE CRIME

The utility of wildlife forensic techniques has been proven again and again throughout the world. The science may be relatively new, but through the methodical and meticulous application of forensic techniques, wildlife forensic investigators have helped law enforcement officials track down and prosecute thousands of people, helping turn the hunters into the hunted.

For example, in a 1993 case handled by the NFWFL specialists were faced with a partial carcass of a radio-collared grizzly bear shot in eastern Washington. The shooter, a Washington-based elk hunter, claimed to have killed the animal in self-defense after it charged at him. Experts doubted the man's story, pointing out that an average person would not have had nearly enough time to aim and shoot at a charging grizzly. A full autopsy

was conducted on the slain animal, revealing that the bullets had entered the bear at nearly right angles. The lab's scientists concluded that the animal was most likely moving away from the hunter, not toward him. Faced with the evidence, the suspect pleaded guilty to the unlawful shooting of the grizzly.

In Texas microscopic techniques were used to determine the validity of a fish caught in a bass fishing tournament. With some tournaments offering cash awards exceeding $50,000, anglers have been known to bring large bass to a tournament site, secure them in a discreet location in the lake prior to the competition, and then enter them as legitimately captured bass. This happened in a 1980s fishing tournament when the winning largemouth bass exceeded the previous record by a significant amount. Tournament officials assumed foul play, and the suspected angler was given a polygraph test. When the results of the test proved inconclusive, officials confiscated the bass for dissection. Examination of the fish's otoliths, or ear stones, which record regular growth patterns in their microstructure, suggested that the bass was 10 years old. Stocking records for the lake, however, indicated that bass had been placed there only six years prior to the tournament date. The scientists con-

cluded that the winning bass could not have come from the lake, and the angler was fined and charged with fraud.

In a 1992 case, several bald eagles, a red-tailed hawk, two coyotes, and several dozen sheep were found dead in a cornfield in north central Kansas. In order to pursue a suspected poisoning of an endangered species (the eagles) and a migratory bird (the hawk), law enforcement agents sent the bird carcasses, sheep tissues, coyote stomachs, and other samples to the NFWFL and to the Veterinary Diagnostic Laboratory at Kansas State University, Manhattan. After ruling out trauma caused by gunshot or electrocution, the scientists performed a chemical analysis on the stomach contents of the coyotes and the birds. They found high levels of the insecticide carbofuran, a highly toxic and strictly regulated organic pesticide developed during World War II as a nerve gas. As a result of the investigation, two people admitted to lacing the sheep carcasses with poison in order to attract and kill problem coyotes. Because of the deaths of the birds, which had also died after eating the insecticide-filled flesh, the legal case was taken to federal court, where the responsible parties agreed to pay a $12,000 fine for their unlawful actions.

Forensic work is also being done on whales, the beleaguered group of marine mammals whose numbers have been drastically reduced by years of commercial hunting throughout the world. Conservationists now have a powerful tool to uncover evidence of illegal whaling. C. Scott Baker of the University of Aukland, New Zealand, and Steve R. Palumbi of Harvard University reported in 1998 that whale meat purchased in some Japanese retail markets was most likely obtained from protected species of whales, including humpback, fin, and minke whales. Using DNA techniques on the purchased meat, the scientists were able to identify the species and the probable geographic source of the whale meat. They concluded that, in spite of the worldwide moratorium on commercial whaling that has been in place since 1986, some nations had been hunting whales under the guise of science and illegally selling the meat. Such information is being used by the International Whaling Commission as it enforces international bans on the commercial hunting of whales.

Not all of the work being done in the field is conducted on large vertebrates. Less glamorous invertebrate species are also receiving protection from wildlife sleuths. In 1998 scientists at the University of Alabama, Tuscaloosa, were using DNA techniques in an attempt to track down the source of a ton of freshwater mussel shells that were confiscated by the U.S. Fish and Wildlife Service from a private collector. Although the collector claimed that the shells were obtained legally, federal wildlife officers suspected that they were collected from protected waterways. The shells have a commercial value of more than $16,000 and could be sold to the Asian cultured pearl industry, which uses shell pieces to encourage the production of pearls in oysters. University of Alabama biologist Charles Lydeard was developing primers for DNA analysis that may allow for a definitive answer as to the origin of the mussels.

THE FUTURE

The science of wildlife forensics has shown great growth in the past several years, and with no shortage of wildlife laws violations, the future looks bright and busy for the individuals and laboratories using these techniques. An important highlight in the ongoing development of the field is planned for 1999, when wildlife forensic scientists are scheduled to convene formally for the first time at the International Association of Forensic Sciences meeting in Los Angeles. Most of the people involved in wildlife forensics are expected to attend.

In the future, individuals who breach state, national, and international wildlife laws will have even more to fear. With forensic techniques, scientists are quickly acquiring the means to expose these criminals with evidence that will help cases stick in the courtroom. Furthermore, judges are stepping harder on people who violate wildlife laws. Tougher enforcement coupled with modern advances in wildlife forensic science is good news for the world's wildlife and those who work to protect it.

Courtesy of NFWFL

Wildlife forensic scientists may not be able to halt the demand for exotic-animal accessories or endangered-species medicinals, but they will continue to give law-enforcement agents the support they need to stop the illegal killing of wildlife in its tracks.

"Witness for the Deceased," Stephanie Pain, *New Scientist* (August 27, 1994, pp. 21–25).

INTERNET RESOURCES

Forensic Science Link Pages
http://www.freeyellow.com/members2/techdev/forensiclinks.html
International Association of Forensic Sciences http://www.criminalistics.com/IAFS-1999/default.html
National Fish and Wildlife Forensics Laboratory http://www.lab.fws.gov
World Wildlife Fund
http://www.wwf.org/index.html

FOR ADDITIONAL READING

"Bodies of Evidence," Jay Stuller, *Wildlife Conservation* (September–October 1997, pp. 29–35).
Forensic DNA Technology, Mark A. Farley and James J. Harrington, eds. (Lewis Publishers, Inc., 1991).
Introduction to Forensic Sciences, William G. Eckert, ed. (CRC Press, 1997).
"When Scientists Become Sleuths," Richard Wolkomir and Joyce Wolkomir, *National Wildlife* (February–March 1992, pp. 8–15).

You Are Here: Navigation in the 21st Century

by Tom Logsdon

In ancient times, explorers relied on the positions of the Sun, Moon, and stars to help cross uncharted lands and oceans. Today the celestial objects that are guiding people from place to place are artificial stars—sophisticated navigation satellites that, under the right conditions, can pinpoint any location on Earth within millimeters.

At this moment, two dozen high-tech satellites are sweeping around Earth approximately 20,400 kilometers (12,700 miles) above the ground. Billions of U.S. military dollars have been spent to finance the satellites, yet the precise navigation signals that they transmit are available free of charge to anyone who chooses to purchase a receiver. For less than $100, a person can buy one of the battery-powered units and, within seconds, pinpoint his or her location on Earth, any time of day or night, in all kinds of weather. Most of the convenient receivers can even gently escort their owners, with user-friendly directions, from any point on Earth to any other.

The constellation of satellites circling the planet are part of the Global Positioning System (GPS), a sophisticated radio-navigation service that may well be one of history's greatest technological developments. Put into place in the 1980s for military needs, GPS was a valuable aid to U.S. forces in Operation Desert Storm in 1991. It helped soldiers direct fuel-starved warplanes toward linkups with aerial tankers, pull in air strikes against Iraqi radar installations, and guide mess trucks toward famished troops scattered across the desert sands. Moreover, when U.S. Special Forces units ventured behind enemy lines, they used GPS receivers to record the map coordinates of natural watering holes in the desert, thus ensuring freshwater supplies for onrushing troops.

Tom Logsdon is a professional lecturer, international instructor, expert witness, and author of 29 nonfiction books, including Understanding the Navstar: GPS, GIS, and IVHS *(1995) and* Orbital Mechanics: Theory and Applications *(1997).*

Today the constellation of GPS satellites has paved the way for a whole new revolution in personal and commercial navigation. Records indicate that approximately 95% of all GPS receivers sold in 1998 were to nonmilitary users. Indeed, industry experts estimate that by the year 2000 annual worldwide revenues from the sale of civilian GPS receivers may top $8.5 billion. The receivers, some of which are no larger than a handheld calculator, are being employed for a multitude of uses, from guiding lifesaving ambulances through the crowded streets of Buffalo, New York, to helping game wardens in The Gambia protect their fish-rich territorial waters against illegal poachers. The system has changed the practice of navigation forever, and with the technology constantly evolving and new applications for it being imagined every day, the Global Positioning System will be guiding people well into the 21st century.

THE ANCIENT ROOTS OF NAVIGATION

Where am I? The question is simple, but the answer, historically, has proved not to be. Since ancient times, explorers and navigators have searched the heavens for celestial bodies that would help them identify their location on Earth with the precision necessary to reach their destination. Early mariners "fixed" their position and navigated by observing the shifting positions of the Sun, Moon, planets, and more distant background stars. The ancient Greek historian Herodotus, for instance, described how Phoenician mariners relied on the position of Polaris (the polestar or North Star) as they plied their extensive trade routes in the Mediterranean Sea during the 1st millennium bc. Centuries later, between AD 800 and 1050, the great Viking explorers guided their ships across the icy waters of the North Atlantic Ocean using simple charts and tables that described the variation of the Sun's noontime elevation at different times throughout the year.

A great development in the history of navigation occurred when mariners—Europeans in the 12th century and Chinese perhaps 200 or 300 years earlier—began making use of the fact that a piece of lodestone (a naturally occurring magnetic ore), when set on a sliver of wood floating in water, aligned itself in the direction of Polaris. These may have been the world's earliest known compasses. One of Western Europe's earliest references to the navigational compass was penned

Early explorers estimated their geographical position using celestial navigation techniques—the art of determining location by means of astronomical observations.

by Englishman Alexander Neckham around 1190. He characterized it as "a needle placed on a dart which sailors use to steer when the Great Bear is hidden by clouds," referring to the constellation of stars known as Ursa Major, which revolves around Polaris.

The sextant, developed in the 18th century, made Polaris and various other celestial bodies considerably more useful to European navigators. When the sky was clear, this simple device, which employs adjustable mirrors to measure the elevation angles of stellar objects, was used to establish a ship's latitude, its location on Earth measured north or south from the Equator. The early sextants, however, had one major drawback—they could not establish a vessel's east-west position, or longitude. Determining longitude depends on both angular measurements and precise time measurements. Superior time-

The Figure of the Quadrant

keeping, in fact, is needed because even a one-second timing error can translate into a longitudinal error of about a half kilometer (1,640 feet). Unfortunately, even on dry land, the best 17th-century clocks were capable of keeping time to an accuracy of only one or two seconds over an interval of several days. Placed on board a ship, clocks became even more unreliable. After being subjected to bouncing

waves, corrosive salt sprays, and unpredictable variations in temperature, pressure, and humidity, most shipboard clocks either stopped running or became too unstable to permit accurate navigation.

The timing problem was solved in 1761 when, after more than 40 years of disciplined labor, a barely educated British cabinetmaker named John Harrison constructed the first practical marine chronometer, an oversized jeweled pocket watch that was nearly twice as accurate as the finest land-based clocks of his day. Finally, mariners had a way to determine both latitude and longitude. For decades thereafter, the precise timing measurements obtained from marine chronometers, coupled with sextant sightings of the celestial bodies, allowed explorers to journey with de-

A woodcut from a 17th-century mariner's magazine depicts a navigator using a backstaff, a predecessor of the sextant. Backstaffs, cross-staffs, and quadrants were among the earliest instruments used at sea to measure the altitude of celestial objects.

pendable precision throughout the world.

GROUND-BASED RADIO NAVIGATION

Celestial navigation remained an important part of exploration and commerce throughout the 19th century and during the early part of the 20th century. A new nautical era began in the 1920s when radio signals from continuously operating onshore transmitting stations began to be used to fix location. The use of electromagnetic waves in position location was particularly useful for ships navigating in darkness and fog. One of the earliest systems employed a radio direction-finding (RDF) receiver. As its name implies, an RDF unit works fundamentally like a radio. Radio signals picked up by a directional antenna are weakest when the antenna is aligned perpendicular to the direction in which the signals are passing. When the antenna is rotated for minimum signal pickup, the direction to the transmitter can be found. This direction, or bearing, can be

(Above and right) The Granger Collection

Self-taught English carpenter John Harrison built the first practical marine chronometer for determining longitude at sea. The chronometer shown, from 1759, was Harrison's fourth, a timepiece that earned him a £20,000 reward from the British government.

plotted on a chart as a line passing through the known reference point—the radio station. When the procedure is repeated with another station, the second position line intersects the first, thus fixing the radio receiver's position.

During World War II, a variety of radio navigation systems were introduced. One system, Loran (for "long-range navigation," later called Loran A), employed hyperbolic ranging techniques. In such systems, a ground-based transmitter broadcasts an omnidirectional pulse, which is picked up by a distant ground-based receiver. A transmitter linked to the receiver then immediately rebroadcasts the pulse on a different frequency. To find a position, the user employs a Loran receiver, which picks up the two pulses and measures the time difference of their arrival to locate itself somewhere on a hyperbola stretching across Earth's surface. A repetition of the process, using two other distant transmitters, provides a second hyperbola, whose intersection with the first determines the user's position.

Loran, one of the earliest hyperbolic systems, was developed to furnish precise navigation for military ships and aircraft. In the intervening years, various countries, includ-

Official U.S. Navy Photo

ing Canada, Norway, England, Australia, and the United States, have cooperated in constructing a variety of ground-based radio navigation systems. More than 100 different types, including Decca, Loran C, and Omega, have been placed in operation over the past 60 years, and a few remain in use. A version of Loran C, for instance, provides radio navigation service for coastal waters around the entire continental U.S. and most of Alaska. In addition, 24 U.S. Loran C stations cooperate with Russian and

Canadian stations to provide coverage in Canadian waters and the Bering Sea.

The engineers who design a ground-based radio navigation system have essentially two choices when they are selecting its transmission frequency, neither of which produces entirely satisfactory results. When a very low frequency is used, the radio signals reflect off the ionosphere—the electrically charged region in Earth's upper atmosphere—and return to the surface, thus allowing broad-area coverage with a small

number of ground-based transmitters. Such a system, however, does not provide accurate navigation, primarily because of uncertainties in the path that the signals follow in arriving at the receiver. On the other hand, transmissions using higher frequency waves provide accurate navigation, but because they penetrate the ionosphere and continue traveling into space, they allow only local, horizon-to-horizon coverage. Consequently, hundreds of high-frequency ground-based transmitters are required to provide accurate navigation to a continent-wide region.

These and other difficulties can be circumvented by placing a navigation transmitter on board a high-altitude satellite. From this vantage point, equivalent to the top of an antenna mast thousands of kilometers tall, horizon-to-horizon coverage is increased tremendously. Building and installing a navigation transmitter along the space frontier typically costs 10–20 times as much as it costs to produce and install a comparable transmitter on the ground. A space-borne high-frequency transmitter, however, combines line-of-sight accuracy with broad-area coverage of a substantial fraction of the globe.

EARLY NAVIGATION SATELLITES

The first successful constellation of radio navigation satellites, the Transit Navigation System, took only limited advantage of the accurate ranging capabilities and broad-area coverage provided by high-altitude satellites. The satellites were first launched in the early 1960s by the U.S. Navy to provide an accurate, all-weather worldwide navigational service for U.S. ships, submarines, and aircraft. The six Transit satellites circled Earth in low-altitude polar orbits with equatorial crossing points spaced evenly around the globe. As they swept through their orbits, they emitted radio signals at known frequencies. A satellite receiver on the ground or, more typically, on a ship or submarine calculated position by measuring the Doppler shifts of the radio signals.

A Doppler shift is an observed change in the frequency of a sound wave or electromagnetic wave traveling from its source to an observer. The phenomenon occurs whenever there is relative motion between the wave source and the observer. Consider, for example, a commuter standing at a train station listening to the whistle emitted by a moving train. As the train approaches the stationary listener, sound waves become compressed and a higher pitch is heard. Then, after the train passes and recedes into the distance, sound waves are stretched out to produce a lower tone. The orbital motion of a Transit satellite sweeping from horizon to horizon produced similar Doppler shift variations in the radio waves picked up by receivers on the ground. Depending on

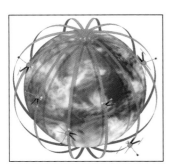

Radio navigation satellites were first employed successfully for position finding in the early 1960s. The U.S. Navy's Transit Navigation System was based on measurement of the Doppler shift of a satellite's radio signal as it transited the sky. Several shortcomings, however, limited the system's military and civilian uses.

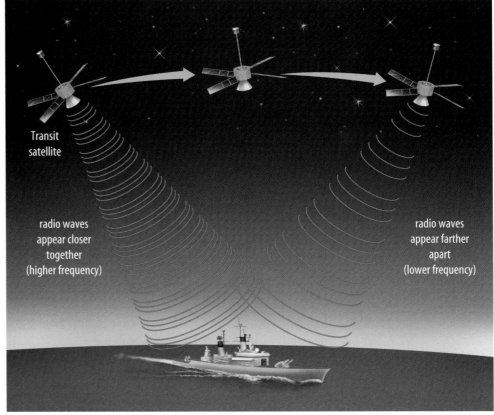

Transit satellite

radio waves appear closer together (higher frequency)

radio waves appear farther apart (lower frequency)

the user's location on Earth, a different variation in the Doppler shift was observed. In actual use, a specially programmed computer processed the Doppler-shifted signals from one satellite in order to obtain latitude and longitude readings.

At the peak of its popularity, the Transit system attracted more than 100,000 users, mostly commercial shipping firms. Although it was financed by the U.S. Department of Defense, civilian use of the system was permitted and encouraged beginning in 1973. Soon civilian users outnumbered their military counterparts by more than 30 to one. The Transit system, however, was plagued by a number of bothersome limitations. The biggest was that, whereas the system did provide reasonably precise longitude-latitude coordinates, it gave no accurate information on a user's altitude. It also yielded no information on the velocity of a moving vehicle and could not be used effectively on rapidly moving vehicles. Lastly, the system's position measurements were inaccurate near the North and South Poles because, being in polar orbit, all the satellites passed directly overhead at those locations, resulting in poor viewing geometry.

THE NAVSTAR GPS

The serious shortcomings of the Transit system were overcome by the Navstar Global Positioning System, which was placed under contract to Rockwell International, Seal Beach, California, in 1973. Once fully deployed, GPS became the first satellite navigation system that could accurately pinpoint a user's longitude, latitude, and altitude anywhere around the world, 24 hours a day, and under the most extreme weather conditions. A basic civilian GPS receiver can usually fix its position within 100 meters (328 feet). Pinpoint accuracy—within a few millimeters—can be achieved with supplementary enhancement techniques. In addition to extremely accurate three-dimensional position information, GPS can provide its users with precise time information and current speed and direction of movement.

GPS consists of three major segments: the space segment, the control segment, and the user segment. The space component is made up of the Navstar GPS satellites in orbit around Earth. The first such satellite was an experimental Block I model launched in

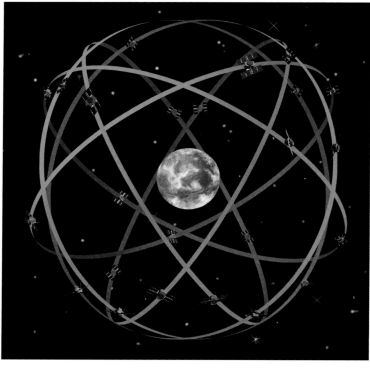

1978. Nine more of these developmental satellites followed over the next decade. From 1989 to 1993, 23 heavier and more capable Block II production models were sent into space. The launch of the 24th Block II satellite in 1994 completed the GPS constellation, consisting of two dozen Block II satellites marching in single file in six circular orbital rings around Earth. The satellite orbits are arranged so that at least five satellites are in view from most points on Earth at all times. As of late 1998, there were a total of 27 active GPS satellites in orbit. Three were reserved as spares.

A typical Block II GPS satellite weighs approximately 900 kilograms (2,000 pounds) and, with its solar panels included, is about 17 meters (56 feet) across. Its key elements are the winglike solar arrays that generate electrical power from the Sun, the 12 helical antennas that transmit navigation

Twenty-four GPS satellites (excluding spares) orbit at 20,400 km (12,700 mi) above Earth and are continuously monitored by ground stations around the world. Their signals are available to anyone equipped with a GPS receiver.

pulses to users on the ground, and its long, spearlike radio antenna that picks up instructions from control engineers. As a satellite coasts through its 12-hour orbit, its main body pivots continuously, keeping its navigation antennas pointing toward Earth's center and its solar arrays aligned perpendicular to the Sun's rays. Each satellite costs about $28 million to build and is constructed from 65,000 separate parts. It is designed to function in space for about 7.5 years.

The control segment consists of one Master Control Station at Schriever Air Force Base, Colorado Springs, Colorado, and four additional unmanned monitoring stations positioned around the world—Hawaii and

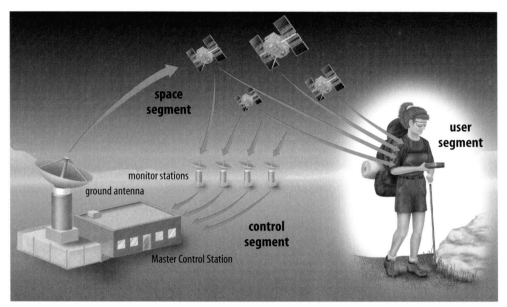

GPS consists of three major segments: space, ground control, and user. The space segment includes all of the Navstar GPS satellites in orbit around Earth. The first GPS satellite, a Block I experimental model, was launched in 1978. Today, the more durable Block II models (below) form the core of the GPS constellation. Ground control consists of five monitoring stations worldwide, including the Master Control Station in Colorado Springs, Colorado. The stations monitor the GPS satellites, checking both their operational status and their exact position in space. The master station transmits corrections to satellites when orbital errors are detected.

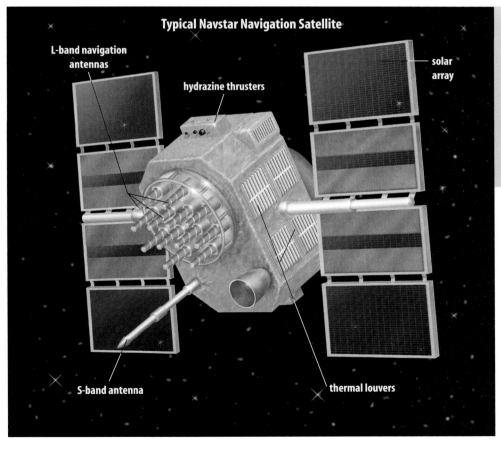

Typical Navstar Navigation Satellite

L-band navigation antennas transmit navigation pulses to GPS users

hydrazine thrusters provide thrust for orbital corrections

solar array converts solar radiation into electrical energy for power

thermal louvers open and close automatically to let heat out or keep it in

S-band antenna receives communications from ground control

In recent years consumers have been able to choose from an increasing array of affordable GPS receivers, such as the handheld model shown below.

Kwajalein Island in the Pacific Ocean, Diego Garcia, an island in the Indian Ocean, and Ascension Island in the Atlantic Ocean. The Master Control Station is the central processing facility for ground control and is manned around the clock by the air force's Space Operations Squadron. Each monitoring station tracks all of the GPS satellites in its view to check for orbital changes. Variations in satellite orbits are caused by gravitational pulls from the Moon and Sun, the nonspherical shape of Earth,

and the pressure of solar radiation. This information is processed at the Master Control Station, and corrected orbital information is quickly relayed back to the satellites via large ground antennas. After an interval averaging 18 months, the satellites within a given

ring have drifted too far from their original configuration and must be nudged back with onboard thrusters fired by ground control.

The user segment consists of the thousands of GPS receivers that pick up and decode the satellite signals. More than 100 different types of GPS receivers were in use in the late 1990s. Some were designed for installation in cars, trucks, submarines, ships, aircraft, and orbiting satellites, whereas smaller models were developed for personal navigation. Most handheld models are about the size of a cellular telephone, but some newer ones are even smaller.

HOW GPS WORKS

The principle behind the unprecedented navigational capabilities of GPS is triangulation from satellites. To triangulate, a GPS receiver simultaneously measures the distance to four or more favorably situated satellites. In theory, three satellites would normally provide an unambiguous three-dimensional fix, but in practice at least four are used. First, the receiver pre-

The basis of GPS is "triangulation" from satellites. Each satellite broadcasts its position and current time to GPS receivers on Earth. A receiver uses the information to find its distance from the satellite, which puts it somewhere on the surface of an imaginary sphere with a radius equal to the satellite's distance. Using the same method for two additional satellites, the receiver calculates a point at which all three spheres intersect. This point is the receiver's location. A fourth distance calculation is made to offset inaccuracy in the receiver's clock.

cisely measures the time it takes for a satellite signal to make its brief journey to Earth—less than a tenth of a second. Then, it multiplies that time by the speed of a radio wave—300,000 kilometers (186,000 miles) per second—to obtain the corresponding distance between satellite and receiver. When signals from three other satellites are simi-

larly processed, the receiver's built-in computer calculates the user's current longitude, latitude, and altitude. In addition, the receiver calculates current velocity (speed and direction) by measuring the instantaneous Doppler shifts created by the combined motion of the same four satellites.

For a receiver to measure exactly how long it takes for a

signal to travel from a GPS satellite, precision timekeeping is crucial. To ensure this accuracy, all Navstar satellites are mutually synchronized and equipped with extremely accurate atomic clocks. For practical reasons, most GPS receivers do not contain these pricey devices. Rather, they rely on inexpensive quartz-crystal oscillators to measure time, much like a wristwatch. As such, the clock in a GPS receiver is never perfectly synchronized with the clocks carried on board the satellites. By incorporating four, rather than three, distance measurements in its calculations, the receiver can make up for its timing deficiency. This approach reduces the cost and complexity of the receiver, but it requires a larger satellite constellation in order to provide continuous coverage for the entire globe.

The GPS constellation is also used to synchronize clocks on the ground and in space. Synchronization accuracies within 1/30,000,000 of a second (0.000000033 second) are routinely achieved using the timing pulses from GPS satellites. Although human beings do not require this kind of accuracy to go about their daily lives, such stringent synchronization accuracies are needed when machines talk to other machines. Computers linked together in

GPS products have been developed for many commercial applications. At sea, GPS receivers are used on commercial and recreational vessels to provide real-time latitude, longitude, time, course, and speed information and to assist with coastline and harbor navigation.

John McGrail/John McGrail Photography

networks, for example, operate much more efficiently if they are precisely synchronized, as do communications satellites, telephone networks, and astronomical observatories. Indeed, some GPS receivers are specifically manufactured for this purpose.

ENHANCING GPS PERFORMANCE

Although the travel time of a satellite signal to Earth is only a fraction of a second, much can happen to it in that interval. Unfortunately, these influences can translate into posi-

tion errors for users. Two of the biggest sources of GPS error are introduced when satellite transmissions pass through Earth's atmosphere. Electrically charged particles in the ionosphere and density variations in the troposphere act to

(continued on page 88)

GPS in Science and Society

G PS has evolved into a technology that extends far beyond its originally intended purposes. The technology has become accessible to just about anyone—scientists, surveyors and cartographers, farmers, pilots, taxi drivers, scout troops, golfers and anglers, and people from many other walks of life. It already has helped countless numbers of people to make their jobs and lives easier, more productive, and safer. As the accuracy of the technology increases and the creativity of its users becomes more sophisticated, GPS will continue to be applied in ever novel and surprising ways.

GPS has become an indispensable research tool to geophysicists studying plate tectonics, data about which could prove valuable in earthquake prediction. In the South American–Nazca Plate Motion Project (SNAPP), Peruvian and Bolivian scientists and American scientists from Northwestern University, Evanston, Illinois, from the University of Miami, Florida, and from the Carnegie Institution of Washington, D.C., used GPS technology to study motion within the Nazca–South American plate boundary. The precise measurements made possible by the technology allowed scientists to monitor plate movements. In 1998 sim-

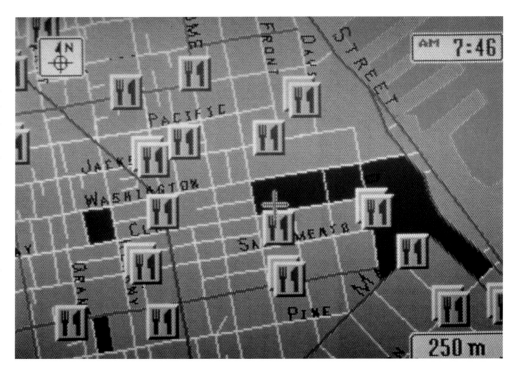

ilar studies were conducted in Missouri's New Madrid seismic zone, research that could lead to better earthquake predictions in the U.S. Midwest.

In 1998 geographer Brad Washburn of the Museum of Science in Boston and scientists from Yale University and the Massachusetts Institute of Technology made the arduous 8.8-kilometer (5.5-mile) climb to the summit of Mount Everest. Carrying GPS receivers, they wanted to determine the height of the world's highest mountain and to gather information about the rate at which it grows each year. The measurements they brought back revealed that Everest was more than 8.5 meters (29 feet) shorter than previously be-

lieved. The mountain continues to grow, however, heaving up approximately one centimeter (0.4 inch) per year.

GPS navigation technology will be critical during the construction and use of the International Space Station, which began its launch phase in 1998. NASA officials expect that the navigational and timing capabilities of the system will be employed for rendezvous and docking and for synchronizing scientific experiments conducted at various onboard locations. (*See* Feature Article: THE INTERNATIONAL SPACE STATION.)

In the United Kingdom, GPS technology has made the often frustrating act of commuting into a somewhat pleasant expe-

Have you ever missed a freeway exit or searched in vain for a restaurant? GPS technology is helping people from many walks of life find their destinations faster and more efficiently than ever before.

Sony/Gamma Liaison International

rience. Buses along Ipswich's Superoute 66 have been fitted with GPS receivers that allow them to be tracked along their entire routes. Radio transmitters on the buses continually broadcast their positions to a central processing station, which relays the information to a Web site every minute. Passengers can check the Internet each day to see how public transportation is running. Monitors set up at bus

(Below, left) Chamoux Initiative/Gamma Liaison International; (top, left) Hank Morgan/Photo Researchers, Inc.; (below, right) Courtesy of Trimble

stops also display the information so that people know when the next bus is expected. Truck fleets, courier services, police and fire departments, and ambulance services around the world have made similar use of GPS technology to keep track of their vehicles.

GPS has evolved into a versatile system with scores of uses. Cartographers and surveyors employ GPS extensively (left). GPS also has been tested in navigational aids for the blind (above). On the golf course GPS receivers calculate yardage to desirable locations and hazards (below).

(continued from page 85)

slow down and distort satellite signals. Timing errors in GPS receiver clocks compound the problem. Other errors are introduced by relativistic time dilations. A satellite's clock is in a weaker gravitational field and travels at a different velocity than a clock in a GPS receiver on Earth's surface. In accordance with Albert Einstein's general and special theories of relativity, the two clocks thus tick at different rates. Various electronic, mathematical, and programming corrections are available to reduce errors acquired in signal transit or caused by relativistic time distortion.

The single greatest source of error to civilian GPS positioning is selective availability, an intentional downgrading of GPS precision by the U.S. government intended to prevent hostile nations, groups, or individuals from making tactical use of the system. Each GPS satellite actually transmits two signals, a civilian signal and a signal for authorized personnel such as U.S. and allied military, certain U.S. government agencies, and selected, specifically approved civilian users. Use of the civilian signal limits positional accuracy to about 100 meters (a meter is about 3.28 feet). Military receivers are specially equipped to pro-cess the second GPS signal, providing positional accuracies of 10–30 meters.

For most GPS users, a position fix within 100 meters is adequate. A ship navigating across open ocean waters, for example, generally can operate safely with this level of accu-

GPS-based precision farming systems assemble data on a field's topography, soil type, drainage patterns, and other characteristics. Farmers can use the information to optimize delivery of agricultural chemicals to the fields.

Photographs courtesy of Trimble

racy. Nevertheless, a number of applications—among them aircraft landing, offshore oil exploration, and land surveying—require much more precision than the basic system provides. Several GPS performance-enhancing techniques

are being perfected to meet these unusually demanding requirements.

When positional information is required with pinpoint precision, users can take advantage of differential GPS techniques to reduce the amount of uncertainty in positional readings. Differential navigation involves the use of a supplementary receiver-transmitter system that sits at a known position on the ground and monitors the sig-

nals being broadcast by GPS satellites in its view. It then computes and transmits real-time corrections to local GPS receivers that have differential correction capability. The U.S. Coast Guard, for instance, maintains a network of such differential monitors and transmits corrections over radio beacons covering much of the U.S. coastline. Other differential corrections are relayed through commercial communications satellites. Still others are encoded within the normal broadcasts of FM radio stations.

Farmers have been among the many commercial users of GPS who have benefited from the differential corrections being broadcast by hundreds of FM radio stations in the United States. In the years before GPS, farmers rigged their tractors to apply uniform amounts of chemical herbicides, pesticides, and fertilizers across all of their crop fields. The approach was simple and easy to implement. However, because soil conditions, topography, and drainage patterns tend to vary both within and between fields, some crops received too much treatment and others too little. As a result, crop yields were lower than optimum, and expensive chemicals were either wasted entirely or ended up polluting nearby streams and rivers.

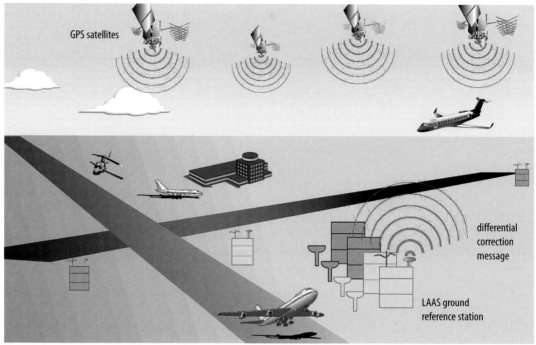

GPS satellites

differential correction message

LAAS ground reference station

Courtesy of Federal Aviation Administration

With the explosion of GPS technology, "precision farming" has become a buzz-word in agricultural circles. By means of a differential navigation receiver mounted in the cab of a tractor, coupled with an on-board computer that supplies information about soil type, topography, and field size, farmers have been able to direct their equipment to tailor the delivery of agricultural chemicals to the varying conditions in their fields. Consequently, crop yields have risen, costs have been reduced, and pollution levels in local streams have declined because less fertilizer and pesticides are applied to the fields.

Another performance-enhancing technique will make commercial air travel a safer and more pleasant experience. Aeronautical engineers are hopeful that the use of pseudosatellites ("false satellites"), or pseudolites, in conjunction with differential correction techniques, will provide precision guidance to commercial and private aircraft during approach, landing, and departure. Unlike true GPS satellites, pseudolites broadcast GPS–like

navigation signals from ground level. Researchers at Stanford University have conducted tests using pseudolites installed at the commercial airport in Palo Alto, California, as part of the Federal Aviation Administration's (FAA's) development of a Local Area Augmentation System (LAAS). The FAA hopes to install the GPS augmentation systems at all major airports. Preliminary tests have shown that a fully operational LAAS can reduce landing errors to less than a meter.

Yet another kind of GPS augmentation technique uses the carrier waves that convey the satellites' navigation pulses to Earth. Because the length of the carrier wave is more than

1,000 times shorter than the basic navigation pulses, this approach has the potential, under the right circumstances, to reduce navigation errors to less than a centimeter (0.4 inch). The dramatically improved accuracy stems primarily from the shorter length and much greater numbers of carrier waves impinging on the receiver's antenna each second.

Indeed, this high degree of accuracy has resulted in a revolution in the use of GPS for land surveying. The techniques were successfully tested in 1985 by professional surveyors working at the Turtmann Test Range, a bowl-shaped valley in southern Switzerland. The test range's unique geometry fos-

ters continuous line-of-sight visibility between eight different benchmarks in a mountainous valley covering 31 square kilometers (12 square miles). The eight benchmarks were initially surveyed with great precision using standard line-of-sight laser-ranging devices. Then, to test the accuracy of GPS, the surveyors used special surveying receivers to fix the positions of the benchmarks using carrier-aided solution techniques. The tests proved that a line of sight on the ground was not necessary for precise surveying—benchmark positions separated by as much as 1,000 meters (3,300 feet) were fixed to 5 millimeters (0.2 inch) or less by GPS.

THE RUSSIAN GLONASS SATELLITES

In 1982, four years after the deployment of the first GPS satellite, Russian aerospace specialists began implementation of the Global Navigation Satellite System (GLONASS). Conceptually, GLONASS is similar to GPS in terms of satellite constellation, orbits, and signal structure. Like GPS, each GLONASS satellite broadcasts two signals—one for civilian use and one for authorized personnel such as military users. GLONASS, like the U.S. system, also determines a user's location through the process of triangulation.

In the late 1990s, GLONASS was functioning but was still under development. When fully deployed, the GLONASS constellation will consist of 24 satellites distributed among three circular 19,100-kilometer (11,870-mile) orbits around Earth. Unlike GPS, the Russian military does not degrade the accuracy of the civilian GLONASS signal. GPS users can take advantage of this with a dual-capability GPS-GLONASS receiver that combines signals from the two sources. Such receivers have been creating waves of excitement among technologists and users alike, as they have proven to be much more accurate and robust than single-capability GPS receivers.

LOOKING TOWARD THE FUTURE

In the short time since its inception, the Global Positioning System has become an invaluable technology that has saved time, lives, and billions of dollars per year. A host of improvements and additions slated for GPS in the new millennium will likely make it an even more important and indispensable resource. Moreover, several GPS augmentation systems are currently under development around the world, meaning that more and more people will soon be taking advantage of the superior navigational abilities that GPS has to offer.

Perhaps the most widely anticipated nonmilitary use of advanced GPS technology in the U.S. is the FAA's new Wide Area Augmentation System (WAAS), arguably the most ambitious and sophisticated GPS augmentation under development. As its name implies, WAAS is a geographically expansive augmentation to the basic GPS service. At a cost exceeding $500 million, the improved navigation sys-

An in-dash GPS car navigation system calculates the most efficient route to any destination. It then guides the driver by means of easy-to-comprehend directional icons and voice commands.

Courtesy of Trimble

tem, expected to be operational in 2010, will employ advanced differential navigation, pseudolites positioned near all major airports, carrier-wave-based enhancement techniques, and additional space-based infrastructure, including navigation transmitters carried piggyback on commercial communications satellites.

In conjunction with LAASs centered around major airports, WAAS is designed to provide seamless navigation for private and commercial aircraft throughout U.S. airspace and in that of adjacent countries, such as Canada and Mexico.

According to many advocates, the new system will also save billions of dollars annually through lower fuel costs and the decommissioning of older and more expensive ground-based navigation equipment. Tests of the system at airports in Mexico, Italy, and Iceland have indicated that safe and dependable air travel can be expected.

In 1998 the European Space Agency began full-scale development of its ambitious Global Navigation Satellite System (GNSS), a worldwide service intended to work in conjunction with and eventually independent of the military GPS and GLONASS. In its initial phase of development, Europe's space specialists will institute a GPS-based counterpart to the U.S. WAAS effort that will improve the availability, integrity, and accuracy of GPS signals and, to a lesser extent, GLONASS transmissions using additional ground- and space-based technologies. Expected to complete operational trials in 2004, it will also have air, land, and marine applications. Europe's long-term objective is to deploy an all-new constellation of navigation satellites that would be entirely under civilian control.

The Japanese Civil Aviation Bureau is also developing a satellite-based GPS augmentation system to provide complete navigation services for all aircraft within Japanese airspace. Like the other wide-area improvements under development, this space-based system, which is scheduled to be finished in 2005, will augment GPS service with additional satellites and ground-control systems.

New satellite-based wireless communications networks such as Iridium and Globalstar will also be useful as navigation services. The Iridium system, which became operational in 1998, is designed to permit any type of telephone transmission—voice, paging, fax, or data—to reach its destination anywhere on Earth. Unlike conventional telecommunications networks, however, the satellite-based system automatically locates a subscriber's portable telephone when a call comes in, providing global transmission even if the subscriber's location is unknown. A properly equipped subscriber will be able to determine his or her position on Earth simply by activating a handheld Iridium telephone. The Globalstar system, conceptually similar to Iridium, is expected to be available in 1999.

On the threshold of the 21st century, the future looks bright for GPS users. In 1998 the White House announced a plan to add a second and third civilian transmission frequency when the GPS constellation upgrading project is completed in 2005. Addition of the two frequencies will greatly enhance the accuracy and reliability of civilian GPS receivers by enabling them to more effectively correct the distortion to satellite signals caused by Earth's atmosphere. Moreover, fresher and more frequent updates of GPS satellites and elimination of selective availability, which may happen as early as 2001, will improve navigation services for millions of users. Industry analysts expect that within a few years GPS technology will be commonplace in such public domains as airport terminals, train and bus stations, taxicabs, highway rest areas, and banks. Automobiles by the thousands are being equipped with GPS receivers that have moving-map displays and give turn-by-turn, synthesized-voice instructions to guide drivers gently to their destinations. One day, for everyone, the fear of getting lost—like that of contracting smallpox—may be just a fading memory, a thing of the past.

FOR ADDITIONAL READING

Electronic Aids to Navigation, L. Tetley and D. Calcutt (Edward Arnold, 1986).

From Sails to Satellites: The Origin and Development of Navigational Science, J.E.D. Williams (Oxford University Press, 1992).

Global Positioning System: Theory and Applications, Brad Parkinson and James J. Spilker, Jr., eds. (American Institute of Aeronautics and Astronautics, 1996).

GPS Satellite Surveying, Alfred Leick (John Wiley & Sons, 1995).

Guide to GPS Positioning, David Wells (Canadian GPS Associates, 1986).

Understanding GPS: Principles and Applications, Elliott D. Kaplan (Artech House, 1996).

Understanding the Navstar: GPS, GIS, and IVHS, Tom Logsdon (John Wiley & Sons, 1995).

INTERNET RESOURCES

The Aerospace Corporation's GPS Primer
http://www.aero.org/publications/GPSPRIMER/index.html

Federal Aviation Administration's GPS Product Team
http://gps.faa.gov/Default.htm

Global Positioning System Overview
http://www.utexas.edu/depts/grg/gcraft/notes/gps/gps.html

GLONASS
http://mx.iki.rssi.ru/SFCSIC/english.html

GPS World Magazine Online
http://www.gpsworld.com/index.html

Navstar GPS
http://www.laafb.af.mil/SMC/CZ/homepage

U.S. Coast Guard Navigation Center
http://www.navcen.uscg.mil

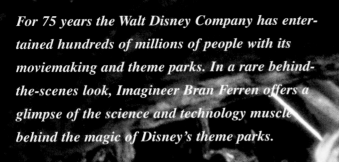

For 75 years the Walt Disney Company has enter-tained hundreds of millions of people with its moviemaking and theme parks. In a rare behind-the-scenes look, Imagineer Bran Ferren offers a glimpse of the science and technology muscle behind the magic of Disney's theme parks.

The Science Behind the Magic: Research & Development at Disney

by Bran Ferren
with Ken Wong and Marty Sklar

On a clear, sunny morning at Disneyland, just minutes after the park has opened, a line of people begins to form outside the Haunted Mansion, one of the theme park's oldest and most popular attractions. For many children and adults alike, a trip to a Disney park is a sort of pilgrimage—an excursion that has to be made at least once in a lifetime. Given the thrilling, special effects-filled nature of Disney's living, breathing fantasy worlds, it is not difficult to understand why. The folks at Disney have mastered the art of using science and technology to tell stories.

Inside the Haunted Mansion, the story begins in the Victorian-era house's darkened waiting room, where guests (there are no "visitors" or "customers" at Disney theme parks) are greeted by Disney cast members (there are no "employees") dressed in butler's tuxedos and maid's uniforms. Assorted shrieks, creaks, and howls echo inside the entry chamber as guests are ushered down a narrow, candle-lit hallway leading to the Doom

Buggies, the show name for the computer-controlled carts that will guide them through the rest of the house. Once safely secured in a buggy, guests are whisked along a track that takes them past dozens of haunting yet entertaining scenes—hanging corpses, cackling ghouls, disembodied heads, and hovering candelabras. In one of the ride's memorable illusions, a Doom Buggy enters a mirror-filled room in which the lighting and other special optical effects make it appear as if guests have been joined by very realistic-looking ghouls.

Typical of a Disney theme park attraction, the Haunted Mansion ride is an awe-inspiring and seamless entertainment experience—stories are outlined, scripts are written, and stage and lighting cues are

Bran Ferren, who started his career as a designer, technologist, and Hollywood special effects wizard, is president of R&D and Creative Technology at Walt Disney Imagineering Research and Development, Inc. He prepared this article with Ken Wong, president of WDI, who has a background in design and business, and Marty Sklar, vice-chairman and principal creative executive of WDI, who has contributed or led the creative development of all Disney theme parks.

carefully rehearsed. Unlike most plays and musicals, however, Disney's enchanting story lines are augmented with millions of dollars' worth of state-of-the-art computer technology, sophisticated robots, special effects, and all manner of optical, lighting, and audio trickery.

The people who dream up and design Disney's famously surreal environments are called "Imagineers"—employees of Walt Disney Imagineering (WDI). It is they who create the convincing illusions that keep the crowds coming to

Disney theme parks every day of the year. For almost 50 years WDI has served as a creative and technical idea factory for the Walt Disney Company. Its first job was to bring Disneyland to life. This involved transforming a fruit orchard in southern California into what has come to be known by hundreds of millions of guests as the "Happiest Place on Earth." Borrowing some technology from other industries and inventing the rest to fit their own special needs, WDI's Imagineers have consis-

tently pushed the boundaries of storytelling.

WDI AND THE IMAGINEERS

After years of success in Hollywood, most notably with his full-length animated features such as *Snow White and the Seven Dwarfs* and *Fantasia*, cartoonist Walter Elias Disney had a vision—a dream to create a "magical little park." He wanted the park to be a joyous place, where parents and children could have fun together while learning some optimistic and educational messages about the world and its future. Disney's plan for the park included natural elements like rivers, waterfalls, and mountains; fantasy elements such as giant teacups, flying elephants, and fairy-tale castles; a bit of history, in the form of pirate ships and steamboats; and a trip into the future on monorails and rocket ships.

Disney hand-picked a collection of his movie studio's most versatile animators, script writers, and technicians to serve as his think tank for the project, and in 1952 he founded WED Enterprises (which later became WDI) to design and create the park. Location was a top priority—Disneyland, as it was to be called, had to be located somewhere within the Los Angeles

Castle Entrance
Fantasy Land

Walt Disney discusses plans for his company's first theme park, Disneyland in southern California, which opened in 1955 (above). Possessed of an extremely fertile imagination, Disney assumed complete creative control of the $17 million project, working closely with a hand-picked collection of his movie studio's best animators, script writers, and technicians (left).

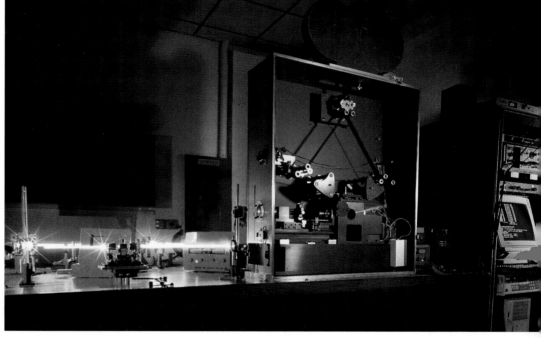

R&D's flexible-format digital film printer prototype is capable of printing high-quality 70mm or larger format films.

metropolitan area and accessible by freeway. Eventually, Disney purchased a 65-hectare (160-acre) orange grove in Anaheim, near the planned Santa Ana Freeway.

During the planning phase of the project, Disney and his crew faced hundreds of tough questions. How do you build realistic-looking animals? What kinds of materials and technology will stand up best to the grueling demands of the park's operation? How do you create the structure of a mountain with a built-in roller coaster? Designing and building an amusement park of this scale was something that had never been done before. There were to be five different themed lands—Adventureland, Fantasyland, Main Street U.S.A., Frontierland, and Tomorrowland—each with its own unique collection of rides, shops, pavilions, and other special attractions.

Construction of the park began in 1954, about a year before it was scheduled to open. Disney supervised much of the work himself, visiting Anaheim several times a week. Progress prevailed despite overwhelming obstacles. For instance, the Rivers of America attraction, carved out of sandy citrus-grove soil, refused to hold water. After much experimentation, WED engineers solved

the problem by laying down a thick layer of natural clay to form an impervious river bed. Bit by bit, Disneyland got ready for opening day. Walt Disney personally maintained complete creative control throughout the project. The $17 million Disneyland opened in July 1955 to the delight of tens of thousands of fans and gawking media people.

Since that time WDI's role within the larger Walt Disney Company has grown considerably. In addition to producing all the attractions at Disney's destination resorts—new theme parks, thrill rides, educational pavilions, resorts, hotels,

restaurants, gift shops, golf courses, gardens, and even wedding pavilions—WDI also serves as the master planning, real estate development, construction resource, and (through its sister company Walt Disney Imagineering Research & Development, Inc.) R&D center for the entire company. As one might expect for a creative design company, WDI encompasses just about every creative and artistic career possible. Puppeteers, architects, engineers, computer scientists, graphic artists, animators, electricians, storyboard writers, special effects designers, landscapers, carpenters,

and lighting specialists are among the more than 250 different disciplines at WDI.

In the parking lot at WDI's headquarters in the quiet Los Angeles suburb of Glendale, many cars have license plate holders proudly bearing the motto, "We make the Magic!" To a person, Imagineers are committed to creating remarkable and memorable entertainment experiences, but the responsibility of envisioning, designing, engineering, and implementing Disney's unique and persuasive illusions ultimately falls on WDI's technologists in its engineering, production, and R&D groups.

R&D also employs a collection of leading technologists and scientists as part of the Disney Fellows program. Initiated by R&D in 1996 in order to remain fluent in computational and communications technologies, the Fellows help Disney business units explore new applications of technology. Danny Hillis, a pioneer in massively parallel supercomputing, and Alan Kay, inventor of object-oriented computer programming (OOP) and the person who first described the personal computer, were the first Disney Fellows and are both based at the Glendale R&D center. Massachusetts Institute of Technology's Seymour Papert and artificial intelligence guru Marvin Minsky also have signed on with Disney as consulting Fellows.

Disney's R&D group is frequently involved in assisting new business ventures across the company. This can be in the traditional R&D role of developing new products and techniques or as consultants to help work through relevant tactical and strategic issues. For example, Alan Kay's Advanced Multimedia Software Group in recent years has been developing a new OOP language called Squeak. When completed, Squeak will enable the company to deliver rich, creative content into people's

Alan Kay, a Disney Fellow, demonstrates the revolutionary Squeak operating environment to a future generation of computer users (left). Below, a WDI technician uses a modern computer-controlled milling machine to design and fabricate an R&D prototype.

homes via the Internet and through computer-based gaming and entertainment systems. R&D is also working with Disney's broadcast division, the American Broadcasting Company, to explore the development of technologies that will enhance or transform television as we now know it. Most industry insiders have a sense that the personal computer and television will somehow converge in the future. A collaborative creative research team, staffed by both ABC and R&D, has been appointed to develop a vision of what a compelling type of convergence might be and to build the first generation of new products.

THE IMAGINEERING PROCESS

Like many companies, WDI is relatively tight-lipped about the science and research behind its products—in this case, its world-class attractions and enabling technologies. The reasons for it go well beyond the need for confidentiality in the competitive entertainment industry. Disney believes that how it does things ought to be invisible to guests, otherwise it could take them out of the story. When guests visit a Disney theme park, they should feel as if they have entered another world and be able to effectively suspend their disbelief.

In line with this philosophy, the focus of Disney's R&D group is very different from research groups in other high-tech companies like General Motors or IBM. Much of the science is the same, but R&D takes an entirely different approach in creating Disney's memorable attractions. For instance, many businesses develop products using a requirements-driven process. In this method a potential new product is identified through a combination of market research, prototyping, and discussions with their customers. All of the knowledge gained is reduced into a document describing an explicit set of requirements. Production people, then, have everything they need to design and build the final product, which, if the requirements research was done correctly, ought to be successful.

WDI makes extensive use of requirements documents during manufacturing and construction efforts but has found it to be a nearly useless model for driving creative concept development. Instead, the process begins with the search for a "Big Idea." Big Ideas are usually quite simple and can be explained in a single sentence. An example of this was Walt Disney's original idea for an attraction called Space Mountain—put a roller coaster in the dark and make it central to a story about an outer space journey. Most products in a creatively driven design organization are born of this method of brainstorming an idea and then designing to support it.

Big Ideas are often generated during so-called Blue Sky brainstorming sessions. The people selected for a session are brought in for their ability to do unconstrained thinking, for their artistic, design, and story skills, or for their track record of contributing innovative or even contrary solutions to challenging problems. Many good-sounding ideas do not survive this initial process. Others have to be reiterated, reconceptualized, or even abandoned when key elements prove to be unworkable or unaffordable. Occasionally, an idea is put on the shelf until technical solutions can be developed through research and experimentation. An ideal Big Idea is one that is practical and exciting and meets certain creative, technical, and operational-quality standards. It also helps for it to be very "cool."

Once an idea for an attraction has been established, it moves into the design and engineering phase of development. Depending on the magnitude of the project, this can be a very expensive process, sometimes involving dozens of people from many different professions, including artists, architects, engineers, lighting designers, special effects designers, audiovisual specialists, and computer software specialists. Often, a rapid-prototyping method of design development is employed, in which a working demonstration model is produced very early on in the construction process. The demo allows Imagineers to receive feedback from test audiences and solicit input on ways to make the attraction better. Nearly every new theme park attraction requires the invention of some new system or device, yet Imagineers often have less than 18 months to design, engineer, and test it.

Construction and production of the attraction is the next step, often an incredibly complex task. A major attraction can sometimes require more than 20,000 individual drawings, many of which are originated on networked, computer-aided design (CAD) computers. Although the construction of an attraction's infrastructure—the site, buildings, and utilities—are the most visible, the production of ride systems, control systems, show sets, special effects equipment, audiovisual systems, integrated controls, and all other technical systems is where it gets complicated. The most difficult task is the integration of all these systems into a seamless environment. This work requires great attention to detail and often a variety of modifications that can only be made after the final product has come to life. Throughout the entire process, the safety and reliability design of the attraction is checked and rechecked.

Final testing of an attraction is, of course, a vital step in the process. Sometimes problems are encountered only when all of the systems are brought online simultaneously. During the testing process, guests are occasionally brought in to see how they will flow through an attraction and react to the story experience. This is also the time when ride operators and maintenance people are trained on any special and unique characteristics of a project. After an attraction opens, it requires constant follow-up to see how the systems function under continuous use. Getting through the entire cycle for a typical theme park attraction takes several years.

THE HIGH-TECH WORLD OF DISNEY

The Disney organization has a long history of using technology to tell stories. In 1928 at New York City's Colony Theatre, a new actor named Mickey Mouse made his debut in an animated short called *Steamboat Willie*—the first cartoon with a fully synchronized sound track. After the overwhelming success of the film, Walt Disney made it a goal to perfect the art of cartoon-making. Disney's Silly Symphony cartoon series in the 1930s was used as a test bed for animation technologies. In particular, *The Old Mill,* released in 1937, was a famous first outing for Disney's breakthrough animation technology—the multiplane camera.

The multiplane camera was a bold new advance in the field of animation and gave Disney cartoons a more three-dimensional, cinematic quality. In traditional animation, separate transparency drawings—one layer showing elements in the foreground, another layer showing the animated characters, and a final one showing background features—are stacked together, and the camera shoots through them, giving the final image. With the multiplane camera, many more drawings could be used, and they were placed on different planes, sometimes several feet apart. The camera could then shift focus in and out among the planes, offering an unparalleled sense of depth and motion.

An R&D cast member manipulates a computer-generated 3-D model of a Rocket Rod ride vehicle at R&D's VR studio.

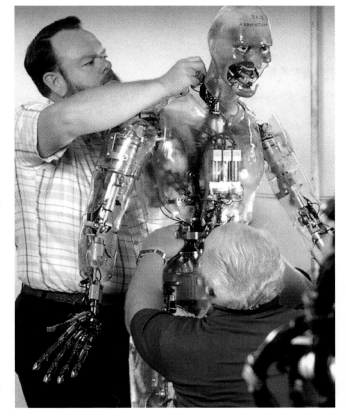

Although computers are now used to produce these kinds of effects, the multiplane camera was a remarkable breakthrough that took animation to a whole new level of creative sophistication. Disney's filmmakers set another technological standard in 1945 with the release of *The Three Caballeros,* the first feature film to combine live action and animation.

Today Disney is pursuing a whole series of new technologies that are as revolutionary as the multiplane camera was when it was introduced. Much of this work concentrates on the application of high-performance computing to the creation of animation and special visual effects. In addition to generating convincing-looking sets and models, powerful computers also help speed up work flow and lower production costs.

Disney hopes to revolutionize the process of movie distribution as well. Imagineers are now developing technologies that will allow movies to be electronically distributed and projected in theaters without the use of film. Within the next decade this "Digital Cinema" technology should make as dramatic an improvement to the movie theater experience as did modern surround sound. Currently, the Disney R&D group is making great progress

on building a next-generation laser-beam film recorder, which will eventually be used to enhance the quality of the images projected in theme park attractions and, later, in local theaters.

In the 1950s it was Walt Disney's interest in creating a theme park that further propelled the company to develop cutting-edge entertainment technologies. Producing fun, exciting, believable, and safe attractions capable of running seven days a week, 365 days per year for 30 years is a completely unique discipline. Much of the time Disney scientists and technicians have to find solutions to their own unique problems.

Consider, for instance, the problem of developing natural-looking skin for the robotic people, animals, dinosaurs, monsters, and other creatures that are central to many attractions. The goal was to develop

a synthetic skin that would not only mimic the malleability and texture of real skin but also withstand repeated bending and stretching due to constant use. Scientists also had to take into account how environmental factors, such as temperature and humidity differences, would affect the skin since Disney's theme parks—Disneyland in California, Walt Disney World in Florida, Disneyland Paris, and Tokyo Disneyland—are located in different climate zones. Temperature fluctuations and high humidity, for instance, can make polymer-based materials fail prematurely. Polyurethane and latex rubber are the most commonly used materials in the special effects industry for making real-looking skin. These materials, however, often exhibit a variety of undesirable characteristics, includ-

Originally developed in the 1960s, Disney's lifelike Audio-Animatronics® robots incorporate silicone-based skins, computerization, and miniature servo valves derived from aerospace technology.

ing flammability, toxicity, and short life span, that make them unsuitable for theme park use. Disney's solution was to modify existing formulas as well as develop completely new technology based upon the use of RTV (room-temperature vulcanizing) silicone compounds. The formulation and methods

In developing synthetic skins for Audio-Animatronics® figures that mimic the look and feel of real skin, Disney scientists have to take into account how climate differences might affect the material. The humidity problems at Florida's Walt Disney World, for instance, offer different challenges than the desiccation caused by California's drier climate. Repeated freezing and thawing at the Paris and Tokyo theme parks add other complications. Each set of conditions requires a slightly different material.

In Disney theme parks, good things can come in small packages. Imagineers integrate their engineering and design talents to invent new storytelling devices, such as Disney R&D's Minimatronics® figures (left). Arty San is the first Minimatronics® figure to entertain guests at Tokyo Disneyland (below).

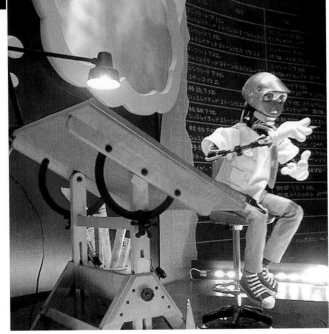

of fabricating these skins vary considerably from project to project. As can be imagined, it is a very different challenge to create realistic skin for Snow White than for a 10-meter (33-foot)-long dinosaur.

In addition to conducting research and developing technologies for their own needs, Disney's Imagineers also work to keep pace with the evolution of technology in other industries that might have applications to entertainment. One of the earliest and best-known examples of this was the development of the very lifelike

Audio-Animatronics® figures. The term means animation with sound, run by electronics, and was first coined by Walt Disney and WED engineers in the early 1960s. To make the robots, they borrowed pneumatic and hydraulic technology that was originally developed for the U.S. aerospace program. Miniature servo valves and other controls intended for rocket engines were built into the robotic systems, enabling the mechanical figures to make extremely fine, reliable, believable motions, such as the delicate wagging of

(Below left) An R&D technician adjusts 3-D park components in real time on a computer-generated model of Disney's California Adventure virtual reality attraction using D.I.R.E.C.T. (Disney's Interactive Real-Time Environment Construction Tools). Guests can now experience many of Disney's new interactive virtual reality thrill rides at DisneyQuest, a new indoor theme park (below right).

a finger or the quizzical raising of an eyebrow.

In more recent years, researchers at Disney have been perfecting the application of virtual reality (VR) technology at its VR studio—a combination research and production facility. Originally, most of the VR technology used by Disney was adapted from U.S. Department of Defense and aerospace flight-simulation technology. Working with leaders in high-performance computing, the VR studio has been producing a wide variety of hardware and software products.

DisneyQuest, Disney's new type of indoor theme park, makes liberal use of the latest in VR technology. Inside each DisneyQuest entertainment center, guests can experience the magic of Disney with a variety of state-of-the-art immersive technologies. The first DisneyQuest opened at Orlando's Walt Disney World in 1998. A second one is slated to open in Chicago in 1999, and a third will debut the following year in Philadelphia. The company also plans to open DisneyQuest centers in other locations worldwide.

Aladdin's Magic Carpet Ride was WDI's first VR project, initially delivered as a trial prototype to Epcot at Walt Disney World in 1992, and then as a finished product for DisneyQuest in 1998. The Aladdin ride is one of the most sophisticated VR experiences ever produced for any entertainment application. It required the development of complex real-time simulation software, special image-generation computers, and high-resolution head-mounted displays. The adventure begins when each guest straps on one of the

virtual reality helmets and boards a personal magic carpet, which very much resembles a stationary bike. Using a lever, guests can change speeds and maneuver their carpets up and down and to the right and left as they fly through the streets of a make-believe city. The attraction even lets guests ride together—up to four at a time in the same virtual space—through nearly 30 different highly detailed virtual environments. True to VR technology, each person can also look around to see the other teammates, all of whom appear as unique versions of the character Abu the monkey, each in a different colored vest.

(Above and right) Imagineers participate in a creative and technical review of a theme park design using proprietary interactive real-time environment construction tools (D.I.R.E.C.T.) in a rear-projection, immersive C.A.V.E. (Cave Automated Virtual Environment).

(Right) This real-time 3-D computer-generated environment was created at R&D's VR studio for the Aladdin Magic Carpet Ride at DisneyQuest.

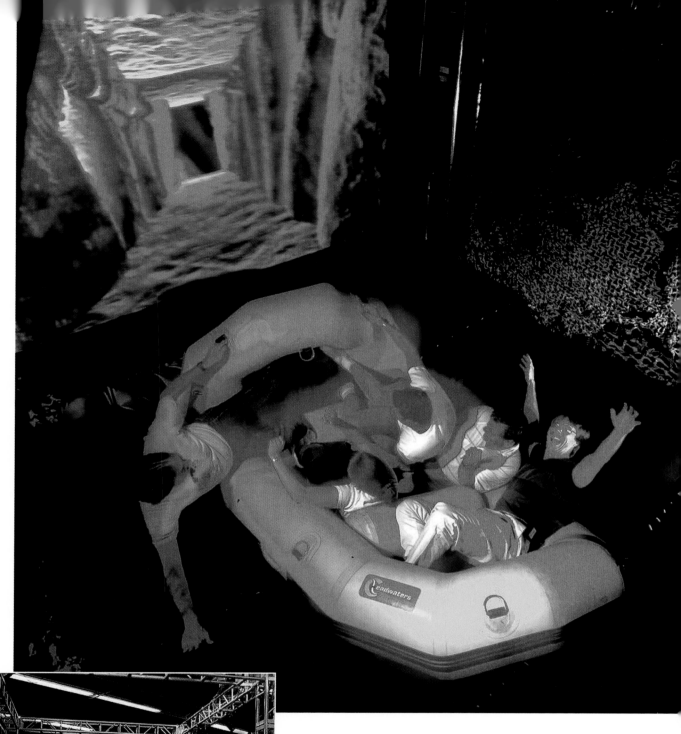

One of the best examples of Disney's new push into interactive virtual reality thrill rides is the Virtual Jungle Cruise, which makes use of two new R&D-developed technologies. The VR computation, control, and player system is a new technology that produces interactive coordinated images and sounds of water motion. To start the ride, guests board a raft that is positioned in front of a large digital projection screen. The raft actually sits on a series of airbags, which, when inflated and deflated in sequence, simulates the motion of a raft on a jungle river. Each guest is also handed a paddle, which is used to control the raft. During the ride, electronic sensors mounted

(Right) Low-profile line array speakers (behind man) enable Disney to optimize audio in unique and challenging venues, such as the New Amsterdam Theater in New York City. (Bottom) R&D technicians assemble line array speakers for use in the Tokyo production of Disney's theatrical show *The Lion King*.

(Opposite page, top) At the R&D lab, technicians test the Turbo Air Cell Motion Base for DisneyQuest's Jungle Cruise interactive raft ride. (Opposite page, bottom) Workers put the final touches on the patented inflatable motion base system.

on and around the raft measure the position of guests as they row their paddles and, in turn, move both the raft and the screen images appropriately. For example, if guests paddle on the right side of the raft, the view on the screen would go to the left. The motion base, which provides the motion cues for the people in the raft, is based upon Imagineering R&D's patented computer-controlled air-bag technology.

WDI is now starting to utilize new Imagineering R&D-developed VR technology to design theme park attractions. Although traditional model-building techniques are still being used to bring ideas into reality, Imagineers are turning increasingly to computer simulation and visualization techniques. Components of Disney's complex attractions are designed, engineered, and tested entirely on the computer, providing a framework for producing more sophisticated designs with a lower risk of running over budget or schedule.

A SOUND EXPERIENCE

The ability to control what guests see, hear, and feel is a big part of what Disney's virtual worlds are all about. Disney researchers are experts at the art of illusion—developing ways to get their guests to believe something happened when it did not (or vice versa). This demands a firm grasp of technology coupled with insight into the emotional dimensions of how people react to particular stimuli. Unlike performing illusions within the medium of film or television, Disney scientists have to develop interactive illusions that are performed live, every few seconds—for decades. Imagineers also expect that guests may revisit the same attraction over and over again; therefore, illusions must be sustainable—good enough to keep their secrets even after repeated encounters.

Audio, of course, is an important factor in any entertainment experience. Sound and music are critical parts of a storyteller's creative tool kit and, as such, play a key role in virtually every Disney show. In some cases a show's sound and music can be handled with traditional professional audio technology. In other cases, however, the requirements go well beyond what can be achieved with off-the-shelf technology. For example, in the Walt Disney World attraction The ExtraTERRORestrial Alien Encounter, much of the show takes place in complete darkness. During this time the entire show depends on a variety of complex sound effects. A key part of this sequence requires creating the illusion of a quite foul-tempered alien creature moving throughout the theater space.

The creation of truly realistic three-dimensional sound effects at high sound intensities usually cannot be achieved without placing a large number of big speakers throughout the space in question. For most Disney applications, however, this is not an aesthetically acceptable solution because the speakers' presence betrays their function. Good theatrical special effects technology should always be invisible to the audience. To solve this dilemma, scientists in the R&D acoustics group borrowed technology that was originally used for high-performance military radar systems (called linear phased arrays) and patented a new acoustic technology called the line array speaker. The three-meter-tall, 10-centimeter-diameter (10-foot-tall, 4-inch-diameter) speakers are surprisingly loud for their size and can beam sound very precisely to any destination required. They behave quite unlike traditional speakers in their ability to produce consistent sound levels over very large distances without audible distortion. The speakers also are produced in a variety of other sizes to best suit each application. The longer units are capable of producing a narrower beam of sound (in one direction), which is useful in theatrical- and sound-reinforcement applications.

For Alien Encounter, R&D designed a special array of nine of these speakers mounted near the ceiling. By combining these line arrays with binaural speakers hidden in each guest's seat back and integrating a variety of other audio and special effects technologies, Disney was able to produce a mind-boggling illusion. Many guests who have experienced this attraction firsthand are convinced that a menacing creature is actually moving around the room, at times only inches away from them. Line array speakers are used in many Disney theme park attractions and a variety of outdoor events, as well as in Disney's Broadway production of *The Lion King.*

BEYOND ENTERTAINMENT

Guests at Disney theme parks and resorts frequently comment about the cleanliness and efficiency of Disney-run operations. This is not by accident. According to Disney entertainment philosophy, what guests cannot see is just as important as what they can see. It is all part of sustaining the illusion. For example, after Disney parades, waves of cast members in themed costumes inconspicuously descend upon the parade routes toting high-powered vacuum cleaners and other equipment to clean up debris almost as soon as it is left.

Weather centers at each theme park also closely monitor forecasts so that restaurants and shops can be warned to set out Disney umbrellas and raincoats before foul weather moves in. It is all meant to be as unobtrusive as possible.

Indeed, imagineers and other cast members go to great lengths to enhance their guests' experiences, sometimes inventing new technologies or unique solutions that go well beyond the realm of entertainment. In 1988, for instance, Disneyland officials found that an insect pest had been causing extensive damage to the Australian brush cherry plants (*Eugenia myrtifolia,* also called *Syzygium paniculatum*) that are used extensively for the visual screening, topiaries, and landscaping of the park. The pest was a Eugenia psyllid (*Trioza eugeniae*), a tiny aphid-like insect, that had inadvertently been brought over from Australia. The troublesome insect was first discovered by a Los Angeles homeowner in May 1988, and by the end of that year scientists learned that it had also spread to Orange County (where Disneyland is located) and other surrounding regions. Early in 1989 the psyllid began to appear in northern California and to date has been found in coastal areas as far north as Marin and Napa counties. In ad-

dition to the problems at Disneyland, the rapid infestation caused a visual blight for tens of thousands of California homeowners and had a significant economic impact on California's plant nursery industry.

Psyllids cause damage to plants by inducing the formation of galls, or tissue swellings, on young developing leaves. The abnormal leaf cell growth is stimulated by the feeding action of psyllid nymphs, which settle on the budding leaves soon after they hatch from their eggs. The galls provide the nymphs with food and protection from enemies. Unfortunately, the galls also protect the pests from insecticidal sprays; thus, severe infestations are nearly impossible to manage with traditional chemical-control techniques. The difficulty of control with pesticides, and concern for the environment, led scientists to believe that the pest was an ideal candidate for biological control.

In late 1991 a search for a natural enemy of the psyllid was conducted at several locations in Australia by scientists from R&D and Walt Disney World, in conjunction with the Center for Biological Control at the University of California, Berkeley. By the end of 1991, the researchers had found a type of eulophid parasitoid wasp (a species of *Tamarixia*) and, following quarantine and intensive study in the U.S., prepared to release it into the southern Calfornia environment. *Tamarixia* wasps prey on psyllid nymphs by laying eggs near the plant galls. Larvae hatch from the eggs and eventually kill the psyllids.

The initial release of *Tamarixia* wasps occurred at Disneyland in July 1992. Within a short time, a self-sustaining population of the beneficial wasps had formed and spread widely across the southern part of California. Subsequent releases were made in 1993 in San Diego, San Luis Obispo, Santa Clara, and Alameda counties; most coastal areas of the state had the wasp by 1994. Monitoring systems were designed and set up to measure the initial psyllid populations and the effects of the introduction of the wasps. Peak psyllid numbers decreased each year from 1992 to 1994 at the Disneyland site. Similar results were observed at the other release locations from 1993 to 1995. The end result was a renewed viability of *Eugenia* as a landscaping plant.

(Below left) Jack Kelly Clark, courtesy University of California Statewide IPM Project/Univ of CA, Davis

When the Eugenia psyllid (above left) threatened to destroy landscaping plants in southern California, including those at Disneyland (above), WDI scientists helped develop a biological control strategy to eliminate the pests. This included releasing *Tamarixia* wasps (right) into the environment to kill the psyllids.

Management of California's eugenia psyllid infestation is just one example of how scientific ingenuity at Disney has benefited the public beyond entertainment. In fact, there is a small group of researchers within R&D whose sole function is to provide scientific guidance to the company on environmental matters. In recent years they have been heavily involved in the design of Walt Disney World's new wastewater treatment plant. As managers of extensive facilities that accommodate tens of millions of people per year, Disney theme park and resort operators are constantly faced with the challenges of managing waste output. A typical wastewater processing plant is sized to accommodate what is calculated to be its peak output requirement. Unfortunately, in most applications the peak load is much greater than the average capacity required. Building in the extra reserve capacity often results in much higher installation and operating costs.

The new wastewater management facility at Walt Disney World, designed with the help of environmental scientists within R&D, is quite revolutionary for the industry. It is based on new computerized process-control technology, which allows plant operators to align peak and average capacities by continuously monitoring and adjusting the water treatment process. The new treatment facility operates much more economically and efficiently and has set a standard that others outside the theme park industry are following.

Disney R&D researchers have also been busy developing technology for more spectacular and environmentally friendly fireworks displays. Disney is among the largest users of fireworks in the world. Each theme park does a full

The Bio-Nutrient Removal Wastewater Treatment Plant at Walt Disney World in Florida operates significantly more efficiently than treatment plants in most municipalities, owing to state-of-the-art computerized process-control technology.

Disney's recently developed computerized air-launch fireworks system (below) produces dazzling displays and eliminates the launch noise and irritating ground smoke associated with traditional fireworks-launching systems.

cluding the ability to coordinate the sequence and position of the explosions to "write" animating graphics across the sky in synchronization to show music.

THE FUTURE OF THEME PARKS

In a world where completely new generations of interactive media arrive at increasingly short intervals, is there a future for theme parks, or will their popularity be eclipsed by cyberspace? The essence of the theme park experience depends in large part upon the value that we place on sharing real experiences, in real places, with other real people. Modern technologies like virtual reality can provide us with thrilling new experiences, but it is likely that these will complement, rather than replace, the traditional theme park experience. While technology does, indeed,

Fourth-of-July-like show every night, so the company has a direct interest in producing more wondrous effects while simultaneously reducing impact on the environment. One new fireworks technology patented by Disney is a computerized air-launch system, which uses a combination of multitube compressed-air launchers and custom microprocessor-programmed igniters to shoot the decorative explosives into the air and set them off. This system also allows creative show-programming options that have not been previously possible, in-change very rapidly, our basic human needs do not. The human need for companionship, family, food, shelter, spirituality, and the desire to tell and be told stories has remained relatively unchanged throughout history.

The shared kinesthetic learning experience of the theme park is unique within the universe of entertainment—nothing in sight seems poised to supersede it. Disneyland was the first example of virtual reality that many of us encountered. Everything seen and experienced there was designed to help tell a variety of thematic stories. The settings placed people in an environment that allowed them to experience what it was like to be part of the story—first person. Guests became part of a completely interactive experience, where they got to choose their own path and level of participation. Disneyland's original virtual worlds were built out of bricks and mortar, not bits and bytes. Even now, no electronic virtual world comes close to approaching the resolution or interactivity of a Disney theme park.

Nevertheless, Disney as a company is committed to understanding the role of new interactive storytelling technologies. As the company moves into the 21st century, guests will begin to see an increasing variety of hybrid theme park attractions that combine real world and cyberspace experiences. The regional Disney-Quest entertainment centers are an example, combining the latest in game play, simulation, virtual reality, and special effects technology.

Disney theme parks will continue to engage and entertain people for years to come. By combining the skills of artists and storytellers with the best new technology developed at WDI and acquired from industry, they will continue to deliver high-tech storytelling experiences long into the new millennium. After more than 45 years of continuous innovation, Walt Disney Imagineering has just barely scratched the surface of what is possible. It is going to be a fun next 1,000 years.

FOR ADDITIONAL READING

Building a Dream: The Art of Disney Architecture, Beth Dunlop (Harry N. Abrams, Inc., 1996).
Designing Disney's Theme Parks: The Architecture of Reassurance, Karal Ann Marling, ed. (Canadian Centre for Architecture, 1997).
Walt Disney Imagineering: A Behind the Dreams Look at Making the Magic Real, The Imagineers (Hyperion, 1996).

INTERNET RESOURCES

Disneyland Paris (available in six languages) http://www.disneylandparis.com/disney/smain.htm
DisneyQuest: The Ultimate Interactive Adventure http://disney.go.com/DisneyQuest
The Official Disneyland Web site http://disney.go.com/Disneyland/index.html
Tokyo Disneyland (in Japanese) http://www.tokyodisneyland.co.jp
Walt Disney World http://disney.go.com/DisneyWorld/index.html

Today, guests can experience futuristic-themed rides and educational exhibits in Tomorrowland at California's Disneyland (opposite page). With the explosion of the Internet and other applications of interactive media, however, is there a future for theme parks? More than likely, modern computer technologies such as virtual reality will complement, rather than completely replace, the traditional theme park experience.

Future and Assumptions

by Edward Tenner

We, the editors of the 2000 edition of the Yearbook of Science and the Future, *are pleased to present a*

distinctive section of five millennium-inspired feature articles on possible futures. Focusing on scientific

and technological developments and their interactions with society, the articles have been commissioned

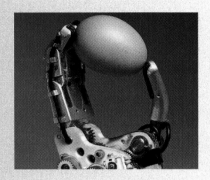 

and prepared with the advice and editorial help of Edward Tenner, guest editor for the collection

and author of the keynote piece to follow. We planned the section on the premise that many similar

collections of speculation will be paying attention to the most likely possibilities whereas, in fact,

the future is certain to produce a number of surprises that will utterly confound the prophets. After

identifying four broad themes—scientific frontiers, the environment, health and biomedicine, and

communication—we engaged expert contributors for each who were willing to look over the heads of

the consensus to exercise their imaginations about outcomes, acknowledge the chaotic aspects of reality,

and consider the unlikely and novel—the heresies, contingencies, and wild cards. To set the stage,

Edward Tenner's essay shows how various assumptions can hobble our capacity to imagine the future

and suggests ways to recognize and question them.

O ther primates, other orders of mammals, and some birds use tools. Chimpanzees even have regional cultures with distinctive ways of handling them. Humanity, however, is unique among animals not only in apprehending the future mortality of physical self but also in envisioning technologies beyond the individual lifetime and in the ability to invest in structures lasting many generations. African termite mounds are magnificent constructions, but a single rainstorm may destroy them. On the other hand, some an-

Edward Tenner *is a writer and lecturer on technology and culture and a visiting researcher in the Geosciences Department of Princeton University. He was recently a scholar at the Woodrow Wilson International Center for Scholars, Washington, D.C., and was the physical sciences editor for Princeton University Press. He is the author of* Why Things Bite Back: Technology and the Revenge of Unintended Consequences *(1996).*

cient Roman buildings and other public works are still in use. We are a species of implicit futurists.

Our capacity to imagine coming things is not so easily exercised. Those who make predictions rarely escape bias—and of two kinds. Men and women who develop, produce, and market new technology need exceptional self-confidence. They see their products and themselves as agents of radical improvement. Yet venture capitalists remind us that of a hundred firms with a new idea, only a handful will ever be viable. In business circles, potential riches coupled with insecurity encourage the boldest and most radical predictions of social transformation. Even many scientists have financial interests and business ties that interfere with dispassionate assessment.

Social critics have biases of their own. Their careers may depend on opposing a conventional optimism that might well turn out to be correct. Just as manufacturers and software producers have products to sell, critics have books and lecture

tours to promote. To stand out, they may have to be bold. Nevertheless, their forecasts may overlook possibilities that neither they nor technology enthusiasts had foreseen.

There is no simple escape from either pitfall, but the history of technology can help us think about the future by recognizing and questioning our assumptions. As our tools for measuring and calculating grow in power and speed, the weak point in our thinking is more and more likely to be in our tacit understanding.

One way to approach this dilemma is to look back a hundred years, to one of the most versatile and gifted young reformers of his time, and to use his career to show the pitfalls of several categories of assumptions over the last century. History cannot predict, but it can expand our outlook in prediction.

One of the outstanding figures of the early 20th century was the economist Irving Fisher (1867–1947). First in his undergraduate class at Yale University, Fisher studied with two of

the greatest American thinkers of his time, the mathematician and physicist Josiah Willard Gibbs and the sociologist William Graham Sumner, and wrote Yale's first Ph.D. dissertation in economics. By 1898 he was a full professor at Yale.

Fisher had boundless and generally justified self-confidence. Although organized futures research was beginning only at the time of his death, Fisher was prominent in many of the advanced-technology movements of his own era. He insisted that mathematical techniques should be used for practical goals. He dedicated himself not just to the advancement of economic theory but also to the enhancement of human life through science and technology. A wrong assumption, however, entangled his career and overshadowed his reputation.

Fisher was farsighted about many things. After contracting tuberculosis in 1898, he became a crusader for hygiene, exercise, and healthy living and coauthored a textbook, *How to Live* (1915), which ultimately sold more than 400,000 copies

Chaos reigned on New York City's Wall Street following the 1929 Stock Market Crash, which took investors by surprise. Between October 29 and November 13 (when stock prices hit their lowest point), more than $30 billion disappeared from the U.S. economy. It took nearly 25 years for many stocks to recover.

neer of the information age with a patented index-card system, a forerunner of today's rotary card files, which made him a wealthy man when Kardex Rand (the forerunner of Remington Rand) bought out his company in 1925.

Unfortunately for Fisher, his greatest public attention was to come from none of these accomplishments but from a prediction he made in October 1929, only 10 days before the stock market's precipitous fall, that stock prices appeared to have reached "a permanently high plateau." Fisher lost as much as $10 million in the market crash, and although he continued to advance measures to rescue the economy and continued his other crusades,

domestically and was translated 10 times. The Life Extension Institute, a preventive medical clinic he helped found in 1913, is still active.

An inventor since grade school, Fisher became a pio-

neither his personal finances nor his popular standing as a prophet ever recovered.

What makes Fisher's case so fascinating is that recent studies have shown that his forecasting methods were justified from the data available to him, even with today's more advanced techniques. It was his assumptions about other factors in the economy, including the role of speculation and fraud, that proved to be Fisher's downfall. All his mathematical mastery—which gave him insights fully appreciated only decades later by a new generation of researchers—could not overcome these gaps. Fisher's history can give us clues to thinking better about the future.

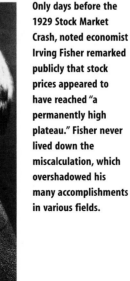

Only days before the 1929 Stock Market Crash, noted economist Irving Fisher remarked publicly that stock prices appeared to have reached "a permanently high plateau." Fisher never lived down the miscalculation, which overshadowed his many accomplishments in various fields.

(Left) Archive Photos; (above) UPI/Corbis-Bettman

ASSUMPTION: THE CENTURY/MILLENNIUM AS A UNIT

Consider how we think of epochs. Behind our fascination with the year 2000 (or 2001 for some purists) is not only that it is a round number. It is also the perception that a century or a millennium conventionally represents a natural milestone in human affairs.

Fisher's own birth and death dates, however, suggest an alternative view. Seventy-five or so years, a full human lifetime, are often a better measure. Politically, 1867–1947 marks a more distinctive era than the 19th or the 20th century as we know them. It coincides with the rise and fall of Germany's aspirations to world power, from the Prussian defeat of Austria in 1866 to the German surrender in 1945. The Meiji restoration and Japan's epochal modernization began in 1868. Technologically and economically as well as diplomatically, America's surge also began after the Civil War.

The period from the Russian Revolution of 1917 to the breakup of the Soviet Union in 1991—74 years—has also been called the "short 20th century," marked by the reactions of the West to the prospect, and failure, of world revolution.

Some epochs can last considerably longer than 100 years. In Japan the Tokugawa Shogunate that preceded the Meiji restoration had endured for nearly three centuries, from the early 1600s, and is often considered as a single period: Edo, from Tokyo's pre-Meiji name. In the West,

Vladimir Ilich Lenin (left) led the Bolshevik Revolution of 1917 and served as the first head of the Soviet state. Marxism-Leninism, however, survived only 74 years, a period often called the "short 20th century." (Below) Workers in Sofia, Bulgaria, remove Lenin's statue after the Soviet Union's collapse in 1991.

historians often write of a "long 19th century" lasting from the French Revolution to the outbreak of World War I.

Our vocabulary is telling: *prewar, postwar, interwar;* or *antebellum* and *postbellum.* Fisher lived through two great convulsions and many smaller ones. Today, despite nuclear proliferation, it is hard to imagine another great conflict of global alliances. Both optimists and pessimists tend to project into the indefinite future our present trend of the rise of world market economies, and especially of global corporations, replacing the struggles of the great powers.

For near-term forecasting, this basis appears to be the most reasonable one, and, indeed, the present trend may persist for 75 years or 120 years or longer. It could also be reversed, and our beliefs about the future come not so much from rigorous analysis as from our lived experience. Fisher, in particular, had every reason to expect a glowing future. He had married young into a wealthy family and had never experienced an economic depression. In the months before the 1929 crash, he had expanded his personal staff of secretaries and assistants with a costly home addition and had bought a luxury car. He must have been reluctant to consider negative scenarios.

All this does not mean that we should be pessimists or optimists but, rather, that we should be explicit about how we periodize our world and be ready to defend the landmarks that we choose in time. The millennium is an invitation to do this, but not a substitute for it.

ASSUMPTION: TECHNOLOGICAL SUCCESSION

Fisher's life reveals not only the difficulties of periodizing but also the coexistence of the periods—the life spans—of multiple technologies. There is a German phrase for this, *Gleichzeitigkeit des Ungleichzeitigen*, literally "simultaneity of the nonsimultaneous." It is another way of saying that old things coexist for a surprisingly long time with new ones. We should avoid the assumption that changes in our lives will be a serial process of succession.

Consider information technology. Fisher's key invention, an index card having a notch that moves along a rail, built on a well-established principle— the rod that keeps library card catalogs in place. Libraries have been shifting to electronic catalogs, but thousands have not yet converted. In fact, some still use the splendidly crafted original oak files from the American librarian Melvil

Michael Newman/PhotoEdit

The pushpin's look has changed little since the introduction of the device by the Moore Push-Pin Company of Philadelphia in 1900. Along with numerous other technologies, pushpins demonstrate that old things sometimes coexist for a long time with new ones.

Dewey's Library Bureau after more than 100 years.

More to the point, after further refinement, Fisher's idea remains an office mainstay more than 85 years after its introduction. Computers and personal organizers have scarcely displaced the rotary card files sold under the Rolodex and Bates trademarks. Business cards are as important as ever, and it is far easier to insert a card into one of these devices than to enter the data by hand. Likewise, it is usually easier to look up an address or phone number by twirling the knob of such a file than by launching a personal database program. In practice, name-and-address software is often used to print the data on sheets of die-cut, separable cards or in address books. Contrary to much 1980s speculation, in fact, computerization

A message is relayed via telegraph (right) by a Western Union worker around the turn of the century. In a modern-day office (below), a newspaper editor composes an E-mail message on a computer. Although the telegraph has been called the Victorian Internet, it may be more appropriate to call E-mail a modern form of telegram.

has multiplied rather than reduced paper consumption.

Paper turns out to be essential especially for advanced electronic work. Even the largest conventional computer monitors are much too small to represent the components of complex multimedia projects. These need storyboards of scenes or text assembled onto large pieces of corkboard or similar material.

To affix these papers most professionals use pushpins introduced by the still-thriving Moore Push-Pin Company of Philadelphia in 1900. The pin's profile has changed little and is optimal for the purpose. Likewise, the mathematics faculty of the Institute for Advanced Study, Princeton, New Jersey, requested not just the latest in workstations and

software for their new building but also slate blackboards, for which newer technologies such as colored markers on white surfaces are no substitute. Old and new are often symbionts rather than competitors.

Some older technologies may be surprisingly resilient for other reasons. Mechanical voting machines, for example, are expensive and cumbersome and need strict scrutiny against fraud. Nevertheless, many computer security professionals are concerned about their replacement by fully electronic systems. It is not yet clear whether it is possible in principle to build an electronic voting system that is fully secure and fully anonymous at the same time. Measures for authenticating electronic voting seem to make results traceable back to individual voters in a way that conventional mechanical counters do not. Internet-based voting systems could have similar problems. In fact, were it not for the anonymity issue, a system of passwords and personal identification numbers could have made possible telephone voting by voice mail menus.

Just as some categories of well-known, apparently simple mathematical problems are expected to resist solution by the most powerful computers that even the cornucopian futurists now foresee, so also may there

be areas of life in which older technology will remain firmly entrenched. In fact, a surprising number of our everyday things have changed remarkably little in the last 100 years. Instead of promoting radically new principles, advanced technology often extends the life of older ones. Internal combustion engines, for example, have persisted for more than a century despite recurrent complaints about their noise and pollution. Electronic communication and on-line shopping have had no measurable effect on distances over which these engines are driven. On the other hand, computerization has transformed the old engine design. Not only does computer-aided design (CAD) software draw and simulate new engines more rapidly but electronic systems in the engines themselves also help reduce noise and vibration to make them environmentally and economically competitive with electric- and natural-gas powered models.

Historians of science and technology point out the high number of current technologies that are at least 100 years old. The first facsimile devices were introduced in the 19th century but found no market. A 1998 book on the telegraph is titled *The Victorian Internet,* but it would be equally correct to call electronic mail a highly ad-

vanced and flexible form of telegram. Today's elevators may use advanced fuzzy logic—programming that uses probabilities rather than rigid decision patterns in responding to changing conditions—to reduce waiting times, but the concept of the elevator itself has changed little.

The safety razor shows how decades and perhaps centuries of refinement can succeed a single rapid innovation. King C. Gillette introduced his new product in 1903, and by the end of 1904 he had sold over 12 million blades. The company he founded still dominates its cate-

gory. Its latest razor product has three blades and a number of other advanced features, yet it remains much closer to the principle of a single disposal blade than Gillette's first product was to the ancient but potentially lethal straight razor—still available and still producing the best shaves in expert hands.

Indeed, the approaching crisis of many computer systems unprepared for the year 2000 has revealed how much vital computer code is reused for decades. Conversion projects have brought many veteran programmers out of retirement.

ASSUMPTION: TECHNOLOGICAL DETERMINISM

Razors bring up yet another issue in prediction: the complex interaction of technology and culture. One error is to imagine invention inevitably begetting other innovations. Fisher gave little thought to values beyond health, prosperity, and efficiency—that was one of his limits. Patterns of culture, ideas, and values, however, are essential in considering the future. The manufacture and sale of razor blades depend largely

Thomas Edison, shown demonstrating an early movie projector, founded the motion-picture industry. His spectacular 1906 film, _The Train Wreckers_, featured special effects hitherto seen only in metropolitan theaters.

on standards of dress and appearance for both men and women. Steam irons, synthetic fabrics, and permanent-press finishes have much to do with a society's view of wrinkled apparel. Many early enthusiasts of the telephone, reflecting the same educated, genteel milieu as Fisher's, predicted that it would be used to deliver sermons and symphonies. (They were not entirely wrong about technology and religion; in the proudly modernizing Iran of Mohammad Reza Shah Pahlavi, cheap tape-cassette recorders in the 1960s and '70s allowed the underground religious opposition to circulate the sermons of the exiled Ayatollah Khomeini.)

A related deterministic assumption sees technology inexorably shaping culture rather than, or in addition to, shaping further technology. The mistake is expecting that innovations in themselves will change patterns of living. Many architects and designers of the 1920s and '30s believed that the common people would embrace dwellings and furniture designed around new materials like steel to proclaim their emancipation from the overstuffed world of the 19th-century bourgeoisie. Instead, the masses clung to upholstered comfort and disliked the award-winning structures designed for their benefit. Today, although buildings and furniture incorporate many new materials, their forms, especially in housing, are likely to be Victorian or Georgian as streamlined "modern" in inspiration.

New technology often embodies and extends existing trends in taste. Consider motion pictures, another technology that rapidly reached a high level and

The development of the modern bicycle depended not only on technological innovations but also on the behaviors of groups of users. The danger of the high-wheel penny-farthing bicycle (right) appealed to many athletic young men. "Safety" models incorporating new features (below) subsequently were developed and marketed to middle-class women.

since has grown more in sophistication than qualitatively. The spectacular, audience-riveting action of early films, like Thomas Edison's *The Train Wreckers* (1906), were not unprecedented consequences of the new medium. To the contrary, as Nicholas Vardac showed in his 1949 book, *Stage to Screen,* early cinema made it possible to exhibit nationally and internationally the kinds of advanced effects that were already drawing audiences to the best-equipped metropolitan theaters. Those stages displayed elaborately painted panoramas as much as

120 meters (400 feet) wide and 18 meters (60 feet) high and presented effects like simulated molten lava and jockeys riding live horses galloping on treadmills. Motion pictures did not create a taste as much as they expressed it.

The modern bicycle appeared at about the same time. As the Dutch sociologist Wiebe Bijker has argued, its emergence depended not only on technical innovations like pneumatic tires but also on complex relationships among groups of users. The upper-middle-class women who could have afforded cycles still wore stiff corsets, so early customers were athletic, affluent young men. The hazards of the high-wheel penny-farthing cycle—a bottle on the road could pitch a rider into a long, head-first fall—actually enhanced its macho appeal. With pneumatic tires, a chain and sprocket drive, and a freewheel mechanism, the path was open to a "safety" model that appealed to young urban women seeking fresh air and exercise. It could also out-race the old penny-farthing design, which soon became a curiosity.

The Internet also is partly a response to established trends. Since the end of World War II, a host of new interest groups, hobbies, associations, and movements had been building memberships and establishing newsletters and mailing lists. In the same period, direct-mail marketing had boomed. By the 1990s millions of people were already accustomed to seeking out new affiliations and products through the mail—and to spending hours sitting before a screen (the TV) and using a handheld device (the remote control) to navigate. The Internet is, in one sense, the expression of a style of getting information that had been developing for years.

Of course, invention does help to change culture. Internet content reflects the public's long-term appetite for gossip

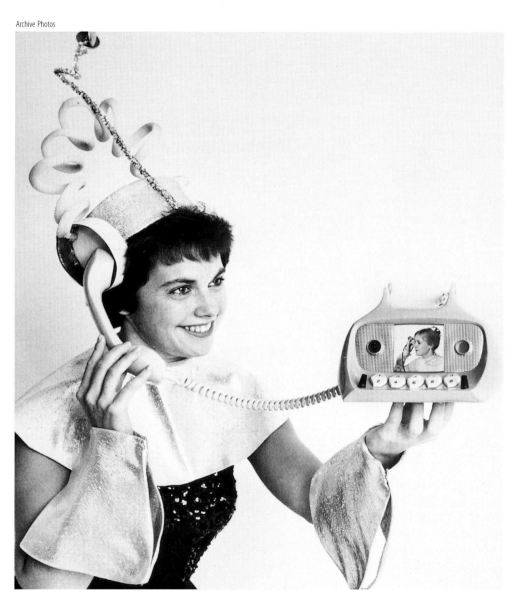

Archive Photos

and erotica that was evident even in 1950s media like *Confidential* and *Playboy* magazines. In applying such appetites to political questions, the Internet has reactivated an even older strain of American journalism,

the scene of often raucous local newspapers and pamphlets that flourished until the rise of more staid metropolitan newspapers in the later 19th century. Today's scandalmongering World Wide Web sites like the Drudge

The future (perhaps fortunately) has failed to turn out quite how some people envisioned. Although video-phones indeed have been produced, they have yet to capture the consumer imagination, in contrast to technologies like the Internet.

Report would not have surprised many earlier 19th-century newspapermen.

Subtle cultural points can also block technically feasible and socially plausible innovations. Videophones have been produced and marketed since the 1960s, yet in contrast to the Internet, they have largely failed. The great majority of our telephone conversations are not with the intimates with whom we would want a form of eye contact. They are often with strangers, and even though users could always turn off their own camera, there would always be the possibility of pressure to keep it on. This does not mean that our descendants might not use them but only that society and its assumptions about communication would have to change before they did.

Unfortunately for forecasters, culture does not take place on easily definable axes. Apparently contradictory trends can move in tandem, for example, faith in conventional biomedical technology and in alternative healing and herbal remedies. Opposites may be only apparent. For people conditioned to believe that there should be a remedy for all ailments immediately, "natural" medicine is yet another technological resource. Because scientific advance reinforces a culture of hope and expectation,

paradoxically it is likely to continue to stimulate interest in the ideas of its holistic critics.

ASSUMPTION: CONTROL

To Fisher and his optimistic contemporaries, nature could be understood and controlled. Underestimating the complexity of natural interactions, most of them still aimed at mastering, rather than working with, the rest of the living world. The 1920s saw a boom in Great Plains agriculture, partly on the theory that "rain follows the plow," that human activity would modify natural patterns to support itself. One reason

for the severity and persistence of the Depression was the resulting erosion of topsoil in what became the Dust Bowl.

We now understand that technologically based human activity has become part of nature. As Stephen Pyne suggests in the accompanying special feature article "The Uncertainties of Environmental Forecasting," we have created an "industrial ecology" that makes Earth's future depend on our decisions on a global scale. The transportation technologies that have promoted regional and intercontinental human movements also create unexpected new biological regimes for humanity. Animals, plants, and microorganisms have been

extending their range, sometimes prevailing in regions where they had been unknown.

The AIDS virus, one of the 20th century's more horrific surprises, is almost certainly not a new organism, but a series of technologies have made it a medical burden often compared to one that seemed conquered—tuberculosis. (Fisher's rare victory over the TB that threatened his life 100 years ago redoubled his energy and transformed him into a medical and social crusader.) Long-distance trucking in Africa and hypodermic delivery of narcotics elsewhere have created an industrial ecology of disease. Blood banks have transmitted the virus inadvertently, and there is always a risk that tests will fail to identify new mutations. Likewise, relatively recent forms of duck and pig farming in China, together with air travel, have transmitted new strains of influenza virus around the world. In his accompanying feature, "Surviving the New Millennium," Robert Desowitz points to the resurgent risk of malaria in the United States as a result of population movements.

New technological systems can interact in bizarre ways with the living world. Investigation of the fatal 1976 outbreak of Legionnaires' disease revealed that the bacillus, soon called *Legionella,* was a surprisingly common one in the

In a familiar scene, customers wait in long lines at a crowded supermarket. Could this be an example of manipulated behavior? Some businesses, in fact, do employ experts to determine the optimum time for keeping customers in line for service.

Rhoda Sidney/PhotoEdit

natural waters of the northeastern U.S. As many as 15,000 people may suffer from it annually in the U.S. Because *Legionella* multiply at temperatures of about 25°–42° C (77°–108° F), they remained isolated until the widespread appearance of recirculating cooling towers and evaporative condensers—with their reservoirs of warm water—for climate control in buildings and industry and of whirlpool baths. The rise in popularity of central air conditioning and whirlpools reflect cultural as well as technological change.

Even machines can be indirectly at risk. The first generation of biocides reformulated against *Legionella* contained minute traces of tin that, once vaporized, were transported through air ducts and contaminated the heads of nearby computer mainframe tape drives, disabling data-processing centers around the United States in the early 1980s. Only rapid detective work by a team of IBM scientists, relocation of the hardware, and later reformulation of the biocide averted disaster.

THE UNASSUMED FUTURE

If there is any tendency that our assumptions have in common, it is to imagine the future as an extended extrapolation of our recent experience. Not only Fisher but also most other leading social prophets have fallen into this trap. In a 1955 book the great Hungarian-American mathematician John von Neumann predicted control of the weather and nuclear power too cheap to meter—both by 1980. David Sarnoff, head of RCA, predicted "a much shorter work week." The experts, nevertheless, are sometimes right in the long run. Fisher was being too cautious as well as too sanguine in 1929 when he said the market would continue at its peak. The postwar boom went beyond his wildest expectations, even though many of the companies in which he had invested went bankrupt in the Depression.

Although we should assume and extrapolate almost nothing, there is at least one trend on which optimists and pessimists about the future agree, without fully realizing it. It may be the basis for a new and more productive round of discussions of the future.

The future will be managed—that is, more and more things will be measured and controlled. One of the strongest tendencies in the later 20th century has been the application of electronic, chemical, and genetic knowledge to specify and tune the performance of a wide variety of manufactured and living things. Notebook com-

Tom Till/Tony Stone Images

This wilderness preserve in Hawaii is one example of efforts to sustain biological diversity by manipulating nature. Some conservationists fear that a managed nature will lose its power to awe and inspire.

puter owners, for example, are familiar with the power-management software that extends time between battery recharges. Battery technology has lagged behind the demands of faster processors and showier screens, but optimization can squeeze more minutes out of an hour.

Our behavior is already more extensively manipulated than we realize; businesses employ consulting mathematicians to compute the optimum time for keeping customers in a queue for service. In his accompanying article, "Communicating in the Year 2075," James Katz suggests another kind of management, the creation of new social codes to shield people from abuses without denying the benefits of new systems.

But management extends beyond the technological, to what was once considered the natural.

The only way to save the diversity of life on Earth appears to be international cooperation affecting more than delimited protected areas, few if any of which were ever free from human influence. (For example, fires set by native Californians suppressed the "natural" scrub vegetation in favor of more diverse stands of oak. Controlled fires may be needed to retain these habitats.) At least one important conservation biologist, Daniel Janzen of the University of Pennsylvania, sees no future for whatever wilderness remains; species can be preserved only in "wildland gardens" where

Nor can we always predict what will happen to the ideas that we are formulating now. Some tasks are much harder than they appear. The French mathematician Pierre de Fermat's last theorem seemed simple enough to tempt countless amateurs, yet when a proof at last was published after more than three centuries, its length and complexity were daunting even to some accomplished mathematicians. Other research has consequences that almost defy imagination. Number theory, a 19th-century mathematical sidelight, became a foundation of cryptography; a Polish mathematician's analysis of the German Enigma cipher machine began the program that proved essential for Allied victory in World War II. It is quite possible that some of today's most abstract ideas, such as string theory, will have deep and socially radical implications in the next century.

There are no theoretical obstacles to some discoveries that have so far been elusive—for example, much cheaper and more abundant energy sources after the false start of nuclear fission reactors and the slow development of fusion. Even the Romanian economist Nicolae Georgescu-Roegen, a pessimist, acknowledged the possibility of what he called a Prometheus III, succeeding the two previous generations of

nature is manipulated to preserve diversity. The roles of governments, international organizations, corporations, and indigenous peoples in management would have to be worked out. If such a plan succeeds, however, the wilderness as a source of awe is likely to be lost in the next century, even if its genetic heritage can be largely preserved.

The fact that the world will be more controlled in the future does not necessarily mean that it will be more predictable. The scenarios imagined by Gregory Benford in the accompanying feature "Expecting the Unexpected" illustrate a fundamental uncertainty about the centuries ahead. The American philosopher Nicholas Rescher has argued that it is impossible either to predict the future course of science or even to declare a question insoluble. Great scientists sometimes speculate on the agendas of their successors, but they are no more likely to foresee them than the great 19th-century physicists were able to sketch the outlines of 20th-century theories of gravitation and relativity.

The image of the ideal female body type has altered drastically over the years, from the plump form exhibited by burlesque dancer Jennie Joyce (opposite page) in 1892 to the slender physique of a runway model (below) in the 1990s. Such fashion changes argue against the wisdom of using genetic manipulation to produce "ideal" children.

Olympia/Gamma Liaison International

carbon-based fuels, wood and coal–petroleum. Moreover, we are far from the theoretical limits of efficiency and of emissions reduction in our use of existing sources. Indeed, the technology analyst Jesse Ausubel of Rockefeller University, New York City, has pointed out that we have been using steadily less fossil carbon per unit of output since the early 19th century.

Control also will have other constraints—the changes in fashion that have been a feature of life in early modern and industrial societies. If, for example, the wealthy attempt to produce "ideal" children through genetic manipulation, these offspring may find that once they have become adults, the body types, physical traits, and temperament that have been engineered for them have gone out of fashion, just as the ample male and female ideals of Fisher's youth gave way to the slender types of the 1920s.

The most likely outlook for the future, as the previous century's evidence and the reflections of our millennium-section contributors suggest, is a delicate balance between our expanded capacities to modify nature and society and the tendencies of both natural and human systems to exhibit novel behavior not accounted for in previous models. Fisher, who

beat the most lethal disease of his time, would have seen this as reason not for despair but for redoubled effort.

FOR ADDITIONAL READING

The Arrogance of Humanism, David Ehrenfeld (Oxford University Press, 1978).

"Expecting the Unexpected," Robert W. Kates and William C. Clark, *Environment* (March 1996, pp. 6–11, 28–34).

Future Imperfect: The Mixed Blessings of Technology in America, Howard P. Segal (University of Mass. Press, 1994).

The Future and Its Enemies, Virginia Postrel (The Free Press, 1998).

The Future in Plain Sight, Eugene Linden (Simon & Schuster, 1998).

"Impact of Technology on the Emergence of Infectious Diseases," Robert P. Breiman, *Epidemiologic Reviews* (vol. 18, no. 1, 1996, pp. 4–9).

Irving Fisher: A Biography, Robert Loring Allen (Blackwell, 1993).

Predicting the Future, Nicholas S. Rescher (State University of New York Press, 1997).

Remaking Eden: Cloning and Beyond in a Brave New World, Lee M. Silver (Avon Books, 1997).

Stage to Screen, Nicholas Vardac (Harvard University Press, 1949).

The State of Humanity, Julian L. Simon, ed. (Blackwell, 1996).

Technological Trajectories and the Human Environment, Jesse H. Ausubel and H. Dale Langford, eds. (National Academy Press, 1996).

Technology in America, Alan I. Marcus and Howard P. Segal (Harcourt Brace, 1999).

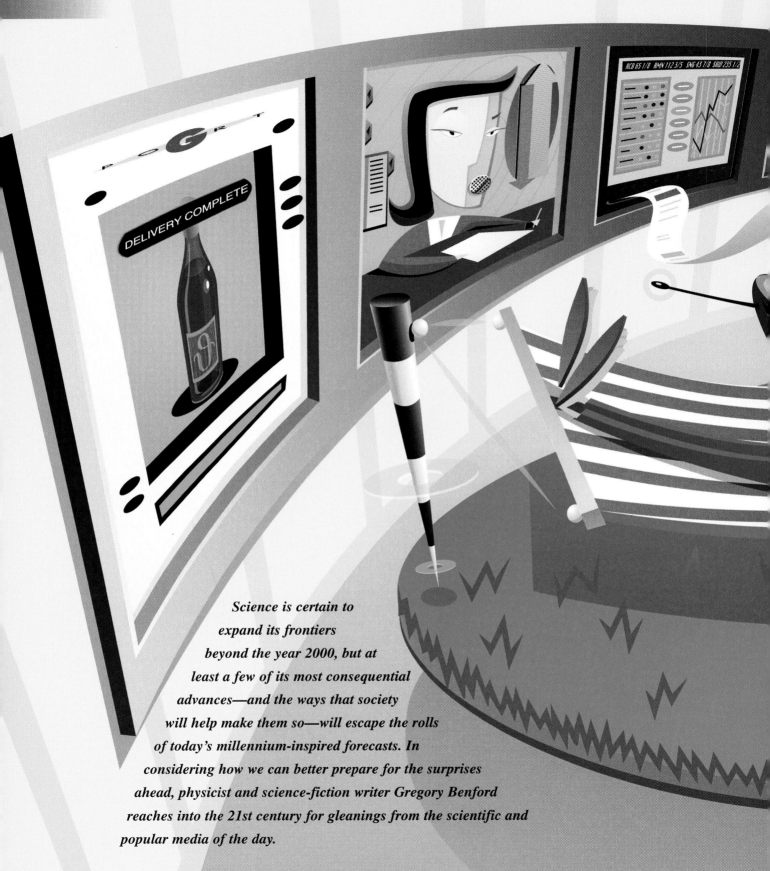

Science is certain to expand its frontiers beyond the year 2000, but at least a few of its most consequential advances—and the ways that society will help make them so—will escape the rolls of today's millennium-inspired forecasts. In considering how we can better prepare for the surprises ahead, physicist and science-fiction writer Gregory Benford reaches into the 21st century for gleanings from the scientific and popular media of the day.

Expecting the Unexpected

by Gregory Benford

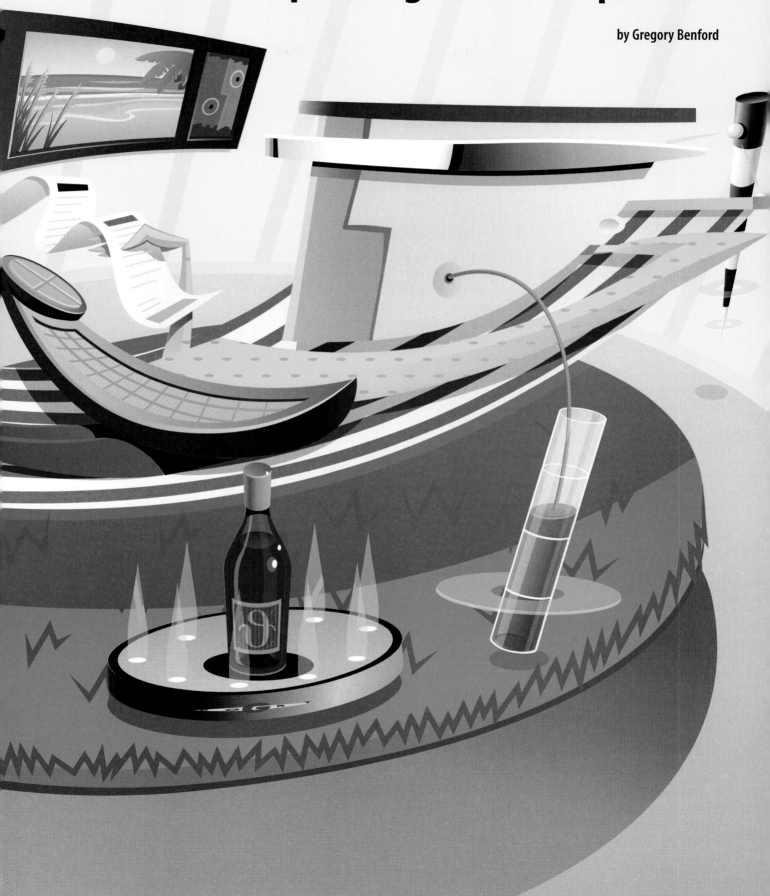

As the next millennium approaches like an overloaded ocean liner, fat with metaphor and passengers, many will attempt to peer beyond the veil of that magical number 2000—for purists, 2001. Some will try to do linear extrapolations from current trends. Others will assume, like southern Californian weather forecasters, that tomorrow will be pretty much like today, only more crowded.

Alas, it will not be that way. Our society is driven by high rates of technological change and exploding social ideas, so powerfully that stasis in any arena is impossible—indeed, inconceivable. One idea that shall surely not survive the 20th century, perhaps to be nostalgically recalled as the mythical TwenCen as language

Gregory Benford is Professor of Physics and Astronomy at the University of California, Irvine, and a prolific author of science fiction. His most recent books include COSM *(1998) and the nonfictional* Deep Time: How Humanity Communicates Across Millennia *(1999).*

compresses under cyber-pressure, is that of the readily foreseeable future.

THE FUTURE AS EMERGENT BEHAVIOR

Many future-oriented thinkers are now less interested in making straightforward predictions and thus in helping determine the future, precisely because they do not believe that linear, programmatic determinism is the right angle of attack. They see themselves more as conceptual gardeners, planting for fruitful growth, rather than engineers designing eternal, gray social machines. Their views of the future are often playful, seeking to achieve an almost impressionistic effect, imagining small scattered details of a future that imply more than can be said. This approach allows them to seek the most vibrant metaphors while cocking a wary eye at society's many looming problems.

Clearly we have come a long way from unblinking wonder at technology, distancing ourselves from the top-down social engineering doctrines that accompanied the optimism of the late-19th and early-20th centuries. Imagining how science and technology could affect society now more often employs the self-organizing principles of complexity

theory popular in biology, economics, artificial intelligence, and even physics. Rather than use monolithic ideas or institutions, we seem poised to operate on smaller, more interactive scales. Today, market competition ideas echo Darwinian evolution. Order, even wholly new species, arise from individual mutations that propagate. In such distant realms as fluid turbulence, small eddies build into larger ones through competition among whorls. In our own brains, somehow the firing of synapses blends into a storm of electrical signals that self-organize into ideas, emotions, and even consciousness. Many phenomena display properties that are more than the sum of their parts, behaviors that emerge from below in ways that science does not fathom.

The TwenCen has been the century of physics, just as the 19th was that of mechanics and chemistry. Grand physical measures still beckon. We could build a sea-level canal across Central America, explore Mars in person, or use asteroidal resources to benefit humanity. Siberia could be a fresh frontier, perhaps better run by a nation other than Russia. Our world will continue to be molded by physics-based technologies.

On the other hand, biological analogies will shape much

more of our thinking to come. The 21st century will be the "Biological Century." We will gain control of our own reproduction, cloning and altering our children. Genetic modification is surely a dynamist agenda, for the many mingled effects of changed genes defy detailed prediction. Although the converging powers of computers and biology will give us much mastery, how such forces play out in an intensely cyber-quick world are unknowable, arising from emergent properties, not detailed all-determining plans. Despite our rather dark impulses to control the shadowy future landscape, to know the morrow, it will be increasingly hard to do so in the years to come.

The most infamous attempt to predict the economic and social future was the Club of Rome's *The Limits to Growth* (1972). Based on a computer model of the interaction of various global socioeconomic trends, the work foresaw only exponential population growth and dwindling natural resources, allowing for no substitutions or innovation. A famous bet over the projected price of metals in 1990 led to the club's public debacle—copper became cheaper, not the fought-over commodity predicted. Although the oil crisis of the 1970s lent the work credence,

The oil crisis of the 1970s appeared to confirm the dire forecast made in the Club of Rome's *Limits to Growth* (1972). Ultimately, the book's predictions of exponential population growth and resource exhaustion proved inaccurate.

James Watson (left) and Francis Crick saw the future implications for reproduction of their discovery of the DNA double helix. In their 1953 paper, however, they took care to express their speculations in terse understatement.

resource markets have since erased the gloomy, narrow view of how dynamic economies respond to change.

WAYS TO LOOK

Rather than looking at the short run and getting that wrong, we should consider peering over the heads of the immediate concerns of the masses, tracing long-run ideas that do not necessarily parallel the present. A historical example of this approach is the Irish-born physicist J.D. Bernal's *The World, the Flesh and the Devil: An Enquiry into the Future of the Three Enemies of the Rational Soul,* which examined the long-term prospects of science and society in terms that seemed bizarre in 1929 but resonate strongly today—engineered human reproduction, biotechnology, and our extension into totally new environments, such as the deep oceans and outer space.

Another, rather enjoyable, way to regard the future is to listen to scientists thinking aloud in a long perspective, making ranging forays into territories seldom illuminated coherently in our era of intense narrowness. Prediction is speculation, normally frowned upon in science, and thus it often arrives well-disguised. Sometimes it is a short-term claim to a notion awaiting exploration, as when James Watson and Francis Crick, in their 1953 paper reporting the discovery of DNA's double helix, laconically noted that they saw its implications for reproduction: "It has not escaped our notice that the specific pairing we have postulated immediately suggests a possible copying mechanism for the genetic material."

In similarly laconic British tradition is a slim tome of a stature comparable to Bernal's, Freeman Dyson's *Imagined Worlds* (1997). In his lofty view, Dyson, an English physicist, shares an advantage with science-fiction writers. Both are good at lateral thinking—the sideways swerve into future scenarios not justified by detail but by their intuitive sweep. In refusing to tell us how we may get to their visions, Dyson and others take in a wider range of possibility than the hobbled futurologists. As Dyson wrote: "Science is my territory, but science fiction is the landscape of my dreams."

Yet another way to broaden the vista of prediction beyond the consensus is to recognize that the future always holds a few wild cards. An unanticipated fundamental discovery or development, or a combination of them in some strange synergy—particularly when mingled with human behavior—can send the future veering from its expected course.

To know that big surprises are in store, we need look only to our recent technological history. As late as the 1950s, not even the most prophetic science-fiction writers foresaw solid-state microelectronics and the personal computer revolution that it would bring. In the 1920s and '30s, who predicted that genetic resistance to those new antibiotic wonder drugs and our indiscriminate use of them would end our rosy expectations for the quick conquest of bacterial infection? Using intuition, educated guessing, random choice—whatever means we wish—we can focus on some of those possible wild

Corbis

The future is bound to surprise us, as a look at our recent technological history demonstrates. No one, for example, anticipated that the behemoth ENIAC computer of the 1940s (left) would evolve into today's laptops and palmtops.

cards, imagining their effects on the future. In so doing, we expand into the realm of the unexpected, where the improbable may become extremely salient.

Physics Today,
April 2008

QUANTUM TELEPORTATION IN THE LAB

. . . teams in Italy showed large-scale transport of quantum information about objects instantaneously to distant points using "entanglement," a connection between separated objects, long known as a purely theoretical feature of quantum mechanics. The achievement, which has its roots in the late 1990s in pioneering demonstrations by Austrian and Italian groups of the transfer of polarization properties between photons, has profound implications for fast computing. . . . Even the concept of instantaneous communication is no longer the fantasy that physicists once believed. . . .

International Electronics Industry, MacroWeb Edition, July 19, 2011

"QUANTUM CHIP" BEATS COMPETITION

Simulation of Human Brain on a Thumbnail Promises Compact Computing, "Smart World"

Chicago Tribune,
May 22, 2027

THIEF "WALKED THROUGH WALLS," GUARD SAYS

FBI Questions Top Scientists

. . . may have employed an application of what Albert Einstein once dismissed as "spooky action at a distance," according to University of Chicago physicist Andreas Rozakis. The entire wave function of even large objects apparently can be "entangled" with a quantum state that exists on the far side of a physical barrier. The object in this case would be the woman who, as witnesses described, passed through the outside wall of

the ultra-secure Nike-Intel vault and then reappeared moments later with several thousand state-of-the-art carbon-based microchips. After looting the vault, said Rozakis, the thief would have needed to entangle herself in another wave function outside the building in order to leave. An FBI spokesperson said that the agency has not even begun considering how such "quantum crimes" might affect future security measures. . . .

As humans we suffer from contradictory demands; our biologically ordained decade-scale thinking contrasts with our social inertia, which requires a century to change. Nearly all of our thinking is bounded within 10 years, although the true agents of change, new institutions and new technologies, take longer than 10 years to grow. Within the next decade, foreseeable advances include a flowering of digital astronomy, completion of the Human Genome Project, and the sequencing of the DNA of many other species.

Single technologies can dominate over the scale of a century, but no more. Dyson has guessed that the next century will dance to the songs of "petroleum, computers, and biochemistry, plus the two

newcomers, genetic engineering and artificial intelligence." Combining these last two alone could give us fresh variants on humans or animals, with microchip-augmented abilities. Such creatures would lie outside any linear mode of our thinking, introducing objects of amusement, wonder, or horror—or all three.

Nature, Vol. 468,
December 16, 2010

BEHAVIOURAL GENETICS FOR THE COMMON MAN

Recently developed procedures for identifying the genes responsible for specific behaviours in animals have now been complemented by a fully automated laboratory technique, announced by BritGen last week, that allows mapping of genetic instructions for advanced abilities, such as programmed seeking, into lower-order organisms and recombinant artificial life forms. . . .

Financial Times,
February 13, 2018

STARTUP BIOTECH FIRM ROLLS OUT LIVING BATH MAT

Can Ease Cleaning Chores, Lives on Soap and Human Dander

Daily National Enquirer, AM Edition, October 29, 2018

"SMART RUG" ESCAPES

Engineered for Home Scrubbing, Living Cleaner Takes to Woods

Rangers, Police Reassure Public: "We'll Shoot on Sight."

The street finds its own uses for things, as a TwenCen writer remarked.

COMPUTERS AND COCOONING

Obviously we have yet to witness the full implications of our fast-evolving computers. Combining the present sensor revolution—the ability of machines to register their surroundings and react—with ever-cheaper computer chips will surely animate our future.

The first changes, coming in a decade or two, will be mild. Appliances will go far beyond obeying voice commands and respectfully replying. Ovens will not merely run and stop; they will know how long to heat a casserole or bake a cake without being told—or at least without being told more than once. Robotic vacuum cleaners will use microwave radar to avoid the walls and furniture. Set to operate when electrical rates are lowest, they will also save money and energy by not overcleaning. Similarly, clothes dryers will run only until the clothes are dry, and washing machines will know how much hot water to use for a load of cotton sheets. Onboard software will allow washers to talk to the embedded chips of the smart clothes loaded into them.

When we wear these clothes, the same chips will sense temperature and send signals to the reactive fabric, which then will adjust itself to suit our personal comfort settings.

There is no reason why a full-blown computer will not be wearable too, perhaps as a fanny pack with a small keyboard fitted to the wrist. Wearable computers will be in especially high demand for people such as doctors, emergency service workers, and real estate agents—those who need immediate information but cannot be tied to a desk or accept

Computer makers are already at work on prototypes of tomorrow's wearable computers. As these devices become lighter and their interfaces more user friendly, they should be popular with people who need immediate information while remaining highly mobile.

Sam Odgen/Science Photo Library/Photo Researchers, Inc.

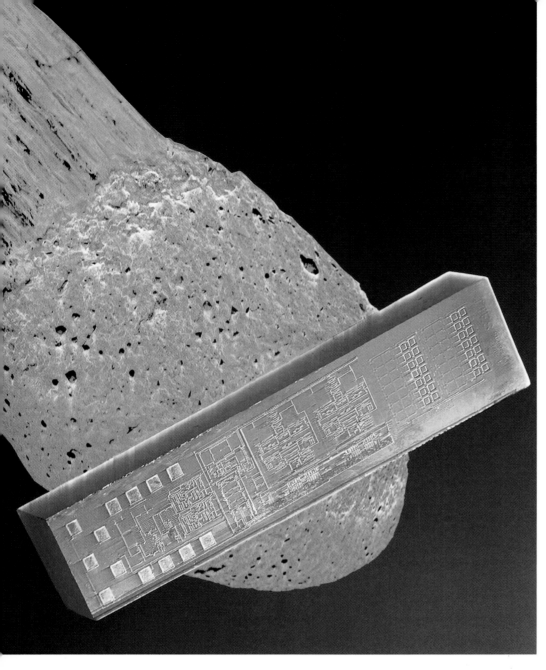

Full-blown computers designed to be built into the body will likely start out as physiological monitoring devices. This implantable, program-mable blood pressure monitor is no larger than a match head.

Volker Steger/Science Photo Library/Photo Researchers, Inc.

the reduced mobility of a lap-top.

Built-ins—computers implanted in the body—will start out as specialized physiologi-cal monitors, say, of metabolic waste for kidney patients or blood-oxygen levels for deep-sea divers, but then they will find myriad applications, sub-stantial and trivial. For simpler tasks, a built-in "social secre-tary" with a small camera or a direct tap into the optic nerve could recognize that vaguely familiar person we might bump into at an office party. It could provide not only the right name but also a short biography, en-abling us to ask without a pause, "Say, Fred, how's that daughter doing at Caltech?"

Robots and artificial intelli-gence generally form the back-ground logic of the future, and the future city will share in their blessings and their prob-lems, for it shall be a living city, the Metropolis, eternally "active" in the computer sense down to its finest details. By the year 2010, computer chips will cost a penny apiece, mean-ing that anything could be made "smart" and able to in-teract with people. Sensing hu-midity and temperature, pre-scription bottles will constantly recalculate the expiration date for the medicine inside and re-mind us with a beep when to take it. A chip in the packaged ham will tell the refrigerator when the ham should be thrown out. Our homes will know which room we are in and tune them to us. Music, scent, art, air temperature, even the views out of flat-screen high-resolution "windows"— all will fit our preferences. Commonplace machines will answer when spoken to, give assistance in their own opera-tion, and automatically self-program to our repeated needs. They will be true "house servants," because houses— indeed, all the Metropolis— will come to be servants. Cocooning will be ever easier.

At our favorite mall, a wall will hail us cheerfully by name, babbling in full-color big-screen enthusiasm about the "bargains a few steps away." We may tell our wearable computer to dis-able all advertisements along our path, but—good luck— somebody will find a way around that, too. Our computer's biomed sensor will discreetly announce if the salesclerk is shedding cold viruses or if the subway car we plan to take back home is a petri dish of flu.

Consumer Litigation News, August 2026

TENANT SUES APARTMENT PSEUDOPERSONALITY FOR INSULT

"It Made Fun of My Weight"

Interactive Software Doorman "Helpfully" Suggested Health Club Membership

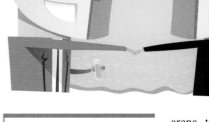

Such environments could yield a new style of human, bred into a comfy, caring culture. The city will not be shadowy and sinister, a TwenCen film-noir future cliché, but welcoming and responsive. In contrast, nature will seem "dead" or other-directed. Trees and animals will be disconcertingly oblivious, unconcerned with our well-being. Strollers in the park will feel uneasy leaving the manicured paths. Children on educational trips into the forest will crowd their tents together, seeking the reinforcement that they expect from their surroundings.

This new sort of human will have political impact as well. "Good-for-you paternalism"—strict rules favoring creature comforts and safety, much like today's no-smoking zones and bans on food ingredients, like peanuts, to which a few have allergies—could become the norm. This is already happening in the voluntary, closed communities favored by the elderly. In California, for example, several cities are wholly walled or gated. Rules set the hours for

The growing popularity of closed, gated communities suggests that the city of the future may produce a new style of human being who not only welcomes a protective, nurturing, all-encompassing environment but also requires it.

mowing lawns and playing stereos and restrict types of pets and numbers of visitors. Those who see the benign, friendly walls of the Metropolis as claustrophobic and subtly threatening will be considered cranks or subversives.

Will this caring city shape a humanity that is missing vital, earthy virtues? The pervasive, softening imagery of this future humanity could be stifling.

Ad Copy, *TV-VR Guide*, October 3–9, 2037

DEATH VALLEY!

A hyper-reality voyage of horror and suspense! You never expected to spend the night in the Yosemite woods . . . or to discover what lives there!

Tonight at 8. Only on the VentuR Network!

U.S. National Park Service Quarterly, 2039, No. 2

28 PARK VISITOR CENTERS SLATED FOR CLOSING

"Nobody Comes Anymore," Ex-Ranger Laments

TAKING TECHNOLOGY TO MARKET

Every new technology can both open and close doors. The same development can encourage cocooning or claustrophobia, depending on use. The first

arena to embrace new technologies is often the market, where every edge could be profitable.

Science, Vol. 379, March 24, 2023

WHO NEEDS ALL THAT CARRY-AROUND HARDWARE?

...few foresaw that these three advances in the physics and chemistry of carbon nanotubes and related fullerene structures would lead in less than 18 months to practical carbon-based semiconductors and then to an explosion of chip-to-tissue interface technology. Designers around the world are at work fashioning microprocessors, sensors, and other microdevices into thin, flexible, highly biocompatible membrane computer arrays that adhere to the body surface and integrate readily into the animal nervous system. Eminently suited for human use, these "smart skins" will have myriad medical, technical, and consumer uses. Industry experts are also predicting a major shake-up for computer and communications-services markets, where conventional handheld and wearable hardware has been a mainstay for decades. . . .

The Wall Street Journal,
June 15, 2026

SKIN-VISION SHOWS PLAY WELL ON BLIND PATIENTS

"Images Not Just on Retinas Now," Say Mayo Doctors

Sight Substitute Could Have Wide Commercial Applications

Bed-Bound Woman "Takes a Hike"

From *Zoomer Extraordinaire: A Biography of Ann Weddon,* by Kris Weddon-Jammeh [Amazon Dot Books, 2087]

The pod wrapped itself around her as tabs and inserts slid into place. This was the latest gear, a top-of-the-line simulation suit immersed in a data-pod of beguiling comfort.

Snug. Not a way to lounge but to fly.

She closed her eyes and let the sim-suit do its stuff.

May 16, 2056. She liked to start in real-space. Less jarring.

Images played directly upon her retina. The entrance protocol lifted her out of her apartment, and in a second she was soaring over rooftops, skating down the beach. Combers broke in soft white bands, and red-suited surfers caught them in passing marriage. All piped down from a satellite view, of course, sharp and clear.

She was a zoomer, one of the ferrets who made markets more efficient. Evolved far beyond the primitivo commodity traders of the late TwenCen, they moved fast, high-flying for competitive edge.

They zoomed through wholly insubstantial spaces, but that was irrelevant. Economic pattern-spaces were as tricky as mountain crevasses. And even in the real world, hard cash just stood for an idea.

Below her, the city was a sprawl, but a smart one. The wall-to-mall fungus from the TwenCen days was gone. High-rises rose from lush parks. Some even had orange grove skirts, a chic nostalgia. Roofs were eco-virtue white, to offset global warming. Blacktop streets had long ago added a sandy-colored coating whose mica sprinkles winked up at her. Even cars were in light shades. All this to reflect sunlight, public advertisements that everybody was doing something about the planet's troubles. High above, man-made clouds did the bulk of the shielding.

The car-rivers thronged streets and freeways (still free, if you could get the license). When parked, cars were tucked underground. Still plenty of scurry-scurry, but most of it mental, not metal.

She felt this more than she saw. Her chest was a map. Laguna Beach on her right shoulder, Irvine over the left. Using neural plasticity, the primary sensory areas of her cortex "read" the county's electronic Mesh through her skin.

But this was not like antique, serial reading at all. No flat data here. No screens. Her body was the medium.

She relaxed. The trick was to merge, not just observe.

Far better for a chimpanzee-like species to take in the world through its evolved, body-wrapping neural bed.

More fun, too. She detected economic indicators on her

augmented skin. A tiny shooting pain spoke of a leveraged buyout. Was that uneasy sensation natural to her, or was it a hint from her subsystems about a possible lowering of the prime rate? She dove into the clouds of event-space. Her skin did the deals for her, working with software that verged on mammal-level intelligence itself. In a sense, she wore her suites of artificial intelligence . . . and in a real sense, they wore her.

She felt her creds—not credits so much as credibilities, the operant currency in data-space—washing like hot air currents over her body.

Losses were chilling. She got cold feet, quite literally, when a new nuke plant piped up with a gush of clean power. That endangered her energy portfolio. A quick flick got her out of the electrical futures market altogether, before the WorldWide Mesh caught on to the implications.

She flapped across the digital sky, capital taking wing in its eternal search.

CONVOLUTED TWISTS

It may help to think not of a smooth future vista, following a steady trajectory upward, but of the odd turns such a future makes all too possible.

3-D Weekly—See What's Coming at You!
January 12–18, 2020

FASHION TIPS FOR THE HERE/NOW

...we clue you to the latest product from the folks at BodyPerfect: real-live "toothpaste." Just pop this little guy—it looks like a bit of strawberry jam—in your mouth, and you're socially safe for weeks! Spreads out around your gums, gobbling up food bits from that sushi or pizza you just had, and maybe it'll even make your breath smell, well, not so bad. It picks off the germs that cause gum disease, too, but who cares if you can't get a date anyway, hey? . . .

Commentary,
Greater USA Today,
October 8, 2032

. . . as the House continues to debate legislation to control the manufacture of pea-sized blobs of synthlife that live in the digestive tract and secrete timed doses of cocaine. Is this illicit production of a drug? It never appears outside of the body and bloodstream. Regardless of the regulations that emerge from Congress, it is clear that far more exotic methods of manufacturing designer drugs and concealing their use will be devised. . . .

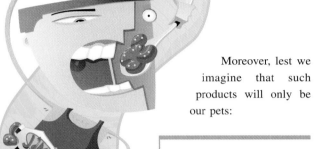

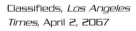

Classifieds, *Los Angeles Times,* April 2, 2067

Animals to your taste. Need a green Siamese to match your futon? A talking collie for those lonely hours? What would you like it to say? Zap us at NewBreeds on the WorldWide Mesh. You imagine—We deliver! Pets reinvigorated while you wait.

Moreover, lest we imagine that such products will only be our pets:

WorldWide Mesh Immersion Ad,
June–July 2072, Subvocal Portion, Inverted Alpha Wave Carrier

Want to work beneath the sea? Or experience space up close and personal? We can let you "breathe" under water or in a vacuum. Always tired? Convert sunlight into quick energy with a custom photosynthetic epidermis! We design for the truly exceptional customer.

NEW HUMANS ASSOCIATES, CLAVIUS BASE, LUNA

We often think that the future belongs to the glitzy professions. Nevertheless, manual labor also will be altered by the changes to come, including the role of the farmer.

New Scientist,
May 2, 2020

CAN WE BECOME QUEEN OF THE HIVE?

As a consortium of corporate labs in Brazil and Germany rushes to complete the Honey-bee Genome Project, a new era is dawning in our genetic understanding of the social insects. . . .

Voice-over, *Toilers in the Field,* CVRI-enhanced vidchip, grade level 9–10, © Yahoo-GM Educational Software, 2039

Consider a field of maize— corn, to Americans. At its edge a black swarm of ants marches in orderly, incessant columns.

Each ant in these long lines carries a kernel of corn or bears bits of husk. In some places, entire teams coagulate around chunks of cob. The streams split, kernel-carriers trooping off to a ceramic tower, climbing a ramp, and letting their burdens rattle down into a sunken vault. Each returns dutifully to the field. Another, thicker stream spreads into rivulets that leave their burdens of scrap at a series of neatly spaced anthills—dun-colored domes with regularly spaced portals, for more workers.

These had once been leaf-cutter ants, content to slice up fodder for their own tribes. They still do, pulping the unneeded cobs, stalks, and husks, growing fungus on the pulp deep in their warrens. They are tiny farmers in their own right. Biotechnologists, however, have genetically engineered them to harvest and sort first for the human masters, processing corn right down to the kernels.

Other talents are being added. For example, acacia ants naturally defend their home trees, weeding out nearby rival plants, attacking other insects that might feast on the acacias. Take that ability and splice it into the corn-harvesters, and we no longer need pesticides or the drudge human labor of clearing the fields.

How were the acacia ants wedded to corn? It was not the immense leap we might expect. Ant species are closely interrelated and multitalented. Evolution has given them a wide, adaptable range.

Following chemical cues, they seem the antithesis of robotic machinery, though insects are actually tiny automatons engineered by evolution, the engine that favors fitness. So the biotechnologists asked, "Why not co-opt their ingrained programming at the genetic level and harvest the mechanics?". . .

Some human farmers will be insect tenders, more like beekeepers than tillers of the soil. Others will find their livelihood threatened.

The Hindu [Orbital Stations Edition], October 31, 2043

AMERICAN FARM-WORKER UNIONS PROTEST "STRIKEBREAKER BUGS"

Mexican Immigrants Return Home—"No Work"

WARNING—HAZARD AHEAD

All of these are mere glimpses of what could await us in the next 100 years. A century is an enormous span, stretching our foresight to the full. H.G. Wells's great visionary novels appeared only a century ago, yet many of their imaginings

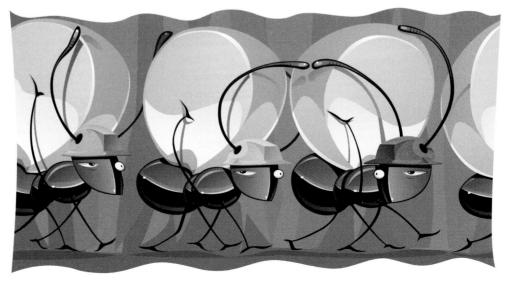

have come true. The point of specific visions is not their accuracy but their implications. Science-fiction writer Ray Bradbury has often remarked that his goal is not to predict the future but to prevent it. Some visions we may not favor but nonetheless should study.

Social reaction will ultimately spell the fate of many innovations, perhaps more so than in the high-flying TwenCen.

. . . so again we see cleverness collaborating with chaos. Defenders like EroCorp's CEO Terry Dixon continue to point out that drug- or VR-enhanced robotic sex is better than having to deal with "quirky, moody humans." Sexbots are always available,

consenting, and disease-free. As welcome benefits, abortions, teen pregnancy, prostitution, and diseases have plunged dramatically since the Food and Drug Administration and the Centers for Disease Control approved national marketing of the first models four years ago.

Strident arguments about the imminent extinction of the species, as we all become sexbot connoisseurs and fail to reproduce, have been summarily dismissed by demographic and population-control experts worldwide. In any case, the World Health Organization is committed to having the first 12 artificial-womb banks up and running

by the end of the decade. At last, society appears to have found the true roots of the problem of sexuality—human beings. . . .

New Puritan activists fought off attacks from a dozen robotic-sex extremists at three street-corner sites in downtown Atlanta today as the Newpies marched and attempted to recruit passersby

for the procedure known as limbic reconfiguration, or LR, which erases the sex drive. . . . Interviewed earlier today on "Good Mornin', AmeriCan," a Newpie leader referring to himself as Ultimata praised LR, the breakthrough discovery pioneered in bonobo apes at the Kinshasa Primate Center, as a "corrective therapy" that is "bringing us to our rational, antianimal senses for the first time in human history." Commenting on clinical findings that children who were given the therapy at birth now find their parents' "obsession" repulsive, Ultimata said that he "can only applaud their perceptiveness."

THE LIMITS TO DREAMS

Although robots will alter much about our laboring life, the greatest promise lies in biotechnology, which could usher in as profound a revolution as industrialization did in the early 19th century. It will parallel and interact with other vast themes—the expansion of artificial intelligence, the opening of the inner solar system to economic use, and more.

The Achilles' heel of predictions is that we have as much difficulty foreseeing the limitations of a technology as we do its promise. A 19th-century dreamer might easily have generalized from the newly invented "wireless" the sending of not merely messages by radio waves but also cargoes and even people. Matter, after all, is at bottom a "message," since it can be turned into energy and propagated. Nevertheless, the awesome radio did not develop into a matter transmitter, which is no closer to reality than it was a century ago.

Undoubtedly, then, some of these analogy-dreams will not come true, particularly in their timing. It seems likely that, despite the current fashion for nanotechnology—artifice on the scale of billionths of a meter, the submolecular level—biotechnology will come first. The latter is easier to implement, because the tiny "programs" built into life-forms have been written for us by nature and tested in its remorseless lab.

In fact, some of the more intriguing prospects for nanotechnological applications derive from our knowledge of the characteristics of biological materials. For example, one of the great quests in biology today is to understand how the linear structure of a protein molecule specifies the way that it will wrap itself into a unique three-dimensional shape, which in turn determines its biological function.

Tekno-Squint Mag,
September 2035

. . . came as essentially a surprise to molecular biologists when the protein-folding problem was solved last year in a series of elegant experiments in microgravity aboard the International Space Station. The scientific community was at first skeptical of the concept that macromolecules, like growing plant shoots, somehow sense the Earth's downward pull and orient themselves accordingly. With general acceptance of the idea, however, came a quick and simple algorithm for predicting the spatial configuration of any protein from its amino-acid sequence. . . .

An obvious long-chain molecule to fold and use as a construction material is DNA, which, given the appropriate molecular machinery, can make more copies of itself. A self-replicating "bio-brick" could be as strong as any plastic. By adding bells and whistles at the molecular level, through processes of DNA alteration, bioengineers could then make intricately malleable substances, capable of withstanding a lot of wear and able to grow more of themselves when needed.

It is not fundamentally absurd to consider sidestepping the entire manufacturing process for even bulky, ordinary objects, like houses. We have always grown trees, cut them into pieces, and then put the boards back together to make our homes. Someday we may grow rooms intact, right from the root, customized down to the doorsills and window sizes. Choose our rooms, plant carefully, add water, and step back. To do fix-ups, simply paint the house with a solution that feeds the self-repairing functions.

Believe It! MacroMesh
site (trans-Mars and
deep-ocean distribution),
April 1, 2099

VAGRANT TRAPPED IN DYNAGROW HOME

"Didn't Know He Was in There," Beijing Developer Claims

How to Get Him Out of Wall? House Has Become His Body

BIO-THINKING

Whether such dreams ever happen, it seems clear that using biology's instructions will change the terms of social debate.

The rate of change of our conception of ourselves will probably speed up from its presently already-breakneck pace. The truly revolutionary force in modern times has been science, far more so than so-called radical politics. Birth control pills changed social relations far more than edicts from the state. Cars and the Internet enhanced the flow of people and information that institutions as varied as corporations and police sought to control.

Nevertheless, many of the examples above underline the implications of leaving genetic choices to individuals. Society has some voice in defining boundaries, but typically we arrive at consensus only slowly, while biotechnology speeds ahead. Perhaps we are poised at the start of a profound alteration in the essential doctrine of modern liberal democratic ideology. There may be genetic paths we will choose to block. How do we recognize them, and quickly?

Our species has made enormous progress through swift cultural evolution. Now, that same fast uptake on changing conditions can come also from deliberate genetic alterations. With knowledge of our genome and the technology to alter it, we will hold the evolutionary steering wheel, however shaky our grip, and no longer rely on pitiless, random mutation.

We stand on the threshold of the Biological Century. Like the 1890s, our decade bristles with striking inventions, though biological rather than physical. Conceptual shifts will surely follow. Beyond 2000, the principal social, moral, and economic issues will probably spring from biology's metaphors and approach and from its cornucopia of technology. Bio-thinking will inform our world and shape our vision of ourselves.

We will emerge from the Biological Century with a profoundly different worldview. Our prospect is both wondrous and troubling. It is as though prodigious, bountiful nature for billions of years has tossed off variations on its themes like a careless, gushing Picasso. Now nature finds that one of its casual creations has come back with a piercing, searching vision and has its own pictures to paint.

The most difficult of all predictions is how all these social and scientific forces will intermingle, yielding a world as different from ours as we are from the optimistic security of 1900.

One thing is certain: the ride will be interesting. Hold on to your hat.

FOR ADDITIONAL READING

Deep Time: How Humanity Communicates Across Millennia, Gregory Benford (Avon/Bard, 1999).

Imagined Worlds, Freeman Dyson (Harvard University Press, 1997).

Paradigms Lost, John Casti (William Morrow, 1989).

INTERNET RESOURCES

The Foresight Institute (nanotechnology) http://www.foresight.org

The Mars Society (human exploration of Mars) http://www.marssociety.org

The Uncertainties of Environmental Forecasting

by Stephen J. Pyne

Will 21st-century generations live in a bright, clean world, or will Earth's environment remain hopelessly mired in its polluted past? Environmental historian Stephen J. Pyne takes an insightful look at the problems of environmental forecasting and points out the critical need for incorporating human behavior, processes, and institutions in our understanding of the planet's future ecology.

In 1989 the U.S. National Academy of Sciences's National Research Council convened a panel on the human dimensions of global environmental change, particularly climatic change. Scientists on the panel believed that they understood most of the natural processes that influence conditions in Earth's atmosphere. A large wall chart traced out the chemistry, physics, and biology involved. Absent from the scientists' calculations, however, was the "human factor," even

Stephen J. Pyne is a professor at Arizona State University, Tempe. He is the author of World Fire: The Culture of Fire on Earth *(1997).*

though people had always been considered important drivers of environmental change. A small circle was placed in the corner of the chart to represent the human dimension. Someone converted it into a smiley face.

Uncertainty about how humans affect the environment is at the core of understanding the future of environmental change. Over the years, an enormous amount of time and money has been spent studying influences on the environment, yet the future will likely depend on human behaviors outside the scope of scientific inquiry, on events beyond rational forecasting. Some future developments will project trends already evident. Others will rely on unique events now being played out on regional scales. The longer future will track the evolution of an industrial Earth, an ecology peculiarly reliant on fossil fuels and technology. Beyond that, events will likely follow from how human populations see themselves and their place in the great scheme of things.

RATES AND REGIONS

The near future of the environment will likely resemble the near past. The trends that define humanity's present relationship to the environment will probably continue. Repeatedly, the projection of the most alarming of these trends leads to forecasts of ecological disaster. The litany is long and practically synonymous with the agenda of modern environmentalism: overfishing the oceans, cutting down tropical rain forests, overgrazing savannas into desert, slashing biodiversity and shrinking vital habitats, expanding cities into the agricultural countryside, and pumping toxic chemicals into the atmosphere, lands, and rivers. The prevailing view is that, if left unchecked, any such trend could prove damaging, if not lethal. In most scenarios, two driving forces stand behind these trends: human population growth and per capita consumption of natural resources. In short, more people are claiming more of Earth's bounty than ever before.

Simple projections can be misleading, however. Natural resources are socially defined, enabled by technology, and subject to fads of fashion and commerce—a synthesis of what people want and what they can get. The value of water in an arid region, for example, depends not only on the local rainfall but also on whether more can be brought from elsewhere by dams and canals and on whether people want it for lawns, irrigated crops, swimming pools, or power plants—or more properly, what price they are willing to pay for each use.

Projections of Earth's environmental future based on existing trends can be misleading. Many trends are nonlinear, even chaotic—the complex product of processes that can compete with one another or interact in other unexpected ways. For instance, as rain forests in some parts of the world are being clear-cut for timber (bottom, this page and opposite) or burned to create agricultural land, tree-planting programs and spontaneous reforestation are going on elsewhere. Similarly, as some ecosystems are being lost to pollution (opposite page, top), other areas are being set aside as nature reserves. An influx of people into the world's major urban centers (below, right) is offset by the outflow of people into the suburbs and surrounding areas.

Similarly, growing mulberry trees as ornamentals consumes water, whereas converting cotton fields to housing tracts can conserve it.

Moreover, most trends are nonlinear, complex, and even chaotic. Like prescription drugs in the body, they can interact in unexpected ways. Many processes have matching or competing counterprocesses, such that trends are reflections of the relative rates between them. For instance, deforestation in the tropics has its counterpart in reforestation in the temperate lands. The clearing and burning of rain forest trees releases carbon into the atmosphere, whereas industrial societies sequester carbon in wood-frame houses, furniture, and libraries bulging with books. Large cities have become the norm for urban life, but they, too, represent a rate between the immigration and emigration of people. Indeed, even as land is paved, mined, and built upon, nature reserves are proliferating.

The competing processes that underlie trends can also change over time, and they do so for various reasons. Some changes reflect a simple pattern of ecological feedback. In the United States, for example, forest fires often burn more intensely because forest management practices have allowed fuels to build up. As a result, the decades-long reduction in land area burned by wildfires is now reversing itself. Trends can also be influenced by economic decisions. When certain goods become expensive, people find substitutes. If wood

becomes scarce and its use cost-prohibitive, people will substitute brick, plasterboard, coal, or some other material for buildings and fuel. Similarly, if meat protein becomes insufficient, people may turn to fish meal or soybeans as protein sources.

Lastly, many processes are most meaningful on local or regional scales. People, endangered birds, rare orchids, and old-growth forests, for example, all live in particular places, not in the world at large. Ecological breakdown in the form of pollution, flooding, or habitat loss occurs locally, not globally. Some places suffer from acute overfishing, others do not. Africa has high population-growth rates, whereas Europe does not. In short, global averages mask these variations.

When the general public becomes alarmed about environmental problems, responses are often expressed as political decisions to intervene. During the 17th century in Japan, 18th-century Germany, and 19th-century America, for instance, serious overcutting of forests prompted conservation responses in each of these countries. When the rates of deforestation reached a certain threshold, they triggered in each society a reaction that forestalled the predicted scenario. The spread of conservation as a transnational doctrine resulted in good measure from the study, by scientists mostly, of the impact of European expansion and industrialization on many parts of the world. People realized that settlement often had undesirable consequences and they sought to intercede, typically with government insti-

tutions, to prevent the worst abuses. Earth today reflects both the shock of impact and the reaction to it. The creation of public forests is one such outcome.

So are the numerous treaties that have helped to spread the conservation response into a global movement. By the mid-1990s, some 200 multilateral environmental agreements (MEAs) regulated the harvesting of such animals as whales, turtles, and elephants; the movement of migratory birds; the production of toxic emissions; and so on. In 1959, for instance, 12 nations signed the Antarctic Treaty, which applied a universal standard of environmental behavior to an entire continent. Other important MEAs are the Montreal Protocol of 1987, which banned trade in the chlorofluorocarbons (CFCs) that threatened stratospheric ozone; the Rio Treaty of 1992, which sought to establish criteria for the protection of biodiversity; and 1997's Kyoto Protocol, which attempted to regulate greenhouse gases. Indeed, MEAs have become as much a part of Earth's environmental status as the processes they regulate.

THE UNIQUE AND THE UNEXPECTED

A simple projection of existing trends, therefore, is not a reliable guide to the long-term future of the environment. Some trends do not express the simple outcome of competing rates. They represent the influence of unique events or circumstances unlikely to be perpetuated or repeated. To discern those unprogrammed events that will tip the scales toward one trend or another—or that

cause gestalt-like shifts in perception and values—is a very difficult trick indeed.

As a historical case in point, consider the existence of large public lands such as wilderness areas, wildlife refuges, and national parks. Such lands are not evenly distributed throughout the world. Most are located in countries colonized by Europeans in which native pop-

ulations largely disappeared through war, disease, or relocation. The vacated lands were then set aside as public or crown lands, while bureaucracies, notably forestry services, were set up to oversee them. They exist most spectacularly in the U.S., Canada, Australia, and Russia and are important features of New Zealand, South Africa,

Argentina, and other former colonies. Russia's story is complicated by the nationalizations that followed the Bolshevik Revolution, but the process was under way in tsarist times.

Most public lands are no more than a century old—at core, they are an imperial creation—and there is no reason to believe that they will continue indefinitely or in their present

form. In the mid-1980s, for example, New Zealand disestablished its forest service, retained about 25% of the reserved lands for conservation purposes, and sold the remainder. Elsewhere, native peoples, for example, in British Columbia, are clamoring to have large chunks of such land returned to them.

When people express concern about the environment, the response typically comes in the form of government interventions. Earth today reflects both the impact of human beings on the environment and their reactions to it.

Despite their uniqueness and short existence, public lands have mattered for several reasons. They are expressions of early conservation efforts, an attempt to halt or even reverse the destruction caused by European contact. Many conservation doctrines emerged from that struggle, and many nature reserves and national parks were created from the wild landscapes so set aside. It is no accident that the scholarly field of environmental history has flourished, particularly in the U.S., and that it has centered on the American West, where much of the landscape consists of public land.

A large fraction of environmental controversies, particularly those involving land use and nature reserves, occur in precisely such lands, where national political values can override local economic interests. These controversies and the concepts that inspired them have, in turn, influenced global environmental thinking. Dealing with those seemingly vacant lands set a pattern—a political paradigm—of human-nature interactions seemingly unencumbered by the usual swarm of competing ethnicities, nationalities, and ideologies. These national commons became, in turn, the model for the global commons that have emerged over the course of the 20th century, including Antarctica, the deep oceans, and the atmosphere. Were the public lands to vanish into privatized lots or be reclaimed by indigenous foragers, agriculturalists, and pastoralists, environmentalism would lose symbols of critical and emotional importance.

As a second example, consider the post–World War II eruption of large-scale development programs in various parts

of the world. In Alaska and the U.S. Intermountain West, Canada, Australia, Brazil, Indonesia, and the Soviet Union, for example, various development projects—pipelines, hydropower dams, irrigation systems, farmland reclamation projects, roads, and oil drilling—all promised to transform the "primitive" into the modern. These programs were only possible, however, because of political, ecological, and historical

circumstances unique to those regions. Most other countries did not possess large "undeveloped" landmasses to which they could direct the new wealth and technologies released after the war; thus their efforts were buried within smaller-scale projects. Furthermore, few large-scale development projects could cross national borders. Only public capital—usually national in origin, but sometimes from the World Bank—could

initiate infrastructure projects of this magnitude. On the other hand, larger countries like the United States and the other above-named nations were not so restrained and could undertake projects in what appeared to be vacant or underused lands. This perception was strengthened where the indigenous peoples did not practice agriculture or did so in forms, such as swidden, that Europe considered primitive and unproductive.

The Snowy Mountains hydroelectric power project, which began in 1949, was a tremendous undertaking by the Australian government to provide electricity and irrigation water to southeastern Australia. Post-World War II development projects such as this one spurred the creation of an environmentalist movement in many developed countries.

Archive Photos

William Bacon/Ken Graham Agency/Accent Alaska

In Alaska, significant petroleum deposits exist under part of the Arctic National Wildlife Refuge, but to recover this oil would require the kind of infrastructure that would drastically and forever alter the landscape of the area, now dedicated to the conservation of Alaska's wildlife and wilderness resources. Such controversies—and the concepts that inspired them—have influenced global environmental thinking.

Many of these places then became scenes of major environmental controversies—nature and indigenous economies pitted against the modernizing state. These conflicts spurred the creation of an environmentalist movement in the developed world that aimed to preserve primitive lands and their residents, impede large infrastructure projects such as the building of dams, and advance another set of values to define the relationship of humanity to nature. The older conservationist movement, concerned with the efficient use of natural resources, transformed into a broader environmentalist agenda replete with nongovernmental organizations and "green" political movements. Without those large postwar projects, it is unlikely that modern environmentalism as a movement and broad philosophy could have emerged. The one required the other. The unique conditions for environmentalism's success, however, make it unlikely that it will continue to survive in its present form.

As a third example, consider the fact that environmental problems are not evenly distributed around the world. The largest division is between those regions that have industrialized and those that are trying to do so. Industrialized countries have problems related to toxic pollution, urbanization, transportation, noise, and issues of public health and quality of life. Indeed, industrialization imposes such vast transformations on the environment that a global overview that merges all regions into a collective average is meaningless. Paradoxically, because industrialized regions have changed so profoundly, their opportunities for further large-scale environmental reform are fewer than in regions that have yet to make an industrial transformation. Even two world wars and a depression did not significantly rearrange the gross ecology of an industrialized Europe. Unless an industrial country has significant amounts of public land, its environmental future will look only incrementally different from its recent past.

This is not the case with industrializing regions, where the opportunities for significant change are greater and the range of possible futures less prescribed. Although such nations as China, India, and Indonesia may be more limited in their options simply from the inertia of their enormous populations, typically rural and poor, the environmental future may be less deterministic elsewhere. The most interesting region—perhaps the surprise of the 21st century—may be sub-Saharan Africa. Today much of sub-Saharan Africa is considered to be an environmental disaster. Little seems to work—industrialization has been spotty, political structures fail regularly, war and famine are endemic, trade moves little more than commodities, and ecological degradation is widespread.

Yet modern technology could redefine, indeed reinvent, Africa. If biotechnology could create vaccines against major diseases like malaria, African demographics could fundamentally restructure, not only among indigenous peoples but also for immigration from elsewhere. With modern biogenetic and materials technologies, it might be possible to establish an agriculture not based on native swidden or European models, industries and technologies not dependent on fossil fuels, and a landscape fashioned in ways different from any known in the past. Africa could move from the degraded nadir to the forefront of desirable habitats. Although the likelihood of this happening is not great, the opportunities for renaissance are better there than elsewhere.

THE ECOLOGY OF INDUSTRIALIZATION

Industrialization has been the primary driver of profound environmental change throughout the world. What, however, does industrialization mean as an ecological phenomenon? A good case can be made for considering fire—humanity's most powerful means for reshaping whole landscapes—as an index of how industrialization began and how it works. In essence, industrialization has revolved around a new kind of controlled combustion—that is, a new kind of fuel and the ways to burn it.

The industrial revolution has long been considered a social and economic event that began redefining the relationship of peoples to one another and to their land. Yet, ecologically, it involved more than machines, factories, and rapid transport. Its critical essence was that this fire, unlike its predecessors, burned fossil biomass in the form of coal, petroleum, shale oils, and natural gas. In themselves, steam engines did not break down the ancient equation between growth and consumption that had governed the degree to which humans could change the environment. To the extent that the new furnaces burned wood, they consumed biomass much faster than it could be grown. Tapping fossil biomass, however, evaded this restriction. By transporting biomass from the geologic past into the present, the amount of fuel available was, for practical

The industrial revolution, which revolved around the controlled combustion of fossil biomass such as coal, fundamentally restructured the world's fire regimes.

purposes, unbounded. It became possible, literally, to make more of everything. This new fire can stand as the ecological definition of industrialization.

The full ramifications of industrialization are still being defined. For at least several centuries, Earth will likely be shaped by industrial processes. No other force comes close to creating the environmental stresses or the occasion for major reforms in Earth's ecology.

It is unclear, however, to what extent the use of fossil biomass is a transitional or an indispensable component of this industrial ecology. For the most part, industrial fire is understood within the context of older fire-ecology models and thus is assessed by how it has perturbed preindustrial ecosystems. Nevertheless, this is not the same as understanding how industrial fire and the ecology that it shapes might function as an integral system in its own right.

What is clear, however, is that industrial fire has added to Earth's fire load through the combustion of a new fuel source. Unfortunately, the new source carries its by-products—soot, smoke, and greenhouse gases, particularly—to old sinks such as the atmosphere. Unlike biomass fires, industrial fires burn without regard to diurnal or seasonal rhythms. They overload the environment with particulates and gases that cause public health problems and affect the chemistry of the atmosphere. Enough greenhouse gases, mostly from combustion, may lead to a greenhouse effect from which Earth's climate could warm dramatically. (*See* Sidebar: *Climates of Earth, Climates of Opinion.*)

The new pyrotechnologies have substituted for many of the old ways of using fire. Most uses of fire as a tool—in kitchens, hearths, forges, and agricultural fields—are vanishing from the developed world. Industrial combustion and its secondary products such as electricity are fast replacing the open burning of wood, charcoal, and other traditional fuels. Domestic fire usage has almost died out and agricultural burning is rapidly fading. Today farmers accomplish with tractor power, pesticides, fertilizers, and herbicides—all derived from fossil biomass—what they had previously achieved with open flame. Indeed, these technologies are even used to suppress natural wildfires.

continued on page 154

Domestic uses of fire—in campfires (far left), hearths, and furnaces—have nearly vanished in the developed world. The use of electricity, for instance, in microwave ovens (left), has replaced the open burning of traditional fuels.

Randy Wells/Tony Stone Images

151

(Top of page and above) North Wind Picture Archives

Climates of Earth,
Climates of Opinion

Along with the loss of the world's biodiversity, no subject has dominated environmental forecasting as much as climate change. Indeed, the atmosphere may be the very symbol of the global environment. Many scientists fear that a sufficiently large insult to the atmosphere could, ultimately, upset Earth's climate. The most likely shock is an accumulation of greenhouse gases such as carbon dioxide (CO_2), hydrofluorocarbons (HFCs), and methane, which may act to increase Earth's greenhouse effect and ultimately lead to global warming. Such a buildup, primarily of CO_2, has occurred over the last century. One of the major sources of additional CO_2 has been deforestation, which has reduced Earth's stockpile of stored carbon. The largest source, however, is the combustion of fossil fuels such as coal and petroleum. Effluents are being released far faster than Earth's ecosystems can absorb them.

In this far-from-understood Earth, however, it is not entirely clear how more greenhouse gases will increase the greenhouse effect or how an enhanced greenhouse effect will induce climatic change in any predictable way. The consequences will likely play out at regional scales, in the form of greater seasonal variability, in shifting proportions of extreme events such as hurricanes, floods, and droughts, and perhaps in local desertification and coastal flooding. Nevertheless, even these speculations are uncertain, for climate models have not proved notably successful in their forecasts. Only recently have they incorporated aerosols, clouds, and other cooling countereffects to global warming. Moreover, as much as 25% of the carbon released by industrial combustion is unaccounted for in global models of the carbon cycle. Scientists have also encountered difficulties interpreting the signatures of climate change.

In itself, climate change is a sure bet. Earth's climate has always changed, and it will continue to do so. On the other hand, the mechanics of climate may well resemble a Rube Goldberg machine, full of unanticipated, misdirected, oddly linked associations with unsyncopated rates and lag times. As such, it is not unlikely

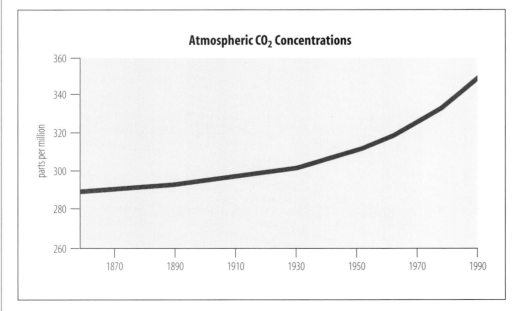

Atmospheric CO$_2$ Concentrations

parts per million

360

340

320

300

280

260

1870   1890   1910   1930   1950   1970   1990

(Opposite page) AP/Wide World Photos; (left) Pete Saloutos/Tony Stone Images

Scientists fear that an accumulation of greenhouse gases, particularly carbon dioxide, in the atmosphere will lead to global climate change. Whereas humans are releasing carbon in record amounts—through the burning of forests (opposite page) and the combustion of fossil fuels—they are also storing large quantities of it in new wood construction (left).

that present predictions about climate change will prove wrong. For one thing, as carbon is being released by humans at record rates, it is also being stored in unprecedented quantities in sinks ranging from cities to spontaneous regrowth outside agricultural lands. Not least is the power of fertilization by increased atmospheric CO_2, which has stimulated plant productivity in many parts of the world. In fact, eastern North America, which is in the process of reforesting, may have become a carbon sink. The public lands of the American West are overrun with woody plants and deepening litter, and many forests have grown into tangled jungles. A century ago the city of Edmonton, Alberta, bordered the edge of a vast prairie. Today that border lies 100 kilometers

(60 miles) to the south, driven back by new forest. Scrub has overtaken large fractions of once grassy Australia. Bush encroachment is a major problem outside intensively managed veldt in Africa. With increased political and economic control over industrial combustion, which is likely, these and other carbon sinks could easily absorb the sources.

This reasoning, however, still leaves several important points unsaid. First, the existing climate cannot be truly stabilized. It will change on its own. Second, today's weather is not the norm, and alarm over its change is fundamentally a cultural judgment. If climate changes, some regions will improve and some will deteriorate. Arguments to stabilize the existing regime are at bottom a political decision to continue

the status quo. Indeed, there is as much reason to intervene to retard these natural movements as there is to halt those that are induced by human activity. After all, some 80% of the past two million years has been glacial. Third, sequestering carbon in sinks has ecological as well as climatic costs. Although reforestation, thickening woodlands, and spreading scrub are stockpiling the carbon that might have otherwise overloaded the atmosphere, in a sense this process is only transferring the overload to existing biotas. Many American forests are now unhealthy, unstable, and prone to high-intensity wildfires.

In short, global climate change is certain to occur and become a crisis, but it may not become the change or crisis predicted. Technologically, the

issue will surely broaden. Climatic engineering will likely join genetic engineering as the macroeconomics and microeconomics, respectively, of nature's mixed economy. The problem may well become one of climatic management, of atmospheric engineering.

Present-day attempts at regulating the perceived causes of climate change resemble a primitive strategy of ecological management in which wild landscapes are simply reserved. This approach has largely failed as a long-term program on land, and so, too, may contemporary efforts to stabilize the climate by an analogous agenda of atmospheric preservation fail. Future societies may seek to coordinate carbon releases and sequestrations in an attempt to dampen the irregularities of climatic fluctuation, not unlike central banks trying to modulate the business cycle through control over the flow of money. Carbon—as living or fossil biomass—may well become the currency of a climatic marketplace.

Fire is an ecologically necessary process. Lodgepole pine trees, for example, have cones that remain closed on the tree. The cones (below) do not open to release their seeds until the heat of a fire melts a waxy layer. In the Rocky Mountains, lodgepole-pine communities have been severely affected by fire-suppression programs.

continued from page 151

Subtracting open fire from the environment, however, has had its costs. Fire is an ecological process as well as a human tool. Expunging fire from fire-adapted ecosystems has upset many biotas. When fuels are no longer allowed to burn routinely under controlled conditions, they can build up and burn episodically and catastrophically as intense wildfires. Species and communities that have evolved under a particular fire regime have suffered because the regime has changed. For example, because of fire-suppression programs, Ponderosa pine forests have become overgrown and experience catastrophic fires instead of mild surface burns. Sweden's extinction of fire threatens beetles equipped with infrared-sensing organs that lay eggs in smoking stumps. In the long absense of fire, many fynbos plants, including orchids, die out. Giant sequoias in California regenerate best in the ash of intensely burned sites. In truth, fire is as powerful removed as applied. Consequently, a major concern of industrialized countries today, particularly those with extensive wildlands, is somehow to reinstate free-burning fires as an ecological presence. Without industrialization, this issue would never have arisen.

practices such as recycling and a search for renewable resources—both materials and energies—as a means to pull the industrial comet into a proper orbit. It may be, however, that among the most radical of industrial ecology's impacts will be the reconstruction of that intellectual model.

A critical element of industrial ecology is the insistent

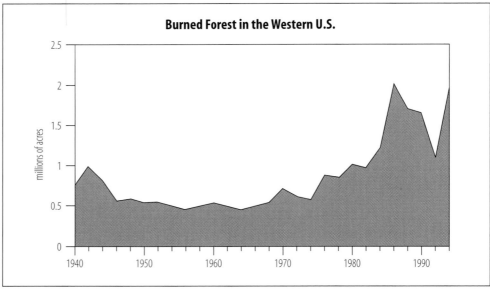

Burned Forest in the Western U.S.

(y-axis: millions of acres; values 0, 0.5, 1, 1.5, 2, 2.5; x-axis: 1940, 1950, 1960, 1970, 1980, 1990)

Finally, the industrial revolution has rearranged fire—that is, restructured fire regimes—through indirect means. It has redefined natural resources, made possible massive urbanization, and literally rewired combustion through roads and rails. It has created new energy pathways powered by fossil-fuel combustion, redrawn nu-

trient cycles often along transport routes and according to the flow of capital, and reorganized the geography and cycling of species and communities. Viewing these changes as disruptions, environmentalists have argued for the reinstatement of an ecology based ultimately on the old agricultural cycles and have encouraged

presence of humans. In the old ecologies, everything humans did could be done by something else—lightning strikes set off wildfires, elephants knocked down trees, wombats dug holes in the ground, bison fed on grass, and wolves hunted ungulates. Preindustrial humans still had an extraordinary capacity to rearrange pieces of the biotic

(Opposite page, graph) The national forests of 11 western U.S. states employed fire suppression programs and now confront a seemingly inexorable rise in wildfires. (Below) The ecological consequences of the 1988 Yellowstone fires far exceeded the park proper. Among the extensive off-site effects was the shutting down, at least temporarily, of many natural fire programs in the U.S.

kaleidoscope, yet if they had left the scene, the basic ecological principles would have continued to apply.

That is not true for an industrialized world. The act of extracting, burning, distilling, or otherwise processing fossil biomass is humanity's alone. If humans leave the scene today, the principles of industrial ecology leave with them. Industrialization can only occur with humans as active agents. It is possible to imagine an ecology of free-burning fires without humans, but it is not possible to imagine an ecology of industrial fire without them. Humans are not only present, but they also are what make the system work. An industrial Earth cannot evade this charge, which means that industrial ecology cannot be understood by natural science alone.

The reasons are several. For one, it has proved very difficult to scientifically describe events in which humans are both observers and participants. When humans describe themselves, the scientific method breaks down. Natural science can describe the brain, but not the mind. For another, human behavior includes processes and concepts that ecological models have not yet absorbed—concepts such as information and institutions. Consider, by way of illustration, the wild-

fires that in 1988 swept through America's first and most famous national park, Yellowstone. Over the course of a droughty summer, fires of multiple origins and various intensities burned more than 364,000 hectares (900,000 acres), almost 45% of the park. At first, park officials accepted the fires as "natural"; later they attempted to supress them at a cost in excess of $150 million.

The Yellowstone fires were widely discussed on radio and television news programs, written about in scientific and popular journals, and debated by politicians and bureaucrats. Indeed, coverage was so extensive that the actual ecological impact of the forest fires was

felt well beyond Yellowstone. As information, it cycled through institutions whose officials then applied what they believed they had learned from the fires. Decisions were made involving not only knowledge but also misinformation, and officials took into account not only assessments of burned area, pine reseeding, and elk migration but also political calculations about public perceptions and cultural values about what a national park should be. In response, wildland fire programs throughout the U.S. were shut down, reviewed, reopened in new forms, or permanently closed. The ecological effects of the fires were manifest in Georgia, Min-

nesota, California, and beyond the borders of the U.S.—in Canada, Australia, South Africa, and Yakutia—places far removed from the flames and smoke of the actual fires.

It is precisely such human processes that an understanding of an ecology of industrialization must incorporate. A globalized ecology involves more than an atmosphere collectively shared by a charcoal stove in Brazil, a wildfire in Siberia, and commuter traffic in Los Angeles. It also involves the prospects for globalizing knowledge, creating suitable institutions, convincing disparate publics that it all matters, and arguing an environmental equivalent to a doctrine

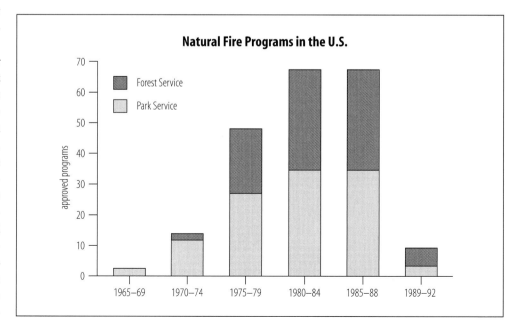

(Below) The charred remains of a pine forest lie in the aftermath of the fires that devastated Yellowstone National Park in 1988. For much of the American public, the Yellowstone conflagrations were a dramatic introduction to fire ecology. News accounts at the time declared the park all but destroyed. More than a decade later, however, Yellowstone was bursting with new life (opposite page) and shattering old notions about fire's role in the natural world.

of human rights. How humans perceive global change is at least as significant as what the change itself may be. In brief, an understanding of industrial ecology must meld science with the indeterminacy of human history and whatever methods humans have to determine what that history means.

THE ECOLOGY OF BELIEF

Here, then, is the wild card in forecasting an environmental future. The human dimension remains stubbornly resistant to scientific self-analysis, predictable historical precedents, and to any assertion other than that it will influence Earth's ecology more thoroughly than any other single factor. Human behavior remains ultimately within a moral universe, with how people in Earth's many habitats see themselves and their place in the great scheme of things. Such considerations are one reason why the future will remain more than the sum of competing

processes or the projection of past experiences forward. (*See* Sidebar: *The Burning of Greece and Canada.*)

The future would seem to belong with that modern technology that has become both the cause of many of human-ity's environmental problems and the near hope for their so-lutions. Increasingly, Earth as a human habitation has become a synthetic creation that not only reorganizes natural elements to suit human purposes but also consists of artificial substances, from reinforced concrete and nylon to silicon wafers and bio-engineered bacteria. Yet the fu-ture really belongs to those who believe in it. To be effec-tive, science and technology must be applied, and more ba-sically, they must be created. Neither is possible without a belief in their rightness, a gut conviction that the future can be made instrumentally better than the past. Cars powered by fuel cells could unburden Earth of greenhouse gases, but only if society commits to fuel cells.

The future requires choices, and choices reflect values. More and more, the decisions people make, even locally, will affect how the global environ-ment works. Those choices are becoming both clearer and more compromised. People will have to choose between necessary goods, between un-avoidable evils, or between cu-rious combinations of the two. Technology may intervene, but it cannot advise. Science may advise, but it cannot choose. The judgment will fall to the murkier spheres of philosophy, aesthetics, history, politics, lit-erature, and religion. Those so-cially constructed values will decide if and why biodiversity matters, at what cost green-house gases should be reduced, and to what extent organic ver-sus artificial fertilizers should be used in agriculture.

What may matter most is not the increasing integration of nature's "hardware" with soci-ety's "software," as powerful as that has become, but the "op-erating system" used to link them. What vision do people have of their relationship with nature? What stories do they tell of their environmental past? What scenarios do they project for the future? Is there a basis for universalizing Western environmentalism into a global code, a "green" ver-sion of human rights? What do

(Left) Raymond Gehman/Corbis; (above) AP/Wide World Photos

The Burning of Greece and Canada

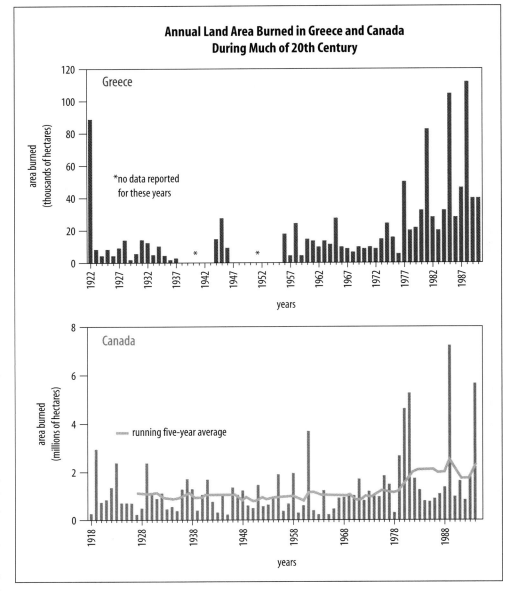

Annual Land Area Burned in Greece and Canada During Much of 20th Century

Greece

*no data reported for these years

area burned (thousands of hectares)

years

Canada

area burned (millions of hectares)

— running five-year average

years

The two graphs indicate the annual amounts of burned land area in Greece and Canada through most of the 20th century. The line passing through the Canadian bars is a running five-year average. Despite the countries' enormous differences in climate, human histories, and land use—two less comparable areas would be hard to find—the trends are strikingly similar. For recent decades in particular, both graphs show a steady overall increase in burned area, punctuated by very large spikes. In fact, according to these records, the largest fires in both countries have broken out in the last two decades. Is this a firm indication of the much-forecasted condition of global warming?

It turns out that there are more proximate causes and that they reside with human behavior. The relatively low amount of burned area in Greece through the late 1960s coincides with a time of military dictatorship. When it ended, two trends set in. One was a surge of internal migration from the countryside to Athens and Thessaloniki. With much of the Greek landscape no longer subject to close cultivation, vegetation blossomed, making fire control more difficult. At the same time, politically motivated arson became

common. The large spikes on the graph coincide with national election years. Both the radical right and the radical left burned the land to provoke and embarrass each other.

The Canadian fire swell has a different explanation. In the late 1970s, Canada extended formal fire protection northward beyond traditional frontiers. Historically, Canada's provinces had only fought fires in their southern, more populated regions. Now many sought to provide universal

protection, sending forces beyond that old fire frontier. This proved both difficult and expensive, and ecological arguments that the practice was unwise mounted. The experiment ceased, but aerial reconnaissance continued to map fires that had previously been ignored in record keeping. The rise in burned area, including the biggest fire years, is an artifact of a change in the way that Canada recorded its fire data. Detailed analysis of boreal forests in the Canadian

Northwest show that fires of equal magnitude occurred there in both the early and the late years of the century. The record of those earlier events lies not in human-kept archives but in the structural pattern of the woods.

The two graphs thus determine nothing about global warming. What they do demonstrate is the inextricable role of humans and the way that human understanding can function to shape the future, in this case, of fire.

Human beliefs, values, and choices will dictate how Earth's environmental future plays out. New science and technology—for example, nonpolluting vehicles—could help unburden Earth of greenhouse gases, but only if people believe in their rightness and commit to creating and using them.

people see as possible, desirable, necessary, or right?

Most modern environmentalism has evolved within the perception that the natural world is good and that humanity corrupts it. The story of European contact narrates a tragedy of ecological atrophy driven by human ignorance, malfeasance, or clumsiness. Human actions will end ironically, if not lethally. According to this logic, the best solution is to limit contact, to set aside nature in inviolable preserves, to accept fatalistically the polluted cost of progress. Such reasoning lies behind many of the core precepts that drive the agenda of contemporary environmentalism in its search to preserve fragments of nature for the future.

Another story is entirely possible, however. Such a narrative would point to places where humans have shaped livable landscapes, transformed raw nature into art, found ways to enhance species diversity and general habitability, and stabilized air, water, earth, and

fire. Such a story requires a human agent; such a nature is meaningless without the human presence. In this environmental comedy, failings are errors—the outcomes of humanity's foolishness—rather than disasters sprung inexorably from humanity's fatal flaws. This perception would categorize the enormous change of the past two centuries as an aberration, a phase transition to an industrial Earth, a kind of historic fire whose flaming front is not, in the end, very deep and from whose ashes a new order is already arising. Such a story would seek out ways to involve humans rather than exclude them.

These two visions, and others that will modify or replace them, will likely drive the future. They will influence what humans deem significant about the natural world and how they will react to predicted and unexpected changes. They will underlie why humans identify one cause or problem over another, support this or that sci-

ence, and select one particular technology among many. Those stories will shape how the natural world will share in the comedy, the tragedy, and the just-plain confusion and muddle of human existence. They will determine which prophecies become self-fulfilling and which self-limiting. How people see the natural world will sculpt how they see themselves; and how they see themselves will ultimately move them to interpret the natural world and their place within it and prescribe what they should or should not do to bring themselves and nature together.

FOR ADDITIONAL READING

The Earth as Transformed by Human Action: Global and Regional Changes in the Biosphere over the Past 300 Years, William C. Clark, Robert W. Kates, and B.L. Turner III, eds. (Cambridge University Press with Clark University, 1990).

Environmental History: A Concise Introduction, I.G. Simmons (Blackwell Publishers, 1993).

A Green History of the World: The Environment and the Collapse of Great Civilizations, Clive Ponting (Viking Penguin, 1993).

Guns, Germs, and Steel: The Fates of Human Societies, Jared Diamond (W.W. Norton & Co., 1997).

The Holocene: An Environmental History, 2nd edition, Neil Roberts (Blackwell Publishers, 1998).

The Rights of Nature, Roderick Nash (University of Wisconsin Press, 1989).

World Fire: The Culture of Fire on Earth, Stephen Pyne (University of Washington Press, 1997).

World Resources 1998–99: A Guide to the Global Environment, World Resources Institute (Oxford University Press, 1998).

INTERNET RESOURCES

Global Fire Monitoring Center
http://www.ruf.uni-freiburg.de/fireglobe

UN Environment Programme, Global Resource Information Database
http://www.grid.unep.ch/gridhome.html

UN Environment Programme, State of the Global Environment
http://www.unep.org/unep/statetxt.html

World Resources Institute
http://www.igc.apc.org/wri

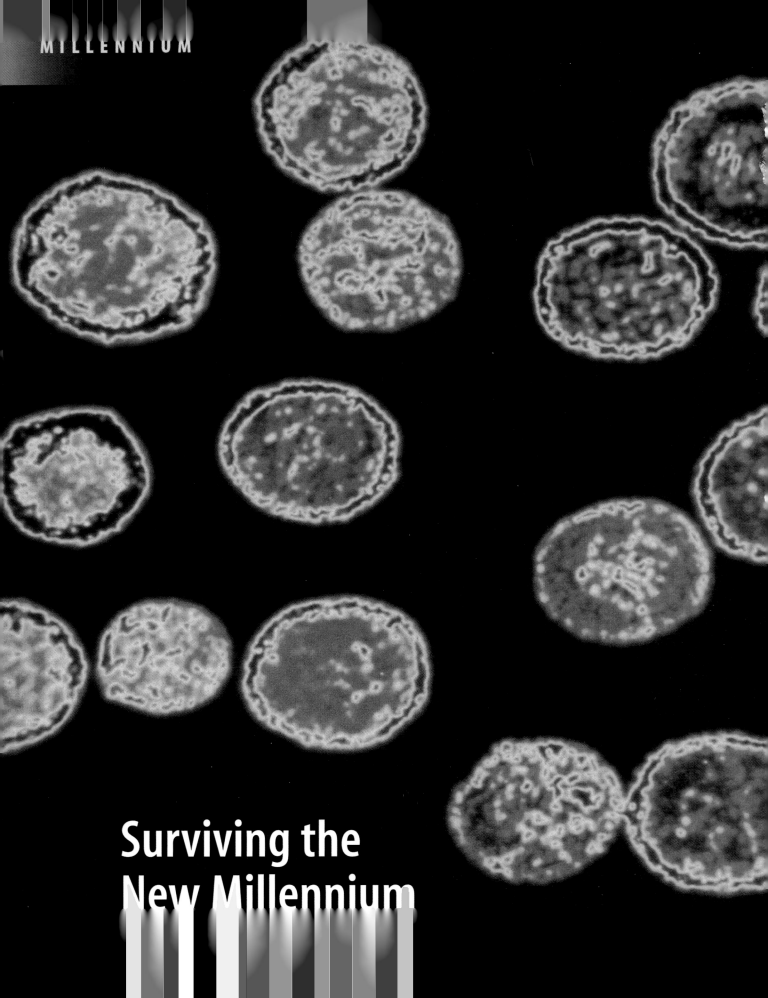

Surviving the
New Millennium

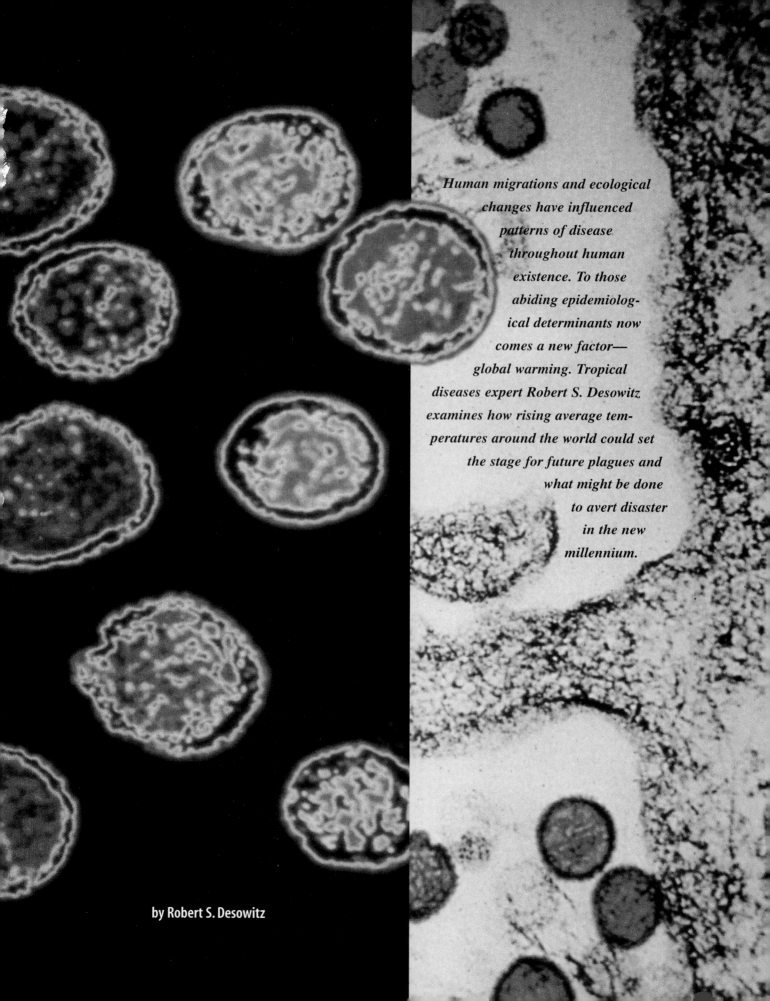

Human migrations and ecological changes have influenced patterns of disease throughout human existence. To those abiding epidemiological determinants now comes a new factor— global warming. Tropical diseases expert Robert S. Desowitz examines how rising average temperatures around the world could set the stage for future plagues and what might be done to avert disaster in the new millennium.

by Robert S. Desowitz

When the 20th century began, pathogenic (disease-causing) microbes still dominated the world. Indeed, throughout at least the past millennium, bacteria, viruses, fungi, parasites, and other infectious agents periodically triggered epidemics that claimed the lives of massive numbers of human beings.

It may not have always been so, however. Many experts believe that during the early period of human history, there was little threat of epidemics. As long as people maintained a hunter-gatherer lifestyle, the risk of infectious, communicable disease was limited. Small, scattered hunter-gatherer bands, comprising 20–30 individuals,

Robert S. Desowitz is Emeritus Professor of Tropical Medicine and Medical Microbiology at the University of Hawaii and Adjunct Professor of Epidemiology at the University of North Carolina, Chapel Hill. His books include Who Gave Pinta to the Santa Maria?: Torrid Diseases in a Temperate World *(1997) and* The Malaria Capers *(1991).*

moved too frequently to pollute the environment with soil- and waterborne pathogens. Even insect-transmitted diseases would not have been a major problem. Malaria, for example, requires about 10 days (the exact time depending on the species of malaria parasite and ambient temperature) after a mosquito extracts blood from an infected person for the parasite to mature into the infectious stage in the mosquito's salivary glands. Before a malaria parasite completed its mandatory developmental cycle in the insect, any potentially vulnerable band of hunter-gatherers likely would

have moved off to another hunting ground.

Small community populations also limited the spread of infectious diseases. Measles, for example, when introduced into a small, immunologically "virgin" population, will have a disastrous killing effect on both adults and children. In the past 500 years, explorers and missionaries unwittingly inflicted this devastation on isolated Amazonian Indian tribes, Pacific islanders, and Eskimos. Nevertheless, after the initial deaths, a form of "herd immunity" supervenes, with too few nonimmune persons to

perpetuate the virus. It requires a population size of about 200,000 to provide a sufficient supply of nonimmunes to maintain and perpetuate the measles virus.

About 10,000 years ago, or perhaps even earlier, humans began a new lifestyle. They settled down and became farmers. Thus began the mas-

An illustration from Father Bernardino de Sahagún's 16th-century treatise, *General History of the Things of New Spain,* shows Aztecs with smallpox contracted from the Spaniards being treated by a medicine man.

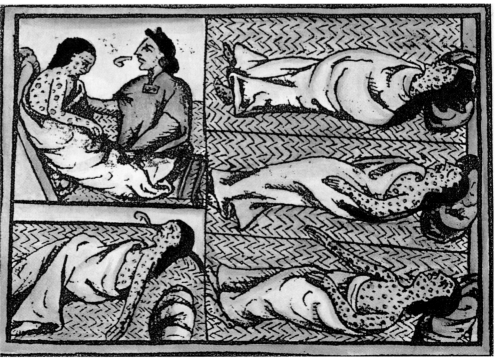

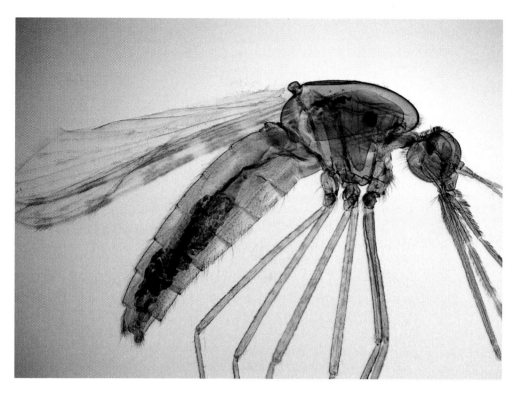

A female mosquito is depicted in this close-up image. Malaria-causing parasites are transmitted to humans by the bite of various species of mosquitoes belonging to the genus *Anopheles*. Global warming is conducive to the spread of such mosquitoes.

sive man-made alterations to Earth's natural ecosystems—first as a concession to agriculture, then later, to industrialization. There were important epidemiological consequences of the ecological changes. For example, many wild animals of the forest and savanna, carriers of microbes having the potential to infect humans, became semidomesticated and began to proliferate, particularly rodents. Zoonotic diseases—diseases that can be passed between humans and other vertebrate animals—became a major factor in human health.

The surplus of food that came with advancing agricultural technology also had an epidemiological impact. It permitted the establishment of nonagricultural communities—towns and cities. Some of the urbanites became technologists who devised ways to increase agricultural productivity. Increased food supplies allowed still more urban growth, until a critical population size was attained that made the epidemiological conditions right for the perpetuation of the "big-population" pathogens such as the measles virus.

FOCUS ON THE FUTURE

This is our world's heritage and its milieu as we stand on the brink of the new millennium, wondering optimistically if the anticipated golden age of "Health for All in the 21st Century"—as the World Health

Human genome researchers hope to map and sequence the estimated 50,000 to 100,000 genes in human DNA—knowledge that could help uncover the genetic factors underlying many diseases.

Organization (WHO) describes its vision of the future—is soon to arrive. Modern biomedical alchemists foresee a time in the not-too-distant future when the mapping and sequencing of the human genome will bring an end to many of the genetic imperfections that lead to illness, disability, and early death. In the current scientific literature are even reports of experiments on inducing cell immortality. These may seem to imply that the fountain of youth is at hand, although the goal of such research is to find cures for chronic and degenerative diseases, including cardiovascular pathologies, diabetes, and cancer.

Nevertheless, even without the help of breakthrough remedies being anticipated from modern genetic and molecular research, preventive medicine and public-health advocacy have done a reasonably good job in reducing the immoderate habits of smoking, bad diet, and

sloth. The influence of environmental factors on health is also being recognized, if not necessarily attended to. The average life expectancies for people in industrialized nations are the highest ever and continue to increase. In Japan, for example, average life expectancy in 1995 was 76.4 years for men and 82.8 years for women, up from 74.2 and 79.8 years, respectively, only a decade earlier.

In the Third World, however, where the full benefits of biomedical science and public-health measures are neither affordable nor available, death continues to come early—between 40 and 50 in such countries as Sierra Leone and Zambia. The attenuation of life span in the Third World is due largely to infectious diseases caused by viral, bacterial, and parasitic pathogens. There is fearsome mortality from malaria, meningitis, pneumonia, tuberculosis, and cholera.

Scott Daniel Peterson/Gamma Liaison International

A malaria victim in Africa lies under a makeshift shelter. Some scientists are worried that as Third World peoples migrate to the West, they may inadvertently bring diseases with them.

intelligence, labor, and culture, they can also inadvertently transport pathogens.

In the past, immigrants to the New World brought with them such diseases as malaria, leprosy, hookworm, filariasis, and yaws. The danger still exists today that immigrants will bring diseases. In the U.S., for example, an estimated 100,000 immigrants from Latin America harbor in their bodies the protozoan parasite *Trypanosoma cruzi,* which is the microbial agent of Chagas' disease, an incurable infection that is a major cause of heart failure in tropical America. In Brooklyn, N.Y., a number of Orthodox Jews recently contracted neurocysticercosis, a condition caused by the larval form of a pig tapeworm; the source of infection was eventually traced to their Mexican domestic help. The AIDS virus is also believed to have spread from Africa via immigrants and other travelers.

In addition to the traditional pathogens, the AIDS virus is taking an enormous toll.

Despite the goodwill and assistance of industrialized countries, it is entirely possible that the health of Third World peoples in the 21st century will not only fail to improve but also actually deteriorate. Already we have entered a new age of infectious diseases, where variants of old familiar pathogens have become resistant to virtually every antibiotic in the pharmacopoeia. Moreover, the fact that Third World peoples, driven by political and economic necessities, are heading to the West in large numbers creates a potentially serious health problem. Although immigrants can vitalize their adopted countries through their

Whereas in years past intercontinental travelers made their way by slow boat, leaving plenty of time for infected persons to develop symptoms or even die before they

Reuters/Sunil Malhotra/Archive Photos

Wearing face masks to avoid contracting pneumonic plague, children wait for a school bus in New Delhi in October 1994.

reached their destination, today it is possible to travel anywhere in the world in less than 24 hours. Pathogens, in effect, now have rapid transit to new colonies of humans.

A CHANGE IN THE WEATHER

In ancient times, prophets, priests, and oracles attempted to divine impending disasters from messages of nature. Modern oracles of medical science also look to nature's signs to predict the behavior and spread of infectious disease in the years to come. One of the omens to which they have been giving particular attention is the phenomenon of global warming, an observed increase in Earth's mean surface temperature during the 20th century. In the 1990s the evidence for the reality of a changing climate was especially telling. According to climate experts, 1998 was the warmest year since reliable record keeping began in the mid-19th century, the second year in a row of record global temperature, and the seventh year in the 1990s with above-average temperature. Unfortunately, such statistics do not appear to portend a bright new millennium for the health of the world.

In the last years of the 20th century, small outbreaks of in-fectious diseases occurred in widely separated areas of the globe. Many are related in some way to weather changes brought on by rising average temperatures, the periodic disruption of ocean-atmosphere system known as El Niño, or both. (Climatologists do not always distinguish between the effects of two phenomena; some studies indicate that they may be related and causally interact.) Three examples given

A recent heat wave in Paris forced many city dwellers to seek relief out-of-doors. With global warming showing no signs of abating as the new millennium approaches, scenes like this are likely to increase in the West.

below help illustrate the relationship between medicine and meteorology.

Wajir is a town in the dry semidesert of northern Kenya. Its normally arid environment restricts the breeding of *Anopheles* mosquitoes, the genus responsible for transmitting malaria. Unlike much of sub-Saharan Africa, Wajir is not seriously threatened by malaria. In November and December 1997, however, the weather changed. Propelled by the 1997–98 El Niño event, which was the strongest of the century (and which, in turn, may have been influenced by global warming), torrential rains inundated the town.

Of the four species of malaria parasites that infect humans, only one, *Plasmodium falciparum*, is potentially fatal. The insect-borne infectious disease could reemerge as a serious threat in the next millennium.

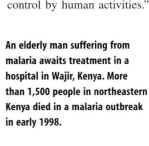

Anopheline mosquitoes bred prolifically. Within two months, malaria struck Wajir; of its 60,000 inhabitants, 40% became infected. At least 108 children under five years of age—the most susceptible age group—died.

About that time, across the Atlantic, the same weather pattern made the desert bloom in the southwestern U.S. This transient garden provided abundant food for the deer mouse (*Peromyscus maniculatus*), whose population increased greatly. The deer mouse is the zoonotic reservoir of the viral pathogen that causes hantavirus pulmonary syndrome in humans. In the normal, sere desert ecosystem of the Southwest, the population of deer mice is low, and there is little contact between mouse and human. The risk of acquiring hantavirus is thus relatively small, with about three or four cases reported in the region each year. This tolerable relationship changed with the 1997–98 rains. Within a few months of their onset, 14 hantavirus cases were reported in New Mexico alone. All patients became severely ill, and five died of the infection. The medical scientists reporting on the outbreak concluded that "the incidence of hantavirus pulmonary syndrome might still be linked to ecological events that are not subject to control by human activities."

An elderly man suffering from malaria awaits treatment in a hospital in Wajir, Kenya. More than 1,500 people in northeastern Kenya died in a malaria outbreak in early 1998.

Scott Camezine/Photo Researchers, Inc.

The third example of a weather-associated outbreak comes from a European city on the Danube River, Bucharest, Romania, where in August 1996 hospitals admitted large numbers of patients stricken with acute central-nervous-system infections of unknown cause. Approximately 10% of the patients died. Blood taken from the patients was sent to the Pasteur Institute in Paris for analysis. The result was unexpected; the laboratory tests concluded that the victims had died of West Nile Fever, a mosquito-transmitted virus common in Africa and the Middle East. In Africa the virus is constantly present (enzootic) in birds, some of which are known to migrate to the Danube River basin. The infection rarely moves to humans because the behavior of the virus-transmitting mosquito species in Africa and the Middle East is genetically directed to favor feeding on birds rather than humans. Abnormally heavy rains in 1996, however, caused extensive flooding in the cellars of buildings in Bucharest. This dank, watery environment was an ideal breeding habitat for another potential vector mosquito species, *Culex pipiens,* which feeds on humans and birds indiscriminately. Later epidemiological investigations revealed that 40% of the wild and do-

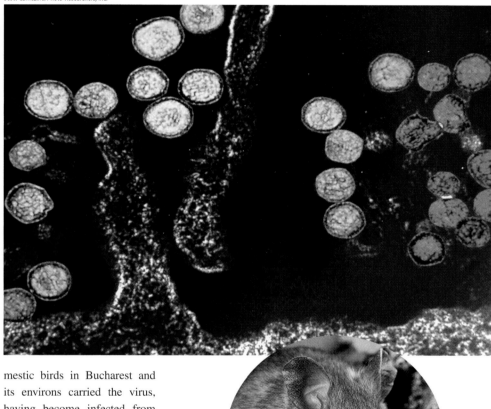

mestic birds in Bucharest and its environs carried the virus, having become infected from the migratory African birds.

Outbreaks of waterborne infections may also be manifestations of global warming. It is a law of physics that, when heated, ice melts. Exactly how much water will enter the oceans as the polar caps thaw has been debated, but according to one projection, if global warming continues unmitigated, sea level may rise as much as 18 meters (60 feet) in the next century. That will result in many backed-up sewers in the inundated coastal regions. Drinking water will be-

come fecally contaminated, leading almost certainly to the spread of waterborne diarrheal diseases such as cholera.

The specter of cholera is particularly frightening. This once-feared, now almost forgotten infection—except in countries like Bangladesh, where the people

(Top) A microscopic image reveals the pathogen that causes hantavirus pulmonary syndrome in humans. The deer mouse (above) is the zoonotic reservoir of the potentially deadly hantavirus pathogen.

Maslowski/Photo Researchers, Inc.

167

A Peruvian girl paddles a canoe through contaminated water to reach her home in the village of Belen. Full of excrement, the water presents a perfect breeding ground for cholera bacteria.

face it each monsoon season—has already returned to the Americas. In 1991 cholera spread through the Southern Hemisphere, with 333,562 reported cases in Peru and 2,690 in Mexico. As if to put the U.S. on notice as to what could happen if its sanitation system was compromised, 26 cases of cholera were reported in the U.S. that same year. Coastal inundation brings with it still another epidemiological risk factor. Static floodwaters favor the proliferation of plankton. Microbiologists have shown that plankton organisms can harbor cholera bacteria and act as a constant reservoir of infection.

PESTILENCE-STRICKEN MULTITUDES?

Will our worst fears come to pass? Will the concatenation of global warming, ecological change, inadequate public health in the Third World, and massive human migrations actually lead to a great plague? If so, what will that plague be like? Signs point to the possibility that, within the next two centuries, if these adverse epidemiological determinants are not redressed, there could be one or more devastating epidemics to rival the Influenza Epidemic of 1918–19, which killed about 550,000 people in the U.S. and an estimated 30 million worldwide.

A future great plague in the West could well be caused by a rapid-killing tropical virus, perhaps one similar to the Ebola or Marburg virus, imported unwittingly by an immigrant or a returning tourist. If, once in its new location, the virus mutated such that it could be transmitted via aerosols (by fine liquid particles in the air), the result could be catastrophic. When the Black Death bacterium, *Yersina pestis,* underwent that kind of transformation, from flea-transmitted bubonic plague to aerosol-transmitted pneumonic plague, it became the horrifically virulent pathogen that wiped out nearly one-third of Europe's population in the 14th century.

The new plague may be caused by a pathogen entirely unknown to present-day science—a virus, bacterium, or parasite that has not previously been seen, characterized, and stored for reference and study in the liquid-nitrogen canisters of microbiologists. It could come as an AIDS-like virus, but one transmitted nonsexually—delivered in the air or contaminated water or by a tropical bloodsucking insect that is able to establish itself in a temperate region made tropical by global warming. It could be a pathogen for which there is no known chemotherapeutic cure or vaccine preventative.

Then again, a new plague may be an old familiar one reestablished in a warmed-over America and Europe. A likely candidate would be an insect-transmitted disease. In places like New York City or London, where the climate would be semitropical, bloodsucking insects would flourish, as they now do in tropical Africa and Asia. They would breed in rapid cycle, feed more often, and live throughout the year; the pathogens that they carried would come to infective fruition more rapidly than at lower temperatures.

One familiar insect-borne infectious disease that could reemerge in the next millennium is malaria, one of the most ancient infections known. Each of the four species of malaria parasites that infect humans can cause high fever and anemia, although only one species, *Plasmodium falciparum,* is potentially fatal in an untreated, nonimmune individual. In North America, malaria had been endemic as far north as Staten Island, N.Y., until the 19th century. Then it subsided, and by 1900 it remained a major medical problem only in the South. In 1919 the U.S. Public Health Service stated that "for the South as a whole it is safe to say that typhoid fever, dysentery, pellagra, and tuberculosis all together are not as important as malaria." In that era, a town in Alabama desperate to attract capital, industry, and jobs attempted to dispel the notion that its citizens were too malaria-enervated to work efficiently by hanging a banner across their Main Street that proclaimed, "Malaria Being Controlled—Come Locate with Us for Health and Prosperity." As late as 1938, an expert council considering the economic plight of the South reported to Pres. Franklin D. Roosevelt, "The pressure of malaria, which infects annually more than 2,000,000 people, is estimated to have reduced the industrial output of the South one-third."

By 1945 the Tennessee Valley Authority and its extensive antimosquito operations, the strategic spraying of DDT, the advent of potent, inexpensive synthetic antimalarial drugs, and the economic recovery that allowed people to live in better housing brought about the virtual disappearance of malaria from the U.S. The anopheline mosquitoes remained, however. In 1993 three cases of malaria were reported in Queens, N.Y. One year later three suburban New Jersey residents were also diagnosed with malaria. None of these people had ever traveled to a malaria-endemic region. The infections were homegrown,

(Left, below and opposite top right)
Culver Pictures; (opposite page
below) Gamma Liaison International

**Workers for the
American Red Cross were
kept busy in 1918–19
removing the corpses of
flu victims. The epidemic
claimed the lives of
some 550,000 people in
the U.S.**

carried by homegrown mosquitoes, although the original sources were never identified.

In at least one instance in the U.S., the turn of the season averted a malaria outbreak. In 1996 a number of Hmong people from the mountains of Vietnam resettled on the outskirts of Charlotte, N.C. One immigrant became ill and was sent to a medical clinic, where doctors discovered *P. falciparum* gametocytes, the sexual stage that initiates infection in mosquitoes, in the immigrant's blood. A follow-up by alerted health authorities showed that more than 25% of the Hmong community members had malaria parasites in their blood. Their settlement was in an area where anopheline mosquitoes bred, but fortunately it was November and the

**Policemen in Seattle, Wash., line up
with protective masks during the
Influenza Epidemic of 1918–19.
The epidemic was the most severe
influenza outbreak of the 20th
century.**

mosquito season was over. The Hmong immigrants were treated, and by the time the mosquito season returned in the spring, they were no longer a source of malaria.

Suppose, however, that the Hmong immigrants had settled in Charlotte at some future time when global warming had made every month the mosquito season. A malaria outbreak would have occurred among nonimmune individuals in Charlotte, and the parasite most likely would have been one of the solidly drug-resis-

This tent hospital (right) was erected in Lawrence, Mass., in 1918 to treat flu victims. (Bottom right) A man sprays a bus with an anti-flu preparation in an attempt to stem the spread of the disease.

tant strains now plaguing Southeast Asia and spreading rapidly to Africa and other endemic regions of the tropics.

Of more immediate concern is the possibility of an insect-borne transmission of the viral disease dengue into North America. Graphically and aptly known as breakbone fever, dengue is characterized by extreme pain in and stiffness of the joints. This acute, infectious, mosquito-transmitted hemorrhagic disease is a major killer of children in Southeast Asian cities and elsewhere in the tropics. Arthropod-borne viral disease experts, such as Tom Monath of the Harvard School of Public Health, have warned that dengue may come to North America. The mosquito vectors of the dengue virus, *Aedes aegypti* and *A. albopictus,* are already established in many regions of the U.S. Moreover, dengue is not a "jungle" disease; it strikes mainly in cities where the aedine mosquito vectors

171

breed in small, diverse pools of water, such as empty flowerpots and discarded automobile tires. If global warming continues to drive up mean temperatures, at some time in the next millennium there will almost certainly be an introduction of the dengue virus into the North American mainland. The unresolved questions are: Will it be of a variety that is highly pathogenic? Will it spread in epidemic proportions, and, if so, can it be controlled by the vaccines that are currently being developed?

MEDICAL STRATEGIES FOR THE NEW MILLENNIUM

Many scientists remain hopeful that, in the new millennium,

extraordinary innovations will be made in the field of biomedical technology that will provide a remedy for every infectious disease. It is helpful, however, to look beyond the promises of science to ask what can realistically be done now to avert a future epidemic.

The first priority should be the strengthening of our epidemiological surveillance capacities. Recently I heard a radio interview in which a U.S. Army general declared that America must be prepared for all unknown threats, plan for every contingency, constantly develop new weaponry, and, of course, be prepared to finance these efforts. His outline for the military could just as well be applied to the question of

new-millennium epidemics—the global uncertainties and needs are essentially the same. Because medical needs, however, are not likely to receive the same attention and level of funding as those of the military, how then do we pragmatically use the resources that we have to prepare for the known and unknown threats of infectious pathogens? Furthermore, where do we even begin if it is not clear that a catastrophic disease will actually emerge, where it will come from, or what its nature will be?

First, we must accept some unpleasant realities. A major concern is that dangerous pathogens may emerge from the tropical Third World. In most of those countries, however, the

imperative surveillance effort—i.e., local epidemiological research and clinical-case detection supported by competent, technologically modern laboratories—is practically nonexistent. Those countries have difficulty enough reaching their meager levels of annual per capita health expenditure—considerably less than $10 in some Third World nations.

If not the tropical nations, who should we look to as an "emerging-diseases police"—a supranational organization such as WHO? Some may disagree, but my observation is that WHO has been rendered unreliable by staffing and budgetary deficiencies and distracting political subversions.

Rather than turning to a global organization, I propose that self-reliance by the industrialized nations should be the first priority. Cooperation and collaboration with multinational health organizations is desirable and even necessary, but in the end, countries must depend on the strength of their own expertise. In the case of the U.S., for example, a highly qualified group of American infectious-disease experts is already in place throughout the

Corbis/Bettmann-UPI

A beach in New York is sprayed with DDT in 1945. The strategic spraying of DDT helped virtually eliminate malaria in the U.S. after World War II.

tropical world, including workers for the Centers for Disease Control and Prevention, the U.S. military, the National Institutes of Health, the U.S. Agency for International Development, and a variety of nongovernmental organizations. This diverse group can be augmented and coalesced into a strong, unified organization or network for surveillance and research purposes. In addition to guarding the health of Americans, this effort would benefit the host countries through collaborative epidemiological surveillance and research, and it would supplement their public-health programs.

The second priority is to address the problem of global warming in a meaningful manner. There must first be universal agreement—by politicians, industrialists, citizens, and scientists of both developing and industrialized nations—that global warming is a real phenomenon, a threat to life as we know it, and a process that we understand sufficiently to control. (For an alternate view of the issue of global warming, *see* Feature Article: THE UNCERTAINTIES OF ENVIRONMENTAL FORECASTING.) Many climate researchers believe that carbon dioxide added to the atmosphere as a result of human activity is the main culprit of global warming, through its en-

hancement of the natural greenhouse effect. Accordingly, there have been international agreements, notably the 1997 Kyoto Protocol, designed to reduce carbon emissions. Nevertheless, those measures may not be sufficiently rigorous. One group of notable climate researchers has stated that, even if the Kyoto Protocol were scrupulously adhered to, global warming would be reduced by only a small fraction of a degree by 2050.

Although the conventional wisdom is to reduce carbon emissions by controlling the inefficient combustion of cars, factories, and cooking fires, some researchers have advocated alternative or additional strategies. For example, Martin I. Hoffert of New York University has suggested a large-scale global reforestation program, trees being marvelously efficient "blotters," or sinks, for carbon dioxide. Two other researchers, Stuart R. Gaffin and

Reforestation projects, like this one under way in Haiti (above), will become increasingly important in the next millennium as scientists strive to reduce atmospheric carbon dioxide. (Left) At a health clinic in Egypt, women learn family planning techniques. Lowering of birth rates has been suggested as another means for cutting carbon emissions.

(Above) Birgit Pohl/Impact Visuals; (left) Donna DeCesare/Impact Visuals

A researcher holds a vial of DNA hepatitis B surface antigen. Despite years of research, effective immunizations still do not exist for some diseases. Scientists hope that efforts to develop a DNA vaccine will open a new path to immunity.

Brian C. O'Neill of the Environmental Defense Fund, have asserted that the growing human population is a significant factor in global warming. They have advocated a global birth-control program that would drop the fertility rate to 1.7 per woman. A proportional reduction in energy need would follow, thus reducing carbon emissions and helping to stabilize the climate.

Will the world's political and economic leaders take heed of the ominous harbingers of global warming and move in a meaningful way to slow or reverse the process? If history is a reliable guide to the collective behavior of humanity, the necessary radical changes will not be undertaken. It may well be that only a catastrophic, climate-change-associated epidemic—or epidemics—will induce governments to impose major regulatory measures.

THE BRIGHTER SIDE

Technologically, civilization's greatest hope for combating the infectious diseases of the 21st century may lie in the ability to transfer the genetic information contained in DNA. Owing to that technology, the biological boundaries that separate humans from animals and animals from plants—boundaries that for so long were considered

fixed—recently have begun to blur and blend. Newly acquired technology that enables the transfer of selected "foreign" genes into plants, whose cells then translate the genetic information into proteins of medical value, is expected to lead to a new agriculture-based method of drug manufacture. Such transgenic plants may abundantly, and inexpensively, produce therapeutic vaccines, enzymes, and hormones and other biological regulators that are today prohibitively costly.

Antigens, the bacterial or viral proteins used in vaccines to immunize humans against a panoply of infectious diseases, are also encoded by specific genes, in this case, genes of the pathogens involved. In the future, vaccinations may be delivered in food rather than the traditional shot in the arm. In 1995 Tariq A. Haq and his colleagues at Texas A&M University's Institute for Biosciences and Technology in Houston reported that they were able to insert the

enterotoxin gene of the potentially deadly bacterium *Escherichia coli* into potato plants. The transgenic plants then produced the powerfully immunogenic enterotoxin peptides (small proteins) as part of their normal protein synthesis activities. When experimental mice were fed potatoes from the plants, they mounted an immune response against the peptides and elaborated specific antibodies that protected them against *E. coli* bacteria.

In the same year, Julian Ma, an immunologist at Guy's Hospital, London, and his colleagues at the University of California, San Francisco, and the Scripps Research Institute, La Jolla, California, reported that they were able to dispense with the antigen "middle man" and synthesize antibodies directly in transgenic plants. Antibodies, which are also proteins, are under the control of genes that encode their synthesis in specialized cells of the immune system. Ma's group

inserted into tobacco plants the specific antibody-encoding genes from a mouse immunized with an antigen from *Streptococcus* bacteria. In a genetic sense, the cells of the transgenic plants functioned as if they were animal immune-system cells, and made anti-*Streptococcus* antibodies. Immunizations based on this approach also can be given orally. The process is one of passive immunotherapy, making use of antibodies expressed in genetically engineered plants. The immediate possibility is one of treatment for bacterial and viral diseases, but treatment for other infections is forseen.

Despite many years of intensive research, practical, effective immunizations still do not exist for some infectious diseases. AIDS is one, malaria is another, and the common cold yet another. Approaches to vaccination presently under study suggest entirely different ways that people will be immunized in the future. The most promising new path to immunity is the DNA vaccine. As noted above, the protein antigens used in traditional vaccines are encoded by genes, which in most organisms (the exception being some viruses) are composed of DNA. Making a DNA vaccine would involve isolating the DNA that encodes a pathogen's immunizing antigen, multiplying it in quantity, and preparing it for direct injection, either carried in a virus or as naked DNA. Once in the body, the DNA would enter cells, become incorporated into their normal complement of DNA, and begin directing them to synthesize the pathogen's antigen. The constant production of antigen would, it is believed, induce the body to mount the prolonged immune response needed for effective immunity.

The year 2000 (or 2001 for precisionists) appears to be the start of the Century of the Gene, wherein research in genetic molecular biology may have far-reaching influence on both therapies and disease-prevention methods. For example, genetic manipulation has the potential to control vector-transmitted diseases more certainly and more efficiently than insecticides. It has long been known that most vector-borne pathogens, such as malaria parasites, fail to complete their life cycle when they are in the "wrong" species of bloodsucking insect. Malaria parasites that infect birds, for example, are transmitted by *Culex* mosquitoes, while malaria parasites that infect mammals are transmitted by anopheline mosquitoes. Mammalian malaria parasites abort their life cycle in *Culex* mosquitoes, and avian malaria parasites do the same in anophe-line mosquitoes. Moreover, of the approximately 150 species of *Anopheles,* only about 50 are biologically capable of transmitting the *Plasmod-ium* parasites to humans. Acceptance or rejection of a pathogen by a potential host is obviously under genetic control—a molecular transaction between the parasite and the insect. Researchers expect that the specific insect genes that deny life to the parasite will be identified and cloned. The cloned genes can then be introduced into populations of the parasite's own insect vectors, which will then spread to nonengineered populations of vectors.

During the international conference on global warming held in Kyoto, Japan, in 1997, two Japanese women pass a Greenpeace banner in front of the Kyomizu Temple. The Kyoto Protocol was designed to reduce global carbon emissions.

Kaku Kurita/Gamma Liaison International

Great new therapies are promised, but unless there is a new way to bring the therapies to market, they will remain intellectual curiosities rather than cures and preventions for the majority of people in the world. On the eve of the 21st century, it takes an average of $500 million and 14.8 years to bring a drug from research to market in the U.S., and few biotechnology-based therapies are being approved. Only if we are very lucky, the promised new therapies will come to us—at a price that everyone can afford and in time to help us all survive the germs of the new millennium.

FOR ADDITIONAL READING

"Global Climate Change: The Potential Effects on Health," Anthony J. McMichael and Andrew Haines, *British Medical Journal* (Sept. 27, 1997, pp. 805–809).

"Strategies for Cutting Carbon," David G. Victor, *Nature* (Oct. 29, 1998, pp. 837–838).

New Guinea Tapeworms and Jewish Grandmothers: Tales of Parasites and People, Robert S. Desowitz (W.W. Norton & Company, 1981).

"Return of a Killer," Brendan I. Koerner, *U.S. News & World Report* (Nov. 2, 1998, pp. 51–52).

Who Gave Pinta to the Santa Maria?: Torrid Diseases in a Temperate World, Robert S. Desowitz (W.W. Norton & Company, 1997).

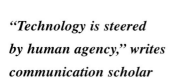

"Technology is steered by human agency," writes communication scholar James E. Katz. *In less than a century we may possess the awesome and potentially dangerous technologies to send messages with the mind and plumb the secret memories of the dead, but it is how we decide to use those technologies that ultimately matters.*

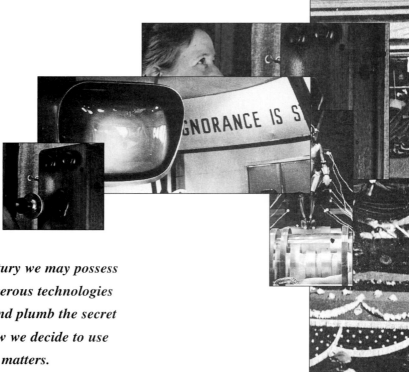

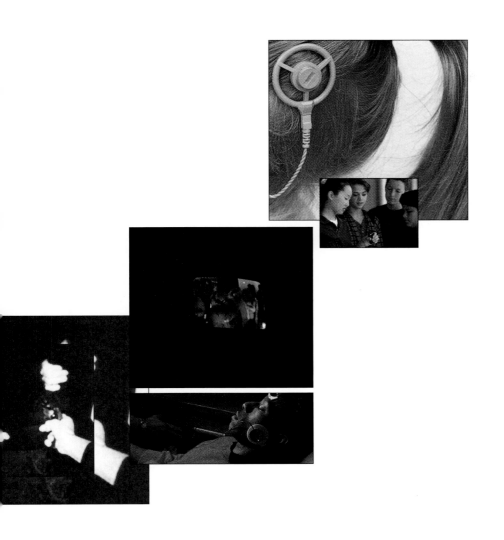

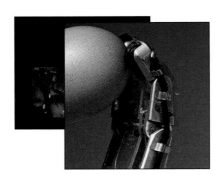

Communicating in the Year 2075

by James E. Katz

S peculations about the future often focus on the machines that surround us. What, for example, will computers and robots in the coming years be able to know, produce, recognize, and do? Those same discussions, however, sometimes neglect questions about the way that advances in science and technology might affect our social relationships and even our inner selves—our human nature. One area that is frequently slighted in machine-oriented discourses is communication. How will the "machinery" with which we now pass information to each other, or keep for later use, be changed, and with what consequences for us? Moreover, what parts of our lives will likely be left relatively untouched by advances in communication technology?

James E. Katz is Professor of Communication at Rutgers University, New Brunswick, New Jersey.

MAN VERSUS MACHINE: AN INTELLECTUAL LEGACY

Although it is an oversimplification, commentators on the future of technology and society generally fall into one of two broad groups: utopians or dystopians. When the topic is the future machine, both groups see machines supplanting humans in the performance of certain activities. Where they differ is on the human condition afterward. Utopians often anticipate that humans will be enjoying superlative service rendered by helpful machines; dystopians, that machines will be enjoying sullen service rendered by helpless humans.

Both traditions of futurism have long and honorable histories, but their emphases are quite different. Utopian specula-

tion stresses those areas in which the quality of life will be most improved—physical comfort, material abundance, and social harmony. The American writer Edward Bellamy's *Looking Backward, 2000–1887* (1888) and the American behavioral psychologist B.F. Skinner's *Walden Two* (1948) are milestones in this tradition. Dystopian speculation, on the other hand, tends to focus on three interrelated areas in which humanity will suffer the most—individual privacy, personal autonomy, and peace of mind. The epitome of the pessimistic view is the British novelist George Orwell's *Nineteen Eighty-four* (1949), which describes a future in which all personal communication and activity is constantly spied upon by a variety of human and electronic agents and in which any deviation from

mindless conformity is punished severely.

Technology plays an important part in the effectuation of dystopias, and in some visions it is the machines themselves that are responsible for the downturn of events. An early treatment of the idea of a takeover by our creations is the Czech writer Karel Capek's dramatic play *R.U.R.: Rossum's Universal Robots* (1920). Its dystopian theme has been a familiar refrain ever since and has received treatment in a variety of media, including many books and films. (A prime example is the 1969 movie *Colossus: The Forbin Project*, about U.S. and Soviet supercomputers linking up to rule the world.) The idea that our technological creations may dehumanize us, if not succeed us altogether, has hit home

In a scene from the 1956 movie version of George Orwell's *Nineteen Eighty-four,* people move dronelike through a world in which all personal communication and activity is continually monitored by human and technological agencies. Orwell's portrait of the future has become the archetype of the dystopian view.

more forcefully and expressly with the advent of artificial-intelligence research. The American computer scientist Raymond Kurzweil has predicted that forms of machine intelligence will integrate with us, then eclipse our old selves, to the extent that "humans who do not utilize such implants are unable to meaningfully participate in dialogues with those who do." Another computer scientist, Hans Moravec of Carnegie Mellon University, Pittsburgh, Pennsylvania, has commented that sentient, nonbiologically based creatures will far surpass us and, in our stead, colonize the wide-open universe.

Along with these more orchestrated visions have been a variety of casual observations, some of them focusing specifically on how communication devices might be used to interfere with the privacy, peace, and liberty of the ordinary citizen. One writer saw that a certain incipient communication technology would assemble "all mankind upon one great plane, where they can see everything that is done, and hear everything that is said, and judge of every policy that is pursued at the very moment when these events take place." Although the statement might seem directed to some computer-intensive technology of the 21st century, it is, in fact,

the British leader Lord Salisbury's assessment in the 1880s of the anticipated social impact of the telegraph. Note that the telegraph was expected to have the same destructive effect on privacy that today's critics of the computer predict for the coming decades. It is easy to overestimate as well as underestimate the influence of an emerging communication technology. Even the telegraph's inventor, Samuel Morse, said

The Granger Collection

In its early years the telegraph was criticized for its interference with privacy. The 19th-century British leader Lord Salisbury believed that its increasing use would eventually break down every barrier that guards our thoughts and actions so that "all mankind . . . can see everything that is done, and hear everything that is said."

in 1838 that the telegraph would soon "diffuse with the speed of thought, a knowledge of all that is occurring throughout the land."

Like the telegraph, the telephone was frequently criticized in its early years for its intru-

siveness and disruption of privacy. In 1895 *The Electrician* magazine ventured that "if a round robin could be got from all quarters we suspect that a majority could be obtained for voting the telephone an unmitigated nuisance which everybody would wish to see abated and perhaps even abolished altogether." In 1913 a writer in *Woman's Home Companion* described the phone as "a noisy intrusion on privacy," com-

plaining about how callers forced themselves on people during meal times, pinning them to the phone "while your dinner turns cold." More modern, but similar complaints have been leveled at telemarketers who draw upon exhaustive re-

search to learn when we are indeed most likely to be at the evening meal and exactly what pitch will most likely keep us pinned on the telephone while our "dinner turns cold."

One of the most recent communication innovations, the cellular telephone, has been scathed for its ruination of concentration and solitude in places ranging from beaches and movie theaters to restaurants and even funerals. Beyond causing inconvenience and embarrassment, cell phones also have had harmful consequences. Surveys demonstrate that drivers distracted by their mobile phones cause traffic accidents that kill and injure numerous people and account for billions of dollars in damages annually. Despite this toll, both subscribership and usage of cell phones continue to rise.

Speculations about the way that technology will affect life and liberty are thus notable in terms of their consistency, concern, and predisposition. My own view, specifically concentrating on communication technology, differs from those of Capek, Kurzweil, and others who see our machines enslaving or dehumanizing us, if they allow us to survive at all. Nevertheless, my view is also different from those who expect that our machines will allow us to achieve bliss.

Like the telegraph, the telephone was first vilified for its intrusiveness. Plays and magazine articles from the early 20th century called the telephone an "instrument of torture" and accused it of "breaking the needed rest of invalids without a qualm" and keeping people tied up while their "dinner turns cold."

By the year 2075, three-quarters of a century from now, I expect that the physical nature of our lives will not differ dramatically from today. Although advancing technology will allow us to explore new ways of living, many aspects of traditional lifestyles will remain as popular as ever. For example, we likely will still be preoccupied with Chippendale furniture and center-hall colonial homes. On the other hand, where I expect some of the biggest changes to take place is in the way that we communicate. In 2075 we will no longer grab at a ringing telephone or peer at a video screen for our electronic messages. We will not have to spend months of study to pick up a new language. We may even be able to learn from dead Uncle Harry why he wrote us out of his will.

BIOMECHANICAL INTEGRATION

How exactly will we be using communication technologies to work, enjoy ourselves, maintain social networks, and, of course, annoy and impose on each other by the year 2075? Before sketching a few specific ideas, I will posit a master trend. I foresee enormous progress in integrating electronic and auxiliary biological systems, particularly genetically engineered systems, with the human body. The input and output of those systems will be linked with the brain, and like our natural limbs and senses, they will meld seamlessly with our consciousness. In both the metaphorical and literal senses, people of the future will grow together with hardware systems and biological enhancements.

Support for this trend can be found today. Surveys suggest that perhaps 10% of the U.S. population carry artificial devices (excluding simple devices like dental fillings and contact lenses) in their bodies. Two hundred years ago the trend was already under way, exemplified by the peg leg and George Washington's famous wooden dentures. Modern devices include software-controlled heart pacemakers and artificial limbs that allow a proxy sense of touch. Increasing varieties of machines, such as cranially implanted electronic devices that give a measure of hearing to the deaf, are enhancing human capacity and functioning. Likewise, biological tissue from other species is being turned to our use. Medical researchers are actively investigating the transplantation of cells and organs from baboons, pigs, and other animals into human patients.

From these steps the trajectory of progress will likely lead to biochemically or genetically manipulated and enhanced biological materials that are highly compatible with the human body. It could also lead to the ready integration of organs and tissues derived from other species, along with their specialized functions. We could, for instance, give ourselves a dog's sense of smell or a dolphin's sonar system. We would be fully conjoined—physically, neurologically, and operationally—with the biological resources of the animal kingdom, modified for our benefit.

The trend toward the continued integration of electronic and mechanical devices and auxiliary biological systems is apparent today. As much as 10% of the U.S. population carry artificial implants. One modern device is the cochlear implant (below), now an increasingly common option for children and adults with a total absence of hearing or profound hearing loss.

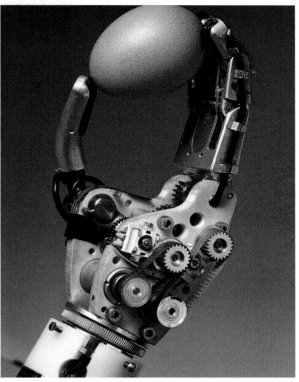

This myoelectric prosthetic hand mimics a living hand's functions. When appropriate muscles in the supporting human arm are flexed, skin sensors relay the actions to a built-in computer, which directs the hand to open, close, or grip. Future research may put such a hand under the direct control of the brain.

Although many of us will welcome these advances, a vociferous minority will perceive such modifications as threats to our essential humanness, ontology, and teleology—with much justification. Others will object to the exploitation of animals for such purposes. These communities will only become further disturbed and energized as technological progress continues.

MIND MAIL

With the master trend in place, consider the way that we send a written message today. At some time in the past, we probably decided to buy stamps and stationary, then acted to acquire them, and finally set them aside for the present use. Now, as we sit at our desk, we think about the purpose of the message and decide on some questions. Will it be postcard or letter? Typewritten, handwritten, or via E-mail? Mass mailing or individualized? We then prepare the message accordingly. Likewise, whenever we get our messages, be they from a mailbox or a computer, we make conscious decisions. In each case we process information and actuate ourselves at two levels: the conscious, mental level and the level of physical action. We plan our actions and then carry them out. The physical actions that we take often result in substantial commitments of time, energy, and

money. We may stand in a post-office line for an hour to send an overseas letter during holiday season or brave a snowstorm just to get to a mailbox. In awaiting E-mail messages, many of us look in our in-boxes several times an hour, and when we expect an important physical document, we may waste time impatiently checking and fretting.

In 2075 I expect that sending a message will involve exactly the same process of planning and acting, but it will all take place at the mental level. We will still decide when to compose a message and by what

modality to send it—voice, video, or written, but perhaps also symbolic or abstract, options that we can implement only clumsily today. If we want to send it in writing, we will compose it much as we do now on a computer screen, but the screen will be replaced by a mental image that we summon up. Rather than typing or speaking aloud to compose our missives, we will use mental dictation. Indeed, numerous voice-recognition dictation programs today can write down our words with surprising accuracy.

These seeming tricks of mental legerdemain, although

not easily attainable with today's technology, should not be as hard to achieve as they may first appear. Indeed, our speech is the physical embodiment of well-established mental routines. We think thoughts and say words; the saying is the neural activation of muscles in our voice box, mouth, and diaphragm. Nevertheless, we also can imagine saying things or can even say them silently. What needs to be done is to harness the neural impulses for these silent actions to biomechanically integrated devices, which would be linked to the communication network of the outside world. Our volition then would invoke these machines rather than our anatomy to send and receive messages. To check our E-mail, or perhaps more accurately mind mail, we would first decide to look at it and then take actions to access, review, and respond to it. The major difference is that we only would have to activate our mind.

Looking at our mind mail would be little different from the way we look at physical mail, except that we would view it literally through the mind's eye. After all, when we read a letter on a computer display, we phenomenologically experience the observation of physical words and letters. Of course, this is a sense, not the reality itself. Our brain assembles a set of sensory signals into what appears to be a solid image. The point is that mentally perceived embodiments of a phenomenon may bear little relationship to its physical reality.

Recent achievements in brain research suggest that the technology of mind mail is entirely plausible. Noninvasive brain-imaging techniques such as magnetic resonance imaging (MRI) can distinguish between the thought patterns required for speaking and reading.

Scientists have demonstrated that people can control the electroencephalograph (EEG) activity of their own brains. In turn, these EEG activities have been used to control computer functions, including cursor movement. Such achievements indicate that we have the nascent capability to compose and send messages using mental activity alone.

EMBALMED MEMORIES

Throughout history people have been killed in the hoary expectation that "dead men tell no tales." For this aphorism to remain valid in the year 2075, killers may have to be a great deal more thorough. As progress continues in our understanding of the biochemical underpinnings of brain function, I expect the appearance of a new "one-way" mode of communication—namely, from the dead to the living. I am not predicting a return to the séance as a form of evening entertainment, but rather that in a number of special cases, the biochemically stored memories of the dead

Using biofeedback techniques, people have learned to control their own brain-wave, or EEG, activity and then use that activity to manipulate various functions on a computer. Such results suggest that we have the capability to compose and send messages using mental activity alone.

Will & Deni McIntyre/Photo Researchers, Inc.

182

Almost 150 years after Abraham Lincoln's death, medical researchers have proposed that his remains be exhumed and genetically tested to determine if he had suffered from Marfan's syndrome. Our ability to gain information about a person from biochemical traces is growing. It may not be farfetched to expect that one day we will be able to tap the biochemically stored memories of both the dead and the still-living.

will be available for inspection by the living.

In one sense, this is not as unprecedented as it sounds. In anticipation of a time when they will be dead, many people arrange to "send" messages to those who will be alive after them. These communiques include letters, wills, videotapes, diaries, and monuments. By year 2075, however, even people who made no such pre-arrangements may be "speaking" to the living—their memories, experiences, and

thoughts open for inspection. Similarly, people who are still alive but in the process of dying may also be candidates for this form of communication.

As was demonstrated in 1998 by the "stained dress" incident in the investigation that preceded U.S. President Bill Clinton's impeachment, extremely salient information can be adduced from the tiniest of biochemical traces. By means of forensic, pathological, archaeological, and anthropological investigations, researchers

regularly gain immense insights from biochemical evidence. (The level of progress is such that some investigators have called for the exhumation of the remains of Abraham Lincoln to determine whether he had suffered from the hereditary disorder known as Marfan's syndrome.) Investigation of biochemical messages also extends to the physical residues of experiences—molecular markers—that are borne by the living. According to a November 1998 report pub-

lished in *New Scientist*, researchers pinpointed a biochemical signature, quinolinic acid, that in children can help differentiate brain injuries caused by accidents from injuries caused by violent abuse. Thus, even if babies cannot speak, they can tell a story.

In 1991 tourists found a body protruding from the ice of an alpine glacier on the Italian-Austrian border. At first suspected to be a murder or accident victim of recent vintage, the body soon was shown to be the extraordinarily well-preserved remains of a 5,300-year-old Stone Age man, nicknamed the Iceman. Numerous scientists subsequently examined the remains in intricate physical and chemical detail, seeking to glean insight into every aspect of the man's physical and social existence—where had he come from, what had he eaten and when, what technologies and skills had he possessed, what injuries and dis-

This model of the possible appearance of the Stone Age Iceman is reconstructed from physical and chemical studies of his remains. As the man waited for death more than five millennia ago, he could have had no idea that we would be gazing at his image and scrutinizing his life and activities.

eases had he suffered and at what age had he experienced them. As the Iceman approached death, cold and alone, he could have had no inkling of the extent to which his life and activities would be scrutinized, and by whom, five millennia later.

Might we suffer a similar fate? Could our secrets, experiences, and longings be pried from us after our deaths, if not millennia later then perhaps within seconds or minutes? A positive answer would seem to undermine our concept of the meaning of death. It is a common and valid supposition in our culture that, when we die, our cognitive structure dies with us. In the year 2075, death may not be the end of us, at least as others know us. We might well be communicating details of our lives that we had believed would go with us to the grave.

Many researchers suspect that our long-term memories are encoded in the chemical or electrochemical substrate of the brain, and that, when we remember, we are accessing those codes. Future technology may allow the codes to be accessible, at least momentarily, to others after we are dead, presuming that the brain tissue has been properly sustained. What could serve as the "decoder" for the memories of the deceased? One possibility is an already existing "machine"— the human brain itself, which has been exquisitely engineered by evolution for that task. The development of external machinery for decoding memories may still be beyond us in 2075, but ultimately it might be possible to do so in such a way as to render thoughts and mental images viewable on an external monitor—or even through the mind's eye, by means of the mind-mail technology described above.

Prospects for the success of such "mind reading" presumably would be highest for people who are only moments dead, when their tissues are intact and nearly viable. The memories of those who have ceased their mental functioning for more than a few minutes, however, could remain forever beyond our grasp. Nevertheless, how much richer would our historical insight now be if we could have plumbed the memories of, say, Lee Harvey Oswald on the cusp of death in order to know for ourselves what he knew

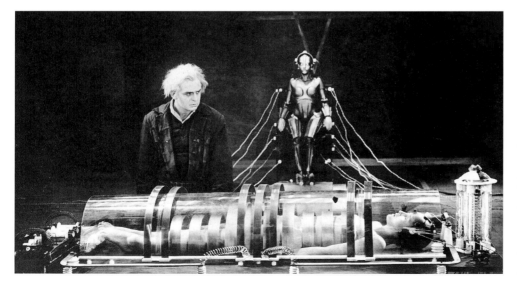

In the 1926 silent-film classic *Metropolis,* the mad scientist Rotwang uses a mind-reading device and other advanced technologies to forcibly transfer the memories and appearance of a woman to a robot. In 2075, might our most deeply hidden thoughts be extracted in a similar way?

What Lee Harvey Oswald knew about the assassination of John F. Kennedy died with him when he met the same fate two days later. If we could have salvaged his memories within a few moments of death, our historical insight into those tumultuous days of November 1963 might now be much richer.

about John F. Kennedy's assassination?

If research in this area surges forward, more of us may be electing cremation after death. At the very least, new rights and legal guidelines would have to be established to deal with biological residues and the information that they contain.

RECOLLECTIONS TO ORDER

As intriguing as a trip down a dearly departed's memory lane might be, the prospects of similar mind reading among the living are far more awesome. Using MRI, scientists already can tell much about an individual's thought processes; for instance, when a person is reading text or whether a person who is speaking a second, acquired language learned it before or after about the age of four. Doubtless this capacity to read the workings of the brain will grow. Consider how much more circumspect and tenuous our own lives would be if we knew that our innermost thinking or darkest deeds might be

opened up for inspection, against our will. Imagine the chill that this might cast over the quality of interpersonal communication and internal reflection.

More intriguing, perhaps, would be the ability not only to mind read but also to "mind feed." Mind-feeding technology, an obvious extension of the mind-reading variety, would allow us to enter extrinsic memories into our brain to the extent that they would be indistinguishable from our own memories. A general observation about information-storage media is that, if a given medium can be read, it can also be recorded on, whether it be paper, magnetic tape, optical discs, or molecules like proteins and DNA. Once re-

searchers know how to read the brain, they should be able to record within the brain as well.

Obviously, implanted memories derived from a native speaker of French would be a great way to learn the language in 10 minutes. We might also benefit from replacing memories of bad experiences—ranging from a boring dinner party to physical abuse or a painful accident—with more pleasant or positive memories. On the other hand, the potential danger would be staggering if some people were able to implant artificial memories without the recipient's awareness. We might be made to believe, falsely, that we owed someone a great deal of money. At the more extreme end of the spec-

trum, what might the consequences be if a normally fair-minded world leader were given selected memories of a racist? Should the technology of mind feeding be realized, society will have to grapple with a problem that makes efforts at the control of nuclear weapons seem like child's play.

BEING THERE FOR EVERYONE

For many, the compelling question is not what tools might we use to communicate in the future, but how such tools might affect our personal lives and society. Today's mobile telecommunication technology can serve as an exemplar of one phenomenological and social problem that will only become worse with future innovations, including mind mail. It is that of finding ourselves having to choreograph multiple realities, the immediate one in which we are already engaged and one or more distant realities that are intruding.

Already many of us are annoyed when our conversation partners decide to "multitask" us with other people who are trying to reach them by pager or cell phone. In observing this process, we also are commonly treated to a new form of body language. To relate a personal, oft-witnessed experience, I will be speaking to a friend—call him Jim—who seems to be giving me his attention. Suddenly, I observe Jim semi-surreptitiously hunch over his midsection in an attempt to read the message that has just announced itself on the pager clipped to his belt. As Jim presses buttons on the pager, he begins tossing out guttural indications of interest ("uh-huh") to compensate for the signs of inattention that his body language is communicating.

If we pay a price for being part of someone's competing reality, those who try to manage too many competing realities may pay an excessively high price. People who are the most "connected"—and I have observed some very connected individuals—are often the most

miserable. Besieged with messages and information, they appear exhausted, harried, and confused rather than informed, exhilarated, and fulfilled. One such acquaintance, whose ar-

may have seen it as the ultimate embodiment of a "good thing," potential users saw it as undesirable. The prospect for most people—even telecommunication executives—of be-

mory of devices included pagers, cell phones, an electronic organizer, an electronic secretary, and a voice-delivered portable E-mail system, spoke of desperation and being overwhelmed.

Perhaps the problem is best highlighted by the inspirational shibboleth of those telecommunication researchers of the 1980s who sought to build a system that would allow us to "reach anybody, anywhere, at any time." Whereas engineers

ing reached by anybody at all (for instance, a telemarketer), at any time they chose (the middle of the night), anywhere (in bed) was disquieting, to say the least.

Obviously, screening and other moderating technologies will be required, no matter what the telecommunication systems of 2075 will be. Those systems will also require new social conventions that can only be achieved through mutual accommodation. We are,

of course, in the midst (as we have always been) of social adjustment to our technological regimes. Today, our attention often is focused on controlling the use of telephone technologies and the Internet in environments—schools or workplaces, for example—where the competing realities that they provide are considered distracting or unproductive.

In schools, telephone communication with the outside world can be limited simply by banking the use of pagers and cell phones and restricting the number of public phones. In the workplace, however, solutions are less straightforward. As the sociologist Paul Attewell has noted, those who are in low-status, low-pay, low-training-cost, high-turn-over jobs, such as people on an assembly line, are heavily monitored; their access to telephones for personal use is quite restricted. On the other hand, people in jobs involving high status, high pay, high training cost, and low turnover are also much less monitored and have ready access to telephones for personal use during work hours.

In addition, with the onslaught of the Internet has come an added problem, the unauthorized use of the technology for viewing materials that the employing organization deems offensive or time wasting. The complexity of this issue was vividly illustrated for me when for my research I recently interviewed the president of a global telecommunications company. As we talked in his office, I noticed stock ticker information crawling across the bottom of his computer screen. During a pause in

David Young-Wolff/PhotoEdit

In schools the distraction of competing realities that the telephone can create can be limited by banning pagers and cell phones. In the future, similar problems of social interaction may be solved if we can formulate guidelines for behaviors that are respectful of everyone involved.

the interview, he quickly swiveled his chair to get an update of the status of his pending trades. If this is how one of the most responsible and highly paid members of the organization behaves, one can only imagine the behavior of the employees below him.

One solution may be found not in ever more panoptic control and monitoring technology but in a modification of our mores and interpretations. Japan's culture might set an example in this regard. When I lectured in that country a few years ago, my hosts warned me not to be concerned if some members of the audience closed their eyes and tilted their heads forward for protracted periods. Knowing of the long hours that the Japanese dedicate to their jobs and schoolwork, I thought perhaps that this behavior would be a sign of tiredness (or the unstated alternative, a lack of enthrallment with my re-

marks). Not at all, I was told emphatically. The audience members desired to be at one with the group. Their behavior would be a sign of respect; they would be trying to listen more carefully to my words. This explanation satisfied me, and I was pleased at the respect that so many members of the audience showed me. There was no loss of face on either side.

To deal with the problems of social interaction that new telecommunication technologies such as mind mail will create, we will have to summon into existence new regimes for social interaction and entirely new standards of etiquette. My experience in Japan encourages me to believe that we can formulate such behavioral guidelines in a way that will allow people to accomplish what they desire, personally and professionally, without inflicting excessive humiliations or indignities on those around them.

INSUFFERABLE OR INDISPENSIBLE?

Another area of speculation beyond the mere machinery of future telecommunication is the way in which that machinery will be used and regarded. My expectations for 2075 are straightforward. We will use telecommunication technology as we always have—to conduct business, find information, and entertain ourselves; to seek and conduct human relationships on myriad levels; and to exploit, cheat, molest, and harm each other. Today's unwanted junk mail, telemarketing calls, and E-mail spam will have their counterparts in tomorrow's mind mail, just as they had in yesterday's roadside hucksters and medicine shows. Machines also will substitute for people when we tire of, or become uncomfortable with, human company, although for some of us it will always be an unsatisfactory substitute.

It is important to realize that just as technology is not frozen and changeless, neither are human values and attitudes. Society continually adjusts and adapts, and what is one era's anathema is another's desiderata. Hence, we must be cautious in projecting our own values into the future and expecting that they will be seen as equally virtuous by later generations.

A good example, as it relates to communication technology, is the telephone answering machine. When this technology became widely available in the 1960s and '70s, its use was decried. Those who called a friend or business associate and encountered an answering machine would often leave a vituperative denunciation of the rudeness and insensitivity of its owner. People intrepid enough to use the device took care to pad their recorded greetings with lengthy apologies. The answering machine was held up as the technological cutting edge of a society bent on dehumanization.

According to my own research, 1987 was a turning point. In that year a majority of people in the U.S. no longer felt it rude to have a telephone answering machine; the view predominated that it was acceptable, or even desirable, to have one. Today, the device is seen as a great convenience, if not a necessity. In fact, in our hurry-up world, our perception has turned completely on its head. People who greet callers with long, mollifying recorded messages are chided for not getting to the point quickly, and a vast segment of the population now judges that those who do not have answering machines are rude and thoughtless.

From the viewpoint of morals and manners, telephone answering machines have introduced a new dilemma. Because they are often used to screen incoming calls, they allow the user to judge whether a particular caller is worthy of attention in real time or sufficiently unimportant to be dealt with later, if at all. The situation is further complicated by the caller's suspicion that the person being called is present and available but not "picking up." Thus, the technology of the answering machine can be held accountable for a tangle of social intrigue that includes heightened distrust, suspected motives, hypersensitivity to nuances, and feigned unavailability. Such entanglements will grow even more Byzantine as new communication technology becomes available.

SEEKING REAL REALITY

In 2075, with all manner of communication delivered directly into our minds and all our thoughts dispatched to others just as effortlessly, how can we fail to arrive at Nirvana? All bliss, at least all information and entertainment, will be available literally for the wishing—and, of course, the appropriate fee.

This ultimate couch-potato existence will not come to pass

in the next century, if ever. By nature, we like the company of others of our kind, and we enjoy full-fidelity experiences. Although it is feasible even now for many people never to leave the comfort and safety of their homes, most of us like getting out and traveling. Indeed, the distance traveled annually by Americans grows year by year. Interestingly, in 1890 the average commute to work took 20 minutes. More than century later, after great advances in the technologies of mobility, untold billions of dollars invested in transportation infrastructure, and, more recently, the promotion of telecommuting, the average commute to work is still 20 minutes.

Today, with little effort, hundreds of millions of us can experience the great works of literature, art, and music. They are available through radio, television, audio- and videotapes, compact discs, digital versatile discs (also called digital video disks), the Internet, and other modes of delivery. Nevertheless, despite such unprecedented electronic access, there seems to be little substitution effect—in-person attendance at museums, concerts, operas, plays, and exhibits continues to set new records. Indeed, the availability of electronic media appears to stimu-

late rather than slacken interest in "being there."

The explanation of this seeming paradox does not lie, as technology enthusiasts would have us believe, merely in the limited vividness of the electronic presentation. I suggest, rather, that it stems from a singular factor: most people enjoy physical immersion in a social setting with other human beings. Furthermore, the benefits of such immersion itself are far from trivial.

This last point may be demonstrated by reference to the behavior of sports fans. By means of clever electronic enhancements developed for sports coverage on TV, a fan can get a hyper-realistic view of a home-team football game surrounded by all the domestic comforts, without having to pay for gas, negotiate traffic, or order tickets. Nevertheless, football stadiums show no sign of extinction. The conveniences and features of TV do not prevent tens of thousands of fans from crowding together in subfreezing temperatures to get a distant, single-perspective view of the game and paying lavishly in time, money, and energy for the privilege.

Sports fans are by no means the exceptions. People of all ages pursue physical hardship and adventure. Mountain climbing, bungee-cord jump-

Most people enjoy the multidimensional richness that real-life experiences provide. The sophisticated electronic presence offered by TV and video and arcade games does not prevent thousands of sports fans from packing into stadiums under uncomfortable conditions, nor do they turn away people from pursuing mountain climbing, paintball fights, or other physically demanding activities.

ing, paintball fights, and deer hunting are all popular activities. All have an element of danger and physical discomfort associated with them. None are in any sense necessary in our society.

Social investment patterns are also interesting in this regard. Despite the emphases on telecommuting, distributed workplaces, and energy conservation, spending on highway construction is expanding. Although billions are spent on optical fiber for telecommunication, so too are billions spent on sports stadiums—what Joseph L. Bast, president of the Heartland Institute, has called "the pyramids of the twentieth century." Moreover, according to studies of the way that we invest our time, the hours whiled away on the Internet

come at the expense of TV watching rather than other activities. This suggests that there may be upper boundaries on the amount of time we are willing to invest in passive forms of entertainment. If, indeed, we are heading in the direction of technologically enabled physical stasis, we are not showing universal inclination to take advantage of it.

Perhaps the best way to look at the issue is in terms of problems and opportunities. As Edward Tenner points out in his accompanying article, "Future and Assumptions," our lives are made from our choices of technology, and we often reject what is possible or efficient for what is appealing or comfortable. Sometimes the lifestyle choices that we make are not as convenient as those

that our forebears might have expected from us, given the anticipated advances in technology. For example, in the early 1950s the magazine *Popular*

Science Monthly produced a newsreel series depicting the near future. One segment showed how our houses and furniture would be made from plastic. This miracle material of modern science not only would offer us a wide array of creative colors, but it also would allow the busy housewife to simply hose down the premises and dispense with dusting and mopping forever. We could have such houses today, but no one does. The rage in the United States continues to be center-hall colonials, as anyone who has tried to sell their "modern" A-frame or Bauhaus-style home has discovered. There are more Doric and Ionic columns in the United States today than were ever built in ancient Greece and Rome. A fireplace can add $1,000 to a home's resale value, even if the home is buried deep in a city and far removed from the nearest forest. Some things simply appeal to us, regardless of their usefulness or modernity. In this sense, there is no technological determinism.

NINETEEN EIGHTY-FOUR BY 2084?

Could the mind-mail and mind-reading technology that I foresee ultimately fulfill Lord Salisbury's nightmarish scenario envisioned for the telegraph, wherein people will "see everything that is done,

In the U.S. the rage in newly built homes continues to be center-hall colonials. Although we could have futuristic plastic homes that probably would be more efficient to maintain, we have made other choices.

and hear everything that is said"? Certainly the potential in us for such application is not lacking. We may wonder what further horrors the early Soviet secret police or German Gestapo would have perpetrated with the armamentaria of modern data-gathering and monitoring technology. From those days of labor-intensive surveillance and paper records to today's computer databases, satellite tracking systems, and automated monitoring devices, it is but the same span of time that separates us from the future to which I refer.

Pessimists justifiably bemoan the steady erosion of privacy by the government and commercial interests. We indeed have less privacy in many spheres than did our parents, but Americans and especially Europeans also have privacy-protection mechanisms that were not afforded prior generations. Powerful public-key cryptography is available worldwide. Europeans enjoy strong juridical protections against illegal privacy invasions. In France, for instance, violators of privacy are liable to jail terms as high as five years.

Those protections notwithstanding, the technology that can be marshaled against personal privacy is astounding. The array ranges from profiling and data-mining software systems to such hardware as infrared cameras that can see through clothing, "pinhole" video cameras that can be hidden in clocks or lamps, and spy satellites that can read the license plates of cars. Even without the spectacular advances that I suggest, our privacy and a wide selection of associated rights and freedoms might seem not only imperiled but on the way to annihilation.

This is far from a foregone conclusion, however. Human society continually defies the pessimistic experts. Rather than extinguishing liberty and privacy, expanding interpersonal communication seems to be extending these treasured rights. In recent years, communication technology has played a critical role in undermining totalitarian regimes in Eastern Europe and Latin America. By means of tape recorders, fax machines, mobile satellite telephones, and the Internet, it is now easier than ever before to bring to public attention such reprehensible acts as police and military abuses, genocide, and suppression of individual expression and to mobilize opposition forces.

At the same time, I do not wish to minimize the widespread abuses that would be possible with advanced communication technologies. For

Pen recorders (above), pinhole cameras, and profiling software are some of the technologies that can be used today to invade our privacy. Tomorrow, without our extreme vigilance, the watcher in the darkened room could be privy not only to what we say and do but also to what we think.

instance, mind reading of the living and the dead could have terrible consequences for both the individual and the larger society. In the hands of criminals, totalitarian regimes, and even indifferent democratic governments, it could lead to massive invasion of privacy, involuntary extraction of information, and mental forms of plunder and rape. As is the case with today's communication technologies, new technologies will require our extreme vigilance to control their harmful misuse.

Technology is steered by human agency. The specific uses depend on the specific personalities involved. As the accompanying articles emphasize, predicting how technology will be used is inevitably surprising,

as are its particular directions of development and the human needs that it will address. Orwell's dystopia was, after all, merely a future extrapolation of the appalling techniques and behavior that typified existing brands of totalitarianism. His predictions were entirely too plausible, and in presenting them in such a compelling way, Orwell bestowed upon us a grammar with which we can today fight the very evils he portrayed. Ironically, his dystopian vision has helped us avoid its realization.

Although issues of the destiny of human freedom are paramount, questions about human nature are also of profound interest. Looking over the millennia of recorded history, I am struck by the amazing consis-

tency of human nature, by how little our drives and conduct have changed, by how powerfully the Greek tragedies and Shakespeare's plays still reach across the centuries to move us. Nevertheless, people and social norms do change, just enough in each new period of history to make the behavior of our forebears seem startling, or at least a little puzzling. Communication technology appears to be an important factor in this constant rearrangement and rebalancing of social processes.

I am confident of one aspect of change. Progress in technology in some way will alter cultural values and the quality of social interaction. Its effects will be such that, despite our smug certainty about our enlightened lifestyles and the cor-

rectness of our values, we assuredly will appear quite bizarre and opaque, if not utterly obtuse, to our great-grandchildren.

FOR ADDITIONAL READING

The Age of Spiritual Machines: When Computers Exceed Human Intelligence, Ray Kurzweil (Viking, 1999).

"Cautions About Car Telephones and Collisions," Malcolm Maclure and Murray A. Mittleman, *New England Journal of Medicine* (Feb. 13, 1997, p. 501).

Connections: Social and Cultural Studies of the Telephone in American Life, James Everett Katz (Transaction, 1999).

Robot: Mere Machine to Transcendent Mind, Hans P. Moravec (Oxford University Press, 1998).

Victorian Things, Asa Briggs (The University of Chicago Press, 1989).

Using the original equipment and techniques,
Brian J. Ford re-creates the work of the earliest microscopists,
revealing what they actually observed with their
simple single-lensed microscopes.

Witnessing the Birth of the Microscope

**Essay and photographs
by Brian J. Ford**

Wonderful was the word that marked the dawn of modern biology. Carefully and with steady hands, the amateur scientist had drawn out a thin glass tube. He drew up into it a droplet of green slime from the surface of a lake, and with a bit of wax fixed it to the end of the specimen pin on his little, single-lensed microscope. Turning a small screw, he brought the tiny tube ever closer to his homemade lens until the image cleared and the tube's contents fell into focus. His own words describe that moment: "I saw so many little animalcules, and the motion of most of them in the water was so swift, and so various, upwards, downwards and round about, that to see it was wonderful." It was August 1674, and the science of microbiology was born.

By the time this astonishing breakthrough was made by Antony van Leeuwenhoek, a middle-aged draper of the Dutch city of Delft, microscopes had already existed for decades. The first examples were compound microscopes, consisting of two lenses. The earliest record of a design for a compound microscope dates from sometime between 1590 and 1608 in the town of Middelburg, Holland, where optician Zacharias Jansen, along with Hans Jansen and Hans Lippershey, constructed a handheld instrument in the form of sliding tubes with a lens at each end. It magnified objects to almost 10 times their actual size and was little more

Brian J. Ford is a research biologist, an authority on the microscope, and the author of many best-selling popular-science books. He is a fellow of Cardiff University, Wales, and serves on the governing bodies of several academic institutes in Great Britain and the United States.

(Overleaf) Onion epidermal cells, as viewed through a simple single-lensed microscope owned by Robert Brown. The nucleus within each cell shows up with clarity in the circular central image at 350× magnification.

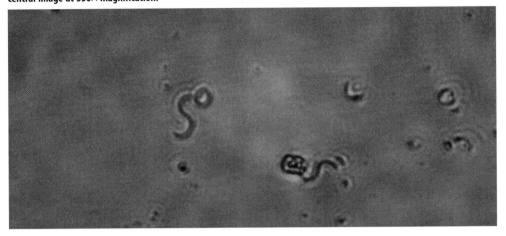

(Left) Free-swimming pond bacteria of the genus *Spirillum* are imaged using a simple single lens. Such a scene may have greeted Antony van Leeuwenhoek when he first examined pond water with his microscope. These remarkable illustrations of rotifers (below left)—drawn by Leeuwenhoek's personal draftsman—reveal that the finest of details can be seen with single-lensed instruments. Leeuwenhoek's early microscopy work was undoubtedly influenced by Robert Hooke's book *Micrographia*. Hooke's most famous discovery occurred as he viewed thin sections of cork (opposite page, bottom, from *Micrographia*). To him, the structures he saw seemed like tiny square rooms, which was why he coined the term *cells*.

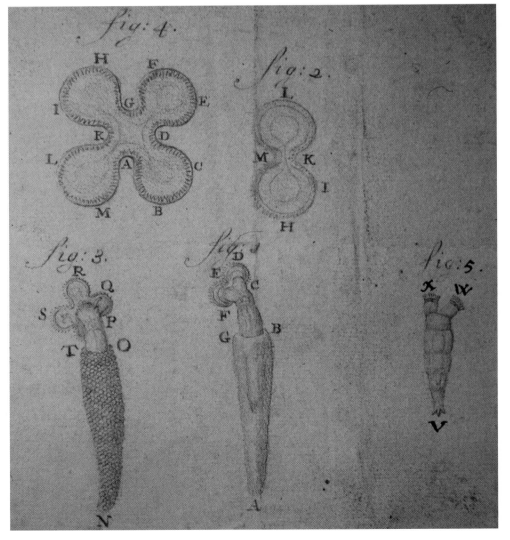

than a version of the astronomical telescope, which was then becoming well known. These experimental microscopes could reveal little fine structure, however.

Ornately designed compound microscopes were popular possessions of wealthy investigators in the mid-17th century. Indeed, throughout the century, compound microscopes were as much upper-class recreational toys as they were scientific tools. Some of the finest were made in London and constructed of cardboard and wood, with a covering of polished fish skin. It was with one of these fine instruments that the English scientist Robert Hooke first saw living cells in 1663, in specimens of moss. Later that year, he made perhaps his most famous microscopical observations when he viewed thin sections of cork. Hooke called the tiny boxlike chambers he saw *cells*—the name they have had ever since.

Hooke's observations were published in his magnificent folio book *Micrographia* in 1665. The highly influential volume, which contains beautiful drawings and accurate and detailed observations of insects, seeds, feathers, leaves, hair, pins, and various other biological and common objects, quickly became a best-seller. The celebrated English diarist Samuel Pepys, who had bought a microscope when he was at the Royal Navy office, wrote in his *Diary* that he sat up half the night reading his newly purchased copy.

The compound microscope has since become the most familiar piece of scientific equipment. To early microscopists, the benefit of using a conventional compound microscope was convenience. The instrument stood upright on a table with the eyepiece comfortably situated for lengthy studies. Nevertheless, it was the single-lensed, or simple, microscope

that provided many of the seminal discoveries on which the modern era of biological science was founded. Whereas much of Hooke's work was concerned with magnifying the intricate detail of objects already visible to the naked eye, it was Leeuwenhoek, with his simple microscopes, who initiated research into the universe of microscopic life and who is thus considered the founder of microbiology.

In the year following publication of *Micrographia*, Leeuwenhoek traveled to England on a trading visit, sailing up the River Thames to London. There he was doubtless shown a copy of Hooke's book, which contains some vivid engravings of textiles. Tucked away in a rarely quoted passage in the book's preface is the first published description of a simple microscope. Hooke's suggested design, in which a tiny handground plano-convex lens (a lens that is flat on one side and

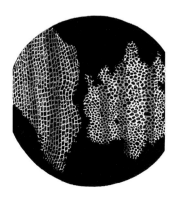

bulging on the other) is sandwiched between holes in a pair of metal plates, was very similar to that used by Leeuwenhoek. Indeed, the first specimens Leeuwenhoek studied—cork, elder pith, and matter from a writing quill—were the same ones Hooke described in his book, and even in the same order.

Simple microscopes were much smaller than the compound type, and they required considerable patience and skill to use. The plates of a Leeuwenhoek microscope were no more than 4.5 × 2.5 centimeters (about 2 × 1 inches) in size. The whole microscope was less than eight centimeters (three inches) from end to end and had to be held between the fingertips and up close to the eye for viewing. In his lifetime, Leeuwenhoek constructed more than 500 of these diminutive instruments and with them observed—in addition to his "animalcules" (protozoans and other microbes)—blood cells, sperm cells, plant cells, fungi, and algae. Even Hooke acknowledged that far clearer images could be obtained with a simple microscope, but he rarely employed them because he found them troublesome to adjust and tiring to use.

To this day, people persist in dismissing simple microscopes as providing poor-quality images. Even recent books reiter-

ate the view that little fine detail could be seen with them. The microscopes are widely misunderstood, their history has been misrepresented, and the achievements of pioneer microscopists like Leeuwenhoek have too often been dismissed as exaggeration or good luck. Few people actually have any idea of what those groundbreaking scientists could truly see. Many textbooks claim that the images from simple microscopes are fuzzy and fringed with an image-degrading halo of colors. To the contrary, simple microscopes produce images of startling clarity. The authors of those textbook accounts apparently never tried to use a simple microscope but, rather, were content to perpetuate a myth from one generation of textbooks to the next. A few scientists have managed to obtain fine images using a simple microscope, but most recent accounts show that modern technicians are unable to discern fine details with these early single-lensed microscopes.

A slightly spurious coloration does exist in the images obtained with high-power simple microscopes. This effect is called chromatic aberration. It is due to the fact that a lens refracts different wavelengths of light by slightly different amounts. Longer wavelengths of

Typical of Leeuwenhoek's handmade microscopes is this brass instrument from Delft (right), dating from around 1700. The basic design of a Leeuwenhoek microscope featured a tiny single lens held between two metallic plates. The specimen was mounted on a pin or within a tiny glass tube. Its position could be controlled by the use of hand-tapped screws. Focusing was done by turning a screw fitted through the block supporting the specimen pin.

specimen pin

focusing control

riveted metal plates

single lens

specimen-positioning screw

adjustment handle

stage-positioning screw

light (toward the red end of the visible light spectrum) are refracted less than the shorter wavelengths of light (nearer the blue end of the spectrum).

In practice, this proves to be far less of a problem with single lenses than might be anticipated. As the photos reveal, the optical phenomenon does not detract from the essential clarity of the image. When used properly, single-lensed microscopes can provide excellent images. Early compound microscopes, in fact, tended to magnify aberrations as much as images. Indeed, the history of the development of the compound microscope is one of many attempts to eliminate chromatic aberrations as well as spherical aberrations caused by lens curvature. Simple microscopes were less affected by these types of optical problems

and were therefore of greater scientific importance during the first two centuries of the microscope's history.

What of the specimens prepared by these great pioneers? Modern writers have perpetrated misunderstandings here, too. According to one book on the preparation of microscope specimens, "No preparations from the seventeenth century have survived, for it is almost certain that all were only of a temporary kind. The detail visible in the usual dry mounts is minimal, and they are prepared with little finesse." In each detail, this popular view is incorrect. In 1981 I found that the first specimens prepared by Leeuwenhoek had survived, after all. With the encouragement of Sir Andrew Huxley, president of the Royal Society of London, I was given access to Leeuwenhoek's papers and among them discovered nine specimen packets, including samples of algae, slices of optic nerve, and hand-cut sections of plant material, all having lain untouched for more than three centuries. The best were of exceptional quality. In fact, Leeuwenhoek's sections of cork and elder pith are better than those reproduced in some recent publications.

In commemoration of the dawn of a new millennium, these historic pictures allow us

A fresh sample of the author's blood is beautifully imaged by the single lens of a 300-year-old Leeuwenhoek microscope (below left). Included among the erythrocytes—red blood cells—is a single leukocyte, or white blood cell (top right corner of photo). A close-up of the leukocyte (below right) shows that this primitive little microscope can reveal extraordinary details, including the characteristic lobed shape of the cell's nucleus. Each lobe is roughly the size of a typical bacterium. (Bottom) Specimens prepared by Leeuwenhoek were found in 1981 among his papers at the Royal Society of London.

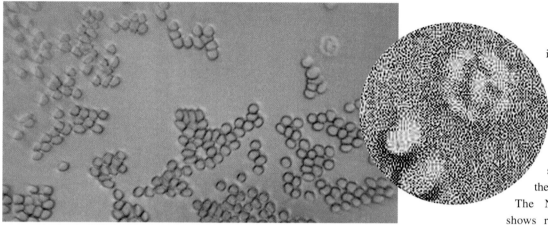

to retrace the steps of some of the great pioneers of modern biology and see what they saw. Using their original instruments, and supplementing the research with newly ground lenses that match the old designs, I have re-created some of the crucial observations made by the early microscopists. They reveal extraordinary detail and show that the most primitive of instruments can provide results that compare with the microscopes used in today's laboratories. Leeuwenhoek's tiny microscopes could clearly reveal living bacteria, for example. One stunning picture, that of a thin film of my own blood, was obtained with a surviving Leeuwenhoek microscope now housed at the University of Utrecht, The Netherlands. That it shows red blood cells is in itself surprising to many scientists. Even more exciting is the revelation that the Leeuwenhoek lens can resolve the lobed shape of a white-blood-cell nucleus, a structure about two-thousandths of a millimeter

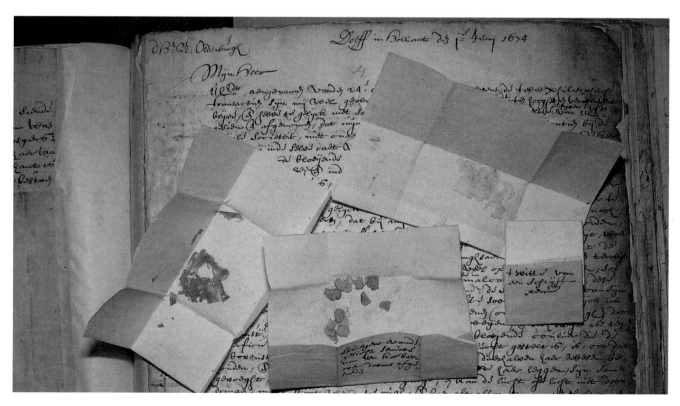

(eight-hundred-thousandths of an inch) in size—smaller than many bacteria.

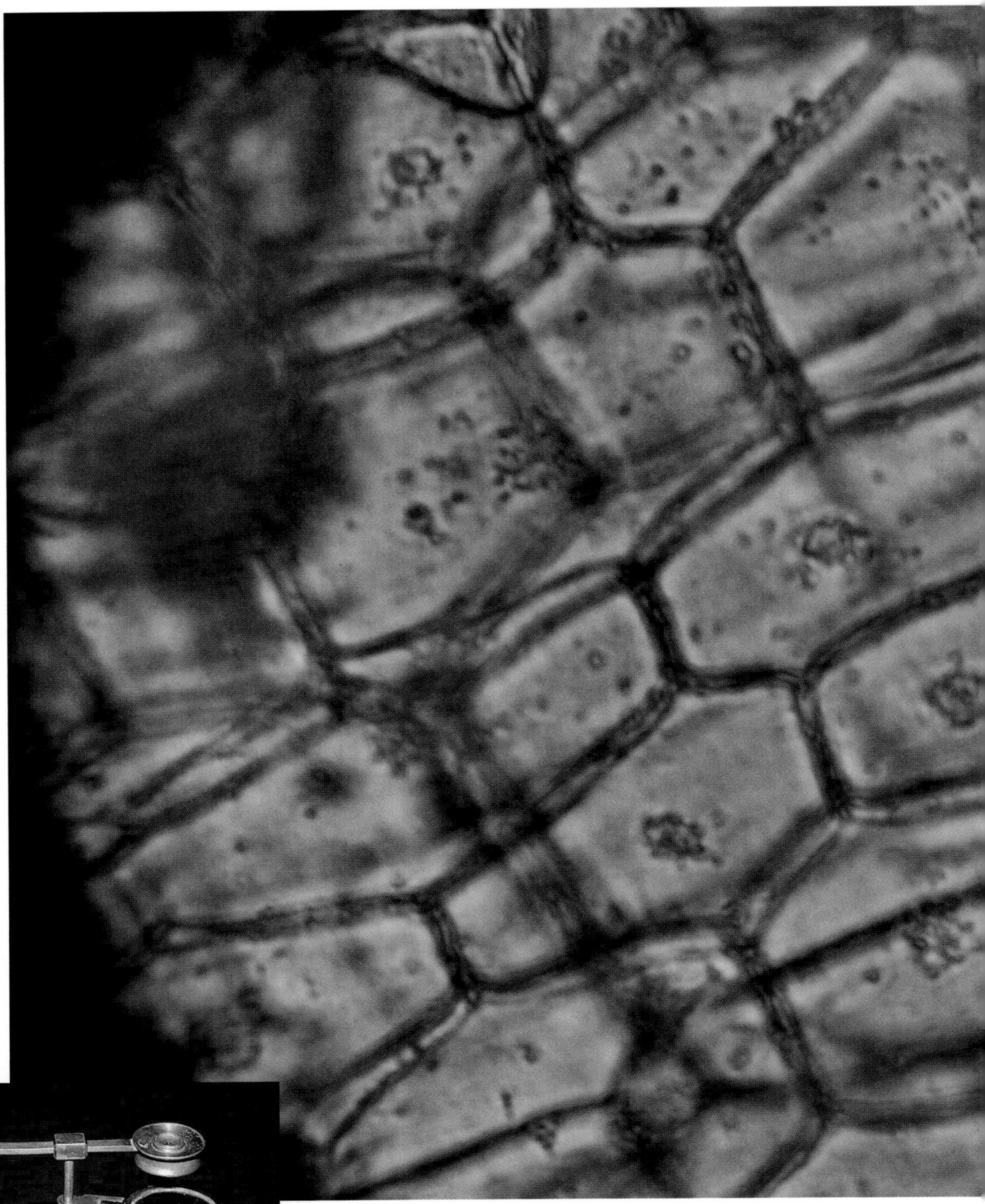

One of the most popular types of simple microscopes was the screw-barrel, a hand-held cylindrical instrument that was held up to the light for viewing. It consisted of a single lens mounted in a circular disk, which screwed into one end of the main barrel. Specimens were loaded into perforated bone or ivory sliders and held between disks of glasslike mica. A spring-loaded aperture al-

Studies on living *Hydra* in the 1700s necessitated the development of the Ellis microscope, named after the prominent 18th-century naturalist John Ellis. The Ellis microscope shown below was used by Swedish botanist Carolus Linnaeus, who established the basic principles for defining genera and species of organisms.

lowed the user to slide them into the barrel from the side. Focusing was accomplished by means of a screw at the end of the barrel opposite the lens. Turning the screw moved the specimen closer to or farther from the lens.

The screw-barrel microscope was easy to use and robust in construction. Not all specimens, however, were suitable for observation with this type of design. In the early part of the 18th century, the single-lens microscope was proving to be a valuable tool in the study of the freshwater cnidarian *Hydra*, an animal first described by Leeuwenhoek in 1702. Pioneering experiments in grafting and regeneration on hydra by the

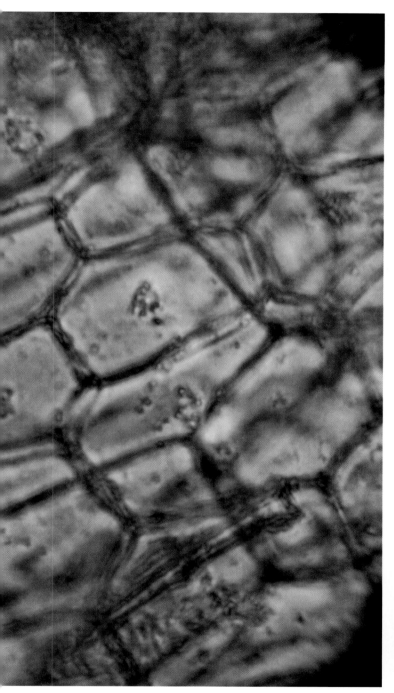

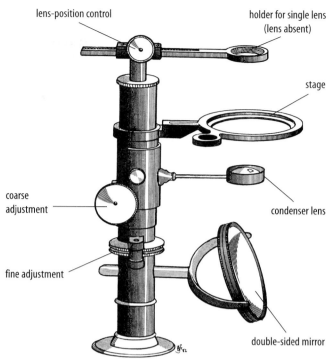

lens-position control

holder for single lens
(lens absent)

stage

coarse
adjustment

condenser lens

fine adjustment

double-sided mirror

Swiss natural philosopher Abraham Trembley stimulated other scientists, and the tiny polyp soon became a popular object for microscopical study. Accommodating the delicate organism—for example, it needed space to expand and would withdraw its tentacles in response to slight vibrations—presented challenges to micro-

scopists. This kind of work necessitated a new kind of instrument. The result was the microscope designed by the English optician John Cuff, a tabletop instrument in which a watch glass containing a specimen in water is rested on a circular stage and the lens brought into focus on a transverse arm set above it. This was the kind of

Robert Brown used simple microscopes made by the London firm of Bancks and Son. Bancks-type microscopes, such as the one shown above, comprise a main brass pillar bearing a circular stage, a substage condenser lens to focus light on the specimen, and a double-sided mirror. Accessories could be fitted to the edge of the stage, such as forceps to hold an insect specimen or a swing-out stage to carry aquatic samples in a watch glass. This view of orchid tissues (this page and opposite), magnified 525 times, was made with Brown's own microscope.

(Left) National Museum of Photography, Film & Television/Science & Society Picture Library

The extraordinary microscope shown at left was made for King George III. Dating from 1760 and constructed of silver, it was fully fitted with accessories—here it is seen with a compound microscope tube in place—but was intended for use as a simple microscope. The exuberantly cluttered design, however, made the instrument difficult to use.

simple microscope owned by the 18th-century Swedish botanist Carolus Linnaeus, which I have been privileged to use in Uppsala, Sweden.

By the early 19th century, an advanced version of this design was being used by a young Scottish surgeon to study plant tissues. Robert Brown, who had traveled to Australia in search of undiscovered plants, was fascinated by the reproductive mechanisms of plants and spent much time studying orchids. As he sat observing tissue structure, a common feature of the living cells under his microscope suddenly attracted his attention. "In each cell of the epidermis . . . a single circular areola, generally more opaque than the membrane of the cell, is observable," Brown wrote. Stimulated by his discovery, he looked again at specimens from other plant families. Brown soon found that this new structure was common to the cells of many organisms. He had recognized one of the most fundamental features of all living cells. Brown did not care for the term *areola*, however, and in 1828 coined the term used today—*cell nucleus*.

Brown was not the first person to observe the nucleus of a living cell. Leeuwenhoek had also observed nuclei, most notably in the blood cells of fish, but he had not recognized their widespread occurrence elsewhere in nature. Leeuwenhoek also had observed the ceaseless and seemingly random movement of tiny particles suspended in fluids. In 1827 Brown made a systematic study of this phenomenon and showed that it occurred in dead matter as well as living cells. It was exhaustively investigated by Albert Einstein in 1905 and is now known as Brownian movement, the result of the bombardment of the suspended particles by moving molecules in the fluid.

Because both Leeuwenhoek and Brown used single-lensed simple microscopes, doubt has been poured upon their veracity as investigators. Leeuwenhoek has been dismissed as a dilettante with a fertile imagination. Brown's abilities to observe the motion that now bears his name have also been misrepresented. Many textbooks claim that Brown observed only the movement of pollen grains, not the movement of far tinier particles within the pollen grains. Similarly, one recent assess-

ment of Brown's microscope concluded that it might have been useful as an aid for dissection, but it could not have discerned structures as small as a nucleus. To the contrary, after using Brown's original microscope preserved at the Linnean Society of London and recreating his experiments, I can confirm that not only are cell nuclei visible using the instrument but also that the phenomenon of Brownian movement is vividly revealed. Published accounts of inadequacies in Brown's microscope are likely based on improper use of the instrument, because when it is set up correctly, it provides images of considerable clarity.

The images presented in this essay have not been enhanced. The lesson to be learned is salutary. The modern era of biology, which is based on a fundamental understanding of the cell, did not result solely from the use of 19th-century compound microscopes with advanced, achromatic lenses—lenses that corrected for chromatic aberration. The key revelations were made with simple microscopes. Indeed, many of the crucial

discoveries could have been made using nothing more than a Leeuwenhoek microscope from the 1600s.

Simple microscopes of the 18th and 19th centuries are made of brass and beautifully finished. One of the most successful manufacturers was the London firm of Bancks and Son. The firm is hardly known to historians of science, however, being listed in a few catalogs of manufacturers but not otherwise documented. Yet, it clearly was influential in its time. Brown used its instruments in his research, as did Charles Darwin. The firm even supplied the Prince of Wales, who later became Great Britain's George IV. The lack of interest in Bancks and Son's products is a symp-

tom of the disinterest shown in simple microscopes as instruments for serious research.

The most fantastic microscope ever made was created in 1760 for Britain's George III by his instrument maker, George Adams. It does have a compound microscope tube as an accessory, although it is primarily designed as a simple microscope. With its grotesque solid-silver construction and Gothic embellishments, it is an unfor-

Robert Brown used this pocket-sized simple microscope (below), made by London manufacturer John Dollond, in his later years. With its mechanical stage and concentric-focusing control, it provides excellent image quality in a space no bigger than a cigarette packet.

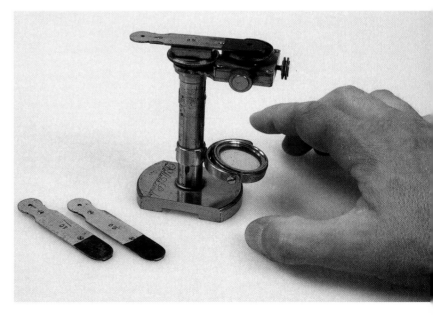

gettable work of art as much as an instrument of science.

Perhaps the most advanced simple microscope of all is a pocket microscope made by the London telescope maker John Dollond in the 1830s. It is rich in design features associated with modern microscopes, including a mechanical stage that allows the observer to rotate the specimen, rack it across from side to side, or move it up and down in the field of view. The microscope is also equipped with a concentric fine-focus control near the base of the body tube and a series of interchangeable lenses, each mounted on a brass slider. Its most powerful lens could magnify objects 480 times actual size (480×). This lens is now missing, though other similar lenses were reckoned to offer magnifications as high as 800×.

Simple microscopes remained popular for longer than most science historians might have anticipated. By 1830 compound microscopes fitted with achromatic lenses were becoming available. Yet, in 1848 Darwin was still advising the use of a simple microscope, and an instrument very much like the microscopes used by Robert Brown in the 1820s, Fields' Simple Microscope, won a major design award in London as late as 1862.

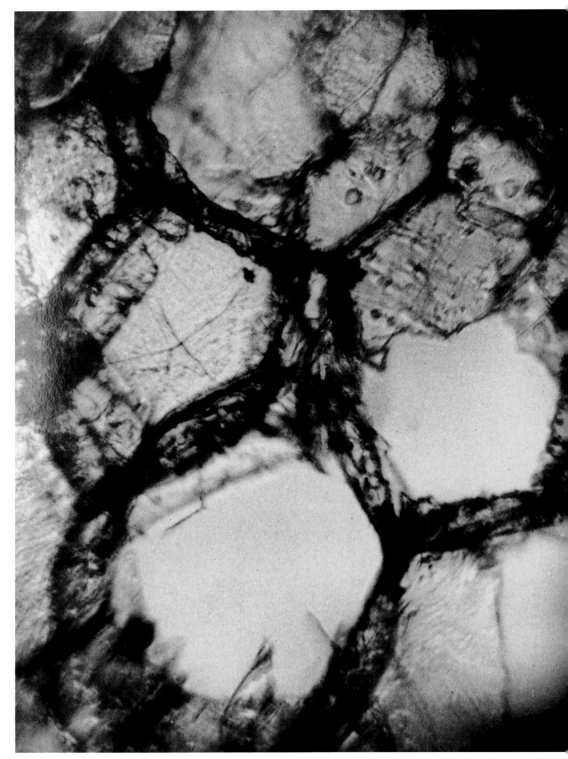

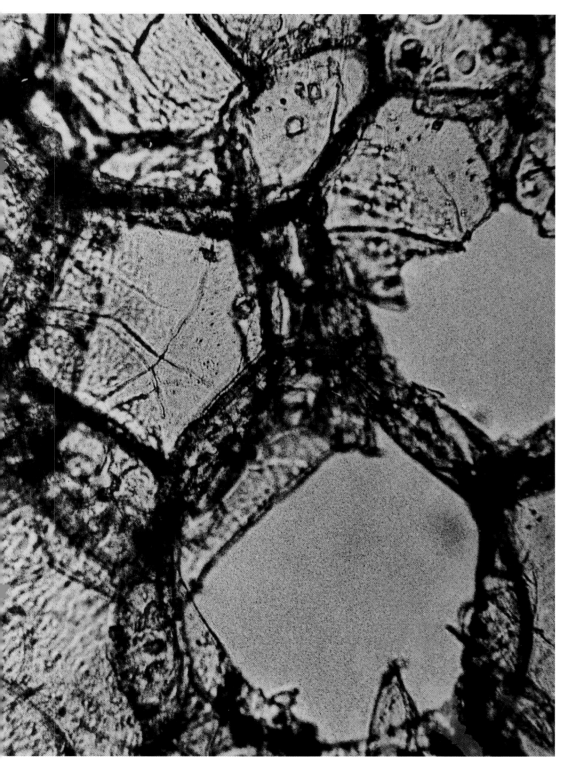

A fine section of Leeuwenhoek's
original elder pith (*Sambucus*)
specimen is imaged through a
Leeuwenhoek lens (opposite page)
and a modern Leitz microscope
(left). Running across the cell walls
are fine fungal hyphae, a legacy
of centuries in storage. The finest
of these hyphae measure 0.7
micrometers (millionths of a meter)
across. A comparison between these
images, from the earliest days of
microscopy to today's optical
perfection, confirms the high image
quality available to the pioneers.

A hand-cut section of wheat stem, infected by the fungus *Puccinia graminis*, is imaged through a single-lensed Leeuwenhoek microscope (right). The clarity of the image is surprisingly good. Single lenses produce remarkably little chromatic aberration, and the appearance of this image compares favorably with many pictures in modern textbooks. The image on the opposite page was obtained with a modern Leitz polarizing microscope. Although an improvement on the Leeuwenhoek image, it is comparable to that available in the 1600s.

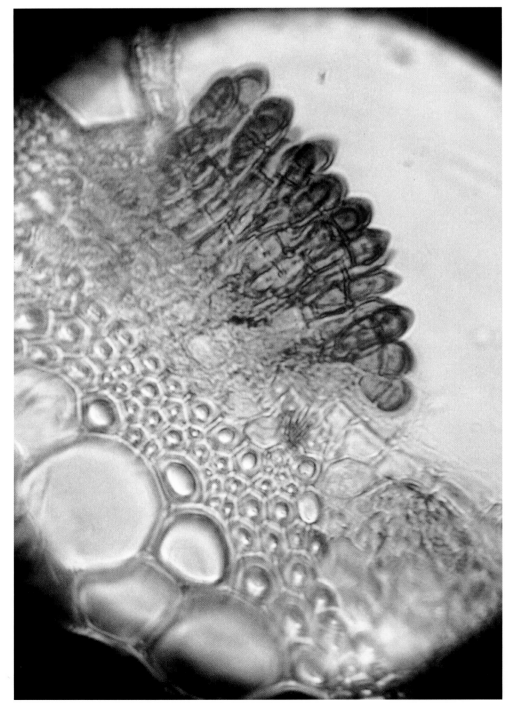

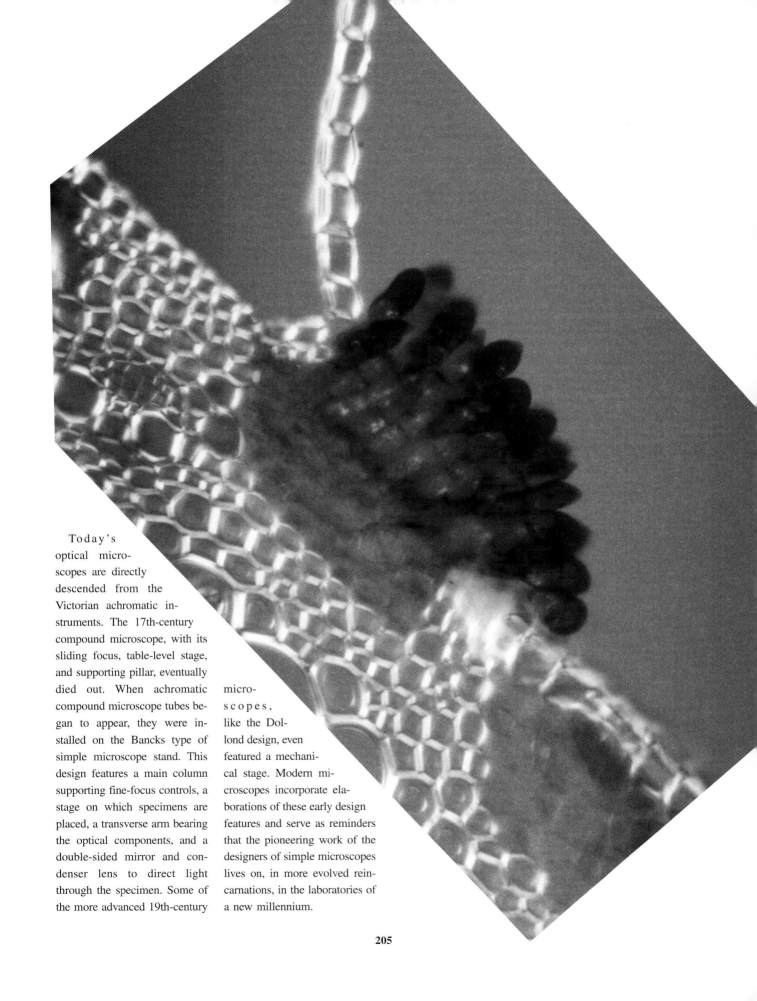

Today's optical microscopes are directly descended from the Victorian achromatic instruments. The 17th-century compound microscope, with its sliding focus, table-level stage, and supporting pillar, eventually died out. When achromatic compound microscope tubes began to appear, they were installed on the Bancks type of simple microscope stand. This design features a main column supporting fine-focus controls, a stage on which specimens are placed, a transverse arm bearing the optical components, and a double-sided mirror and condenser lens to direct light through the specimen. Some of the more advanced 19th-century microscopes, like the Dollond design, even featured a mechanical stage. Modern microscopes incorporate elaborations of these early design features and serve as reminders that the pioneering work of the designers of simple microscopes lives on, in more evolved reincarnations, in the laboratories of a new millennium.

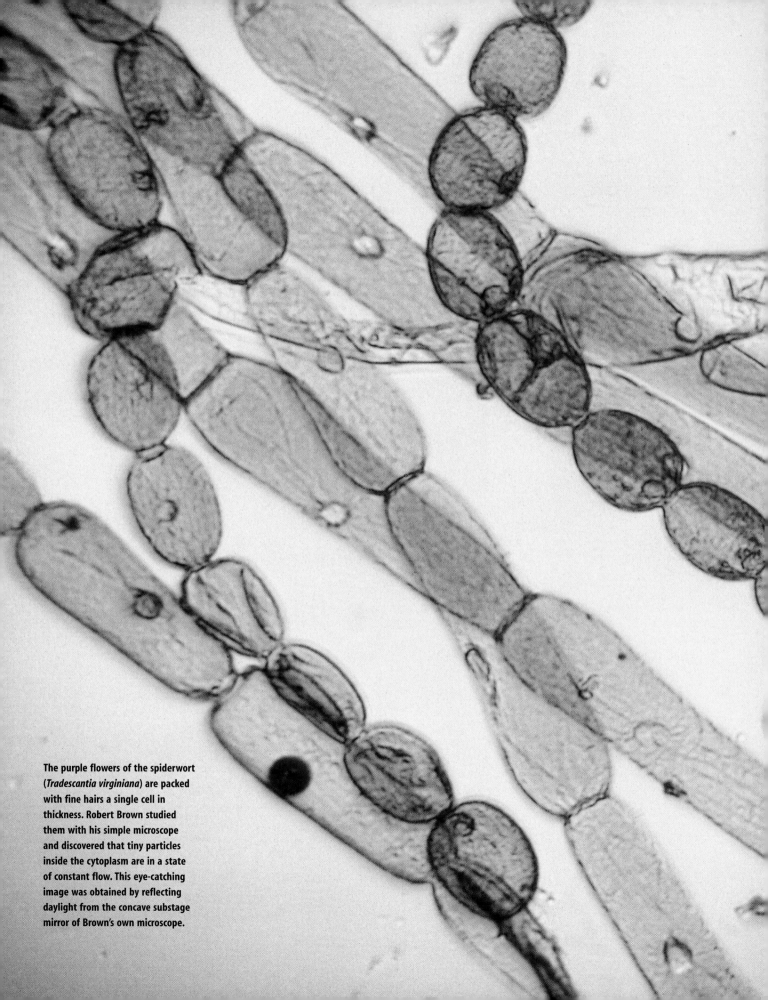

The purple flowers of the spiderwort (*Tradescantia virginiana*) are packed with fine hairs a single cell in thickness. Robert Brown studied them with his simple microscope and discovered that tiny particles inside the cytoplasm are in a state of constant flow. This eye-catching image was obtained by reflecting daylight from the concave substage mirror of Brown's own microscope.

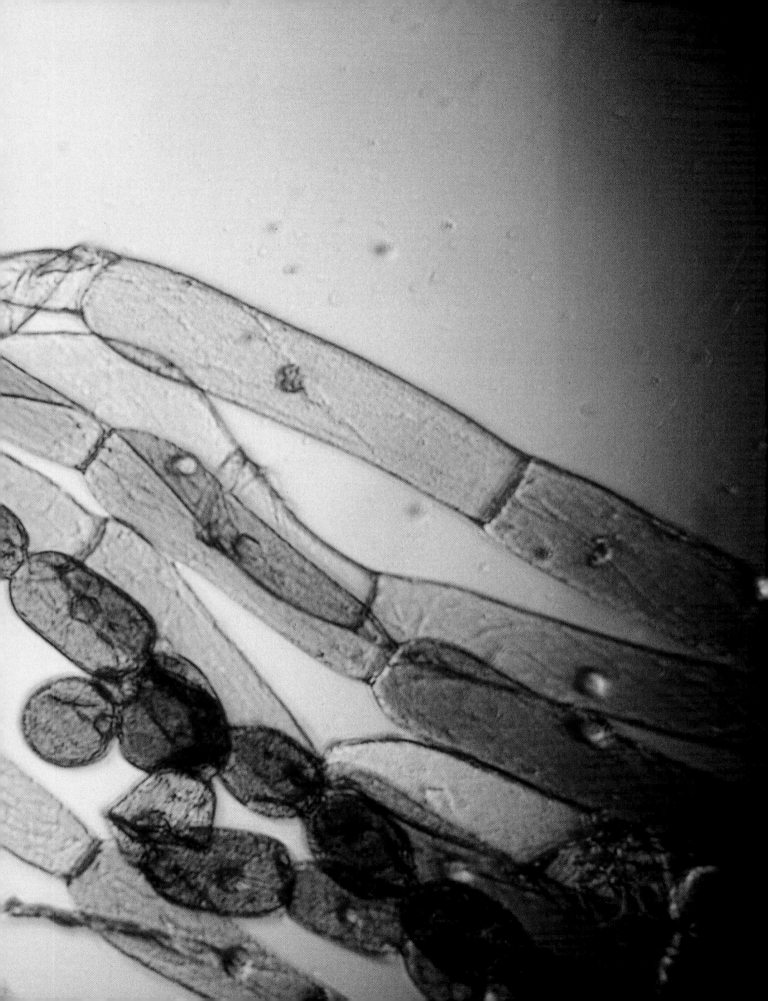

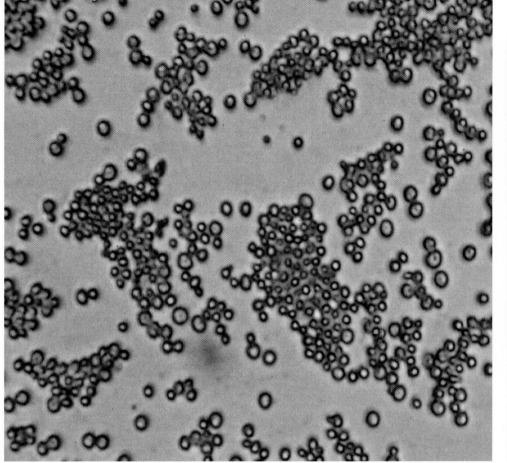

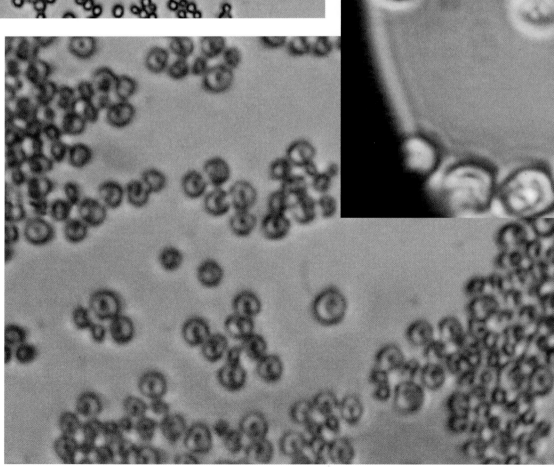

These images show brewer's yeast (*Saccharomyces cerevisiae*), as viewed through single-lensed simple microscopes. The image above was obtained using a low-power lens from Robert Brown's microscope (120×). The structure of the cells is more clearly seen through the high-power lens from this instrument (right, 325×). Leeuwenhoek's view would have been similar to the image on the opposite page, top, which was taken through a replica lens, giving an image magnified 750 times.

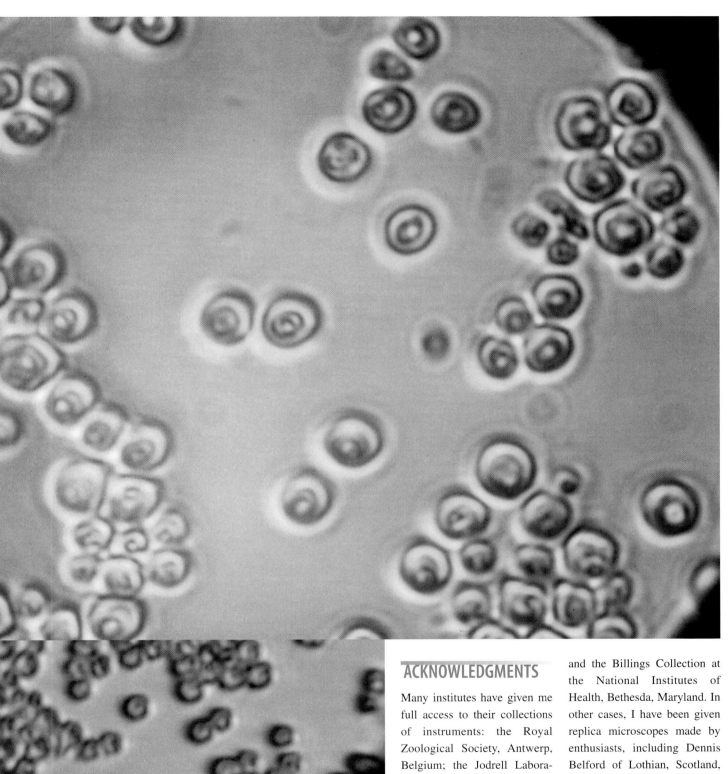

ACKNOWLEDGMENTS

Many institutes have given me full access to their collections of instruments: the Royal Zoological Society, Antwerp, Belgium; the Jodrell Laboratory at Kew Gardens, London; the Deutsches Museum, Munich, Germany; the Museum for the History of Science at the University of Utrecht, The Netherlands; the Museum for the History of Science, Oxford; and the Billings Collection at the National Institutes of Health, Bethesda, Maryland. In other cases, I have been given replica microscopes made by enthusiasts, including Dennis Belford of Lothian, Scotland, Henri Hansen of Antwerp, and the late Horace Dall of Luton, England. To all these sources, and others, I am grateful.

SCIENCE
YEAR IN REVIEW

CONTENTS

THE YEAR IN SCIENCE:
AN OVERVIEW
by Robert P. Crease

One of the most provocative science books of 1998 was John Maddox's *What Remains to Be Discovered*. The title was paradoxical: how can one write about what one does not yet know? Taking the reader on a delightful tour of a diverse array of fields, from cosmology and particle physics to genetics and mathematics, Maddox, a former editor of the journal *Nature,* pointed out the existence of fundamental, as-yet-unsolved technical problems in known science—problems whose resolution will be the task of scientists of the next century.

Even as Maddox's work hit the bookstores, scientists were making inroads on the technical problems that he identified. Key scientific events of 1998 included the sequencing of the first animal genome, the presentation of the strongest evidence yet that the neutrino has mass, the rare finding of a dinosaur fossil with preserved soft tissue, and the observation of the oldest- and farthest-known galaxy to date. Scientists also found evidence of more planets around other stars, of frozen water on the Moon, and of asteroid impacts with Earth, and they collected data suggesting that the rate of the universe's expansion is accelerating.

To resolve certain outstanding scientific problems will require the construction of new accelerators or other specialized facilities or the completion of such programs as the U.S. Department of Energy and the National Institutes of Health's Human Genome Project. Although many projects

Robert P. Crease is Associate Professor of Philosophy at the State University of New York at Stony Brook and Historian at Brookhaven National Laboratory, Upton, N.Y.

were under way in 1998, some encountered problems. Nuclear reactors continued to arouse opposition and were politically unpopular; accelerators also incited fears in some communities. Even the Human Genome Project gave rise to ethical concerns. An important lesson of the year in science seemed to be that the social problems of science can be as formidable as its technical problems—and that science itself may have to change in resolving them.

Reactors and accelerators

Scientists in many fields have complained for decades about the shortage of neutron sources for research. Neutrons are an invaluable tool not only in physics, where they provide clues to the structure of atomic nuclei and the magnetic structure of matter, but also in chemistry, biology, and engineering, where they yield information important in determining the structure of tissues and metals, in designing new drugs, and in making new polymers and superconductors. Research reactors are the traditional sources of neutrons, but none have been built in recent years for a number of reasons, ranging from their escalating cost to fears about their safety.

The neutron shortage grew particularly acute in 1998. One existing source of research neutrons, the High Flux Isotope Reactor at Oak Ridge (Tenn.) National Laboratory, was shut down for a quarter of the year, partly due to a routine inspection and partly for scrutiny in the wake of an operational error. Another source, the High Flux Beam Reactor (HFBR) at Brookhaven National Laboratory, Upton, N.Y., remained closed throughout the entire year. The HFBR's operations were initially shut down at the beginning of 1997 following the discovery of a small leak in its spent fuel pool. No significant safety problems were found in the reactor or its operation, and a Nuclear Regulatory Commission report stated early in 1999 that "the safety programs at the HFBR were found to provide adequate protection of the health and safety of the public, the workers, and the environment." Nevertheless, community opposition made it politically impossible to reopen the reactor.

One new neutron source, a research reactor called FRM-II, was under construction in Germany, at the Technical University of Munich at Garching. Its fate, however, was thrown in doubt by a newly elected governing coalition involving the Green Party. The Green Party had called for the end of nuclear power in Germany (19 nuclear power stations were responsible for 36% of the country's electricity) and made the phasing out of nuclear power part of the coalition agreement. The Green Party had also taken a critical stance on FRM-II, which uses highly enriched uranium, but, to the considerable relief of neutron researchers, the reactor—for the moment, at least—was left out of the coalition agreement.

In the 1980s and early '90s, the U.S. Department of Energy developed plans to build an Advanced Neutron Source, a

A new neutron source, the FRM-II research reactor (right), was under construction during 1998 at the Technical University of Munich at Garching, Ger. Plans to phase out nuclear power in Germany did not target the FRM-II. (Below) Workers exchange words inside the High Flux Isotope Reactor at Oak Ridge (Tenn.) National Laboratory. The reactor, another source of scarce research neutrons, was closed for part of the year.

large research reactor at Oak Ridge, but the project was terminated in 1996, thanks in part to escalating costs. Realizing that building a new large research reactor in the U.S. was unlikely because of expense and popular opposition, neutron physicists asked for and received a commitment from the Department of Energy to build another, complementary kind of neutron source, called a spallation source, which was driven by an accelerator rather than a reactor. The Spallation Neutron Source (SNS) is to be built at Oak Ridge with the participation of four other national laboratories. The first construction funds for the SNS were approved in 1998, and it was scheduled to be completed in 2006.

Accelerators, too, have faced social problems in recent years. The year 1998 marked the fifth anniversary of the termination of the Superconducting Super Collider by the U.S. Congress, which was unconvinced that the scientific value of the project was worth the cost. The largest accelerator under construction as of early 1999 was the Large Hadron Collider (LHC) at the European Laboratory for Particle Physics (CERN) outside Geneva, on the border between France and Switzerland. In 1998 both of those countries gave formal approval to tunnel construction for the machine. Some physicists in the U.S. began calling for a still larger accelerator, saying that even the LHC would be unable to address current problems of particle physics. Meanwhile, an accelerator called the Relativistic Heavy Ion Collider (RHIC), designed to study the nuclear physics of quark plasma, neared completion at Brookhaven. Some of the same activists who opposed the restart of Brookhaven's reactor, however, likewise opposed the completion of its new accelerator.

Fusion power research also suffered recent setbacks. The largest fusion project was the International Thermonuclear Experimental Reactor, which involved a collaboration between the U.S., the European Union, Japan, and Russia, but in 1998 the U.S. Congress instructed the Department of Energy to terminate participation in the project, partly for budgetary reasons and partly in response to the feeling that the promise of fusion as a practical power source had been oversold. A smaller and somewhat different U.S. project, the National Ignition Facility, a $1.2 billion fusion facility under construction at Livermore, Calif., came under fire for possibly being in violation of the Comprehensive Test Ban Treaty, signed by the U.S. in 1996.

Astronomy and space research

Progress was made in the development of new telescopes in 1998. The first of four telescopes to comprise the Very Large Telescope, which on completion would be

the world's largest optical telescope, took its first images in May at the European Southern Observatory in Cerro Paranal, Chile. Scientists from the U.S. and Europe discussed collaboration on the Next Generation Space Telescope, which would be the successor to the Hubble Space Telescope. South Africa committed itself to supporting half the costs of the planned Southern African Large Telescope, which at 9 m (354 in) in diameter would be the largest single optical telescope in the Southern Hemisphere.

Spacecraft, like telescopes, had a high public visibility and were politically popular—too much so, according to some crit-

ics in the scientific community. The International Space Station, supposedly a collaborative project primarily between the U.S. and Russia, was first proposed in 1984; originally intended for completion by 1994 for $8 billion, it had been plagued by escalating costs and repeated delays. Not until 1998, with $20 billion spent and

Astronomer Jason Spyromilio tests the azimuthal mount of the telescope UT1, part of the Very Large Telescope (VLT) in Cerro Paranal, Chile. The UT1 was the first of four VLT telescopes to become operational. Each telescope is housed in a separate building.

the total projected cost climbing to $75 billion or higher, were the first two components of the space station finally launched and joined in space. The American Society of Cell Biologists, whose researchers had been expected to be integral to the project, called it "the most expensive and inflexible research laboratory ever." The *Economist* advocated cancellation of the entire project, calling it "a black hole in the sky."

Even the space shuttle was criticized for being higher on hype than science. In late 1998 the mission of the shuttle *Discovery* (STS-95) became the most publicized space flight in recent years because its crew included 77-year-old retiring U.S. Sen. John Glenn—the man who, in 1962, had become the first American to orbit Earth. NASA defended Glenn's presence on board for scientific reasons, and Glenn called himself a "science passenger." Nevertheless, his role, which included an in-space guest appearance on late-night TV via a communications link with *The Tonight Show,* seemed to many of dubious scientific value, and Glenn had to drop out of one "high-priority" experiment. Critics maintained he was being awarded a "victory lap" for having strongly supported U.S. Pres. Bill Clinton's political programs.

Biology and biomedical sciences

The single largest project in biology and the biomedical sciences, and one whose completion will permanently transform these fields, was the Human Genome Project (HGP). In 1998 the HGP came to the end of its first five-year plan. It also reached several milestones, such as the ge-

nomic sequencing of a number of microorganisms (including the syphillis microbe and the tuberculosis bacterium) and the first complete sequencing of the genetic program of an animal, a microscopic roundworm known as *Caenorhabditis elegans.* This last feat was a key step in the effort to sequence the human genome; it became the "brightest lighthouse," said one researcher, "for the navigation of all animal genomics." The focus of the HGP's next five-year plan (1998–2003) was the complete sequencing of the human genome; a nearly complete "rough draft" was due by the end of 2001 and the complete sequence by the end of 2003, two years ahead of the original schedule.

Another major goal of the HGP's new five-year plan was to explore the ethical, legal, and social implications created by the information gathered by the project. As several events of 1998 testified, humanity still seemed uncertain as to how to make use of the new understanding of human genetics brought about by the project. Some feared the misuse of this knowledge so strongly that they preferred to halt or severely restrict the acquisition and application of genetic information.

In December, for instance, Iceland's parliament passed a bill that granted a single, privately owned licensee, deCODE Genetics Inc., the right to create and operate for profit a single electronic database with medical, genetic, and genealogical information on that country's entire population. Given Iceland's relatively uniform genome, such a database would be especially valuable for health researchers, but the project also raised ethical issues about privacy and the informed consent of experimental subjects. "The ethical and legal

issues under consideration are not unique to Iceland," wrote an Icelandic official in the research journal *Science* in defending the action. "The dilemmas we are facing in developing a system that facilitates progress while preserving patient rights are complex and deserve a thorough analysis." Iceland was certainly not alone in facing controversy over genetic databases. In the U.K., an official of the British police force stirred heated debate when he called for a national DNA database of the entire population to aid in investigating crime. In the U.S., similar debates arose when the New York City police commissioner proposed to collect DNA samples from any person who was arrested in that city and when the governor of New York called for a DNA database of all of the state's felons.

Battles over genetic engineering continued in 1998—especially in Europe, where several governments banned genetically altered products of various kinds and others imposed restrictions. Proponents of genetic engineering argued that the engineered products were not only safe but also essential for coping with humanity's pressing need for improved food. Former U.S. president Jimmy Carter argued that if unnecessarily rigid restrictions on genetically engineered medical, agricultural, and environmental products were imposed, "the real losers will be the developing nations." (India was giving high priority to transgenic crop research for what it called its "urgency to enhance food production.") Opponents argued that genetically engineered products harbored unsuspected dangers, and for some the issue had heavy theological overtones. Said Great Britain's Prince Charles, "I happen to believe that this kind of genetic modification takes

(Below) Eric Vandeville/Gamma Liaison International

Scientists in Italy take samples from the sarcophagus of Frederick II (1194–1250), king of Sicily and Holy Roman emperor. The opening of the sarcophagus on live Italian television was one of a number of controversies involving science in 1998.

mankind into realms that belong to God and to God alone." In parts of Europe the controversy turned violent, with protestors destroying trial fields of genetically modified plants.

In Switzerland, a proposal for strict limits on biomedical and other research involving genetically altered plants and animals was made into a national referendum. The proposal was highly controversial in a country that was home to two of the world's leading pharmaceutical companies, Novartis and Roche, which saw tremendous promise in genetic engineering. Although the proposal was defeated (the pharmaceutical companies poured money into the opposition and far outspent the measure's supporters), the very fact that the winner was decided by popular vote made many researchers extremely nervous. Referendums on such issues will not disappear, however. In 1999 the Swiss were scheduled to vote on legislation to ban all assisted reproduction techniques, including in vitro fertilization.

Controversy over cloning was more muted in 1998 than in 1997, when the biggest and most controversial single science story was the creation, in Scotland, of a sheep named Dolly through cloning of the differentiated cells of an adult animal. In 1998 cloning techniques seemed to spread with unsuspected ease. Various teams around the world announced successful cloning of cows and mice. ("Aren't there already enough mice for everybody?" wondered humorist Russell Baker. "Are so many people complaining of mice shortages that we have to clone them?") Texas A&M University received a $2.3 million grant for a two-year project to clone the anonymous donor's pet dog, a

mixed-breed husky-collie named Missy. The most controversial cloning episode occurred in December, when—in a report challenged both for its ethics and its accuracy—a team of South Korean scientists said they had cloned a human cell but had terminated the procedure when the embryo reached the four-cell stage of development.

A more serious ethical controversy was sparked by the announcement in November that a team of scientists had isolated and cultivated undifferentiated human embryonic stem cells. The work was of enormous importance for medical research, and prospective applications included growing transplant tissue and gene therapy. The development was savagely attacked by anti-

abortion activists, who regarded such cells as persons. In the U.S. the use of federal funds for human embryo research was banned for ethical reasons, and a battle erupted over whether that restriction covered embryonic stem cells. Still murkier ethical issues were raised when a private company in Massachusetts announced that its researchers had created embryos by fusing human DNA with the DNA of a cow's egg.

Even certain genetic tests were controversial. A team of Italian scientists opened the sarcophagus of Frederick II (1194–1250), king of Sicily and Holy Roman emperor, and took samples of his body and the tomb environment to use in

settling lineage and other questions. The opening of the sarcophagus, shown live on Italian television, was criticized by certain church authorities as disrespectful. In the U.S. a team led by a retired pathologist established a link between DNA sequences in the Y chromosome of descendants of the third U.S. president, Thomas Jefferson, and of descendants of Jefferson's slave Sally Hemmings. That finding, plus circumstantial evidence, suggested that Jefferson had fathered a child with Hemmings. Astoundingly, that was not the only, or even most sensational, DNA analysis of a U.S. president in 1998. During his investigation of President Clinton, special prosecutor Kenneth Starr ordered a DNA analysis of a stain on a blue dress of former White House intern Monica Lewinsky, which confirmed that the stain came from the president's semen.

Life and death

Certain medical technologies achieved notoriety in 1998—chief among them the male impotence drug Viagra (sildenafil citrate), which in March won approval by the U.S. Food and Drug Administration. The drug was accidentally discovered by researchers at Pfizer, who were seeking a drug to ease chest pain in heart disease but found one that enhanced erections instead. Although folk remedies for impotence date back to ancient times and other effective remedies exist, Viagra was the first approved pill. The drug inspired legions of jokes on late-night television, but it also created concern about its use. Like other newly approved wonder drugs, it had poorly understood side effects and was likely to be not only overused but also

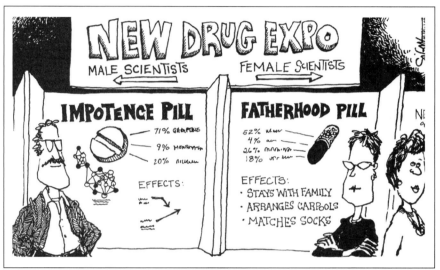

Signe Wilkinson/Cartoonists and Writers Syndicate

taken by those who would be better served by other forms of treatment.

As in 1997, fertility drugs were also controversial in 1998. The reason stemmed from their increased likelihood of producing "high-order multiples" (triplets or more). When this happened, parents were forced to decide whether to try to carry all the fetuses to term—with a substantial risk of defects and permanent health problems in the children, not to mention huge medical costs—or to abort some fetuses to allow the others to develop in a more healthy manner. Some medical ethicists argued that it was bad faith to appeal to God's will as a reason for not aborting fetuses in this situation, since one has used advanced technology to get pregnant in the first place. In 1997 the problem was spotlighted by the birth of septuplets and in December 1998 by the birth of octuplets—none of which weighed over 0.8 kg (less than two pounds) at birth—to a couple in Houston, Tex., Nkem Chukwu and Louis Udobi.

One of the octuplets died before the end of the year, and the total hospital bill was estimated at more than $2 million. The use of fertility drugs, and the incidence of multiple births, was increasing. More medical cases highlighting painful ethical issues are surely to come.

Even as technologies involving birth were controversial, so were technologies involving death. In September Thomas Youk, a terminally ill man who could barely speak or breathe from amyotrophic lateral sclerosis (Lou Gehrig's disease), asked for, and was given, a lethal injection by Jack Kevorkian, an American pathologist and an activist for euthanasia. Although Kevorkian previously had assisted more than 100 suicides by terminally ill patients, this one was different. Not only did he directly inject Youk with the fatal drugs, but he also made a videotape of the various stages in the process of euthanasia, which was subsequently given to TV reporters, broadcast by CBS on *60*

Minutes, and then given by CBS to the police. Kevorkian was charged with murder, and in March 1999 a Michigan jury convicted him of second-degree murder and a drug violation for administering a controlled substance. Whereas some critics charged CBS with sensationalism, other commentators said the airing of the videotape fulfilled the mandate of responsible journalism by, as one said, forcing "public attention to a subject that is so hard to think about that many find excuses for looking away."

Science in society

Many other events of 1998 could be cited to show that what appear to be simple technical issues to a scientist may turn out to have unsuspected and controversial social ramifications. Even statistics became a hot political issue in the U.S. during the year. In preparations for the 2000 census, a well-established method of sampling was thought potentially to favor one political party over another, and the battle over its use ended up in the U.S. Supreme Court.

Society, not just science, has a stake in properly using technical information in a social context, but the obstacles can be high. One telling example took place last year in Italy, where a physiologist named Luigi Di Bella claimed to have cured thousands of cancer victims with a miracle treatment. Some public health advocates demanded that the government conduct trials on human volunteers in state-run clinics, and the government capitulated. The results showed the Di Bella treatment to be of no clinical value, but many ethicists said it was unethical for the government to have sponsored the trials in the first place. As

one said, "It is malpractice on the part of public health services to offer an untested, unscientific method as a real alternative."

Another example of the sometimes difficult relationship between science and society involved a recent lawsuit over the alleged health hazards of silicone breast implants. Despite a lack of scientific evidence for these hazards, the lawsuit had dragged on for more than half a dozen years and brought about bankruptcy proceedings for Dow Corning, the largest of the companies involved. In 1998 a panel of four scientists appointed by a U.S. federal court determined that there was no evidence that breast implants caused disease or abnormalities of the immune system. It was a milestone decision for the role of science in the courtroom and a terrifying

Demonstrators gather in front of the White House in July 1998 after a federal judge ordered silicone breast implant manufacturer Dow Corning to pay $3.2 billion in damages to some 170,000 women.

Georges De Keerle/Gamma/Gamma Liaison International

lesson in how would-be saviors can contribute to the suffering of the very people they purport to want to help. As Malcolm Gladwell, writing in *The New Yorker,* put it, "In the end, one may find that the true health toll of breast implants was the seven years of needless anxiety suffered by implant wearers at the hands of all those lawyers and health 'advocates' who were ostensibly acting on their behalf."

Pseudoscience was another area in which the potential social cost of ignoring technical information was high. In

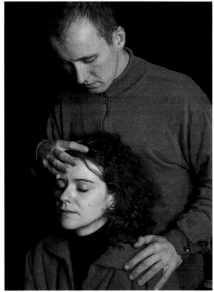

(Left) A practitioner of touch therapy, a controversial form of alternative medicine, places his hands on a woman's head and shoulders in an effort to channel "healing energy" into the patient. (Below) Actors perform a scene in Michael Frayn's play *Copenhagen*, about a meeting between two great quantum physicists.

September *The New England Journal of Medicine* reported cases in which people had died from taking herbal remedies. In April the *Journal of the American Medical Association* reported the results of an experiment that disproved the validity of touch therapy, an alternative medical practice used by more than 40,000 health professionals and more than 70 hospitals in the U.S. Touch therapy had often been shown to be ineffective before; this experiment attracted front-page headlines, however, because it was planned and executed by a nine-year-old girl.

Science appeared in a number of movies in 1998, but as usual its role was almost always as a pretext for something else—a chase, a whodunit, a good-versus-evil conflict—with the science itself receding into the background. An interesting example could be seen in the premier blockbuster movie of 1998, *Titanic*. The movie was celebrated for the supposed lengths to which the director went to get the ship's details accurately, down to the rivets and

patterns on the china. The director, however, did not bother to do the same when it came to the stars in the sky overhead; the movie evidently attempted to portray the constellation Corona Borealis, or Northern Crown, but gave it the wrong number of stars. Nature, apparently, deserves far less respect in setting a movie scene than do the dishes. Neil deGrasse Tyson, director of Boston's Hayden Planetarium, noticed the mistake and lamented that more Hollywood studios did not recognize that "valid science can actually enhance your storytelling, not limit it."

Two excellent plays of 1998, both staged in Great Britain, addressed some of the social dimensions of science. One was

Copenhagen, by the British novelist and playwright Michael Frayn, about a 1941 meeting between Werner Heisenberg and Niels Bohr. The other play was Stanford University chemist Carl Djerassi's *An Immaculate Misconception,* about treating male infertility.

In an interesting editorial in *Science* in 1998, physicist John Ziman discussed the post-World War II evolution of science past a division between "academic" and "industrial." Some of his colleagues dismissed the escalation of social and ethical concerns about science "as no more than a natural consequence of the increasing influence of science on society, magnified, perhaps, by media frenzy," but Ziman disagreed. What the new concerns manifested, he said, was "symptomatic of the transformation of science into a new type of social institution," as its products were woven ever more tightly into the social fabric. The heightened level of the social involvement of science, he seemed to be saying, is here to stay.

ANTHROPOLOGY

In another impressive year in paleoanthropology, new fossil discoveries and reinterpretations of earlier finds added to scientists' understanding of human ancestors, particularly the australopithecines, the apelike forerunners of modern humans. By far the most dramatic event of the year was the discovery in a South African cave of an extraordinarily well-preserved skull and associated skeleton of an australopithecine. Thousands of kilometers to the north in East Africa, scientists unearthed a trove of new *Australopithecus anamensis* fossils, greatly increasing the known sample of this recently named species of hominid (a bipedal primate within the family Hominidae). Analyses of previously recovered hominid fossils also produced interesting surprises during the year, including a new estimate of the cranial capacity of *Australopithecus africanus* and the discovery that this species—at least in terms of limb proportions—is more apelike than its geologically older cousin, *Australopithecus afarensis.* Comparative anatomical studies also provided insight into the evolution of human language.

Oldest hominid skeleton

In a find called "momentous," paleoanthropologists Ron Clarke and Phillip Tobias of South Africa's University of the Witwatersrand discovered the first complete skeleton of an ancient human ancestor dating back more than three million years. How the scientists came upon the australopithecine skeleton at Sterkfontein Caves on the outskirts of Johannesburg, S.Af., reads like a good mystery. The story begins in the 1920s or early 1930s, when miners blasted through a limestone forma-

tion in the Silberberg Grotto, an underground chamber at Sterkfontein. Some 50 years later, in 1978, Tobias began removing chunks of rock left from the blasting. Technicians subsequently found fossil bones in the rubble and stored them away in boxes in a work shed at the site.

More than a decade later, Tobias and Clarke returned to Silberberg Grotto to look for additional fossils in some of the older deposits of the cave. The rocks proved to be rich in monkey and carnivore fossils but seemed to lack the bovid (hoofed mammals, such as antelopes, dik-diks, sheep, goats, and cattle, in the family Bovidae) bones that were so plentiful in other areas. Puzzled, Clarke decided to check through some of the material left from 1978. Among a collection of miscellaneous animal foot bones, he identified several bones belonging to the left foot and ankle of a hominid. This dramatic find was published in 1995 and given the name "Little Foot." The foot, cataloged as Stw 573, not only represented the oldest known hominid from Sterkfontein but also revealed apelike as well as humanlike characteristics, indicating that the individual spent at least some time in the trees, as well as on the ground. In 1997 Clarke found additional ankle and leg fragments that fit perfectly with Stw 573. In all, he had recovered 12 foot and lower-leg bones of one australopithecine individual—the left tibia and fibula, which joined to the Little Foot specimen, and fragments of a right tibia and foot bone. Over the course of that year, Clarke organized excavations to trace more of the skeleton. A major breakthrough occurred in September 1998, when workers uncovered the individual's virtually complete skull. By the close of

the year, most of the legs and the left side of the skull and mandible had been exposed.

Past finds of South African *Australopithecus* had been either a partial skull or partial skeleton, but never both from the same individual. Paleomagnetic dating at Sterkfontein revealed that the skeleton was 3.2 million to 3.6 million years old, making it slightly older than the famous 3.2-million-year-old "Lucy" fossil (*A. afarensis*) discovered in East Africa in 1974. Until Clarke's discovery, there had been no definitive evidence of australopithecines living in southern Africa before three million years ago. Because much of the skeleton, as well as the skull, were still embedded in rock, it remained to be determined what kind of australopithecine it represents.

Early steps in East Africa

Paleoanthropologists led by Meave Leakey of the National Museums of Kenya confirmed that bones of *A. anamensis,* discovered in 1995 at the site of Kanapoi in northern Kenya, are more than four million years old, making the species the earliest known two-legged ancestor of humans. At the time of the discovery, Leakey believed that *A. anamensis* was a very ancient bipedal creature, but some scientists questioned the antiquity of the Kanapoi evidence, particularly a leg bone that had been found in a higher, and therefore younger, layer of sediment. Writing in *Nature,* Leakey and colleagues reaffirmed the early age of the species by reporting that a layer of volcanic ash just above the level of the leg bone is roughly 4.1 million years old, meaning that the fossil is at least that age.

Ron Clarke (center) holds a model of a foot, while his assistants, Isaac Molefe (left) and Steven Motsumi (right), show some of the bones from the virtually complete australopithecine skeleton discovered in South Africa in 1998.

Leakey's team also announced the discovery of 38 new specimens of *A. anamensis* from Kanapoi and nearby Allia Bay, which paint a more complete picture of the species. Among the more important of the discoveries were juvenile teeth, skull pieces, wrist and finger bones, a maxilla, and pieces of a large, presumed male, mandible. The new evidence confirmed what scientists had learned from earlier finds—namely, that *A. anamensis* was a primitive hominid with numerous apelike characteristics. The mandible, for instance, is extremely thick and robust like an ape's and has parallel tooth rows, unlike human jaws, in which tooth rows diverge toward the back of the mouth. The wrist bone is also very apelike and similar to that of other australopithecines. In addition, *A. anamensis* individuals were probably chimpanzee-like in height and weight, the researchers said. Males were probably about 1.5 m (5 ft) tall and weighed be-

tween 54 and 68 kg (120 and 150 lb). Females were more diminutive, perhaps as small as 1.1 m (3.5 ft) and 27 kg (60 lb). On the other hand, features of the leg bones clearly reveal that the species was able to walk upright like humans, rather than on all fours like apes.

The brain of Mr. Ples

A. africanus had a much smaller brain volume, or cranial capacity, than previously believed, reported a team of researchers led by Glenn C. Conroy of Washington University, St. Louis, Mo. The new brain size estimate was made on "Mr. Ples" (cataloged as Stw 505), an *A. africanus* skull discovered in 1989, calling into question ideas about human brain evolution. Conroy and colleagues nicknamed the presumably

male cranium Mr. Ples because it was found at Sterkfontein, where scientists in 1947 found "Mrs. Ples," the first nearly complete adult australopithecine skull. The Mr. Ples fossil, which includes the face and the left side of the cranium, was originally estimated to have a cranial capacity of about 600 cu cm (about 37 cu in). Although small compared to a 1,250–1,350-cu cm (76–82-cu in) modern human brain, it was large for australopithecines, whose brain volumes range between 400 and 500 cu cm (24 and 31 cu in).

Using computed tomography (CT) scans of the Mr. Ples cranium, the researchers were able to construct a three-dimensional computer model that replaced the missing portions on the right side. The endocranial cavity was then rendered as a separate object, and the brain volume was estimated.

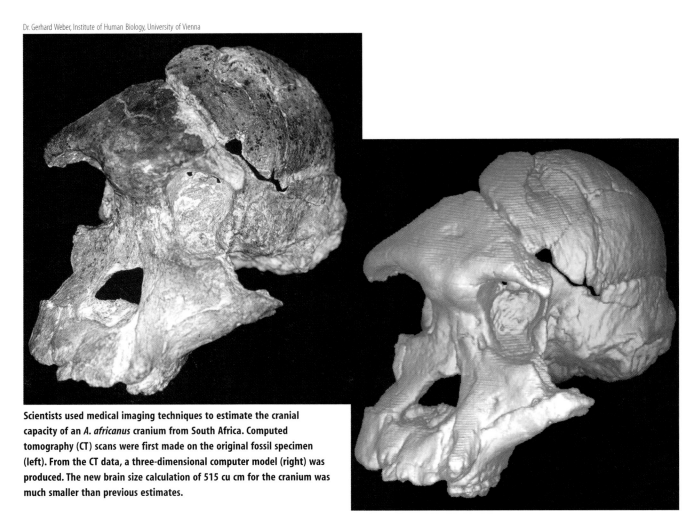

Scientists used medical imaging techniques to estimate the cranial capacity of an *A. africanus* cranium from South Africa. Computed tomography (CT) scans were first made on the original fossil specimen (left). From the CT data, a three-dimensional computer model (right) was produced. The new brain size calculation of 515 cu cm for the cranium was much smaller than previous estimates.

The result was a cranial capacity of 515 cu cm (31.4 cu in), significantly smaller than original estimates. Two other methods of determining cranial capacity provided similar estimates. Since the method allows a relatively objective means of estimating brain size from fragmentary remains, the researchers recommended that analyses of other early hominids are needed in order to place anthropologists' understanding of the tempo and mode of human brain evolution on a firmer foundation.

Sizing up *Australopithecus*

Many contemporary interpretations of early human evolution assume an ancestor-descendant relationship between *A. afarensis* and *A. africanus*. South African *A. africanus* is known from approximately 2.6 million to 3 million years ago and had more humanlike cranial and dental features than *A. afarensis*, which roamed East Africa from about 3.6 million to 3 million years ago. An analysis of australopithecine

limb bones by Henry McHenry of the University of California, Davis, and Lee R. Berger of the University of the Witwatersrand, revealed, however, that the pattern of changes in body proportions is not as straightforward as is the evidence from the crania and teeth.

McHenry and Berger measured the forelimb and hindlimb joints of more than 100 partial *Australopithecus* skeletons discovered at Sterkfontein (*A. africanus*) and the Hadar site in East Africa (*A. afarensis*).

Using mathematical formulas calibrated with studies of modern humans and apes, the researchers derived body-weight estimates of the australopithecines from the limb-joint measurements. From their calculations, a surprising pattern emerged— the average size of *A. africanus* forelimb joints correlated to a modern human with a body weight of 53 kg (117 lb), whereas the hindlimb joints corresponded to a 33-kg (73-lb) person. It had been assumed that such top-heavy limb proportions were found only in apes, who employ a fore-limb-dominated pattern of movement in the trees. In contrast, *A. afarensis* more closely approximated a modern human ratio of forelimb to hindlimb joint size. The investigators were then left with an apparent paradox: How could *A. africanus* be more apelike in its body proportions than the earlier and craniodentally more primitive *A. afarensis*?

The implications of the research remained unclear, but the finding clearly suggested that the path to modern humanity was not simple or straightforward. The results of the study implied that *A. africanus* probably did not evolve from Lucy's kind, the researchers contended. Rather, both *A. africanus* and *A. afarensis* probably evolved independently from a "missing link" ancestor, with the southern australopithecines retaining the primitive limb proportions of this ancestor.

Origin of language

A hallmark of humanity is our ability to talk. Unfortunately, language leaves few obvious clues in the fossil record; thus, scientists do not know precisely when language developed or which of our ancestors had the ability to speak. Instead, indirect inferences about language capability are made through anatomical and behavioral comparisons of humans and their closest living relatives, apes and monkeys. For instance, one investigation, conducted by a team of researchers led by Patrick Gannon of Mount Sinai School of Medicine, New York City, showed that a region of the human brain thought to control language is proportionately the same size in humans and chimpanzees, disproving a theory that the brain section was enlarged only in humans.

Modern human speech is associated with tissue located mostly in the left hemisphere of the brain. For instance, Broca's area, a region in the left frontal lobe discovered in 1861 by French neurosurgeon Paul Broca, has been connected with speech production. Similarly, Wernicke's area, named after German neurologist Carl Wernicke, has been related to language comprehension. In normal human brains, a fingernail-sized piece of tissue called the planum temporale (PT), located within Wernicke's area, is more pronounced in the left hemisphere than in the right. Such asymmetry had been assumed to be unique to humans until Gannon's team reported in 1998 that 17 out of 18 chimpanzee brains dissected also had enlarged left PTs. The marked differences in the two sides of the chimpanzee brain were first observed by Gannon during a magnetic-resonance-imaging (MRI) study. Following that discovery, he sought the help of noted paleoanthropologist and primate brain expert Ralph Holloway of Columbia University, New York City, who assisted in measuring the ape brains.

The groundbreaking discovery provided further evidence of the profound similarity between humans and chimpanzees and suggested that the anatomical substrate for language was already present in the last common ancestor of chimps and humans, which is thought to have lived some five million to six million years ago. The work should encourage development of new theories of language origin that build more directly on primate, especially chimpanzee, communication systems and lead to more conservative interpretations of the utility of fossil endocasts (brain castings, in which the cranial cavity serves as a mold).

Another study using the comparative approach was conducted by Richard Kay, Matt Cartmill, and Michelle Balow of Duke University, Durham, N.C., who measured the hypoglossal canals, a pair of bony grooves in the base of the skull, of modern humans, gorillas, chimpanzees, bonobos, and several fossil hominids. Kay's team discovered that the canals— which transmit branches of the hypoglossal nerve, a cranial nerve that controls most of the musculature of the tongue— are large in humans and their more recent fossil ancestors but small in apes, monkeys, and australopithecines. Theorizing that the large size of the hypoglossal canal in humans reflects a greater control of the tongue in this species, Kay and colleagues concluded that human speech may have originated as early as 300,000–400,000 years ago.

Less than a year after this research was published, however, the picture became cloudier when graduate students from the University of California, Berkeley, hinted that the hypoglossal canal may not be an important skeletal signpost of speech after all. Led by David DeGusta, the Berkeley students measured the hypoglossal canals

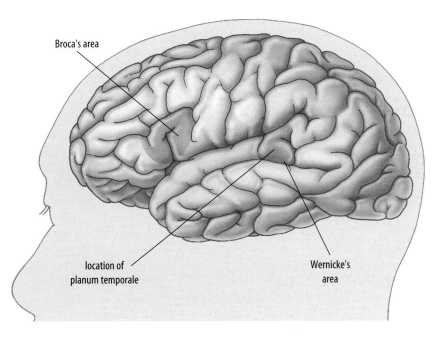

Broca's area

location of
planum temporale

Wernicke's
area

of 104 modern humans, 75 nonhuman primates representing 32 different species, and 4 three-million-year-old australopithecine specimens. After correcting for size, the team found that 15 nonhuman primate species had hypoglossal-canal sizes larger than the modern human average. Hypoglossal canal size in *A. afarensis* and *Australopithecus boisei* also fell within the range of modern humans. Consequently, the researchers concluded that hypoglossal canal size is not a reliable indicator of humanlike speech ability.

—David L. Carlson

ARCHAEOLOGY

A number of exciting developments in archaeology occurred during 1998. Several studies were concerned with the emergence of uniquely human traits that accompanied our evolution. In one study examining the origin of speech, scientists showed that a bony landmark on the base of the skull may hold clues about our ancestors' verbal capabilities. Another highlight was the report that humankind's first sea voyager may not have been a fully modern human after all but a slightly more distant ancestor who lived hundreds of thousands of years earlier. A reanalysis of Paleolithic artifacts from France reaffirmed that, at least culturally, Neanderthals were in many ways similar to their modern human contemporaries.

When did we start to speak?

Without question, speech and language are uniquely human traits. Indeed, some consider speech to be the essence of being human. A long history of heated scientific debate has occurred over the evolutionary origin of speech and language. The core of

the debate has centered around the issue of whether biological characteristics associated with speech emerged only in anatomically modern *Homo sapiens* sometime between 100,000 and 40,000 years ago or in earlier members of the human lineage.

In the past, archaeologists and paleoanthropologists made inferences about the capability of speech and language in human ancestors by means of arguments about the degree of interpersonal interaction and information transfer that would have been necessary for such social behaviors as group hunting, food sharing, tool manufacture, territorial knowledge, and the passing of such information from generation to generation. Other scientists, citing data collected from studies of nonhuman primates and other animals, argued that, whereas some form of communication may have been required for such activities, humanlike speech was not.

In recent years, investigators have searched for direct physical evidence of speech capability through the analysis of human fossils. Several scientists have tried to glean information about language from fossil endocasts, those crude maps of surface features of the brain. Traditionally, Broca's area, visible as a small bump on the left hemisphere of the brain, has been associated with the production of speech. Evidence of Broca's area has been found in the endocasts of a two-million-year-old

Homo rudolfensis and later species of *Homo* but not in humans' apelike ancestors, the australopithecines.

The origin of human speech has also been probed through studies of the voice-producing apparatus itself—the larynx. Like language, the human vocal tract is unique in the animal world. In mammals, the position of the larynx in the neck assumes one of two general patterns. One position is high up in the throat near the base of the tongue, which enables an animal to swallow and breathe simultaneously. The second pattern is located lower in the throat, well below the back of the tongue, requiring temporary closing of the air passage during swallowing. Adult humans have the second pattern, while all other mammals—and infant humans—possess the first. The low position of the larynx enlarges the throat space above it, enabling us to make a wide variety of sounds with our mouths.

Larynxes are not preserved in the human fossil record, but scientists have learned that laryngeal position is reflected skeletally on the base of the skull, or basicranium. In adult humans, the shape of the basicranium is arched. In nonhuman primates and newborns, it is much flatter. The presence of an arched basicranium in a human ancestor, therefore, may suggest something about the capacity for language in that species. Fossil studies have shown that *Australopithecus* had a relatively flattened basicranium, indicating that its vocal tract was much like that of a modern monkey or ape. By contrast, the basicranium of the long-lasting and widespread ancestor *Homo erectus* is slightly arched, suggesting that the hominid was capable of complex communication, probably including

many kinds of meaningful sounds even if they were not truly humanlike speech.

In 1998 Richard F. Kay of Duke University, Durham, N.C., and colleagues showed that the hypoglossal canal—a short bony tube in the base of the skull—is another anatomical feature that might hold clues about the origin of speech. Kay knew that an important organ of speech, the tongue, is controlled by the hypoglossal nerve, which passes through the hypoglossal canal as it exits the brain cavity. Finding that the hypoglossal canal is small in apes and other nonhuman primates but large in modern humans, the scientists theorized that the larger the canal, the greater the number of nerve fibers that can go through it, thereby permitting finer control of the tongue.

An analysis of hypoglossal canal size in the human fossil record again hinted that speech and language probably did not arise until human brains reached a certain, near-modern, size. Kay and colleagues learned that the hypoglossal canals of *A. africanus* and an early *Homo* specimen that is probably *Homo habilis* were within the size range of apes. In contrast, human-sized hypoglossal canals were discovered in two 60,000–70,000-year-old Neanderthals *(H. sapiens neanderthalensis),* a 90,000-year-old early *H. sapiens,* and two other specimens of *Homo* ranging from 300,000 to 400,000 years old. (For additional information on the relationship of the hypoglossal canal and human speech, *see* Year in Review: ANTHROPOLOGY.)

An interesting question arose from the fossil research. Why does the origin of speech fail to show up as a major change in the organization or structure of archae-

ological sites dated between 400,000 and 500,000 years ago? Was the advent of speech merely a point along a line of increasingly complex communication, such that it was accompanied by few if any changes in material culture or archaeologically recognizable social structure? The archaeological record does not show many cultural innovations until 30,000 to 40,000 years ago. It was during this time that the archaeological records of Europe, Africa, and the Near East blossomed with new ideas, such as art, personal adornment, reverence for the dead, religion, and a variety of new and different kinds of artifacts. It remains a fascinating area of research to discover how and why speech and language developed.

Very ancient sailors

Although the evidence for speech in *H. erectus* is not entirely clear, scientists are reasonably certain that members of this species left Africa by at least 1.8 million years ago and spread out into the temperate areas of the Old World over the next million years. *H. erectus* is thought to have made clothing and various weapons and traps and to have controlled fire for warmth, protection, and cooking. They were excellent hunters, scavengers, and perhaps fishers, and they probably knew of and used the abundant food and medicinal plants that grew in the areas that they inhabited. Anatomically they remained relatively unchanged between 1.8 million and 800,000 years ago. Average brain size grew somewhat, but postcranially *H. erectus* was very similar to modern humans, even from its appearance in Africa almost two million years ago.

One intriguing question regarding the widespread distribution of *H. erectus* has been how the species was able to colonize several islands in Southeast Asia and Indonesia. Most archaeologists assumed that the hominid was not advanced enough intellectually and culturally to make sea crossings. *H. erectus* may have arrived on the Indonesian island of Java, for example, by crossing land bridges that formed between the Asian mainland and the Indonesian archipelago when sea levels dropped dramatically during the glacial advances of the Pleistocene Epoch (1.6 million years ago to 10,000 years ago). Other islands that lay to the east were never connected to mainland Asia, even when sea levels were at their lowest. Consequently, scientists had assumed that Indonesia was colonized by *H. sapiens,* who presumably had the intellectual capacity and cultural ability to build boats.

In 1998 M.J. Morwood of the University of New England, Armidale, N.S.W., Australia, and his colleagues reported evidence that hinted that *H. erectus* may have indeed built watercraft for sea crossings. Working on Flores, a small island east of Java, Morwood's team excavated two fossil sites, one of which contained numerous stone tools previously dated to about 40,000 years ago and attributed to *H. sapiens.* Fossils found along with the tools included remains of the an-

Archaeologists working on the Indonesian island of Flores discovered a cache of stone tools that date from 800,000 to 900,000 years ago. If the dates are accurate, it suggests that *Homo erectus* (above)—the only hominid species in Asia at that time—used some kind of watercraft to cross at least 20 km (12 mi) of open sea to reach the island.

cient elephant *Stegodon,* crocodiles, giant rats, freshwater mollusks, and plants. More ancient human remains had yet to be found on the island.

Using an absolute dating technique called fission-track dating, the archaeologists showed that the period of hominid occupation on Flores was considerably older

than previously believed. In fission-track dating, scientists count the microscopic tracks created in volcanic-rock crystals as atoms of uranium and other radioactive isotopes decay and emit neutrons. Crystals of volcanic origin work best for this dating method because large numbers of tracks are formed at the same time when lavas cool from their molten state. Since the decay rates of uranium and other isotopes are well known, the ages of the crystals are determined by measuring the number and types of fission tracks in those crystals.

The new dating analysis showed that the layers of volcanic ashes bracketing the stone tools were laid down 800,000–900,000 years ago. The stone artifacts, previously thought to be made by *H. sapiens,* instead were probably manufactured by *H. erectus,* the only hominid species in Asia at that time. Even at the time of the lowest Pleistocene sea levels, two water crossings of between 20 and 80 km (12 and 50 mi) would have been required to reach Flores from the Asian mainland. The scientists, therefore, concluded that *H. erectus* probably did build seaworthy watercrafts to get there.

French Neanderthals

Interpretations of another group of hominids, the Neanderthals, were also called

Tom McHugh/Photo Researchers, Inc.

The discovery of the first known Neanderthal in 1856 touched off a lasting fascination with this enigmatic hominid species. How much like us were the Neanderthals? How intelligent were these short, stocky, barrel-chested people, who inhabited Europe and the Middle East starting about 200,000 years ago? What caused their relatively abrupt disappearance about 30,000 years ago? These questions are among the more hotly debated in anthropology today.

into question in 1998. Ever since Neanderthal remains were first discovered in Germany in 1856, people have questioned their cognitive and cultural capabilities. Did Neanderthals rival modern *H. sapiens* in their art and technology, or merely copy us? Were they subhuman bestial creatures, or indistinguishable from humans?

A 1998 reanalysis of Châtelperronian artifacts recovered from sites in Arcy-sur-Cure, France, reaffirmed what archaeologists had been learning in recent years—namely, that Neanderthals were quite humanlike. Scientists first thought that the artifacts, which were discovered in the 1950s and early '60s, were left by early

modern humans soon after they migrated into Western Europe. Later, following studies in the late 1960s and '70s, some archaeologists began to attribute the Arcy artifacts—which include carved bone tools and personal ornaments such as pierced animal bones, claws, and teeth—to Neanderthals, whose skeletal remains had been recovered from the same sites.

Not all scientists were convinced, however, that Neanderthals made the artifacts. Many thought that Neanderthal peoples did not have the intellectual capacity or the cultural needs to develop and use personal adornments on their own. Some argued that Neanderthals obtained the tools and

ornaments through trade with their modern neighbors, the Cro-Magnon people, who had long been associated with Châtelperronian technology. Others suggested that if Neanderthals did manufacture the artifacts, they merely copied or mimicked the techniques and styles of their more thoughtful modern human contemporaries.

Research by a team of archaeologists led by Francesco d'Errico of the Institute of Prehistory and Quaternary Geology in Talence, France, showed that the traditional view of Neanderthal replacement by more advanced, anatomically modern people is outdated and probably wrong. Careful review and reevaluation of the evidence from the Arcy sites indicated that the Châtelperronian tools were made by Neanderthals, not their modern neighbors. Moreover, the team showed conclusively that the Châtelperronian tools and ornaments were not just imitations of modern human Aurignacian-style objects but independently derived and fashioned using techniques that stem from even older Neanderthal bone-working methods.

What is the significance of Neanderthal personal adornment? Anthropologists believe that ornaments, such as rings, necklaces, and pendants, transmit information about the wearer and his or her status in the social group. The need for transmission of such information is related to acute awareness of identifying self, group membership, group status, and nongroup individuals. Adornments first appear in the archaeological record of both Neanderthals and anatomically modern humans around 40,000 years ago and coincide with the origins of cave paintings, art, intentional burials, ritual behaviors, and, presumably, religion. Although the situation is not completely clear, evidence from throughout Europe suggests that modern humans created most or all of the artwork, but that Neanderthals, like modern humans, buried their dead, built altars, and participated in rituals.

In their concluding remarks, d'Errico and colleagues suggested that the initial contacts between anatomically modern humans and Neanderthals were extremely important events in human prehistory. They argued that the contacts, which may have been shocking and unnerving for both groups, may have stimulated an intensive use of symbols (ornaments) in the two cultures, perhaps owing to the problems of personal, social, and biological identity that surely arose from the meetings. Whether Neanderthals were a separate species or not, the cultural dynamics of the friction created when anatomically modern humans migrated into Neanderthal territories might have been the catalyst for the great leaps in cultural evolution that occurred between 30,000 and 40,000 years ago.

—James D. Wilde
See also Feature Article: UNLOCKING THE MYSTERIES OF THE MAYA.

A reanalysis of Châtelperronian artifacts from the French site of Arcy-sur-Cure, including worked-bone tools (above), personal ornaments, and stone tools, suggested that the traditional notion of Neanderthal acculturation by anatomically modern humans is inconsistent with the evidence. Models of independent invention best explain the Arcy artifacts, archaeologists argued, and suggest that a thorough reevaluation of Neanderthal cognitive abilities is needed. (Right) A close-up view of one of the worked-bone tools shows a pattern of regularly spaced notches, which may have been intended to communicate a visual message.

Dr. Francesco d'Errico

ARCHITECTURAL AND CIVIL ENGINEERING

Transportation was an important theme in architectural and civil engineering in 1998. While a major airport was finished in China and engineers worked on a permanent rail and road link between Denmark and Sweden, plans to replace an earthquake-damaged bridge in San Francisco were finalized. The year may also be remembered as one of superlatives in the architecture world, as a number of buildings and structures staked claim as the world's or region's largest, longest, or tallest.

Architectural engineering

The new Hong Kong International Airport was completed and opened in July 1998, capturing global attention for both its architectural- and civil-engineering bravura. Eight years in the making, the $20 billion airport is expected to become the largest in the world in terms of international passenger movements, having been designed to handle as many as 35 million passengers annually. By 2040, with the addition of a second passenger terminal, the airport could accommodate more than 87 million travelers per year. The opening of the airport marked the completion of China's Airport Core Program, an ambitious multiproject plan to compliment the airport with new infrastructure, including 34 km (1 km = 0.62 mi) of expressways and tunnels and a high-speed railway that connects the airport to Hong Kong and surrounding areas.

The massive airport effort was coordinated by the Mott Consortium (Foster and Partners, architects; Mott Connell Ltd., engineering and project management; and the British Airport Authority, airport planning and operational systems) and required input from more than 230 experts in the field—including 72 architects. Renowned British architect Sir Norman Foster designed the colossal Y-shaped passenger terminal, which features 288 check-in counters, 38 gates, and a baggage-claim center as large as New York City's Yankee Stadium. With a whopping 516,000 sq m (5.6 million sq ft) of floor space, the terminal became one of the largest enclosed spaces ever constructed. The bright and spacious terminal supports a series of

In July 1998 flights touched down for the first time at the new Hong Kong International Airport. Designed by the Mott Consortium, led by the architectural firm Foster and Partners, the airport is one of the most ambitious civil engineering projects of the 1990s. The vast arrival hall, shown below, is among the largest enclosed public spaces ever built.

36.5-m-wide (1 m = 3.28 ft), lightweight-steel shells connected to form continuous barrel vaults that run east and west, parallel to the building's 1.3-km-long main axis leading from entry to gates. The structural engineering firm Ove Arup & Partners designed the building's distinctive, multivaulted roof. Due to their great size, the roof's steel-frame vaults appear to curve along their length, but, in reality, flat segments were progressively tilted and built of uniform straight beams clad in rectilinear panels.

Another notable project that opened in 1998 was the extension to the Hong Kong Convention and Exhibition Center. The new facility, which more than doubles the original center's capacity, was built on an artificial island that projects into Victoria Harbor, just offshore of Hong Kong's congested business district. One challenge to project managers was to make a seamless connection between the old center and the new building, a task made all the more difficult by the presence of a 100-m-wide water channel that separated the buildings. Engineers resolved this issue by designing an atrium link, a massive glass-enclosed bridge supported by two huge trusses cantilevered off the site of the old convention center. The main entry to the new building is fronted by a 40-m-tall glass wall that opens onto a spacious lobby. From there, visitors can take escalators up to the vast convention halls, which are stacked on three levels, each 15 m floor-to-floor. The roof may be the most impressive feature, however. Made up of a series of undulating, overlapping planes, it provides a striking contrast to the squared-off buildings in downtown Hong Kong.

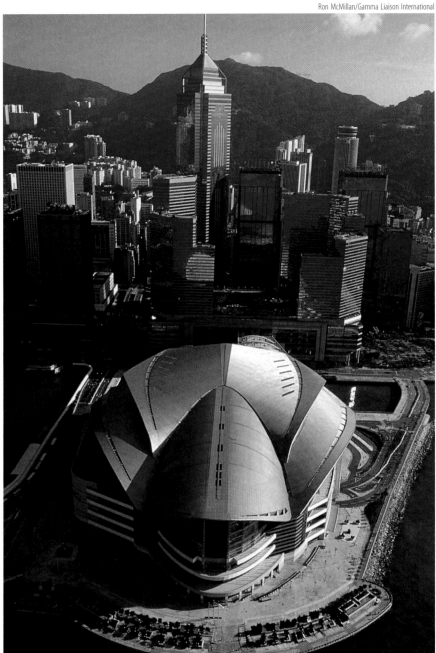

The new extension to the Hong Kong Convention and Exhibition Center opened in 1998. Among the most impressive features of the building is its massive aluminum roof, which is made up of a series of undulating, overlapping planes.

The new buildings in China could not be criticized for displaying engineering timidity—nor could some new ones in Europe. In Frankfurt, Ger., Commerzbank opened its new headquarters in what some observers called the world's first environmentally friendly office building. Standing 259 m tall, Commerzbank Tower became the tallest office structure in Europe and ranked 24th in the world at the close of 1998. The towering edifice is more than another high-rise bank, however. Viewed up close, the architectural design is striking. The building plan is of an equilateral triangle, with the floors organized around a 50-story ventilation and light shaft. Four-story-high "sky gardens" spiral up the inside of the triangular tower, offering each office a view of greenery and providing the building's interior with ample light. Botanically, the vegetation in the nine sky gardens reflects the geographical orientation; thus, eastward-facing gardens contain primarily Asian plants, westward-facing gardens contain North American vegetation, and southward-facing gardens have Mediterranean flora. The sky gardens work with the building's outer skin, which has vents through which fresh air can enter, to provide the tower's sophisticated, energy-efficient natural ventilation system.

The world's largest domed structure was completed in London as part of Great Britain's celebration of the new millennium. Constructed on the prime meridian (the imaginary line used to indicate 0° longitude) near historic Greenwich, the Millennium Dome, as it is known, will contain numerous exhibits and attractions in celebration of the 21st century. The cable-supported dome has a maximum diameter of 320 m, making it almost twice as large as the previous record holder, Atlanta's Georgia Dome.

In addition to providing office workers with communication and recreation areas, Commerzbank Tower's sky gardens form part of the building's ventilation system.

The Millennium Dome—the world's largest domed structure—was completed in London near historic Greenwich. The enormous fabrication, which will be used in observances of the new millennium, is scheduled to open on New Year's Eve 1999.

Civil engineering

Construction of the Øresund (The Sound) Link between Denmark and Sweden continued as planned but was not without problems. Set to open in the year 2000, the 16-km bridge-tunnel system that spans The Sound, separating the cities of Copenhagen and Malmö, Swed., is a massive engineering project. From west to east, the traverse begins with a 3.8-km immersed tunnel starting near Copenhagen International Airport. The tunnel—the longest immersed tube tunnel for both road and rail traffic in the world—leads to a 4.1-km-long artificial island from which a 7.9-km bridge continues to Malmö. Construction workers encountered several problems in 1998. Minor leaks were discovered in several of the bridge's concrete caissons, or foundations. Project managers said that the damage had occurred when the caissons were cast on land. Another setback occurred when one of the enormous 57,000-ton concrete tubes required to form the tunnel sank before it could be placed.

In the U.S., controversy arose when the California Department of Transportation finally approved a plan for a single-tower suspension bridge to replace an earthquake-damaged section of the Oakland–San Francisco Bay Bridge. Both the proposed design of the bridge and its planned route were debated. Mayor Willie Brown of San Francisco disagreed with the route, which would take the new bridge north of the present link between Yerba Buena Island and Oakland, thus interfering with the city's future Yerba Buena development projects. Oakland mayor-elect Jerry Brown questioned the aesthetic aspects of the bridge's design. Construction of the con-

tentious span was to begin in the year 2000. Meanwhile, a replacement for the 854-m Tacoma (Wash.) Narrows Bridge also moved toward a 2000 construction start after delays over funding. It promised to be the first major cable-suspension bridge built in the U.S. in the past 30 years.

Other U.S. civil engineering projects were aimed at reclaiming marginal land in urban areas. San Francisco announced a multibillion-dollar plan to build office buildings, medical facilities, labs, and housing on its 123.5 ha (305.2 ac) of abandoned railroad yards. In nearby San Jose the U.S. Army Corps of Engineers started construction on lengthy bypass channels to prevent flooding from the Guadalupe River. The work, however, was held up over concerns about skyrocketing land costs and the project's potential effect on salmon migration and a planned riverfront park. (For further information on engineering projects, *see* Year in Review: TRANSPORTATION.)

Honors and awards

In 1998 both of the prestigious awards bestowed by the Boston Society of Architects and by the American Institute of Architects (AIA) were denounced by critics for their lack of technological verve and for favoring stylistically correct buildings on conventional structures. Although notable for their pleasant appearance, most of the winning projects were hardly outstanding for technological innovation or expression. The exception, recognized by both organizations, was Ventilation Building Number 7 at Boston's Logan Airport, the only utilitarian structure so praised. Architects TAMS Consultants Inc., Stull & Lee Inc.,

and Wallace, Floyd, Associates Inc. designed the aluminum, stainless-steel, and concrete building to be monumentally expressive of its combined intake and exhaust functions. Other AIA awards went to biomedical manufacturer Becton Dickinson's Building 2, Franklin Lakes, N.J., which was designed by Kallmann, McKinnell & Wood Architects Inc. and recognized for its modular system of office partitions, and the Chapel of St. Ignatius in Washington state, designed by architect Steven Holl and the firm of Olson & Sundberg Architects and noted for its composite structure of tilt-up concrete and steel panels. More technologically inspired was another AIA award winner, the renovation of the 1905 U.S. Court of Appeals building in San Francisco by Skidmore, Owings & Merrill LLP, which incorporated a seismic-protection mechanism that allows the building to move independently of the ground beneath it during earthquakes. Among international award winners, Renzo Piano, architect of the Debis Tower in Berlin, won the Hyatt Foundation's 1998 Pritzker Prize.

In January 1999 *Engineering News Record* recognized outstanding achievement in civil engineering by naming its 1998 Top 25 Newsmakers. Among those honored were Ian Liddell of Buro Happold Ltd., who engineered London's Millennium Dome; South Florida Water Management District's Joseph A. Schweigart, who supervised construction projects to help restore water-flow patterns in the Everglades; and J. Muller International's principal engineer James Lockwood, who continued to advocate the use of innovative technologies in bridge design.

—Charles King Hoyt

ASTRONOMY

Jupiter's rings, planets in other solar systems, gamma rays from deep space, and the expansion of the universe were among the major subjects of research in astronomy during 1998. A surprising discovery was that there may be nearly as many stars between galaxies as there are within them.

Solar system

On any clear night, a person at a dark site is likely to see a half dozen "shooting stars," or meteors, per hour. They are produced when specks of interplanetary dust fall to Earth at speeds of about 100 km (60 mi) per second. They are vaporized by friction with Earth's atmosphere, producing a bright streak of light. A few times each year, there are meteor showers during which this rate increases to about one per minute. Meteor showers occur when Earth crosses the orbital path of a comet. When a comet is in the inner solar system and warmed by the Sun, some of its ice sublimates and releases the impregnated dust. In this way the orbital paths of comets become littered with particles of dust. These become meteors upon entering Earth's atmosphere. Meteor showers are named for the constellation from which the meteors seem to radiate.

The intensity of a meteor shower depends on the dust content of the comet and on the distribution of the dust along the comet's orbit. Because the dust tends to disperse, it is densest close to the comet. If Earth crosses the orbit of the comet within a few weeks or months of the comet's passage, the result is not a shower but a meteor storm. Such an event was predicted for the Leonid meteor storm for Nov. 17, 1998. Predicting the exact time of a meteor storm is impossible because the precise distribution of the dust is unknown. The location on Earth from which the storm will be visible is also difficult to predict. As Earth moves in its orbit, it also turns on its axis. The portion of Earth facing "forward" toward the oncoming dust will see the strongest display.

For the 1998 Leonid storm, China and Japan were predicted to be the best sites. In fact, the storm peaked a few hours later than predicted, causing the best location to be the

Every November, when Earth passes through the dusty debris along the orbit of comet Tempel-Tuttle, a meteor shower becomes visible. The "shooting stars" are called Leonids because they seem to radiate out of the constellation Leo. The 1998 display was particularly strong, as Tempel-Tuttle passed closest to the Sun in February.

Photri

eastern Atlantic Ocean. There, observers in the Canary Islands reported a few hundred to a few thousand meteors per hour. This display was dominated by bright meteors, many of which left smoky trails that lingered for several minutes. While only a few people were in the right location to see an intense storm, observers throughout the world reported a significant number of bright meteors for several nights. Another, but somewhat lesser, Leonid storm was predicted for November 1999.

Although interplanetary dust can fall harmlessly to Earth, kilometer-size asteroids cannot. The public got a scare during the past year when the possibility of a collision with an asteroid was announced. In December 1997 James V. Scotti discovered a new asteroid as part of the ongoing program of the Spacewatch Project of the University of Arizona's Lunar and Planetary Laboratory. Asteroids are small rocky objects that orbit the Sun. The vast majority orbit between Mars and Jupiter, but a small percentage have paths that cross Earth's orbit, leading to the possibility of a collision. This new asteroid later received the designation of 1997 XF_{11}. By early March Brian Marsden of the Minor Planet Center in Cambridge, Mass., had calculated an orbit for 1997 XF_{11} that revealed the possibility of a collision with Earth in the year 2028.

A collision with even a small asteroid can be catastrophic. Such a collision 65 million years ago is believed to have triggered worldwide mass extinctions that terminated the reign of the dinosaurs. Asteroid 1997 XF_{11} was predicted to pass between Earth and the Moon in 2028 at a distance from Earth of approximately 45,000 km (28,000 mi). This was too close to rule out the possibility of a collision. The announcement received worldwide attention. All orbit calculations contain a certain amount of uncertainty, however, due to the limited precision of the observations on which they are based. Marsden called for more observations and searches of archival images that may have accidentally recorded the asteroid. The additional observations refined the orbital calculation and indicated that in 2028 the asteroid will safely miss Earth by approximately 950,000 km (590,000 mi).

Most schoolchildren know about Saturn and its beautiful ring system. Far fewer people are aware that Jupiter also has a ring system. Unlike Saturn, the rings of Jupiter are much darker and are very dif-

ficult to see from Earth. The rings of Saturn are composed of individual particles of ice, dust, and ice-covered rock, ranging in size from specks to a few meters in diameter. Each ring particle orbits the planet like a miniature moon. The ice causes the ring particles to be shiny and, therefore, easy to see from Earth. By contrast, the particles that make up Jupiter's rings are not very reflective and are only the size of smoke particles. On average they are spaced 30 m (100 ft) apart. Consequently, Jupiter's ring system was not discovered until the Voyager 1 space probe explored the planet in 1979. Since that time astronomers have wondered how the ring system is maintained. The orbits of particles this small are easily affected by magnetic fields, the solar wind, and the gravity of the Jovian moons. This should spread the particles both inward toward the

planet and outward into space. As a result, the ring system will disappear unless the ring particles are continuously replaced. It had been suggested that new dust is generated by the collisions of tiny (and still undetected) moons within the ring system.

By 1999 the mystery of the dust replenishment appeared to be solved. Joseph A. Burns, Maureen E. Bell, and Joseph Veverka of Cornell University, Ithaca, N.Y., studied new images of the ring system taken by the Galileo space probe orbiting Jupiter. They found a close coincidence between the radial and vertical extent of the ring system and the orbits of the Jovian moons Thebe, Amalthea, Adrastea, and Metis. Apparently micrometeorite impacts on those moons generate dust particles that easily escape the weak gravitation of the moons. In this way dust lost from the rings is continuously replaced.

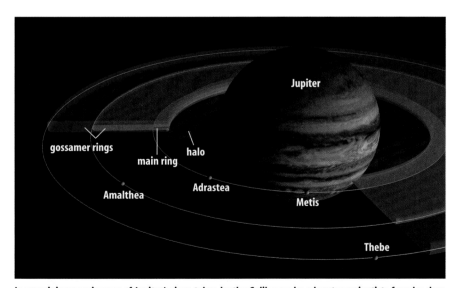

In examining new images of Jupiter's rings taken by the Galileo probe, planetary scientists found a close coincidence between the ring system and Jupiter's innermost moons. The rings appear to be replenished by dust from the moons, the orbits of which correspond to the rings' boundaries, as diagrammed above.

Stellar astronomy

The year 1998 marked a significant milestone in humanity's quest for knowledge. For the first time, astronomers knew of more planets existing outside our solar system than there are within it. By the year's end, 22 extrasolar planets were known to exist. Three of them orbit a single neutron star, and the remaining 19 orbit nearby sunlike stars. None of these planets has been seen directly; they are too small and faint. Instead, they were detected by their gravitational effect on the star they orbit. As a planet orbits a star, it pulls the star, causing it to move back and forth. Although this motion is extremely small because the star is very massive compared to the planet, the wavelengths of the starlight change as the star periodically moves toward and away from the observer. These wavelength changes are also very small and, until recently, were undetectable. Only the effects of massive planets, the size of Jupiter or more, can be seen. The masses of the planets found orbiting the sunlike stars range from 0.4 to 11 times that of Jupiter.

For most of these planets, the orbital periods are only a few days. This indicates that they orbit their stars very closely; all but a few have orbits smaller than Mercury's. This came as a surprise to astronomers, because in our solar system all the massive planets are found much farther from the Sun. The standard theoretical model for the formation of massive planets requires the presence of ice grains of water and methane. These cannot be found close to the central star. Thus, either these massive planets formed in a way very different from that posed by the theory, or

they formed farther from the star and then migrated inward. The latter situation could have been produced by a drag on the planet's orbital motion from friction with the dust in the disk that formed the planets.

Most of the planets of our solar system have very nearly circular orbits. Many of the newly discovered planets, however, have highly elliptical orbits. One way this could come about is if those solar systems began with several massive planets. In such a case, the gravitational interactions would have forced most planets into very large orbits or ejected them from the planetary system. The remaining planets would have small and highly elliptical orbits. The picture emerging from these observations, therefore, suggests that our solar system may be unusual. One reason may be that Jupiter's circular orbit prevents violent interactions and provides our solar system with a measure of stability.

While the number of known planetary systems has increased, so too has the number of suspected stars with planets in the making. Astronomers believe that planets form in flattened disks of dust and gas that surround young stars. The planets grow in the disk by gravitationally sweeping up nearby disk material. Evidence for this process exists. For more than a decade, astronomers have known that some stars are surrounded by dusty disks. They are visible in the infrared, where the warm disk glows brightly. The list of known pre-planetary disks is growing and with it the understanding of planetary formation. The star HD 141569 is a recent example. This young star is 320 light-years from Earth. Its disk was imaged with the infrared camera of the Hubble Space Telescope by Alycia Weinberger, Eric Becklin, Murray

Silverstone, and colleagues. The image revealed a disk 120 billion km (75 billion mi) across with a gap (about 6.5 billion km [4 billion mi] wide) dividing it into two parts. The most likely explanation is that the gap was cleared out by a planet forming in the disk. This protoplanet accreted the material from the gap and/or forced that matter into different orbits.

Another star, HR 4796A, also showed evidence of planets being formed. The Hubble Space Telescope image obtained by Brad Smith, Glenn Schneider, and colleagues revealed a narrow ring surrounding the star. Left to themselves, rings are unstable; the interaction of the particles causes the ring to spread into a broad band or disk. The narrow rings that have been detected in the solar system (around Uranus) have been maintained by the gravitational effects of small moons near the edges of the ring. Thus, the narrow dust ring surrounding the star HR 4796A strongly suggests the presence of planets near the ring. In addition, the youth of this star reveals that planets can form in less than 10 million years.

More than two decades ago, Earth satellites that had been launched by the U.S. to detect the gamma-ray emissions produced by testing nuclear weapons discovered, instead, bursts of gamma rays from deep space. These arrive at Earth at a rate of one or two per day and typically last for a few seconds to a few minutes. Their origin has been a mystery. For many years it was not clear if these events took place comparatively near Earth and were of relatively low energy or were very distant and tremendously energetic. In 1997 and 1998 several gamma-ray bursters were found to have a faint counterpart in visible light. In several

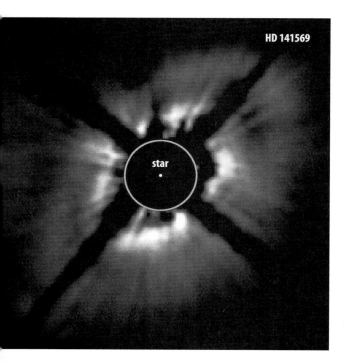

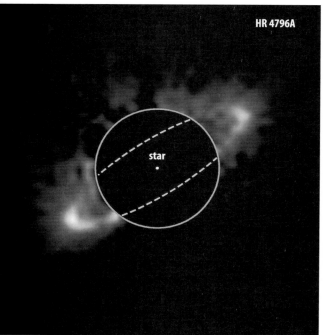

Using the Hubble Space Telescope, astronomers imaged a dusty disk around star HD 141569 (top). The disk had a gap that suggested the presence of a forming planet. Hubble's image of a second star, HR 4796A, revealed a narrow ring (above), an inherently unstable configuration that is likely being maintained by planets orbiting near the ring.

B. Smith (University of Hawaii), G. Schneider (University of Arizona), E. Becklin & A. Weinberger (UCLA) NASA/Newell Color Lab Inc.

cases, optical astronomers found a faint, fading point of light imbedded in a very distant galaxy. New images of some earlier burst locations revealed galaxies that had not been orignally detected. Consequently, the origin of gamma-ray bursters in external galaxies now seems established, though the source of their energy is not.

Because they are detectable over distances of millions of light-years, gamma-ray bursters are the most powerful explosions known in the universe, 10–100 times that of a supernova. The bursters are also smaller than our solar system because they fluctuate in brightness on a time scale of just minutes. An early explanation of a burster was that it involved the collision of a pair of neutron stars orbiting in a binary star system. Neutron stars are believed to be the highly compressed cores of stars produced in supernova explosions. They have the mass of the Sun compressed to an object only 10–20 km (6–12 mi) in diameter. The general theory of relativity predicts that binary neutron stars will lose orbital energy by emitting gravitational radiation and will slowly spiral together. The merger would be a titanic event that forms a black hole. Even this energetic event, however,

may not be enough to explain the strongest bursters. In a new model proposed by Wlodzimierz Kluzniak of the University of Wisconsin-Madison and Malvin A. Ruderman of Columbia University, New York City, the energy of the bursters comes from intense magnetic fields in neutron stars. In their concept, a neutron star with a magnetic field of 1,017 gauss has an interior that spins 1,000 times per second faster than its solid crust. (The gauss is a unit of magnetic flux density; Earth's magnetic field is about one gauss.) This process causes the magnetic field lines of force to wind up like a clock spring. Like a spring that breaks, these field lines explosively expand into space. The authors claim that this process can account for the energy release of even the strongest bursters. The test of this and other models will require follow-up observations with ground- and space-based telescopes.

Introductory astronomy students are taught that stars are members of galaxies. The possibility of isolated stars existing outside of galaxies in intergalactic space is rarely, if ever, raised. Several recent studies, however, indicated the existence of a substantial population of stars between the galaxies. Individual stars in intergalactic space are very distant and very difficult to see with ground-based telescopes. To detect them, Roberto H. Mendez of the Munich (Ger.) University Observatory and colleagues looked for some-

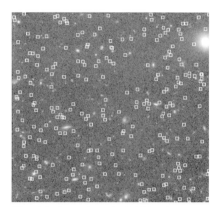

(Above) An image from the Hubble telescope shows many of the several hundred red-giant stars (boxes) found in a dark region of the Virgo Cluster of galaxies. The telescope also captured a portrait of the distant host galaxy of Gamma Ray Burst 971214 (below, marked with arrow) four months after the burst was detected.

thing else. When low-mass stars like our Sun age, they pass through a brief phase during which they shed their outer atmospheres and produce planetary nebulas. These clouds emit all their light in discrete emission lines rather than across the entire spectrum, causing them to be very bright at those wavelengths. It is possible to detect planetary nebulas at very great distances with images taken with filters tuned to those wavelengths. In this way, the researchers found planetary nebulas in the "blank" regions between the galaxies of the Virgo cluster of galaxies. Since planetary nebulas make up only a small fraction of the stellar population, the researchers concluded that there must be many stars in intergalactic space. This was confirmed by Harry Ferguson of the Space Telescope Science Institute, Baltimore, Md., and colleagues who used the Hubble telescope to find a few hundred red-giant stars in a dark region of the same cluster.

Many of the stars in intergalactic space probably once belonged to a galaxy. Collisions and near collisions of galaxies are rather common in galaxy clusters. The result is that large swarms of stars are teased from the galaxies. This is evident in many photographs. The surprise, however, was that the new studies indicated that there might be almost as many stars between galaxies as there are within them.

Extragalactic astronomy

In the 1920s astronomer Edwin Hubble discovered that the light from almost all galaxies is red-shifted, or displaced toward longer wavelengths. This indicates that the galaxies are receding from our galaxy, the Milky Way. Furthermore, the more distant the galaxy, the faster it is receding. Simply put, the universe is expanding. The distances between galaxies and galaxy clusters are increasing with time. The rate of expansion, H_0, is today called the Hubble constant. The expansion of the universe implies that in the past everything was much closer together. The universe must have been much denser and hotter. The expansion, and our universe, began from that state. This is the basic idea of the big-bang theory.

Much of modern cosmology has been devoted to determining two numbers, the Hubble constant and the deceleration parameter. The Hubble constant is important because it tells the age of the universe. By knowing the rate of expansion, astronomers can calculate the time required for our region of the universe to grow from a single point to its present size. The deceleration parameter measures the slowing of the expansion due to the gravitational attraction of the galaxies on each other. If the deceleration parameter is small, it indicates that the universe will expand forever. If the deceleration parameter is large, the universe will eventually collapse.

Both these important constants have been exceptionally difficult to measure well. The key to determining the parameters of both is to measure the distances and speeds of the farthest visible galaxies. The speeds can be determined by using the Doppler shifts in the spectra of the galaxies, but the distances have been difficult to obtain. In recent years, however, significant progress has been made. Two international groups, one led by Brian Schmidt of Mount Stromlo and Siding Spring Observatories in Australia and the other by Saul Perlmutter of the Lawrence Berkeley

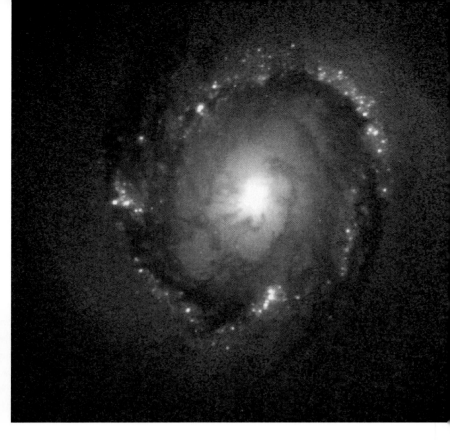

(Below and right) G. Fritz Benedict, Andrew Howell, Inger Jorgensen, David Chapell (University of Texas), Jeffery Kenney (Yale University), Beverly J. Smith (CASA, University of Colorado), and NASA/Space Telescope Science Institute

The barred-spiral galaxy NGC 4314 (below) is shown in a ground-based telescopic image. In the past year astronomers presented a close-up image of the galaxy's core (right), taken by the Hubble Space Telescope, that reveals a ring of clusters of infant stars (bluish-purple knots). This stellar nursery formed within the past five million years and appears to be the only place in the galaxy where new stars are being born.

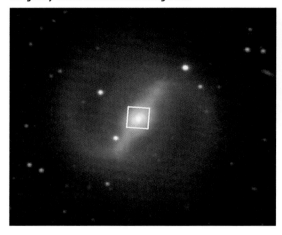

National Laboratory in California, used a class of supernovas as a standard for determining distance. These exploding stars are extremely consistent in their luminosity. If a galaxy contains one of these stars, the distance to it can be computed from the supernova's apparent brightness and its known luminosity.

Based on these measurements, preliminary estimates of the deceleration parameter indicated that the universe is open and will expand forever. In addition, the deceleration parameter indicated that the expansion of the universe is accelerating rather than slowing down. This requires a repulsive force to drive the expansion of space. Albert Einstein once considered such a force. At the time that he finished his general theory of relativity, the universe was thought to be static. His theory predicted that the universe must either expand or contract. To achieve consistency with a sta-

tic universe, he added to his equations a repulsive force term called the cosmological constant. This force prevented the galaxies from falling inward toward each other. When the expansion of the universe was discovered, Einstein dropped the term, referring to it as his "greatest blunder."

By 1999, however, the cosmological constant was being revived to explain two problems. The first was the (still tentative) observation of an accelerating universe. The second was that inflationary theory, the currently favored version of the big-bang theory, predicts that the universe should be perfectly balanced between open and closed. This is called the flat universe. The density of matter and energy determines whether the universe is open, closed, or flat. Measurements taken by researchers indicated only about 0.3 of the needed density for a flat universe. While this finding was consistent with the recent determination of the deceleration parameter, cosmologists were reluctant to abandon the inflationary model because it had been so successful in other areas.

A way out of this problem is that the energy density of the universe has been underestimated. The physics of subatomic particles views the vacuum of space as anything but empty and featureless. Instead, at every instant throughout space, subatomic particle pairs of matter and antimatter instantaneously pop into existence. To produce these particles, energy is "borrowed" from the vacuum. This violates no laws of nature as long as the particles combine and are converted back to energy in a very tiny fraction of a second. Because the vacuum has this property, it also has an energy density and so will produce the repulsive effect required by the cosmological constant. This could both explain the observed acceleration of the expanding universe and provide the energy density necessary to make the universe flat. By early 1999, however, researchers had not succeeded in deriving the size of the deceleration parameter from the theory of the vacuum energy. This remained an important unsolved problem for cosmology.

—Ronald H. Kaitchuck
See also Feature Article: BAD SCIENCE.

CHEMISTRY

During the year chemists made important advances in the pursuit of mild chemical reactions, modeled after biological processes, that convert atmospheric nitrogen into useful nitrogen compounds. They also prepared a propeller-shaped molecule and, using scanning tunneling microscopy, observed it rotating on a surface like a ball in a bearing—a potentially important step in the development of molecular machines. Several anti-impotence drugs in addition to Viagra were developed or made available; a new "heart healthy" fat substitute called Nu-Trim appeared; and a variety of improved adhesives were announced, including one, intended for wound dressings, that is deactivated by light.

INORGANIC CHEMISTRY

Bioinorganic chemistry

Enzymes are biological catalysts that carry out many types of chemical reactions in living systems. (A catalyst is a chemical compound that speeds up a reaction but is not consumed during the process.) They are built from large protein molecules having exquisitely complicated three-dimensional structures. Frequently the enzyme structure includes one or more metal ions that provide the essential reactivity of the enzyme. Such a system is called a metalloenzyme.

Chemists would like to synthesize metal compounds of low molecular weight that faithfully reproduce the catalytic reactions promoted by the naturally occurring high-molecular-weight systems. Nevertheless, because of the complicated structures of metalloenzymes and the uncertainties about how the surrounding protein structure affects re-

Copper Active Site in Galactose Oxidase

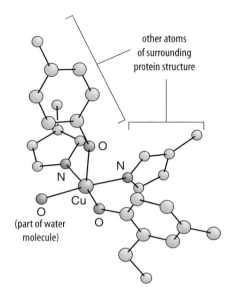

other atoms of surrounding protein structure

N

O

N

Cu

O

O

(part of water molecule)

activity at the metal site, they have found the task difficult. Interest in understanding how metalloenzymes promote chemical reactions is more than academic; the development of new industrial chemical processes that are inspired by efficient enzyme-based reactions promise considerable economic benefits. In particular, reactions that are promoted by synthetic metal compounds modeled after metalloenzymes should operate at moderate temperatures in water or another benign solvent and, therefore, should consume less energy and be more environmentally friendly than traditional reactions.

In the past year, a research team headed by chemist Daniel Stack of Stanford University reported the synthesis of a copper complex that reproduces the essential reactivity of galactose oxidase, a copper-containing enzyme that oxidizes alcohols to aldehydes while reducing molecular oxygen (O_2) to hydrogen peroxide. An earlier

crystallographic determination of the structure of galactose oxidase had demonstrated that the protein backbone binds a copper(II) ion (copper in the +2 oxidation state) by means of two oxygen atoms and two nitrogen atoms. The oxygen atom of a water molecule forms a fifth bond to copper, and the atoms bonded to copper are arranged in a square pyramidal form. The Stanford chemists were able to mimic this unusual geometry by preparing the copper(II) complex shown in the upper portion of the illustration below. The ligand (the molecule providing the atoms that bond to the metal

Proposed Catalytic Cycle for Galactose Oxidase Model Complex

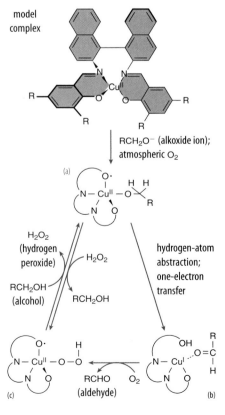

model complex

RCH_2O^- (alkoxide ion); atmospheric O_2

(a)

hydrogen-atom abstraction; one-electron transfer

H_2O_2 (hydrogen peroxide)

H_2O_2

RCH_2OH (alcohol)

RCH_2OH

(c)

RCHO (aldehyde)

O_2

(b)

239

atom) in the model complex was specifically designed to create the same type of geometry around the copper atom that was observed in the crystal structure of galactose oxidase.

When the model complex is allowed to react with an alkoxide ion—an anion derived by the removal of a proton (a hydrogen ion, H^+) from an alcohol—in the presence of atmospheric oxygen, a copper(II) alkoxide radical compound is formed (structure a in the illustration). A radical is a compound with an unpaired electron, and in this radical species, the unpaired electron is delocalized on the six-membered carbon ring bonded to one of the copper-coordinated oxygen atoms. The radical compound then undergoes a hydrogen abstraction reaction in which a carbon-hydrogen bond of the alkoxide is broken to form a copper-bonded aldehyde group (b). During this step, a new oxygen-hydrogen bond is thought to form, and the copper(II) ion is reduced to copper(I) (+1 oxidation state). In the next step, the copper(I) compound reacts with O_2; the result is the displacement of the copper-bound aldehyde and the formation of a copper-bound hydroperoxide group through oxidation of the metal atom from copper(I) to copper(II) and concomitant transfer of a hydrogen atom (c). The final step of the catalytic sequence involves displacement of the hydroperoxide group by an alcohol molecule, producing a molecule of hydrogen peroxide (H_2O_2) and restoring the copper(II) alkoxide radical species (a) for another reaction cycle. Although reaction rates measured for the model complex were too slow to be useful for preparative chemistry, its exhibited reactivity is remarkably like that of galactose oxidase. Based on the success and promise

demonstrated in this model system, the mimicry of useful enzyme reactivity patterns by enzyme analogs of low molecular weight will continue to be an active and important area of research.

Advance in nitrogen fixation

Molecular nitrogen (N_2) makes up about 78% of Earth's atmosphere and, therefore, represents a potentially large source of nitrogen atoms for applications in chemical synthesis. Unfortunately, N_2 is extremely inert, and very few reactions are known that fix it—convert it to useful compounds—in a cost-effective manner. At present, ammonia (NH_3) is prepared industrially from N_2 using the Haber-Bosch process, an energy-intensive reaction between nitrogen and hydrogen molecules at high temperatures. NH_3 and other nitrogen compounds are important industrial chemicals and are used to make more complicated compounds ranging from drugs and fertilizers to rocket fuels. Remarkably, some bacteria are able to convert N_2 to useful nitrogen compounds at ambient temperature and pressure by means of an iron-molybdenum-sulfur enzyme called nitrogenase. Whereas the mechanism of N_2 fixation by the nitrogenase enzyme is still being unraveled, the existence of such a mild process for converting N_2 to nitrogen compounds has inspired several generations of inorganic chemists to pursue new methods of fixing N_2. Despite years of study, however, chemists have not been able to devise an efficient metal-catalyzed process that converts N_2 to NH_3 or other useful nitrogen compounds. Development of such a process would be a monumental achievement and could provide a low-cost

and environmentally friendly route to low-molecular-weight nitrogen compounds.

A significant report in the past year brought chemists one step closer to this goal. A research team led by Masanobu Hidai of the University of Tokyo described a tungsten complex bonded to an N_2 molecule that reacts with molecular hydrogen (H_2) in the presence of a ruthenium complex to afford moderate yields (up to 55%) of NH_3. It had been known from previous work that the starting ruthenium compound reacts with H_2 to yield a new ruthenium compound with a coordinated H_2 molecule and that this new compound is acidic enough to serve as a source of protons. Indeed, Hidai found that the compound would transfer protons to the tungsten-N_2 compound at room temperature to form tungsten compounds with new nitrogen-hydrogen groups and, ultimately, free NH_3.

The study has several important implications. The mild conditions of the experiments, done at room temperature and atmospheric pressure, are in stark contrast to the high temperatures and pressures required for the Haber-Bosch process. A room-temperature, atmospheric-pressure metal-catalyzed process for the production of NH_3 would significantly drop the price of this important chemical feedstock and could reduce the environmental impact of the manufacture of NH_3. Additionally, demonstration of a ruthenium-H_2 compound as the proton-transfer reagent suggests that cheap and abundant H_2 gas can be used as the hydrogen source in reactions that are catalyzed by transition-metal compounds. Finally, the results of Hidai's study raise the interesting possibility that the nitrogenase enzyme in bacteria also uses H_2 as a reagent in the fixation of N_2.

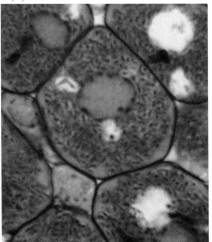

(Left) M.W. Kellogg Company; (right) Carolina Biological Supply Company/Phototake

An industrial Haber-Bosch plant (left) and the bacteria that pack the root-nodule cells of legumes (above) have in common the ability to fix atmospheric nitrogen, although the bacterial approach is far superior. In the past year chemists made significant strides in their work to develop nitrogen-fixing processes modeled more closely on nature.

These and other issues relating to the metal-promoted production of NH_3 from N_2 are certain to come under intensive study in the future. (For more information on nitrogen fixation research, *see* APPLIED CHEMISTRY, below.)

New molecules

One of the great discoveries of recent years has been the isolation and structural understanding of fullerenes, which are all-carbon molecules having a hollow spherical cage structure. Intense worldwide research activity beginning in the mid-1980s has resulted in the characterization of many new fullerenes and a deeper understanding of the properties of this form of carbon and its compounds. Despite the isolation and characterization of many fullerenes, which

have even numbers of carbon atoms ranging from 32 (C_{32}) up to several hundred, some members have not been prepared in macroscopic quantities. In particular, C_{72} and C_{74} were thought to be unstable and highly reactive structures.

In the past year, a research team headed by Hisanori Shinohara of Nagoya University in Japan reported the synthesis and characterization of C_{72} and C_{74} in which a calcium atom is contained in the hollow core of each of the carbon spheres. (These atom-in-a-cage structures are represented by the notations $Ca@C_{72}$ and $Ca@C_{74}$, respectively.) Remarkably, $Ca@C_{72}$ and $Ca@C_{74}$ are stable and soluble and were obtained as pure compounds after separation from other fullerenes that were produced in the synthesis. The fact that they could be isolated demonstrated

that the presence of the caged metal atom stabilizes the otherwise reactive structures. Theoretical work by the Shinohara team suggested that two electrons from the calcium atom are transferred to the fullerene cage structure, stabilizing it against further reactivity. The results of the study suggested that as-yet-unprepared fullerenes likewise may be stabilized by incorporation of metal atoms inside the carbon cages.

Unexpected explosions of chemical compounds are among the most frightening and dangerous situations that chemists can face. In spite of this threat, a research team headed by Roland A. Fischer of the University of Bochum, Ger., described a remarkable study in which nanometer-sized particles of gallium nitride, an important semiconductor material, were produced by the deliberate and carefully controlled detonation of gallium compounds bonded to azide ($N=N=N^-$) ions. (A nanometer is a billionth of a meter.) Compounds of metals with azide ions are frequently explosive and dangerous to handle because they readily release N_2, which in a confined space can build rapidly to high pressure. Fischer and co-workers managed to prepare gallium azide compounds that were stable enough to be handled safely at room temperature. On rapid heating in sturdy, sealed steel cylinders, the gallium azide compounds exploded safely to afford nanometer-sized particles of gallium nitride, along with N_2 and other gaseous products. Isolated in the powdery residues of these explosions, the gallium nitride particles were shown to have properties characteristic of high-quality materials. The success of the study implied that controlled detonation of explosive compounds may offer new and interesting routes to desirable materials.

Among the significant paradigm shifts that have taken place recently in chemistry is the realization that even the most weakly basic organic functional groups are capable of bonding to transition metal atoms. This new understanding has profound implications for reactive processes that are promoted by metal complexes, since many solvents and reactants that were previously thought to be noncoordinating may actually play significant roles in a reaction by bonding weakly to metal compounds at critical points in the reaction sequence.

Arguably the most interesting weakly basic potential ligands for metal atoms are alkanes (compounds of carbon and hydrogen atoms joined by single bonds), because they should form extremely weak bonds to metals. Their coordination to

metals could pave the way for new mild reactions that would convert the alkanes, normally among the least reactive of organic molecules, into more reactive compounds. Such reactions are difficult or impossible to carry out with current chemical methodology. Alkanes are abundantly available from crude oil, and metal-catalyzed processes for converting them to more useful products would be highly desirable. Although indirect evidence for alkane coordination has increased steadily in recent years, stable and experimentally observable metal-alkane compounds have remained poorly characterized and elusive.

A recent report from the research group of Graham E. Ball of the University of New South Wales, Sydney, Australia, described the generation and direct characterization of a rhenium compound that contains an alkane, a cyclopentane (C_5H_{10}) molecule, bonded to the rhenium atom. Because the rhenium-C_5H_{10} compound was stable only at low temperatures, a key innovation in Ball's work was the construction of an apparatus that allowed the compound to be generated and studied spectroscopcally at $-80°$ C ($-176°$ F). The Australian workers used carbon and proton nuclear magnetic resonance (NMR) spectroscopy to characterize the rhenium-C_5H_{10} compound—the first such characterization of the bonding be-

tween a metal and an alkane. The study should serve to inspire new thinking about metal-alkane complexes and promote new work in the area. It appears to be just a question of time before stable metal-alkane compounds are actually isolated.

—Charles H. Winter

ORGANIC CHEMISTRY

Fullerene research

Chemists have synthesized a wide variety of fullerene molecules since 1990, when the soccer-ball-shaped, 60-carbon molecule buckminsterfullerene (C_{60}), the first member of this new family of carbon molecules, was produced in large quantities. All of the fullerene molecules structurally characterized during the period, however, have had a minimum of 60 carbon atoms. Some chemists argued that C_{60} was the smallest fullerene stable enough to be synthesized in bulk quantities. During the year Alex Zettl and colleagues of the University of California, Berkeley, overturned that notion with the synthesis of the "minifullerene" C_{36}. They used the arc-discharge method, in which an electric arc across two graphite electrodes produces large quantities of fullerenes.

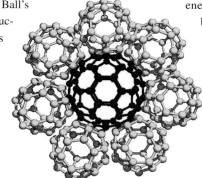

A computer model shows the fullerene molecule C_{60} surrounded by seven C_{36} "minifullerenes." In 1998 chemists at the University of California, Berkeley, reported their success in synthesizing C_{36} in bulk quantities, overturning the notion that the molecule might be too unstable to make the feat possible.

The bonding in C_{36}, like that in C_{60}, comprises three-dimensional arrangements of hexagons and pentagons, with the minimum possible number of shared pentagon–pentagon bonds.

Nuclear magnetic resonance measurements indicated that the adjacent pentagons are highly strained in the fullerene's tightly bound molecular structure. Theorists speculated that the bond strain is so severe that C_{36} would likely prove to be the smallest fullerene to be made in bulk quantities. The extreme strain may also turn out to enhance the molecule's superconducting properties. Like C_{60}, C_{36} displays increased electrical conductivity when doped with alkali metals. Zettl speculated that C_{36} may prove to be a high-temperature superconductor with a higher transition temperature than that of C_{60}. (For other fullerene research, see *Inorganic Chemistry,* above.)

Polymer chemistry

Polyethylene's great versatility makes it the single most popular plastic in the world. Although all polyethylene is made from repeating units of the same building-block molecule, the monomer ethylene, catalysts used in the polymerization process have dramatic effects on the physical properties of the plastic. Mixing ethylene with certain catalysts yields a polymer with long, straight, tough molecular chains termed high-density polyethylene (HDPE). HDPE is used to make plastic bottles, pipes, industrial drums, grocery bags, and other high-strength products. A different catalyst causes ethylene to polymerize into a more flexible but weaker material, low-density polyethylene (LDPE). LDPE is used for beverage-carton coatings, food packaging, cling wrap, trash bags, and other products.

American and British chemists, working independently, reported discovery of a new group of iron- and cobalt-based catalysts for polymerizing ethylene. Experts described the discovery as one of the first fundamentally new advances in the field since the 1970s. The catalysts were as active as the organometallic catalysts called metallocenes in current use for HDPE production—in some instances more active. They also had potential for producing a wider range of polymer materials at lower cost. In addition, the iron-based catalysts were substantially more active than current materials for the production of LDPE. Maurice Brookhart of the University of North Carolina at Chapel Hill headed the U.S. research team. Vernon C. Gibson of Imperial College, London, led the British group.

A "green" synthesis

Adipic acid is the raw material needed for production of nylon, which is used in fabrics, carpets, tire reinforcements, automobile parts, and myriad other products. In the late 1990s about 2.2 million metric tons of adipic acid were produced worldwide each year, which made it one of the most important industrial chemicals. Conventional adipic acid manufacture involves the use of nitric acid to oxidize cyclohexanol or cyclohexanone. Growing interest in environmentally more benign chemical reactions, often called green chemistry, is making the traditional synthesis undesirable because it produces nitrous oxide as a by-product. Nitrous oxide is believed to contribute to depletion of stratospheric ozone and, as a greenhouse gas, to global warming. Despite the adoption of recovery and recycling technology for nitrous oxide, about 400,000 metric tons are released to the atmosphere annually. Adipic acid production accounts for 5–8% of nitrous oxide released into the atmosphere through human activity.

Kazuhiko Sato and associates at Nagoya (Japan) University reported development of a new, "green" synthetic pathway to adipic acid. It eliminated production of nitrous oxide and the use of potentially harmful organic solvents. Their alternative synthesis used 30% hydrogen peroxide to oxidize cyclohexene directly to colorless crystalline adipic acid under solvent- and halide-free conditions. Sato reported that the process is suitable for use on an industrial scale and could be the answer to the worldwide quest for a "green" method of synthesizing adipic acid. The major barrier is cost—hydrogen peroxide is substantially more expensive than nitric acid—but stricter environmental regulations on nitrous oxide emission could make the new synthetic process more attractive.   —Michael Woods

Chemotherapeutic advances

In the year in which the male anti-impotence drug Viagra made its appearance (*see* Year in Review: MEDICAL SCIENCES: *General Medicine*), a major focus of organic chemistry, appropriately, was the development and synthesis of biologically important molecules, including more efficacious drugs. Gary H. Posner of Johns Hopkins University, Baltimore, Md., synthesized a new generation of antimalaria drugs, based on the natural plant product artemisinin, that is cheaper and more eas-

CHEMISTRY

1 Viagra (sildenafil)

2 papaverine

3 prostaglandin E₁

ily synthesized than others currently available. Paul A. Wender of Stanford University designed molecules that have a simpler structure and greater activity than the important anticancer agent bryostatin, a natural product derived from a marine invertebrate.

A variety of anti-impotence drugs in addition to Viagra (sildenafil; *see* 1) were synthesized and in clinical trials or made available for use. They include papaverine (*see* 2), prostaglandin E₁ (*see* 3), phentolamine (*see* 4), and apomorphine (*see* 5). Several other compounds also were under investigation as impotence remedies.

Taxoids are derivatives of the natural product taxol, a powerful anticancer agent first isolated from the bark of the Pacific yew. During the year Iwao Ojima of the State University of New York at Stony Brook incorporated fluorine into taxoids, designing a second generation of drugs with stronger cell-killing effects and better tumor specificity than existing taxoids. Daniel Kahne of Princeton University developed a strategy to alter the terminal disaccharide (a molecule composed of two linked molecules of simple sugars) of the antibiotic vancomycin. The advance may lead to antibiotics with increased activity against bacteria that have become resistant to vancomycin. An epilepsy drug, vigabatrin (*see* 6), was shown in animals to suppress the effects of nicotine that make it addictive. The drug was also found to stem the buildup of extracellular dopamine in baboon brains following cocaine intake,

which suggests that vigabatrin may be useful in treating cocaine addiction.

Catalysts and catalytic processes

Alois Fürstner and Günter Seidel of the Max Planck Institute of Coal Research, Mülheim/Ruhr, Ger., developed an olefin metathesis reaction that uses a tungsten alkylidyne complex developed by Richard R. Schrock of the Massachusetts Institute of Technology (MIT) to generate macrocyclic rings of the kind that are present in many important organic molecules. Wolfgang A. Herrmann of the Technical University of Munich, Ger., reported a new class of catalysts for olefin metathesis that contain an alkylidene group and two nitrogen-containing heterocyclic carbenes attached as ligands to ruthenium. Shrock and Amir H. Hoveyda of Boston College discovered an asymmetric ring-closing metathesis of acyclic diolefins using a chiral molybdenum catalyst.

A new, nontraditional catalytic process developed during the year involved zeolites, inorganic compounds of great value as catalytic molecular sieves. Zeolites possess a crystalline structure riddled with tiny pores and voids, which select for reactants or products of a particular size and shape. Mark E. Davis of the California Institute of Technology (Caltech), Pasadena, developed a technique to modify the catalytic activity of zeolites by coating their interior with organic groups.

Shu Kobayashi of the Science University of Tokyo immobilized the water-soluble Lewis acid scandium trifluoromethane-

sulfonate by way of microencapsulation and found it to be recoverable and reusable. The scandium compound is trapped in little beads that can be added to a reaction, filtered off when the reaction is done, and then used again. The catalyst proved to be effective in many useful carbon–carbon bond-forming reactions.

Richard A. Lerner and co-workers of the Scripps Research Institute in La Jolla, Calif., used a catalytic antibody called 38C2 to prepare intermediates to epothilones—which currently are exciting anticancer-drug prospects—by catalyzing the kinetic resolution of the racemic mixture of a compound into one of its enantiomers. (The molecules of some compounds can exist as mirror-image structural arrangements, or enantiomers, of one another. A sample of the compound in which its two enantiomers are present in equal amounts is called a racemic mixture.)

Synthesis of complex molecules

The total synthesis of important organic molecules is always of major importance. In addition to some of the chemotherapeutic agents described above, there were several important advances in the synthesis of natural products. K.C. Nicolaou of the Scripps Research Institute completed a total synthesis of brevetoxin A, one of the toxins produced by the single-celled organisms responsible for discolorations of seawater called red tides. Chemists reported three independent syntheses of dysidiolide, a potential anticancer compound isolated from a marine sponge. Dysidiolide was the only known natural inhibitor of a protein phosphatase called cdc25A, which is involved in a signaling system for cell

4 phentolamine

division. Jeffrey D. Winkler of the University of Pennsylvania completed a synthesis of another sponge-derived compound, manzamine A. The compound, one of the most complex polycyclic alkaloids known, has a structure that includes a rare 13-membered ring.

Peripheral areas

Many different scientific endeavors are influenced by organic chemistry. James K. Gimzewski of the IBM Zürich Research Laboratory in Switzerland and co-workers prepared a propeller-shaped molecule, hexa-*tert*-butyl-decacyclene, and made it function as a molecular rotor. When deposited as a single layer completely covering a copper surface, the molecules in the layer are immobilized by interactions with each other. Less-complete surface coverage, however, creates a random array of tiny voids. Scanning tunneling microscopy revealed that individual loose molecules present within the voids spin spontaneously like a rotor in a bearing. The molecular rotors can be switched between spinning and immobilized states by moving the rotor axis only a quarter of a nanometer (billionth of a meter). The achievement may be important to the future development of miniature gears, motors, and other molecular-based mechanical devices. (For further information on molecular rotors, see *Physical Chemistry*, below.)

Seth R. Marder and Joseph W. Perry of Caltech and the University of Arizona prepared a series of organic molecules (*p*-diphenylamino stilbene derivatives, linked by a dicyanobenzene styryl unit) that have a high probability of absorbing

5 apomorphine

two photons from intense laser pulses. These molecules were expected to be useful in three-dimensional optical-data-storage applications, photonics, and biological studies.

A new method for detecting explosives was based on work by Timothy M. Swager of MIT, who developed a robust chemical sensor for TNT based on a porous fluorescent polymer containing pentiptycene units. The units form voids that trap TNT molecules present as vapor in the air. As the TNT is trapped, the fluorescence of the molecule diminishes—a change that can be converted into a detection signal. The polymer was incorporated into a portable prototype device for finding land mines. A very practical observation made by Peter V. Coveney while working at Schlumberger Cambridge Research in the U.K. showed that macrocyclic organophosphonate compounds delay the onset of setting of cement slurries without altering the properties of the cement when set.

Awards

The American Chemical Society's (ACS's) prestigious Priestley Medal was presented to Ronald Breslow of Columbia University, New York City. Breslow was honored for his pioneering research in physical and bioorganic chemistry—in particular, biomimetic chemistry, which involves studying biochemical systems such as enzymes and mimicking their

6 vigabatrin

reactions—as well as his lifelong commitment to chemistry education.

Ralph F. Hirschmann of the University of Pennsylvania won the ACS Arthur C. Cope Award for his contributions to peptide and medicinal chemistry. Over the past decade Hirschmann's research has involved the design and synthesis of peptidomimetics, chemical compounds that retain the biologically active properties of peptides (small proteins) but are not degraded by digestive enzymes when ingested. The work has led to the development of drugs, including one for treating HIV infection, that can be administered orally instead of by injection.

Albert A. Carr, a retired pharmaceutical chemist with Hoechst Marion Roussel, received the Perkin Medal, awarded by the Society of Chemical Industry to scientists and engineers who have made significant contributions in applied chemistry. In his almost 40-year career Carr developed a number of important medicinal compounds, including the antihistamines terfenadine (Seldane) and fexofenadine (Allegra). —Michael B. Smith

PHYSICAL CHEMISTRY

Views of one molecule spinning

The power of the scanning tunneling microscope (STM) to reveal atomic-level details became increasingly apparent in 1998 when it provided exciting images of single molecules that rotate on a surface like a ball in a bearing. The STM passes a small electric current between a surface and a very sharp metal tip by means of a quantum-mechanical effect known as tunneling.

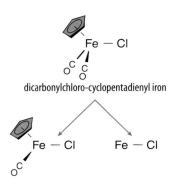

dicarbonylchloro-cyclopentadienyl iron

Figure 1 (left): The structures of *cis*-2-butene and *trans*-2-butene are compared.

Figure 2 (right): Two reaction pathways are shown for dicarbonylchloro-cyclopentadienyl iron. Either the iron atom (Fe) loses only a CO group, or it loses all but the chlorine atom (Cl).

CH₃ group structures:

cis-2-butene   *trans*-2-butene

As the tip passes over a molecule, the tunneling current varies with the nature of the atoms making up the molecule and can be used to construct an image of the surface and the adsorbed molecule with atomic-level resolution.

The IBM Zürich Research Laboratory in Rüschlikon, Switz., the birthplace of the STM, was once again the center of activity. A team from IBM led by James K. Gimzewski collaborated with researchers from the National Center for Scientific Research, Toulouse, France, and the Risø National Laboratory in Denmark to construct a single-molecule "rotor" that turns inside a "bearing" made up of other like molecules. The molecule in question had a core made up of twisted rings of carbon atoms and six bulky hydrocarbon groups that stuck out somewhat like a propeller. The researchers deposited the molecule on a cold copper surface and imaged the surface using an STM. When the surface was completely covered with a layer one molecule deep, the molecules were locked in position in a two-dimensional crystalline array, and the six tips of the "propellers" of each molecule could be separately seen in an STM image. At slightly lower coverages, individual molecules that happened to lie in small voids in the array could be imaged only as a doughnut shape. This change was attributed to the molecule's rotating faster than the STM could follow inside a bearing made of its neighbors. Such a dry, wear-free bearing may be an important step in the development of molecular machines.

Other STM experiments that observed the rotation of a single molecule on a surface were performed by Barry Stipe, Mohammad Rezaei, and Wilson Ho of Cornell University, Ithaca, N.Y. They saw that a diatomic oxygen molecule (O_2) adsorbed on a very cold platinum surface would rotate by 120° on being shocked by a small voltage pulse from the STM itself.

Researchers at the Canadian National Research Council's Steacie Institute for Molecular Sciences, Ottawa, showed one more facet of the STM's ability to image single molecules. G.P. Lopinski, R.A. Wolkow, D.J. Moffat, and D.D.M. Wayner adsorbed two very similar molecules on a silicon surface. The two molecules were isomers of each other—that is, they had the same overall chemical composition, but the atoms in the molecules were arranged in space differently. In this case, the researchers used *cis*-2-butene and *trans*-2-butene (*see* Figure 1), which differ by the arrangement of methyl (CH_3–) groups around the central double bond. The STM clearly differentiated between the two molecules. One molecular image showed these groups both on one side of the molecule (*cis*), and another image showed the groups on opposite sides (*trans*).

Lasers that learn chemistry

A holy grail of physical chemistry is to be able to make and break bonds selectively to produce exactly the desired products in a chemical reaction. Usually, heat is used to supply the energy for chemical reactions. Unfortunately, that heat energy is available to reaction pathways other than the one desired; the result is often a mixture of desirable and unwanted products. For many years chemists have regarded lasers as a way to inject energy into just the part of the molecule that they wish to react, by means of selective absorption of the laser light, but nature has defeated the most straightforward attempts by quickly redistributing the energy to other places in the molecule.

One of the most promising newer approaches is known as coherent control, in which the wavelength and timing of pulses from a very fast (short-pulse) laser are continuously tuned to favor a particular reaction pathway. G. Gerber and seven colleagues of the University of Würzburg, Ger., used a computer-controlled laser to pulse very short bursts of light at a beam of molecules of the compound dicarbonylchloro-cyclopentadienyl iron ($C_5H_5Fe(CO)_2Cl$). This molecule can react in two ways (*see* Figure 2), either via the breaking of an Fe–CO bond,

$$C_5H_5Fe(CO)_2Cl \rightarrow C_5H_5Fe(CO)Cl^+,$$

or via a process in which only the Fe–Cl bond remains intact,

$$C_5H_5Fe(CO)_2Cl \rightarrow FeCl^+.$$

These researchers observed the production of the two products and fed this information back to the laser computer in a feedback loop. A special "evolutionary algorithm" in the computer software then learned the best pattern of laser pulses to force the reaction along one pathway or the other.

A different approach to understanding the details of chemical reactions came from A. Welford Castleman, Jr., Daniel E. Folmer, Eric Wisniewski, and Lutz Poth of Pennsylvania State University, who used a technique developed by atomic physicists called a Coulomb explosion to

Depicted in this artist's conceptualization is a Coulomb explosion, wherein an intense laser beam causes a molecule to become multiply charged and then abruptly fly apart. During the year the technique was used to follow the details of a chemical reaction by stopping it at various points in its progress.

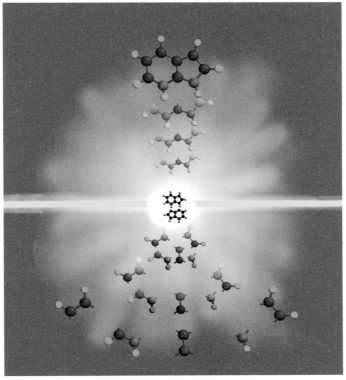

stop a reaction in its tracks. A Coulomb explosion occurs when an intense laser beam causes a molecule to become multiply charged. Coulomb's law, which describes the force between charged objects, predicts that many like charges confined to a small volume would repel one another explosively. If a Coulomb explosion occurs during the course of a reaction, the reaction grinds immediately to a halt as the molecule breaks apart. By changing the time delay between starting the reaction and stopping it with an intense laser pulse that causes a Coulomb explosion, the chemists were able to follow the transfer of protons between base pairs that mimic similar processes known to occur in DNA.

Order out of disorder

As many parents observing their child's room can attest, the second law of thermodynamics—the tendency for the universe to become more disordered—is hard to overcome. It thus may be something of a surprise that this tendency toward disorder, known as entropy, can sometimes be used to produce more order. As long ago as 1958 it was known that two large particles adrift in a sea of smaller ones would eventually meet and remain together. Scientists have been rediscovering this phenomenon as a method to produce ordered structures.

Recent speculation suggests that membranes in living cells might use such tricks. Marie Adams and Zvonimir Dogic of Brandeis University, Waltham, Mass., and Sarah L. Keller and Seth Fraden of the University of California, Santa Barbara, studied a mixture of microscopic particles of two different shapes—rodlike particles (a virus) and polymer spheres. They found that, depending on the relative sizes and concentrations of the rods and spheres, an amazing variety of ordered structures were spontaneously created from the disordered mixture by the force of entropy. One such phase consisted of layers of rods alternating with layers of spheres, whereas another consisted of columns of spheres with intervening rods, packed into a crystalline array.

Honors

The Wolf Foundation, based in Herzliyya, Israel, awarded its $100,000 Chemistry Prize for 1998 to Gerhard Ertl, professor of chemistry and director of the Max Planck Society's Fritz Haber Institute in Berlin, and Gabor A. Somorjai, professor of chemistry at the University of California, Berkeley, and the Lawrence Berkeley National Laboratory. The scientists were honored for "outstanding contributions to the field of surface science in general and for the elucidation of the fundamental mechanisms of heterogeneous catalytic reactions at single crystal surfaces in particular."

Both Somorjai and Ertl pioneered the use of simple surfaces of metal crystals as models for the complex ceramic-supported metal catalysts used in many chemical and petrochemical processes. Such surfaces can be investigated in exquisite detail by a battery of surface-sensitive techniques that reveal the atomic structure of the surfaces themselves and of molecules that adsorb on them. Furthermore, the fundamental reactions that occur during a catalytic reaction can be explored on these well-characterized simple-surface models without the complicating effects of the many different types of surfaces found on a typical catalyst. Using such methods, Ertl uncovered the detailed mechanisms of ammonia synthesis over iron catalysts and the palladium-catalyzed oxidation of carbon monoxide. Somorjai was the first to recognize the unique reactivity of defects such as steps and kinks on surfaces. His research has revealed a wealth of detail about many of the important reactions that occur in petroleum processing, particularly the platinum-catalyzed interconversion of hydrocarbons into different forms.

—Philip R. Watson

APPLIED CHEMISTRY

Nitrogen fixation

Nitrogen is an important constituent of all plant and animal protein as well as of fertilizers, explosives, and numerous industrial products. Although life literally exists in a sea of this gaseous element, which constitutes about 78% by volume of Earth's atmosphere, the cells of most living systems cannot assimilate nitrogen from the air for use in making proteins. Notable exceptions are certain bacteria that live in the root nodules of beans, clover, alfalfa, and other legumes, which have long been cultivated to restore depleted nitrogen to the soil—a technique known as rotation of crops.

The conversion of atmospheric nitrogen (dinitrogen, N_2) into nitrogen compounds was first accomplished in 1909 by the German chemist Fritz Haber in one of the first great applications of chemistry on an industrial scale. This direct combination of N_2 and molecular hydrogen (dihydrogen, H_2) to form ammonia (NH_3), however, requires iron catalysts, a large expenditure of energy, and high temperatures and pressures. Consequently, through the years scientists

have tried to devise ways to fix atmospheric nitrogen under less extreme conditions.

Because the catalysts used in the Haber, or Haber-Bosch, process involve metal surfaces to which oxygen is bound, Carlo Floriani of the University of Lausanne, Switz., decided "to use a preorganized set of oxygen donor atoms to bind a metal, then use that metal to reduce dinitrogen to make a real simulation of the active site in heterogeneous catalysis." Working with colleagues Antonio Zanotti-Gerosa, Euro Solari, and Luca Giannini at Lausanne and Angiola Chiesi-Villa and Corrado Rizzoli at the University of Parma, Italy, he reduced a solution of a complex of the transition metal niobium with a calix[4]arene—a bowl-shaped organic ligand (complexing agent) capable of binding metals through four oxygen atoms—in a solution of the solvent tetrahydrofuran (thf) with sodium metal under an atmosphere of the inert gas argon for two days to yield a mixture of three products. When a thf solution of one of the products, $Nb_2(calix[4]-(O)_4)_2Na_2(thf)_6$, was saturated with dinitrogen (N_2, which contains a strong N–N triple bond) and stirred overnight, it yielded the dinitrogen-containing complex $Nb_2(calix[4]-(O)_4)_2$ $(\mu N_2)Na_2(thf)_6$. The weak N–N single bond in this compound, reduced by stirring in a thf solution with sodium metal at room temperature for four days under an argon atmosphere, was broken to form the nitride dimer complex $Nb_2(\mu_3-N_2)Na_2(thf)_{12}$. This stepwise reduction of dinitrogen to form an electron-rich dinitrogen bonded to two niobium atoms, which then decomposed to two separate nitrogen atoms, each bridging the niobium atoms but no longer bonded to each other, has several analogies

to previous work by Christopher C. Cummins of the Massachusetts Institute of Technology. Cummins used transition metal complexes to cleave the bond in dinitrogen in 1996. Floriani intended to use his procedure to introduce reduced nitrogen into organic molecules, for example, in the synthesis of carbohydrazide ($H_2NNHCONHNH_2$) from N_2 and carbon monoxide (CO).

In another attempt to improve upon the Haber-Bosch process by using dinitrogen- and dihydrogen-containing transition metal complexes, Masanobu Hidai of the University of Tokyo, with co-workers Yoshiaki Nishibayashi and Shotaro Iwai, treated the ruthenium compound $[RuCl\{(C_6H_5)_2P(CH_2)_3P(C_6H_5)_2\}_2]X$ (in which X is BF_4, PF_6, or OSO_2CF_3) with H_2 to yield an equilibrium mixture of this complex and its dihydrogen adduct, trans-$[RuCl(\eta-H_2)\{(C_6H_5)_2P(CH_2)_3P(C_6H_5)_2\}_2]X$. Heating the mixture together with the tungsten dinitrogen complex cis-$[W(N_2)_2\{P(CH_3)_2C_6H_5\}_4]$ under relatively mild conditions (55° C [131° F] for 24 hours) produced ammonia in a moderate yield (45%) with traces of hydrazine (N_2H_4). According to the Japanese researchers, during the reaction heterolytic cleavage (the breaking of a covalent bond to produce two oppositely charged fragments) of H_2 occurred at the ruthenium atom. One of the two hydrogen atoms then reacted with the coordinated N_2 on the tungsten atom, yielding a hydrazido intermediate, while the other hydrogen atom remained bonded to ruthenium as a hydride (H^-). Additional reaction of hydrogen to the tungsten complex then yielded ammonia. (See *Inorganic Chemistry,* above.)

Yet another potential competitor for the Haber-Bosch process was developed by chemical engineers George Marnellos and Michael Stoukides of Aristotle University of Thessaloniki, Greece, who synthesized ammonia in 78% yield in a solid-state proton-conducting electrochemical cell from N_2 and H_2 at atmospheric pressure (compared with 150–300 atmospheres needed for the Haber-Bosch process) and a temperature (570° C [1,058° F]) only a little higher than the temperature range (430°–480° C [806°–896° F]), used in the Haber-Bosch process. Their apparatus consisted of a nonporous strontia-ceria-ytterbia (SCY) ceramic tube closed at one end and enclosed in a quartz tube. The inner and outer surfaces of the ceramic tube were coated with films of porous polycrystalline palladium that acted as cathode and anode, respectively. An electric circuit connected the two electrodes. Hydrogen gas flowing over the anode was dissociated into protons (H^+ ions). The protons diffused through the ceramic tube wall to the cathode, over which nitrogen gas was passing, and reacted with the nitrogen to form ammonia. Electrical work rather than pressure drove the reaction.

Until the beginning of the 20th century, almost all nitrogen compounds were produced naturally from atmospheric nitrogen by lightning or soil microbes. Now, paradoxically, Earth is suffering from an overload of nitrogen caused by an exponential increase in synthetic-fertilizer application and a rise in atmospheric nitrogen oxides from automobile exhausts and in nitrates from fossil fuel emissions. According to Stanford University ecologist Peter Vitousek, "Fixed nitrogen is essential for all life, but the added nitrogen is literally too much of a good thing." The correction of the current nitrogen glut probably lies in the substitution of crop rotation for fertilizer use and the production of smaller, more efficient cars.

Fat substitutes

Fats in foods are high in calories and may result in artery-clogging deposits that can cause heart disease. Consequently, scientists in countries such as the U.S., where an increasingly large proportion of the population (more than half of adults and nearly one-fifth of adolescents and children) is overweight, have sought to produce low-calorie, low-cholesterol fat sub-

USDA Agricultural Research Service/Information

USDA chemist George E. Inglett (below) developed the recently unveiled fat substitute Nu-Trim (bowl in foreground). Baked goods made with the "heart-healthy" oat and bran product (below right) are rich in beta-glucans and have fewer calories without compromising taste or texture.

stitutes to fill a market niche worth billions of dollars annually.

The latest fat substitute—to be marketed as Nu-Trim—is the first to be specifically designed to meet U.S. Food and Drug Administration (FDA) requirements for food products that can be advertised as good for the heart. Developed by George E. Inglett of the U.S. Department of Agriculture's (USDA's) Agricultural Research Service (ARS), Peoria, Ill., the fat substitute was prepared by thermal and mechanical shearing of milled oat bran, oat flour, or barley flour. The process removes coarse fiber components to form a fat-mimicking hydrocolloid rich in beta-glucans—soluble fibers known to reduce blood cholesterol levels, a factor linked to heart disease. Billed as a "new generation of fat replacer," the product can be used as a nutritious ingredient in bakery goods, nondairy cheeses, and ice cream and as a substitute for coconut cream in Asian foods. Inglett, who has worked on

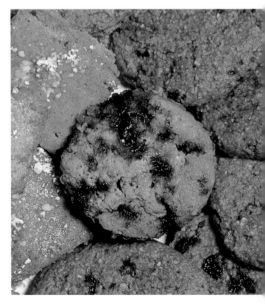

oat- and barley-based fat substitutes for the past decade, previously developed Oatrim (widely used in the food industry) and Z-Trim (in the process of being licensed), but neither of those earlier products qualified as "heart-healthy."

According to Wallace H. Yokoyama of the USDA Research Center, Albany, Calif., Nu-Trim makes more beta-glucans available to the digestive system than does a comparable quantity of whole-grain oats or barley. Studies by Judith Hallfrisch and Kay M. Behall of the ARS Human Nutrition Research Center, Beltsville, Md., suggested that beta-glucans play a role in regulating blood sugar by lowering insulin levels. David Busken of Oak State Products, Inc., Wenona, Ill., reported that Nu-Trim imparted extra body and moisture to his company's cookies. Inglett stated that the product can transform cookies, cakes, and creamy deserts into low-calorie, high-fiber foods and that only $5,000–$10,000 would be required for food manufacturers to add Nu-Trim processing to their plants.

In a related development, on June 17, 1998, the FDA approved as a food additive the product olestra, a no-calorie, no-cholesterol fat substitute that Procter & Gamble Co. had developed for use in potato chips and snacks. Rejecting the contention of a consumer advocacy group, the Center for Science in the Public Interest, that this fat substitute posed a health hazard, the FDA concluded that there was a "reasonable certainty" that olestra would not cause significant health problems. The FDA did insist, however, that products made with olestra continue to carry a label warning consumers that olestra may cause cramps and diarrhea.

Improved adhesives

Removal of adhesive bandages from wounds not only causes pain but also can strip off skin, posing problems for the elderly and for those who need frequent changing of dressings. For their development of a pressure-sensitive, light-switchable adhesive that allows painless removal of bandages, polymer chemist Iain Webster and co-workers at Smith & Nephew Group Research Centre, York, Eng., were awarded the 1998 Industrial Innovation Team Award by the Royal Society of Chemistry. The dressing was backed by two layers laminated together—an outer opaque layer, when peeled off, allows light to reach and deactivate the adhesive under the transparent layer, permitting painless removal of the dressing.

Webster decided to use a light-switchable adhesive rather than a water- or heat-switchable one, because water could potentially spread infection and the proper amount of heat could be difficult to deliver safely. The adhesive was based on a commercial acrylic adhesive—a co-polymer of n-butyl acrylate, 2-ethylhexyl acrylate, and acrylic acid—to which were added vinyl ($CH_2=CH-$) groups and a commercial titanium-containing, visible-light photoinitiator. On exposure to light in the presence of the photoinitiator, the vinyl groups cross-linked, making the co-polymer nonadhesive. The sticking power of the adhesive was reduced 90% by light, with the switching speed depending on the light source. Smith & Nephew was considering applications other than health care for the adhesive.

Because glues exuded by mussels and barnacles are excellent moisture-resistant adhesives, scientists have attempted to pre-pare synthetic versions of such glues for medical uses. At the University of California, Santa Barbara, Timothy J. Deming and Miaoer Yu developed systems for preparing large amounts of simple random co-polymers of the natural amino acids L-dihydroxyphenylalanine (L-dopa) and L-lysine, which, in aqueous solution in the presence of oxidizing agents, yielded cross-linked networks that stick to a variety of surfaces. The researchers were able to tailor the adhesive properties for specific applications by varying the polymer's composition, molecular weight, or conditions of oxidation.

Introduced in the 1960s, glues based on soybean proteins (soya proteins) were soon routinely replaced by stronger and more water-resistant petroleum-based glues. Xiuzhi Susan Sun of Kansas State University (KSU) recently modified soya protein to produce a much improved and environmentally friendly glue that was free of the noxious formaldehyde fumes associated with conventional glues. Sun unraveled the folded three-dimensional structure of native soya protein to expose its adhesive and hydrophobic (water-repelling) functional groups. By employing nontoxic reagents for this process, she was able to avoid the health problems for both workers and consumers of using phenyl formaldehyde as a cross-linking agent to increase water resistance in the usual glues. Not only was the new glue stronger than conventional glues, but it also could be used in humid or wet conditions both indoors and outdoors. It was also less viscous and more thermally stable than unmodified soya-protein glue. The potential applications are numerous, and the KSU Research Foundation has applied for a patent.

Chemist Xiuzhi Susan Sun (right) of Kansas State University and assistant Ke Bian display their improved, environmentally friendly glue made from modified soybean protein.

Hydrogen from water via sunlight

Hydrogen, the lightest element, is an environmentally friendly, nonpolluting fuel that produces only water when burned, in contrast to fossil fuels such as natural gas and petroleum, which produce polluting products. Because water (H_2O), its most common compound, is abundant, researchers have devoted considerable effort to liberating hydrogen, which many think is the fuel of the future, from water. The splitting of water into its elements by electricity (electrolysis), however, has been too expensive and inefficient to be economically feasible.

In a recent major development, John A. Turner and Oscar Khaselev of the National Renewable Energy Laboratory (NREL), Golden, Colo., used a semiconductor-based system, powered only by light, to electrolyze water for more than 20 hours. The integrated, immersible system set a world efficiency record of 12.4%, almost twice as high as hitherto achieved and approaching the theoretical limit for a two-layered semiconducting system. Previous workers had been hampered by the corrosion of the semiconductors used to construct the photocells and electrodes, which deteriorated when exposed to light while immersed in water. The alternative of employing separate subsystems, one to convert sunlight into electricity and the other to use the energy to split the water, was inefficient because of the energy loss between the components.

The NREL researchers overcame this difficulty by layering two types of cells based on different semiconductor materials. The outer layer comprised a gallium indium phosphide photochemical cell that absorbed visible light and resisted corrosion. The inner layer, a gallium arsenide photovoltaic cell, absorbed near-infrared light transmitted through the outer layer, providing the voltage boost needed to electrolyze the water. Their "novel, integrated, monolithic photoelectrochemical-photovoltaic device" absorbed light as the only energy input to produce electrons that directly split water into hydrogen and oxygen. Because the semiconductors that were employed are expensive, commercialization of the process probably will require at least a decade. According to Turner, "we can use cheaper semiconductors but the efficiency drops off." He admitted that even in a decade conventional methods for producing hydrogen from natural gas would still be three times cheaper than using sunlight, but he hoped to develop cheaper semiconductors with higher efficiencies.

Detection of war weapons

Two techniques involving fluorescence were developed for different purposes by two groups of chemists in 1998. Timothy M. Swager and co-workers of the Massachusetts Institute of Technology employed fluorescing polymers to detect 2,4,6-trinitrotoluene (TNT) and 2,4-dinitrotoluene, the main constituents of an approximately 120 million unexploded land mines around the world (see *Organic Chemistry*, above). Although other detection methods such as metal detectors, dogs, neutron activation analysis, electron capture, ion mobility spectrometry, and biosensors have been used, Swager stated that "there still exists a need for real-time TNT chemosensory devices that not only complement existing methods, but also provide the advantages of low cost and simplicity."

Robert S. Pilato and colleagues of the University of Maryland, College Park, developed a system for rapidly and selectively detecting volatile fluoro- and cyanophosphates, the major constituents of chemical warfare agents or nerve gases. They immobilized in a cellulose acetate-triethyl citrate polymer a platinum 1,2-enedithiolate complex with an appended alcohol molecule. The complex functioned as a sensor, fluorescing in the presence of selected phosphate esters at room temperature. They tested their system against phosphate esters with vapor pressures too low to create a lethal dose, and they intended to test it with actual nerve gases in the future. —George B. Kauffman

DEFENSE RESEARCH

As U.S. military forces in 1998 continued to reorient their defense mission from their Cold War responsibilities of countering a single adversary, the former Soviet Union, their supporting research activities were reoriented accordingly. The large strategic weapon systems of the past received less attention, and additional funds were invested in developing new communications networks and other tactical systems capable of responding to smaller, more focused threats, such as terrorist groups.

The core of this new trend, called "networkcentric" warfare, represented a shift away from the traditional emphasis on weapons platforms, such as aircraft, ships, and ground combat vehicles. Instead of upgrading the individual weapon systems to make them more capable in combat, military planners directed their efforts toward

creating more powerful command, control, communications, computer, and intelligence networks in order to integrate the weapons into a coordinated fighting force.

Networkcentric warfare, moreover, began to resemble the commercial world from which it was derived. Dedicated military communications systems were giving way to distributed systems featuring multiple inputs and multiple access—much the way the Internet works. In fact, the Internet, firmly grounded in commercial off-the-shelf (COTS) technology, became the model for this new military capability.

In parallel with the Defense Department's effort to establish distributed networks in order to tie its platforms into a more effective fighting force, the department's research arm began spearheading a drive to upgrade the existing Internet to

make it 100 to 1,000 times faster. The effort was known as the Next Generation Internet Initiative, and the lead agency was the Defense Advanced Research Projects Agency (DARPA). The initiative was launched Oct. 1, 1996, with such other participants as the National Aeronautics and Space Administration (NASA), National Institutes of Health, National Institute of Standards and Technology, and National Science Foundation. The idea was to create an end-to-end network capable of such advanced techniques as multicast and video and network management for allocation and sharing of bandwidth. A "100 ×" test bed was developed to connect at least 100 sites at speeds 100 times greater end-to-end than the present Internet, to be followed by an even faster "1,000 ×" test bed to connect 10 additional super sites via the multiagency Advanced Technology Demonstration Network and DARPA's own network by using NASA's Advanced Communications Technology Satellite.

The networkcentric concept originated with the U.S. Navy's requirement for over-the-horizon targeting for its Tomahawk cruise missiles, in which targeting was done from a series of sensors tied into a network; the sensors were external to the missiles and the ships from which they were launched. The network then became the focal point for development, and demand grew for increased communications bandwidth in order to accommodate more types of information, such as battlefield video, radar, and signal intelligence. This, in turn, contributed to the Joint Chiefs of Staff's concepts for what has become known as the revolution in military affairs.

The result was horizontal movement of information rather than the vertical move-

NASA's Earth-orbiting Advanced Communications Technology Satellite was part of a new initiative by the U.S. Defense Department to increase the speed of the Internet dramatically. The satellite would help connect a test bed of sites at speeds as much as 1,000 times faster than the present Internet.

NASA/Glenn Research Center

ment up and down the military chain of command, as practiced in the past. This, however, created security problems because more nodes in a network represented more opportunities for an adversary to intercept or jam the flow of information. On the other hand, the new method increased the opportunities for essential information to be transmitted where it was needed because there were fewer single points of failure. One broken link would not negate the entire chain. Also, given the need to embody many mobile platforms in what military planners called a "system of systems" network, the principal means of transmission among platforms remained radio-frequency communications, which were vulnerable to detection.

The U.S. Army in particular was struggling to meet the growing bandwidth and security requirements inherent in its tactical mission. With many small units operating over broad stretches of the battlefield, the army faced a command and control problem posed by the need for an ever-greater two-way flow of information in areas in which the information was vulnerable to interception and jamming. The changing operational environment dictated the need for new technical solutions. Observers agreed that the commercial telecommunications industry could answer at least some of these problems, and the army began using both terrestrial and space-based COTS systems spanning the traditional high-frequency and very-high-frequency bands devoted to military command and control.

Another facet of networkcentric warfare was the advanced displays needed to complement the ever-more-powerful communications networks, but in this regard

the army was caught in a dilemma. Cathode-ray tubes (CRTs), such as those used in home television sets, provided sufficient resolution but were not rugged enough for battlefield use, whereas the newer technology of plasma displays could be deployed in the field but provided resolution that was considered unsatisfactory. During the year, the army began evaluating 107-cm (42-in)-diagonal plasma displays from such producers as Fujitsu, NEC, Panasonic, and Mitsubishi. They provided 852×480-line resolution, good enough for high-definition television but not good enough for the army. Moreover, plasma displays cost about four times as much as CRTs, which in a demonstration at Ft. Monmouth, New Jersey, provided $1,152 \times 900$-line resolution in segments that could be combined, without unacceptable seams, to provide a total display. The CRTs, however, were also considered unsatisfactory. According to an army spokesman, "They're fragile, and they take a long time to set up." What the army sought was a family of displays tailored to the users. CRTs (or some acceptable flat-panel display equivalent) would be the best solution for the relatively benign environment of division- and brigade-level tactical operations centers, but something more rugged would be needed for vehicles and dismounted soldiers.

The 256-gigaflop supercomputer installed at the U.S. Air Force Research Laboratory in Rome, N.Y., consisted of 384 processors that could operate as a single system or independently at user sites.

Displays became increasingly important because of the army's stress on situational awareness and collaborative planning, which required the commanders to see a common picture. This was considered another opportunity for a COTS approach, such as developing software programs for Sun and Silicon Graphics Unix workstations and then transferring them to personal computers using the Windows operating system. This was considered particularly important, as more information flowing to the displays was coming from heterogeneous sources. In the past a fire-finder radar (a radar that can track where rounds are fired from), for example, could be optimized to detect moving targets, but under the new concept it might also have to serve as an advanced sensor for other targets.

Another necessary supporting technology was more powerful computers, and in 1998 the Air Force Research Laboratory (AFRL) took steps to provide signal- and image-processing computational services throughout the military research community with its new 256-gigaflop (billions of floating-point operations per second) supercomputer installed at AFRL headquarters in Rome, N.Y. The $2.9 million system, delivered by Sky Computers Inc., consisted of 384 processors that could operate as a single system or independently at user sites. Another option was to access the system via the Internet.

Regardless of the method of usage, the basic idea of the system was to process data from radar, sonar, optical, infrared, and other sensors and to develop new techniques in synthetic aperture radar, synthetic aperture sonar, space-time adaptive processing, automatic target recognition, and wavelet-based compressions of signals and imagery. Other supercomputers in the past tackled such computationally intensive problems as fluid dynamics and weather modeling, but this was considered the first system available to all military services for algorithm development, real-time implementation, and field demonstration in the processing of signals and images.

The new machine at Rome, part of the U.S. Defense Department's commitment of $1,237,000,000 through 2003 to upgrade its supercomputers, was described as the U.S. Air Force's most powerful and about the 20th most powerful computer in the world. It delivered approximately 85 gigaflops per $1 million. The Defense Department's goal was to improve the price-performance ratio by a factor of about 10 every $3\frac{1}{2}$ years, eventually reaching a teraflop (a trillion floating-point operations per second) per $1 million by 2001.

At the other end of the computing spectrum, the U.S. Navy in 1998 began tests at sea of a sonar signal processor in an attaché case that would be capable of achieving the same performance as an entire rack-mounted antisubmarine warfare console installed in a P-3C patrol aircraft. The tests were conducted on frigates and destroyers operating in the Pacific. The problem in the past with such sonars was that they needed high-throughput processing from multiple sensors. This tended to pile up the work on the human operators and also made it difficult to distinguish false alarms. The new instrument was designed to preprocess as much data as possible and thereby relieve the load on the operators. The displays combined alphanumeric and graphic data. Parallel processing was also performed across multiple personal computers in order to increase total processing power. In the post-Cold War period, the navy had become increasingly concerned about detecting quiet diesel submarines in shallow waters in which adversaries were likely to be dispersed and operating covertly to elude detection from the air.

Another technological challenge that emerged from the revolution in military affairs was logistical support of deployed forces—getting the right military hardware to the right users at the right time. The problem first received public attention during the Vietnam War, when the relationship of fighting forces to support forces—often called the "tooth-to-tail ratio"—was skewed toward more tail and fewer teeth.

Developed by the Department of Defense, MicroSTAR was a very small and lightweight (about 80 g, or 3 oz) battery-powered reconnaissance vehicle that achieved altitudes of 15 to 90 m (50 to 295 ft) above the target in preliminary flight tests.

Courtesy of Lockheed Martin Corp.

The effectiveness of combat forces declined accordingly. Similar problems occurred in the Persian Gulf War and, more recently, in the Bosnian peacekeeping mission. As the weapons become "smarter," and therefore more lethal, however, it made sense to shift money and personnel into the support functions, according to David Mills, principal deputy for logistics at the Army Materiel Command in Washington, D.C. The idea was to put more firepower at the front lines with less manpower (and therefore fewer soldiers exposed to risk) and to support those on the front lines with a logistics system that provided them with what they needed when they needed it in order to achieve information dominance.

The result was the use of what the military termed "best commercial practices" from the civilian sector. This extended down to putting tags on containers, similar to the bar coding of items on grocery shelves. "Five or six years ago our problem was knowing where the container is," Mills said. "Now it's what's in it and who's supposed to get it." Although special tags were provided in the past for what he called "sensitive" items, such as munitions and chemicals, there was still considerable confusion at the front lines in trying to figure out what was where.

One of the lessons learned from the Persian Gulf War was that twice as much material was delivered as was needed, but it arrived twice as late as usual. Rather than taking what amounted to the brute-force approach of sending everybody everything that might be required, the army concluded that an effective logistics system had to answer the questions of what the troops needed and who already had it. This also meant taking into account what were called the assets of the forces, such as their own transportation systems.

In regard to another part of the logistics system, the supporting industrial infrastructure, it had been accepted for years that operations and maintenance accounted for 60% of the life-cycle cost of a weapon system and, accordingly, that this should be the place to apply best commercial practices. Anthony LaPlaca, director of the army's Logistics and Readiness Center at Ft. Monmouth, said that it made sense for the army to operate like civilian corporations by shipping materiel directly to the users from the manufacturers. As part of this effort, the army began what it termed the direct vendor delivery program, in which commercial suppliers shipped spare parts, modules, and other equipment directly from their plants to the field, assuming responsibility for transportation, storage, and handling.

Perhaps one of the most advanced technologies being tailored to the revolution in military affairs was unmanned aerial vehicles, specifically a new class of very small, battery-powered reconnaissance vehicles, capable of being launched by hand by troops in the field, that would transmit back video images of the battlefield from distances of up to five kilometers (three miles) on missions of up to 20 minutes. State-of-the-art technology was needed to produce vehicles as light as 85 g (3 oz). To achieve this, a 42-month, $10 million advanced concept technology demonstration was begun by the Defense Department in 1995; it entered the flight-test stage in 1998. The basic idea was to achieve autonomous operation for the miniature vehicles and provide on-demand situational awareness to ground units at the brigade level and below. Preliminary flight tests encountered propulsion problems, but subsequent flights achieved altitudes from 15 to 90 m (50 to 295 ft) above the target to be observed. The estimated cost of the craft was $3,000–$5,000 in production volumes of 50,000–100,000 units. The new vehicle was named MicroSTAR.

One of the constraints was that the vehicle have a wingspan of no more than 15 cm (6 in), which represented an aerodynamics challenge and forced the designers to reduce the payload to no more than 20% of the system weight. Half the weight, 44.5 g (1.6 oz), was taken up by the battery, which produced 13 w, and the engine and airframe required another 20.5 g (0.72 oz).

Using such advanced electronics packaging technologies as multi-chip modules (MCMs), the development team was able to reduce the payload to 18 g (0.64 oz), including the charge-coupled-device (CCD) camera, onboard processing, and the automated flight controls. The packaging technique, known as Chip-on-Flex, was developed by General Electric Corporate Research and Development, Schenectady, N.Y. The CCD camera was a standard COTS device that provided a resolution of 512×512 lines at either the standard video rate of 30 frames per second or freeze frames at one image per second. Other payloads, such as jammers, could also be carried into battle by MicroSTAR. Regardless of the payload, the vehicles were to be controlled by troops using wearable computers. They could even be launched by devices similar to slingshots. The vehicles were considered vulnerable to small-arms fire, and so the likely operational scenario was that they would be launched in sufficient numbers to saturate the target area.   —John Rhea

(Opposite page left) Spot Image/Gamma Liaison International;
(opposite page right) AP/Wide World Photos

EARTH SCIENCES

Strong new evidence that an asteroid impact caused the mass extinction that killed the dinosaurs, measurements revealing that the Earth's average surface temperature in 1998 was the highest since instrumented records have been kept, one of the strongest El Niños ever experienced, and the discovery that multicellular life possibly existed on the Earth as long as 1.1 billion years ago were among the highlights of the past year in the Earth sciences. New light was also shed on the "Snowball Earth" hypothesis, and researchers discovered that the southernmost end of the Arctic ice pack had retreated hundreds of kilometers closer to the North Pole from 1996 to 1998.

ATMOSPHERIC SCIENCES

Global climate change

According to the World Meteorological Organization (WMO), the Earth's average surface temperature in 1998 was the highest since 1860, when instrumented records became common. The average global temperature in 1998 was nearly 0.6° C (1.1° F) above the recent long-term average and represented the 20th consecutive year of above-normal worldwide temperatures. Scientific evidence continued to mount that activities by humans were causing a significant portion of the observed warming.

Some scientists had been skeptical about the existence of global warming because 20 years (1979–98) of satellite data indicated a slight cooling of the atmosphere rather than the warming at the surface found by other observing systems. The satellites, orbiting at altitudes of about 850 km (525 mi), carried Microwave Sounding Units, which measure radiation emitted by oxygen molecules. The intensity of the radiation is directly related to the mean temperature of relatively deep layers of the atmosphere. After correcting for several factors, including the effects of El Niños and volcanoes, decay in the orbits of the satellites, and methods of splicing together records from different satellites, scientists found a slight warming rather than cooling trend, bringing the satellite temperature record much closer to the record based on surface observations.

A new statistical analysis of 115 years of observed global temperature data, compared with output from two leading climate models, strengthened the argument that human-caused emissions of greenhouse gases are causing much of the observed global warming. The study, by scientists at the National Center for Atmospheric Research, the University of North Carolina, and the Lawrence Livermore National Laboratory, examined each year's average temperatures for the Northern and Southern Hemispheres by correlating them with the readings taken up to 20 years earlier or later. If the numbers rise and fall randomly over time, the correlations are weaker than if there is a consistent long-term trend. The correlations were found to be far stronger for the 115-year temperature observations than for temperatures derived from two global climate models (from the United Kingdom's Hadley Centre and the Geophysical Fluid Dynamics Laboratory of the National Oceanic and Atmospheric Administration) that purposely omitted the 20th century's increase in greenhouse gases. With their assumptions of constant concentrations of greenhouse gases, the models replicated only the natural year-to-year variability of the climate system. These studies therefore imply that the warming trend in the 20th century has overpowered the climate system's natural variability.

In analyzing the differences between the data and the models, the scientists also considered volcanoes and changes in solar output. Volcanic eruptions are so infrequent and their effects so short-lived that they were rejected as an explanation for the differences. Variations in solar output during the last century could, however, have been large enough to affect the long-term trends. Global temperature rose sharply from about 1900 to 1940, leveled off until the 1970s, and then began another period of warming. The scientists concluded that both human activities and solar output have significantly affected global climate and that the Sun's output alone was insufficient to explain the behavior of the observed temperature data.

Weather disasters

Some theories of climate change suggest that the frequency and intensity of severe weather will increase as the climate warms. Although this connection is not proven and other factors, including growing numbers of humans and such practices as deforestation and building near disaster-prone areas, have undoubtedly played a role, the decade of the 1990s has experienced an unusually high incidence of severe weather around the world. During 1998 alone severe weather caused a record $89 billion in losses, more than was lost in all of the 1980s. In addition to the economic losses, an estimated 32,000 people were killed and 300 million displaced.

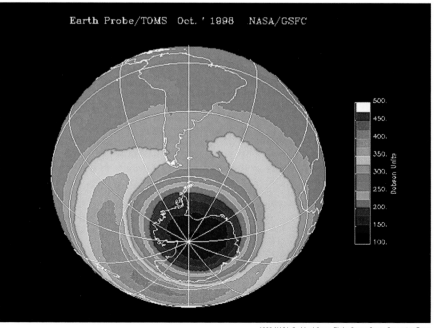

The most severe events of 1998 included the flooding of China's Yangtze River valley, Bangladesh's most extensive flood of the century, and Hurricane Mitch, which devastated Honduras and Nicaragua. The deadliest Atlantic hurricane in history, Mitch killed some 9,000 people.

This record loss of ozone occurred in spite of a gradual decrease in ozone-depleting chemical compounds (chlorofluorocarbons and halons, which peaked in 1994) as a result of the actions taken by nations in accordance with the Montreal Protocol.

This apparent inconsistency does not mean that the Montreal Protocol has been ineffective; without it the ozone decline would have been even greater. The continued decrease in ozone is associated with a cooling of the stratosphere, which fosters

Ozone hole

The ozone deficiency (ozone hole) observed over Antarctica in the austral spring (September–November) of 1998 was the largest and strongest on record, covering an area two and a half times the size of Europe and exposing not only Antarctica but also the southern tip of South America and vast swaths of the Pacific and Atlantic oceans to harmful ultraviolet rays. More than 85% of the ozone in the lower stratosphere was destroyed, and the deficiency was 25% greater than the average during the spring seasons of the previous years of the 1990s.

The ozone hole over Antarctica in September– November 1998 was the largest ever recorded, two and a half times the size of Europe.

Earth Probe/TOMS Oct. ' 1998   NASA/GSFC

1999 NASA Goddard Space Flight Center Ozone Processing Team

the formation of aerosols and ice crystals upon which the ozone destruction occurs. The stratospheric cooling in turn is caused by both warming in the troposphere (which causes the stratosphere to expand and cool) and the depletion of ozone itself, which reduces the strong absorption of solar radiation by ozone molecules.

In addition, although emissions of the chemicals that destroy ozone have decreased, it takes many years before the chemicals are removed from the stratosphere. Even with full compliance with the Montreal Protocol by all nations, a full recovery of Earth's protective ozone shield is not expected to occur until the middle of the 21st century.

Global Positioning System

In recent years the U.S. and Russia have put in orbit 48 brilliant radio beacons in a constellation collectively known as Global Navigation Satellite Systems. The U.S. component consists of 24 Global Positioning System (GPS) satellites, which broadcast microwave signals with precise wavelengths near 19 and 24 cm (7 and 9 in). These signals are delayed and bent along their path by interactions with free electrons in the ionosphere and by interactions with dry air and water vapor in the stratosphere and troposphere. Scientists are taking advantage of the GPS system to measure a number of important atmospheric variables.

GPS measurements of the atmosphere can be made either from the ground or from space. Ground-based networks including thousands of GPS receivers have been established around the world (more than 1,000 in Japan alone) for precise sur-

veying, navigation, and earthquake research. Data from these networks can be used to make detailed estimates of ionospheric electron density and tropospheric water vapor. From space, a GPS receiver in low-Earth orbit can observe the 24 GPS satellites rising and setting roughly 500 times per day. Each time this occurs, the GPS signals traverse the atmosphere, a process called "occultation." During an occultation the atmospheric layers are successively scanned by the radio waves. The resulting occultation data can be converted into precise vertical profiles of atmospheric refractivity, electron density, temperature, and water vapor.

Validation studies of occultation data from the GPS/Meteorology (GPS/MET) experiment during 1995–97 demonstrated accurate high-resolution vertical soundings of electron density in the ionosphere and temperature and water vapor in the neutral atmosphere. Scientists at the Institut d'Estudis Espacials de Catalunya in Barcelona, Spain, reported a successful three-dimensional analysis of the electron density in the ionosphere using tomographic techniques and ground- and space-based GPS data.

Future satellites carrying GPS receivers and an increasing global network of surface-based receivers are expected to contribute significantly to the observation and understanding of the atmosphere. Practical applications of these observations are expected to be in the improved forecasts of terrestrial weather and "space weather." (For additional information on satellite navigation systems, *see* Feature Article: YOU ARE HERE: NAVIGATION IN THE 21ST CENTURY.)

—Richard A. Anthes

GEOLOGY AND GEOCHEMISTRY

Possible asteroid impact in Argentina

P.H. Schultz of Brown University, Providence, R.I., and co-workers reported during the past year on their study of abundant glassy fragments measuring up to two meters (6.6 feet) across within a single thin stratigraphic layer in the Pliocene Pampean Formation. The Pampean rocks are predominately very fine-grained wind-deposited clays called loess, so these fragments are quite anomalous. Locally called "escorias," they were interpreted by the authors as fragments of solidified impactite liquid from an asteroid impact somewhere in Argentina. By early 1999 the impact crater itself had not been found and may have been eroded away or buried.

The escorial blocks are slabs of glass that have the same chemical composition as the local sediments, from which they were probably formed. Schultz and his colleagues described the glass as having "a distinctive folded and twisted texture with deformed vesicles, indicating a dynamic process of formation and emplacement similar to glasses from other known impact sites." The glass contains the rare mineral baddeleyite, ZrO_2, that formed from crystals of the common accessory mineral zircon, $ZrSiO_4$, at temperatures above approximately 1,700° C (3,100° F); this temperature is far above those of magma and consequently supports the impactite model for the escorial glass.

The escorial layer was accurately dated to 3.3 million years. This coincides with a widespread interval of extinction of major vertebrates in South America and with a major shift in the ratio of oxygen isotopes, indicating a drop in ocean temperature of 2° C (3.6° F). These effects might be expected as the consequences of a major impact.

Distant disruption of Jurassic sediments

Walter Alvarez and his colleagues during the year studied Jurassic (about 165 million-year-old) wind-deposited sandstones of the Entrada and Carmel formations within Arches National Park in Utah. The rocks exhibited unusual severe folding and disruption within a narrow stratigraphic interval above and below undisturbed flat-lying beds. The structure was very different from that of a typical folded body of rock, in which the folding extends vertically through the entire crust.

The folds generally terminated sharply downward near the base of the Carmel and faded out gradually upward over several tens of meters. The folded beds varied irregularly in thickness, indicating lateral flowage within them. In places, the sediments were so extremely deformed they disintegrated to form breccias, sharp fragments embedded in a fine-grained matrix. In addition, sandstone dikes and plugs were common in the area; these develop where water-saturated sand has been forced upward from its original layer into overlying sediments.

Alvarez and his colleagues suggested that these effects were due to a nearby asteroid impact just after the sediments were laid down and had not yet solidified. The probable site is preserved at Haystack Butte, some 45 km (30 mi) southwest of the park. Modeling the energy release of a large impact revealed that sufficient energy would have been generated to deform the sediments many miles away.

Isotopic evidence for asteroid impact

Ever since the proposal in 1980 that the extinction of the dinosaurs and most other plants and animals at the end of the Cretaceous Period 65 million years ago was caused by an asteroid impact, the hypothesis has been hotly debated. Although various kinds of evidence have accumulated in support of the hypothesis since 1980, it has not been universally accepted by all geoscientists, especially paleontologists. During the past year, Alexander Shukolyukov and Gunter Lugmair of Scripps Institution of Oceanography, University of California, San Diego, obtained geochemical and isotopic data on the element chromium from the clay at the Cretaceous-Tertiary boundary at Stevens Klint, Den. These data prove that material from a large carbonaceous chondrite asteroid or possibly a comet is part of the boundary clay and provide strong support for the impact scenario.

Chromium is a rare element in surface sediments on the Earth. It is notable, therefore, that the boundary clay has a chromium abundance 20–30 times the normal terrestrial levels. Even more notable is the isotopic nature of this chromium. All terrestrial and lunar rocks of whatever source have the same ratio of the two chromium isotopes, chromium-52 and chromium-53. In meteorites, however, the ratios are different and fall into two groups. In most meteorites chromium is noticeably enriched in the heavier isotope, chromium-53. In carbonaceous chondrites, on the other hand, the chromium is noticeably enriched in chromium-52. (The reasons for these isotopic relationships in

different meteorite types are not clear, but they are experimental facts.) The abundant chromium in the boundary clay has the same chromium-52-enriched character as carbonaceous chondrites and thus cannot have a terrestrial source.

Although no geochemical data on comets exist, the researchers pointed out that some scientists expect comets to be composed of the same type of material as carbonaceous chondrites and thus cannot be ruled out as the impactor material. The case for an impact by an asteroid or comet as the cause of the Cretaceous extinction is a strong one.

Lead pollution in ancient times

Kevin J. Rosman, of the Curtin University of Technology, and his colleagues undertook geochemical and isotopic studies of lead isotopes in dated zones of an ice core drilled from the Greenland ice cap and discovered implications for life in Roman times. Minute amounts of lead, probably of volcanic origin, are found in the ice. The ratio of the two main lead isotopes, lead-206 and lead-207, is 1.201 in ice that is 8,000 years old; this is assumed to be the pre-pollution natural ratio. In the interval from 600 BC to AD 300, however, the ratio dropped as low as 1.183, indicating the temporary introduction of a new source of lead (in vapor form) to the air.

The Romans used lead extensively and employed several mines as sources; each of these deposits has a particular isotopic ratio of lead-206/lead-207. The big lead and silver deposit at Rio Tinto, Spain, extensively mined today and as far back as Roman times, has a unique lead isotope ratio of 1.164, almost identical to the lead from this time interval in the Greenland ice cap. Presumably the lead escaped as vapor from Roman smelters where the lead ore was processed.

The "Snowball Earth" hypothesis

About 700 million years ago, according to the "Snowball Earth" hypothesis, almost the entire Earth was covered by ice. Life would have ceased in all but a few continental refuges, where local bare rock and meltwater pools provided favorable environments. Paul F. Hoffman, of the Department of Earth and Planetary Sciences, Harvard University, and his colleagues during the past year summarized a considerable amount of stratigraphic information from that time and matched it to carbon isotope data; their results supported the hypothesis. In stratigraphic successions throughout the world for that time period, they found glacial deposits capped by a thick fine-grained limestone. They then determined that carbonate minerals in the matrix of the glacial deposits and in the lower part of the limestone caps revealed an almost total absence of living organisms on the planet.

This latter information was gained because of the way photosynthetic organisms fractionate two isotopes of carbon, carbon-12 and carbon-13. They strongly select the light isotope, so the ratio of carbon-13/carbon-12 is low in them compared to an Earth average. Conversely, the ratio is high in the water where the photosynthetic organisms live, because much carbon-13 has been left behind by the organisms. If there is no photosynthetic life in the water, no change occurs in the ratio supplied by streams to the ocean. Simple chemical precipitation of carbonate minerals from an oversaturated ocean

does not change the isotope ratio of carbon; therefore, these minerals provide information on biological activity in the ocean.

In the African sedimentary section studied by Hoffman and his group, the carbon isotope ratio of marine carbonates was typically heavy, showing considerable photosynthetic activity up to within about 20 m (65 ft) below the base of the glacial deposits; at that level the isotopic ratio changes rapidly, with all trace of photosynthetic activity gone just below the glacial deposits. At the top of the glacial deposits worldwide, the cap carbonate appears; it has the same low percentage of carbon-13 as the rock just below the glacial sediments. As one moves upsection, perhaps 200 m (660 ft), the carbonate gradually returns to normal carbon isotopic ratios, signaling the return of normal photosynthetic activity and abundant plant life.

The researchers concluded that for unclear reasons probably connected with the position of the continents at the time and the pattern of oceanic circulation, sea ice began to form and reflected increasing amounts of solar energy back into space as it grew, in a runaway feedback effect that quickly led to the coverage of the world's oceans with ice and the complete extinction of oceanic photosynthetic organisms. These are called icehouse conditions, and the planet that results from them is the Snowball Earth. This interval is accompanied by a rapid drop in the carbon-13/carbon-12 ratio of carbonates.

The ice that covered the oceans prevented carbon dioxide (CO_2), which came from continental volcanic sources, from being dissolved in the ocean; consequently, the CO_2 content of the air rose. CO_2 is a greenhouse gas, so the atmospheric temperature increased. Calculations have de-

termined that at a CO_2 concentration of 120,000 parts per million, a sudden transition from icehouse to greenhouse conditions would occur, and the sea ice would suddenly melt. The CO_2 in the air would rapidly dissolve in the sea and just as rapidly be precipitated as carbonate; a layer approximately 5 m (16 ft) thick could cover the entire ocean floor. In this way would the capping carbonate atop the glacial deposits form. Once the ice was gone, photosynthetic life would emerge from its refuges and repopulate the seas, and over the next few millennia the carbon isotope ratio would return to normal, which is what the data show. Thus at that time in Earth's history, a total extermination of photosynthetic life was narrowly avoided, and the evolution of life leading to humans was able to continue.

Borehole temperature profiles

Henry N. Pollack and Shaopeng Huang of the Department of Geological Sciences, University of Michigan, during the past year described how temperature measurements in shallow boreholes can be used to provide the surface temperature history of the Earth over the last few hundred years. This history is of great use in interpreting present temperature change in the context of the global warming hypothesis.

Data collection from such boreholes is simple. A hole is drilled to a depth of 500 m (1,640 ft), and the temperature of the rock along it is taken, giving a temperature-depth profile. The profile can be interpreted in terms of temperature change at the surface over the last few hundred years. Hundreds of such data sets have been gathered over the last few decades.

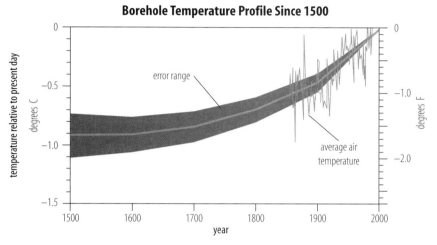

Borehole Temperature Profile Since 1500

y-axis: temperature relative to present day

degrees C: 0, −0.5, −1.0, −1.5

error range

average air temperature

degrees F: 0, −1.0, −2.0

x-axis: year — 1500, 1600, 1700, 1800, 1900, 2000

A temperature-depth profile is obtained by drilling a borehole to a depth of 500 m and taking the temperature of the rock along it. The profile can be used to determine temperature change at the Earth's surface. Data analysis from such boreholes worldwide reveals a net surface warming of a little under 1° C (1.8° F) since 1500, most of it coming after 1750.

Analysis of the data shows that approximately 75% of boreholes worldwide reveal a net surface warming, a little under 1° C (1.8° F) since 1500. Almost all this increase has taken place since about 1750, when the Industrial Revolution began, and about half the change occurred in the 20th century. Should this trend continue, a simple extrapolation suggests a global temperature rise of about 1.0° C during the next century. This increasing temperature rise is assumed to be caused by human-generated changes to the atmosphere, mainly resulting from the burning of fossil fuels.

Helium isotope analysis

During the past year, helium isotope ratios were used to detect comet showers that have impacted the Earth. Kevin Farley of the California Institute of Technology in Pasadena and colleagues decided to look for comet dust in sediments approximately 35 million years old because two large asteroid impact craters of that age were already known, and the researchers believed that they might have been associated with a comet shower. Their analytical detector for comet debris was helium isotope ratios. Helium has two isotopes, helium-3 and helium-4. The ratio of helium-3 to helium-4 is more than 3,000 times higher in comet debris than in normal terrestrial sediments, so it provides a fine detector.

The investigators studied sediments at Massignano, Italy, in which they found a two-million-year-long interval of high levels of helium-3, which peaked 35.5 million years ago, the time of the big impacts. Farley and his colleagues concluded, therefore, that, in addition to the asteroid impacts, a large number of comets struck the Earth during this time. An interesting feature of this interval is that no evidence was found for any exceptional disruption of the biosphere during that time—there was no major extinction.

Major awards

The Geological Society of America presented its major awards for 1998 in Toronto at its annual meeting. The R.A.F. Penrose Medal, awarded in recognition of research in pure geology, was given to Jack E. Oliver of Cornell University, Ithaca, N.Y., for his extensive efforts in developing seismological tools and interpretations over the past 40 years. Oliver was one of the discoverers of subduction zones, a major part of the plate tectonic hypothesis, and helped found the Consortium for Continental Reflection Profiling (COCORP), which pioneered the use of seismology in determining details of continental structure.

For outstanding distinction in contributing to geological knowledge through the application of physics and chemistry, the society awarded the Arthur L. Day Medal to Edward B. Watson in recognition of his work in experimental petrology. Watson was the first to determine how trace elements were partitioned among major minerals during magmatic crystallization as the magma evolved from basaltic to rhyolitic compositions. He also quantified diffusion rates in magmas, work that has had major implications for understanding the evolution of silicate melts.

The society gave its Young Scientist Award (Donath Medal) to Terry A. Plank of the University of Kansas, Lawrence, for her work on several aspects of the plate tectonic geochemical cycle. Plank discovered that in subduction zones the composition of basalts correlates with crustal thickness and that volcanic-arc output correlates with subducted-sediment input. In other work she presented new values for the chemical composition of the world continental crust and resolved the dispute between various factions over the mean extent of melting in the mantle.

The American Geological Institute (AGI), comprising more than 30 professional organizations, presented its most prestigious award, the Ian Campbell Medal, to Charles Groat in recognition of his long service to the AGI. Groat was the institute's director (1990–92) and in November 1998 became the 13th director of the U.S. Geological Survey.

—Rolfe Erickson

GEOPHYSICS

Two severe earthquakes in the Afghanistan Tajikistan border region and a tsunami along the north coast of New Guinea each killed several thousand people and left thousands more injured or homeless in 1998. Other deadly quakes struck China,

Guatemala, Iran, Bolivia, Turkey, and Indonesia. Researchers tried to quantify seismic hazards in the central United States and studied volcanic processes at oceanic ridges.

Earthquakes and volcanoes

On Jan. 10, 1998, a magnitude-6.2 earthquake struck northeastern China near Zhangjiakou. The quake killed at least 50 people, injured more than 11,000, and damaged parts of the Great Wall of China in northwestern Hebei province. Also on January 10, a magnitude-6.1 earthquake shook southwestern Guatemala near Quezaltenango, causing landslides and injuring several dozen people. A magnitude-6.1 earthquake in the mountainous Afghanistan-Tajikistan border region near Rostaq on February 4 killed more than 4,000 people and destroyed more than

8,000 buildings. Houses in the epicentral region were constructed of mud and brick and were unable to withstand strong ground shaking. Earthquake-triggered landslides also claimed many victims. A magnitude-6.4 earthquake in the same region on February 20 caused additional damage but resulted in a much smaller human toll. On March 14 a magnitude-6.6 earthquake in southern Iran near Golbaf killed five people and destroyed 2,000 houses. On May 20 a magnitude-6.8 earthquake in central Bolivia near Aiquile killed more than 100 people and destroyed hundreds of buildings. Analyses of seismograms showed that this earthquake had a complex source, with two large events occurring 8 and 12 seconds after the onset of faulting.

A magnitude-6.9 earthquake in the Afghanistan-Tajikistan border region near Rostaq on May 30 killed as many as 5,000 people. Like the quakes several months earlier in this remote area between the Hindu Kush and Pamir mountain ranges, landslides and poorly constructed houses contributed to the devastation. On June 27 a magnitude-6.3 earthquake in southern Turkey near Ceyhan killed at least 129 people and destroyed more than 17,000 houses and 6 large buildings. The main shock was followed one week later by a damaging magnitude-5.3 aftershock. A magnitude-5.8 quake in the Azores Islands on July 9 killed 10 people and left 1,000 homeless. On July 17 a magnitude-7.0 earthquake generated a 10-m (46-ft)-high

Survivors of an earthquake in Afghanistan on May 30, 1998, sift through rubble in the mountain village of Dashtak. More than one-fifth of the village's approximately 5,000 residents were killed during the quake.

Powerful eruptions of the Soufrière Hills volcano on the Caribbean island of Montserrat began in 1995 and continued into 1998. The volcano produced huge ash plumes and extensive lava flows.

tsunami that killed more than 2,500 people and left 4,500 homeless along the north coast of New Guinea. Also on July 17, five people were killed by a magnitude-6.2 earthquake in Taiwan. On August 4 a magnitude-7.1 earthquake near Bahia de Caraquez on the central coast of Ecuador killed three people and caused considerable shaking and landslide damage. A magnitude-5.2 quake struck southern Santa Cruz county in central California on August 12, injuring two people and damaging a church in San Juan Bautista. On August 27 a magnitude-6.3 earthquake struck southern Xinjiang province, China, killing at least three people and destroying more than 3,000 houses. A magnitude-7.8 earthquake centered beneath the Ceram Sea in eastern Indonesia on November 29 killed more than 40 people. Most of the casualties and damage occurred on Mangole Island, 2,000 km (1,240 mi) east-northeast of Djakarta.

Popocatepetl volcano near Mexico City was active throughout 1998. A violent eruption on November 27 cracked walls and broke windows in a village 60 km (37 mi) away. Other eruptions showered ash on parts of Mexico City, closing the city's airport for several hours on December 21. The eruption of the Soufrière Hills volcano on the Caribbean island of Montserrat that began in 1995 continued in 1998. A major eruption on July 3 produced a 10-km (6-mi)-high ash plume, and lava flows that reached the sea.

The deadly eruption of Merapi, the most active of Indonesia's more than 130 active volcanoes, that began in 1994 continued in 1998. Lava and ash from strong eruptions in July and October forced temporary evacuations of thousands of people. Other noteworthy volcanic activity in 1998 occurred at Grimsvotn, Ice.; Colima, Mex.; Cerro

Negro, Nic.; Nyamuragira, Democratic Republic of the Congo; Guagua Pichincha, Ecuador; Manam, Papua New Guinea; Pacaya, Guat.; Korovin, Alaska; Karymsky, Russia; and Arenal and Rincon de la Vieja, Costa Rica.

Seismic hazard in the Mississippi embayment

Earth scientists know from historical accounts that three very large earthquakes struck near New Madrid, Mo., on Dec. 16, 1811; Jan. 23, 1812; and Feb. 7, 1812. The best estimates of the sizes of these pre-instrumental quakes came from two sources: descriptive reports of shaking and damage tied to the Modified Mercalli intensity scale (which in turn was tied to magnitude by using instrumental data) and the size and distribution of liquefaction features in the alluviated epicentral area. Although imprecise, both lines of evidence suggested that all three earthquakes were magnitude 8 or larger. Scientists then addressed the questions as to when the next damaging earthquake in that region would take place and how large it would be. The only clues (since there were no exposed

faults to study) came from liquefaction deposits from pre-1811–12 earthquakes, preserved in near-surface sediments and datable by means of radiometric methods. By the mid-1990s, the best studies concluded that earthquakes of the magnitude of those in 1811 and 1812 had occurred as often as every 500–1,000 years at New Madrid. These results had important implications for building codes and land-use plans in the Mississippi embayment region.

At the American Geophysical Union (AGU) meeting in San Francisco in late 1998, Seth Stein of Northwestern University, Evanston, Ill., and his colleagues presented new geodetic evidence that the rate of large earthquakes in the New Madrid region might have been overestimated. Using six years of Global Positioning System data, they measured very small relative motions between sites (less than one millimeter (0.04 inches) per year across one possible 1811–12 fault, for example). Consequently, the implied strain rates were also very small, possibly consistent with a magnitude-7 quake every 500–1,000 years or a magnitude-8 quake every 5,000–10,000 years, but not indicative of a magnitude-8 quake every 500–1,000 years, according to

Stein. Other scientists were cautious in assessing these results. They argued that the validity of plate tectonics theory near plate boundaries, where plate motions seemed to cause regular seismic activity, did not translate to midplate settings, where the forces driving earthquakes were poorly understood. Perhaps, some seismologists speculated, the force exerted at New Madrid was not constant but occurred rapidly immediately after a large earthquake and then slowed.

Seafloor spreading at oceanic ridges

An early cornerstone in the development of plate tectonics theory was the recognition that crustal plates were formed by volcanic processes at oceanic ridges. By the 1990s Earth scientists had long recognized that molten magma ascended from the mantle and cooled into fresh crust along the trailing edges of the spreading plates, but the details of the process were elusive. At the AGU meeting in Boston in May 1998, a team of geophysicists reported some results from a several-years-long study at the East Pacific Rise (EPR) that had been designed to discriminate between two popular models of ridge upwelling. In one model, melt formed in a narrow zone directly beneath the spreading ridge. This model was compatible with observations that new crust formed within a few kilometers of the ridge axis, but it also required high concentrations of melt in the mantle. In the other model, lower concentrations of melt were present in a much wider zone, but some mechanism was required to concentrate magma along the ridge axis. Geophysicists used seismic and electromagnetic methods to address these questions.

The seismic team was coordinated by Donald Forsyth of Brown University, Providence, R.I., and included scientists from the Scripps Institution of Oceanography in La Jolla, Calif., the Woods Hole (Mass.) Oceanographic Institution, the Carnegie Institution of Washington (D.C.), and the Universities of Oregon, Colorado, and Washington. From November 1995 to May 1996 they deployed more than 50 ocean-bottom seismometers in two 800-km (500-mi) arrays perpendicular to the ridge axis. They hoped that, because seismic waves traveled slower in magma than solid rock, the spatial pattern of travel times from distant earthquakes would reflect the distribution of melt in the upper mantle. Scientists found that travel-time delays were largest near the EPR axis but remained large several hundred kilometers away. This result favored the second hypothesis (at least for a fast-spreading ridge like the EPR), implying melt concentrations of 1–2% over a broad zone. The EPR was known to spread asymmetrically, and some intriguing asymmetries were found in the seismic data. In particular, travel-time delays decreased much more rapidly with distance east of the spreading ridge than west, suggesting that the faster-spreading Pacific Plate to the west held more magma than the slower-spreading Nazca Plate to the east.

Seismologists also explored the hypothesis that upwelling at ridges was related to convection deep in the mantle. They found no perturbations in the 410-km (255-mi)- and 660-km (410-mi)-deep worldwide seismic discontinuities beneath the EPR, suggesting that upwelling was not driven from deep within the mantle but instead was probably a shallow, passive process, related to the separation of the plates.

The electromagnetic team was led by Alan Chave and Rob Evans of Woods Hole and included geophysicists from Scripps, Flinders University in Adelaide, South Australia, the University of Western Brittany, the University of Tokyo, Chiba (Japan) University, and the University of Washington. They deployed electromagnetic sensors near the EPR from May 1996 to July 1997. They expected to find high electrical conductivity where magma was present in interconnected zones and low conductivity elsewhere. Preliminary results of the research were generally consistent with the seismic data, allowing for 1% of interconnected magma in a broad zone beneath the EPR.

Awards

The 18th Medal of the Seismological Society of America (SSA) was presented to Lynn Sykes of the Lamont-Doherty Earth Observatory, Palisades, N.Y., at the society's annual meeting in Boulder, Colo., on March 31, 1998. In the 1960s Sykes studied the mechanisms of earthquakes occurring at the crests of oceanic ridges and in the fracture zones between ridge segments; his work was crucial in the development of plate tectonics theory. Throughout his career, Sykes was a leader in the field of seismotectonics, the use of seismology to inform tectonic interpretations. The SSA Medal is awarded for outstanding contributions in seismology and earthquake engineering.

David J. Stevenson of the California Institute of Technology was awarded the Harry H. Hess Medal of the American Geophysical Union at the AGU spring meeting in Boston on May 27, 1998.

The Hess Medal recognizes outstanding achievements in research on the constitution and evolution of the Earth and other planets. Stevenson was cited for his skillful application of comparative planetology methods to important research problems in the origin and structure of the planets and for the breadth of his contributions.

Norman H. Sleep of Stanford University was awarded the Walter H. Bucher Medal of the American Geophysical Union at the AGU fall meeting in San Francisco, on Dec. 8, 1998. The Bucher Medal recognizes original contributions to knowledge of the Earth's crust. Sleep was cited for his elegant use of simple thermal, mechanical, and chemical ideas to address geodynamic problems. He made major contributions to the understanding of oceanic ridges, subduction zones, continental margins, the thermal evolution of the mantle, mantle plumes, and even Martian tectonics.

Also at the AGU fall meeting, Richard P. Von Herzen of Woods Hole was awarded the Maurice Ewing Medal. Presenter Seiya Uyeda of Japan's Tokai University called Von Herzen "undoubtedly the world's greatest researcher in the field of marine heat flow," noting his "many great contributions to the understanding of Earth's thermal structure and to the technology needed for doing heat flow research."

—Charles S. Mueller

HYDROLOGY

A number of scientists during the past year reported on the intimate link that exists between hydrologic processes, the geochemistry of groundwater and surface water, and the impact of water resources development on both human settlements and sensitive ecosystems. For example, in South Asia there was considerable concern directed toward the hazards of long-term exposure to arsenic in drinking-water supplies. Arsenic is a naturally occurring element that is usually present in both surface water and groundwater in minute concentrations. The problem of elevated concentrations of arsenic in South Asia was most pronounced in Bangladesh. It was recognized that the health of millions of people in that country was at risk because of high levels of arsenic in the water supply. During the past 20 years, the people of

Bangladesh had been encouraged to convert from water supplied from surface ponds to the use of inexpensive wells that extracted groundwater from shallow aquifers. This change contributed to a tremendous decline in deaths caused by waterborne diseases such as cholera. The sediments that form the shallow aquifers, however, contain minerals that are enriched in arsenic, and geochemical conditions favored the release of arsenic from those minerals. The dissolved arsenic was then transported by flowing ground-water to water supply wells.

The seriousness of the problem came to light with the dramatic increase in the number of people developing symptoms of long-term arsenic poisoning, which include neurological damage and cancer. In preliminary surveys it was reported that a relatively high proportion of the wells currently in use in many parts of Bangladesh had arsenic con-

A young woman pumps water from a well in Bangladesh. The extensive use of groundwater from shallow aquifers in Bangladesh has caused arsenic to be released from minerals in the sediments that form the aquifers and has produced a sharp increase in the number of people with symptoms of long-term arsenic poisoning.

The Colorado squawfish, already an endangered species, may have suffered a loss of spawning habitat because of water resource development projects on the upper Colorado River.

centrations well above the recommended drinking water standard of the World Health Organization. Hydrologists worked to better understand the physical and chemical processes that control the migration of arsenic to the water supply wells. Meanwhile, government agencies in Bangladesh set out to document arsenic concentrations in the several million wells that are in use and to plan strategies for dealing with this severe problem.

Concentrations of arsenic in rivers used for drinking water supplies also gained considerable attention during the year in the U.S. With evidence accumulating on the long-term health impacts of exposure to arsenic in drinking water, the U.S. government began to reevaluate its drinking water standard with a view toward lowering the allowable arsenic content. The standard as of early 1999 was 50 micrograms of arsenic per liter of water. To better manage the consequences associated with a possible reduction in the safe-drinking-water standard, it was important to understand sources of arsenic that enter streams, the pathways followed by arsenic within a watershed, and the processes that may modify the arsenic concentration in surface water. Lawrence Baker of Arizona State University and his colleagues reported the results of their study on the movement of arsenic through the upper Salt River watershed in central Arizona. They found that an arsenic-rich geologic deposit, which com-

prised only 4% of the area of the watershed, contributed one-third of the total arsenic load to the river. Rainwater infiltrating through this deposit leached the arsenic from the sediments, where it was then transported by groundwater flow to the channel of the Salt River. Although abandoned mines and geothermal springs located within the watershed also had elevated levels of arsenic, the researchers determined that these sources were minor contributors to the total arsenic load.

Baker and his colleagues also estimated that approximately 15% of the total arsenic was retained in two reservoirs in the watershed, due to sedimentation and chemical precipitation of minerals that removed arsenic from the water column. Studies of this kind provided important insight into the features of the natural environment that contributed to higher concentrations of arsenic in surface water systems. If the drinking water standard for arsenic were lowered, additional and more costly treatment would have to be adopted by affected water supply agencies.

Dams and water diversions from river channels can result in a significant modification of downstream habitat that may be critical to the maintenance of native fish populations. Mark Van Steeter and John Pitlick of the University of Colorado, Boulder, demonstrated how water resource development projects have altered the natural flow of the upper Colorado River.

Reductions in the magnitude of high flows in the upper Colorado River reduced the capacity of the river to transport the sediment carried to the main channel by its tributaries. The consequent changes in the geomorphology of the river channel may have affected the population of endangered fish species such as the Colorado squawfish. These fish need clean gravels for spawning and tend to reside in side channels and backwater regions. Van Steeter and Pitlick found that peak discharges in sections of the Colorado River near Grand Junction, Colo., that are used by squawfish were 29–38% lower during the period from 1950 to 1995 in comparison with the years prior to 1950. While the average annual flow remained the same, flows during spring snowmelt were typically much lower and receded more quickly.

From 1964 to 1978 the average sediment load carried by the river was at least 40% lower than the long-term average, primarily because high flows were less frequent during that time. Sediment was deposited in the river channel rather than being carried farther downstream. For the section of the river they studied, Van Steeter and Pitlick concluded that since 1950 there had been a 10–15% reduction in the width of the main channel and a 25% reduction in the area of side channels and backwater regions. These changes were reversed to a limited extent by very high flows in 1983 and 1984, but the researchers suggested that, in general, it would be difficult to restore habitat under natural flow conditions. Van Steeter and Pitlick argued that these changes may have limited the reproductive success of the squawfish, and they questioned whether this change in channel morphology represented a critical loss of habitat for the squawfish.

Van Steeter and Pitlick also estimated the amount of flow in the upper Colorado River that would be required to maintain existing habitats for endangered fish species. They concluded that fish habitats were maintained by flows in the range from 50% of bankfall discharge to bankfall discharge. At bankfall discharge the water level in the river is such that the entire cross-section of the river channel is carrying water, but water does not encroach on the adjacent floodplain. At the lower end of this range, the water velocity was high enough to initiate gravel transport within the river, which flushed fine-grained sediment from the riverbed. At the higher end, sediment was eroded from the side channels, and it maintained existing backwater habitats, where the squawfish resided. Under current conditions, flows needed to initiate gravel transport occurred on average only 26 days per year, while sediment erosion from side channels occurred on average 8 days per year.

Scientists continued to gain valuable insight into the hydrologic behavior of steep hill slopes at an experimental site established at Coos Bay, Ore. in the mountains of the Oregon coast range. A team of researchers led by Raymond Torres of the University of South Carolina suggested that the hydrologic properties of the soils above the water table could be a primary factor in determining the timing and magnitude of the pore pressure response and the discharge of water from a hill slope. (Pore pressure is the stress transmitted through the interstitial fluid of a soil or rock mass.) Higher water pressures are significant because they can contribute to failure of the slope and to landslides. The researchers observed that the response of the saturated zone and the peak discharge of water from the hill slope occurred much faster than expected on the basis of the time it would take for rainfall to move from the soil surface to the water table. Torres and his colleagues proposed that a pressure wave moved through the soil horizon (the partially saturated soil layer) and generated a rapid hydrologic response at the water table. They noted that such a rapid response could explain how short-duration rainfalls can trigger slope instabilities and landslides if the hill slope was initially quite wet. These observations suggested that there might be limitations in the current generation of simulation models used to examine the spatial variability of runoff across mountainous terrain, because of the simplified manner in which water flow through partially saturated soils was treated.

Ignacio Rodriguez-Iturbe of Texas A & M University received the Horton Medal of the American Geophysical Union in recognition of outstanding contributions to the geophysical aspects of hydrology. Rodriguez-Iturbe made numerous advances in the understanding of hydrologic processes and land-atmosphere interactions. These contributions included the development of methods to aid in the prediction of extreme hydrologic events and the formulation of new theories that explained the organization of river basins and the resulting landscape patterns. Mary Anderson of the University of Wisconsin, Madison received the Meinzer Award of the Geological Society of America for her contributions to modeling groundwater flow systems and for studies of the interactions between groundwater and surface water systems.

—Leslie Smith

OCEANOGRAPHY

The 1997–98 El Niño

Called the climate event of the century, the 1997–98 El Niño was one of the strongest on record, causing a reported $30 billion in damages and contributing to the loss of 24,000 lives, according to the U.S. National Oceanic and Atmospheric Administration (NOAA). This oceanic warming arrived in mid-1997, when the water temperatures started rising dramatically in the central and eastern equatorial Pacific Ocean. The warming peaked around the end of 1997, but El Niño remained strong until a precipitous oceanic cooling in May 1998.

El Niño warmth in the central part of the Pacific fueled the growth of towering thunderstorms, which redirected normal atmospheric circulation patterns. Like rocks in a river, these thunderheads deflected the Pacific jet stream and skewed the track of storm systems heading toward North and South America. Torrential rains washed California in the winter of 1997–98, particularly during the early part of February. Parts of the state received between 200% and 400% of their normal wintertime precipitation. Other storms related to El Niño swept through the southeastern U.S., causing $1 billion in damages. On the western side of the Pacific Ocean, El Niño conditions caused a drought that fueled devastating fires in Indonesia. Atypically abundant rainfall in East Africa aided the spread of Rift Valley fever and other diseases.

This episode of El Niño marked the first time that scientists succeeded in charting the entire course of a strong Pacific warming, from start to finish. A string of 70 buoys across the equatorial Pacific helped

A "black smoker" on the ocean floor is viewed from a deep-sea vehicle. Seawater heated by volcanic energy produces black brines that spew out of vents on the seafloor.

C. Allan Morgan/Peter Arnold, Inc.

pick up initial signs of El Niño in the late spring of 1997 and enabled researchers to predict its development later that year. Satellites in space revealed that average sea levels swelled by 20 mm (0.8 in) during El Niño and then subsided to their previous heights. The oceanic disruption sped up atmospheric winds and temporarily slowed the Earth's rotation, adding 0.4 milliseconds to each day. In addition, the warming of Pacific waters played a strong role in raising the Earth's surface temperature for 1998 to its highest mark in more than a century.

El Niño started dying out in May 1998, when the water temperatures plummeted in the central equatorial Pacific by as much as 8° C (14.4° F) in 30 days in key regions. The drastic temperature change heralded the beginning of a cooling phase in the Pacific known as La Niña. In some ways the flip side of El Niño, the Pacific chill also upset regional weather patterns. It fostered the development of Atlantic hurricanes in 1998, leading to an above-normal number of tropical storms. One of these, Hurricane Mitch, lashed Central America and has been blamed for 11,000 deaths. (See *Atmospheric Sciences,* above.)

Pacific eruption

When a seafloor volcano located 500 km (310 mi) off the coast of Oregon erupted in January 1998, oceanographers managed for the first time to observe critical details of a submarine volcanic outpouring. The lava eruption occurred at Axial Seamount, a broad-shouldered mountain sitting atop the Juan de Fuca Ridge. The ridge is part of a 65,000-km (40,000-mi)-long underwater mountain chain that winds its way through the world's oceans.

On Jan. 25, 1998, underwater microphones revealed that a swarm of earthquakes was coming from Axial Seamount. More than 8,000 tremors were detected during the next two weeks, indicating that an eruption had occurred. During February the research vessel WECOMA from Oregon State University set out through punishing winter storms to visit the Axial Seamount site. Two more expeditions of university and government scientists returned during the summer with the ALVIN submersible and a remote-controlled robotic sub.

Oceanographers were able to document aspects of the eruption because they had previously set out several instruments on Axial Seamount in hopes of detecting any activity there. One gauge located near the summit of the mountain recorded a rapid drop in the ocean floor at the time of the first earthquakes. Geologists suspected that during the eruption, magma within the volcano migrated toward the southern flank of the mountain and squirted out there, causing the summit of Axial to drop like a deflated soufflé. This same process had been documented on Hawaii and elsewhere, but researchers had never previously witnessed it at an underwater volcano.

Sensors tethered to the ocean floor near the eruption site measured an abrupt increase in the water temperature, as volcanically heated fluids rose like a mushroom cloud. From these data, oceanographers learned more about how volcanic eruptions season the ocean with minerals and with colonies of underground microorganisms.

Black smoker

Marine geologists for the first time pulled up examples of the rocky chimneys that sit on the seafloor and spew out superheated fluids. Known as "black smokers," these sulfur-rich formations house a rich assortment of microorganisms adapted to some of the most extreme conditions on the planet.

Discovered in the 1970s, black smokers form along tears in the ocean crust wherever two of Earth's great tectonic plates are gradually pulling apart. This process, called seafloor spreading, causes molten rock to rise from deep inside Earth and erupt occasionally at the surface. Seawater in the crust is heated by the volcanic energy, creating black brines that shoot out of vents in the seafloor at temperatures in excess of 300° C (570° F). As the mineral-laden fluids mix with the near-freezing ocean water, sulfides and other minerals preci-

Scientists from the ice-locked Canadian Coast Guard ship *Des Groseilliers* (above) deploy instrumentation through a borehole in the Arctic pack ice (left). The researchers discovered that the ice north of Alaska was much thinner than it had been in the 1970s.

pitate onto the seafloor, building up spire-shaped chimneys.

In a joint project carried out by the University of Washington and the American Museum of Natural History in New York City, oceanographers traveled to a field of black smokers located on the Juan de Fuca Ridge, 200 km (125 mi) north of Axial Seamount. The team sawed off four 1.5-m (4.9-ft)-high chimneys, weighing between 550 and 1,800 kg (1,200 and 4,000 lb) each. Subsequent tests revealed that the chimneys were full of so-called hyperthermophiles, or heat-loving microbes. Researchers planned to try to culture new species of bacteria and archea to determine the upper temperature limits of life and how organisms live under such extreme conditions.

Arctic ice camp

An international team of researchers spent a year trapped amid the floating Arctic pack ice in order to collect clues about the climate of the far North, the place where some of the earliest and most obvious signs of greenhouse warming are expected to occur. Their data indicated that the Arctic Ocean underwent significant changes in the 1990s.

The oceanographers and atmospheric scientists traveled onboard the Canadian Coast Guard ship *Des Groseilliers,* an icebreaker with a hull fortified to withstand the crushing forces of the Arctic ice cover. *Des Groseilliers* steamed north from Canada in October 1997 and was intentionally frozen into the pack ice. During the next year, the ship floated almost 3,000 km (1,860 mi) with the ice, while a cadre of researchers collected meteorological and oceanographic measurements. The ship broke free of the ice in October 1998.

The experiment, called Surface Heat Budget of the Arctic Ocean (SHEBA), was designed to study how the perennial ice cover in the Arctic controls the way heat moves back and forth between the atmos-

phere and ocean. In wintertime the Arctic pack ice reaches the size of the contiguous U.S. and forms a cap over the ocean, preventing heat from escaping into the atmosphere. During summer the pack ice shrinks by half. When SHEBA researchers arrived in the fall of 1997, they discovered that the ice north of Alaska was far thinner than it had been during a research program in the 1970s. The ocean below the ice was also much fresher than expected, indicating that above-average amounts of ice had melted during the summer of 1997. By October 1998, the pack was thinner than it was when SHEBA began its observations a year earlier.

Satellite measurements showed that the southernmost edge of the pack ice near Alaska retreated hundreds of kilometers closer to the pole between 1996 and 1998; consequently, that much less ocean area was insulated by ice. Without this white cover, which reflects most of the Sun's radiation, the dark ocean water readily absorbs heat from the Sun. One potential result is that a small loss of the Arctic pack ice could warm up the ocean and rapidly thin the rest of the ice. As of early 1999 it remained unclear as to whether the recent changes are temporary or whether they are part of a warming trend expected to result from greenhouse gas pollution. Researchers believed, however, that the data gathered by the project would improve their methods of forecasting future changes.

Ocean temperatures

Oceanographers successfully demonstrated an extremely precise method for measuring the ocean's temperature by using sound waves. The $40 million project, known as Acoustic Thermometry of Ocean Climate (ATOC), exploits the principle that sound travels faster in warm water than it does in cooler water. Therefore, by repeatedly measuring the time it takes a sound signal to propagate across an ocean basin, this technique can determine whether the water temperature is changing.

When researchers first proposed this project in 1992, some environmental groups criticized the technique as a potential threat to marine life, particularly marine mammals that communicate with low-frequency sounds. As a result of the protests, the ATOC team modified the experiment and gave biological researchers control of the sound transmitter, located on the Pioneer Seamount about 100 km (60 mi) southwest of San Francisco. After 15 months of testing, marine mammal researchers found that the sound transmissions caused minor changes in the behavior of humpback whales in the area.

Data collected during this trial phase showed that the technique worked even better than expected for measuring ocean temperatures. Using underwater microphones near Hawaii, Christmas Island, and New Zealand, the ATOC team measured the sound signal's 4,800-km (3,000-mi)-long trip across the Pacific with a precision of 20 milliseconds, which translated into temperature measurements with a precision of 0.005°–0.01° C (0.009°–0.018° F). With this kind of system, researchers believed that they could determine in a decade whether greenhouse gases are warming the planet.

The legal obstacles posed by environmentalists, however, drained funds from the program and cut short the ATOC experiment. The Pioneer transmitter ceased working in 1998, and a second transmitter, installed off the island of Kauai, was designed to operate only through the end of 1999.

Deadly tsunami

An earthquake struck just north of New Guinea on July 17, 1998, spawning a giant set of waves that killed more than 2,500 people. Debris hanging from trees indicated that the waves, known as a tsunami, reached heights of 14 m (46 ft) above the ocean surface.

The devastating waves perplexed researchers because they were generated by an otherwise ordinary earthquake of modest size, measuring 7.1 on the moment magnitude scale. An international team of scientists that visited the site to survey damage concluded that the earthquake may have triggered an underwater landslide, which in turn generated the large tsunami. That scenario raised concern among U.S. officials, because the seafloor off the west coast of North America has many faults capable of producing earthquakes similar in size to the New Guinea shock.

The disaster came at a time of heightened sensitivity to the dangers of tsunamis. In 1996 NOAA coordinated with Hawaii, Alaska, California, Oregon, and Washington to develop a mitigation program for these waves. The federal-state task force started educating coastal residents about tsunamis and producing maps of the most vulnerable areas. In 1998 NOAA tested new deep-sea sensors capable of detecting distantly generated tsunamis that are heading toward U.S. shores.

A new natural gas resource

Several nations explored the feasibility of exploiting deposits of frozen natural gas, called methane hydrates, that are locked beneath the seafloor and under Arctic permafrost. Rough estimates suggest that this as-yet-untapped resource contains more energy than all conventional sources of coal, oil, and natural gas. In 1998 Japan and Canada drilled an exploratory well in northwest Canada to learn more about methane hydrates and located an extremely rich concentration of them. In 1999 the Japan National Oil Co. planned to drill an underwater well off the east coast of Japan to assess the concentrations of methane hydrates beneath its waters. The U.S. Congress considered bills in 1998 that would establish a national methane hydrates research program.

Bacteria in the ocean

Oceanographers discovered that the frayed remnants of bacterial cell walls make up much of the dissolved matter in the open ocean. The finding emerged from a study by researchers at the University of Washington and the University of Texas who collected thousands of liters of water from remote ocean sites. When the scientists passed the water through a series of extremely fine filters, they isolated amino acids characteristic of bacterial cell walls.

The discovery overturned the traditional view that most of the ocean's dissolved organic matter is derived from marine algae. Oceanographers previously believed that algae were the ocean's principal primary producers, but the amino acid data and other recent findings suggested that bacteria play a critical role as primary producers in nutrient-starved areas of open ocean.   —Richard Monastersky

PALEONTOLOGY

Oldest animals?

Researchers announced in the journal *Science* the discovery of what appeared to be traces of wormlike animals in Indian sandstone dated to 1.1 billion years ago—nearly twice as old as any other evidence of multicellular life yet discovered. The surprising report from the team of scientists headed by Adolf Seilacher of Yale University both intrigued and puzzled invertebrate paleontologists, leaving them scratching their heads and scrambling for verification.

Traditionally, animal evolution had been thought to have begun with a sudden "explosion" of different forms and species at the start of the Cambrian Period, about 540 mil-

lion years ago. This argument was based primarily on the fact that no fossils of multicellular organisms had been found in rocks much older than the Cambrian. Seilacher's discovery, however, was consistent with previous genetic studies, which had suggested that the major groups of animals diverged from a common stock more than a billion years ago. Nevertheless, paleontologists were cautiously skeptical of the new fossils. R.J. Azmi of the Wadia Institute of Himalayan Geology, Dehra Dun, India, called into question the actual age of the fossils. Three weeks after the *Science* article appeared, Azmi reported in the *Journal of the Geological Society of India* that he had found millimeter-sized "small, shelly fossils"—firmly dated to 540 million years ago—in rocks just above the purported trace fossils. He also argued that the mineral grains in the sandstone on which the 1.1-billion-year date was based could have formed long before the wormlike animals left their tracks. Consequently, the wormlike animals that left their tracks might be only about 600 million years old, Azmi said. Other scientists questioned the identity of the fossils,

Paleontologist Paul Sereno displays the fossil remains of *Suchomimus tenerensis*, an 11-m (36-ft)-long carnivorous dinosaur discovered by his research team in the Sahara.

wondering whether the tracks were not instead inorganic artifacts of sedimentary rock formation. Resolution of these questions will either sink the worm fossils into relative obscurity or elevate them to evolutionary stardom.

Dinosaur discoveries

Dinosaur popularity outside the paleontological community was matched by new discoveries within the world of vertebrate paleontology. Emerging from 90-million-year-old rocks from New Mexico, *Zuniceratops christopheri* is the oldest

O. Louis Mazzatenta/National Geographic Image Collection

A model reveals the possible appearance of *Caudipteryx zoui*, a turkey-sized dinosaur of 120 million years ago. Recently discovered in northeastern China, the dinosaur had feathers fanning out from its forearms and tail.

horned, or ceratopsian, dinosaur ever found, a group that includes the three-horned *Triceratops*. The new species, which extended the Cretaceous history of the ceratopsians, was named after its eight-year-old discoverer, Christopher Wolfe, by the boy's father, Arizona paleontologist Doug Wolfe.

A team of researchers led by Paul Sereno of the University of Chicago announced the recovery of a new crocodile-like dinosaur from 100-million-year-old rocks in the Sahara. Reporting in *Science,* the paleontologists said that the 11-m (36-ft)-long *Suchomimus tenerensis* was a fearsome carnivore with a mouth filled with hooked teeth for snatching and holding prey and surprisingly dexterous fingers tipped with foot-long (about 30 cm), sickle-shaped claws. *Suchomimus* belongs to a small group of dinosaurs called the spinosaurids, which are part of the larger theropod group that includes *Tyrannosaurus rex.*

The long, slender head of *Suchomimus* strongly resembled that of a modern-day crocodile, Sereno said. The crocodile analogy, however, does not apply to the remainder of the skeleton, which shows no other specializations for aquatic life. The resemblance in skull shape is an interesting example of evolutionary convergence between distantly related animals and indicates a similar solution to a shared problem—how to best catch fish for dinner.

When it was first named in 1979, *Majungatholus atopus* was thought to be a dome-headed, plant-eating pachycephalosaur. A nearly complete and exquisitely preserved skull of the species discovered in 70-million-year-old rocks from Madagascar revealed, however, that the 7–9-m (23–30-ft)-long dinosaur

was actually a member of an enigmatic family of meat-eating theropods. The discovery provided scientists with new information about a dinosaur group previously found only in Argentina and India and expanded their understanding of how Earth's continents split apart millions of years ago.

A persistent topic in the field of dinosaur paleobiology was whether some dinosaurs, particularly the large-bodied sauropods, might have given birth to live young. This notion was put to rest when paleontologists reported in the journal *Nature* the discovery of a sauropod nesting ground strewn with thousands of fossilized eggs, many of which held complete dinosaur embryos. In addition to the tiny skeletons, some of the eggs contained small sections of fossilized skin, offering scientists a rare glimpse at the soft-tissue features of dinosaurs. The remarkable new fossils, found in 70-million–90-million-year-old sediments from Argentina, represented several paleontological firsts, including the first dinosaur embryos to show fossilized skin and the first known embryos of the plant-eating sauropods

Although the skull, jaws, and teeth are traditionally the most important anatomical regions for determining the feeding preferences of dinosaurs, what comes out the other end may be equally as interesting. Reporting in *Nature,* Karen Chin of the U.S. Geological Survey and three colleagues described a chunk of fossilized feces that—based on its size, age, and location—was

most likely formed by the celebrated carnivorous dinosaur *Tyrannosaurus rex.*

The 7-kilogram (15-pound) mineralized excrement, or coprolite, discovered in 65-million-year-old sediments from saskatchewan, contained bone fragments of cow-sized dinosaurs, confirming what paleontologists had already suspected about the dietary habits of the dinosaur king.

Dinosaur or bird?

The widely held hypothesis that birds evolved from theropod dinosaurs was supported by new fossil discoveries in China and Madagascar. Writing in *Nature,* Ji Qiang of China's National Geological Museum, Beijing, and his collaborators announced the discovery in northeastern China of three 120-million-year-old turkey-sized dinosaurs. Two of the new creatures were named *Caudipteryx zoui,* or "tail feather," for the unmistakable feathers that fan out from the animals' tails. Downlike impressions are also visible on the fossils, hinting that the animals' bodies were feather-covered. *Caudipteryx*'s wing feathers were symmetrical, however, suggesting that the structures probably did not evolve for flight but instead may have been used for thermal insulation, sexual display, or some other purpose, scientists said. The other new species, *Protarchaeopteryx robusta,* is similar to *Caudipteryx* in that most of its body was probably covered with feathers, although no evidence of wing feathers had been discovered.

Another fossil also hinted at a close relationship between birds and theropod dinosaurs. Catherine Forster and David Krause of the State University of New York at Stony Brook announced the discovery of a raven-sized, 65-million–70-million-year-old creature in Late Cretaceous rocks from Madagascar. The new species was initially given the name *Rahona ostromi* but was changed shortly thereafter to the genus name *Rahonavis* due to a conflict with a previously named animal. In addition to its birdlike traits, which included a feathered wing, a perching foot, and several other features in its hips and legs, *Rahonavis* also retained many primitive dinosaurian characteristics, such as a long, bony tail and a sickle-shaped, second toe claw.

Fossil whales

Studies of new fossil-whale skeletons in 1998 increased scientists' knowledge of marine mammal evolution. The Himalayan foothills of India yielded a jawbone and teeth of a fossilized whale called *Himalayacetus*, pushing the origin of the marine mammals back before 53.5 million years ago, several million years earlier than previously thought.

In addition, a 40-million-year-old whale fossil—found in 1983 near Augusta, Ga., by workers building the Plant Vogtle nuclear power facility—was described and named *Georgiacetus vogtlensis* in the *Journal of Paleontology*. The extremely

(Right and below) AP/Wide World Photos

The 142-million–148-million-year-old fossil remains (right) of the world's oldest-known flowering plant were recently discovered in China. Below a scientist holds in his right hand a pelvic bone of a 40-million-year-old whale and in his left hand the much smaller pelvic bone of a dog. The whale's pelvis was similar to that of a land animal.

well-preserved fossil documents a crucial ancestral phase of adaptation from living on land to living in the ocean. Scientists said that the Vogtle whale was an aquatic animal that had already changed anatomically from its land-dwelling ancestors, but it still possessed a pelvis and legs, suggesting that the animal may have been able to drag its body on land, perhaps to give birth.

The fossil of a previously unnamed species of whale was put on display at the Burke Museum of Natural History and Culture at the University of Washington, Seattle. The 28-million-year-old specimen was discovered in 1993 on Washington's Olympic Peninsula. Unlike whale fossils that predated it, this whale had no teeth. Instead, like modern-day humpback and gray whales, it possessed a baleen—a specialized feeding structure used to filter small

plants and animals from the sea. Museum officials said that the whale represented a missing link that will aid paleontologists in understanding the 55 million years of whale evolution.

First flower?

Chinese and American researchers announced in *Science* the discovery in China of 142-million–148-million-year-old plant remains that represented the world's oldest-known flowering plant. Previously, the oldest-known flower was a 115-million-year-old specimen found in Australia. A key in identifying the new fossil as an early flowering plant was the presence of seeds that were preserved in the fossil. Although the plant lacked petals and looked nothing like present-day flowers, such as roses or chrysanthemums, it is a flower by scientific definition because it had carpels—leaflike pods that opened to release seeds. Nonflowering plants have no such structures.

—Matthew J. James

ELECTRONICS AND INFORMATION SCIENCES

The convergence of electronics, telecommunications, and computers became ever more pronounced in 1998. The use of inexpensive, low-end microprocessors dominated consumer electronics, ranging from toys to digital cameras to cellular telephones, while new generations of high-end microchips brought increased power to personal computers. Laser technology, which was already central to photonics and optical research, made inroads into fiber-optic–based consumer uses. More advanced telecommunications systems relied directly on computers and lasers for such developments as packet switching and high-speed data transmission.

ELECTRONICS

The distinction between electronics and computing continued to blur during the year, as almost all electronic devices incorporated some form of built-in computer. Computer chips that were being used as embedded controllers ranged from 64-bit Intel Pentiums and Motorola PowerPCs to 8-bit microcontrollers; the latter, which often employed 20-year-old architectures, remained popular because of their low cost, sometimes as low as $1 per chip, and their simple programming. Microchip Technology, Inc., and Amtel Corp. introduced low-cost microcontrollers that required no external circuitry except a power supply, for use in place of oscillators, level detectors, timers, and other functions that would normally require one conventional integrated circuit (IC) or two or three transistors.

The programmability of the microcontroller was a compelling advantage; the microcontroller served as a customizable IC offering far more versatility than a conventional circuit of comparable cost. Programming equipment was inexpensive, well within the reach of small entrepreneurs as well as hobbyists.

At the high end of built-in computers, children's toys went far beyond the limited computer functions that had appeared in the 1980s. "Virtual pets" were among the most popular. A virtual pet is a simulated animal that demands attention and (virtual) food (administered by pressing a button); its "health" depends on how it is treated, and it will "die" if neglected. Calculator-sized "Tamagotchi" virtual pets (from Bandai Co., Ltd., Tokyo; named for the Japanese *tamago,* or "egg") beeped for virtual food in school classrooms throughout the year.

At Christmas 1998, the most sought-after toy was the Furby (Tiger Electronics, Ltd., Vernon Hills, Ill.), a fuzzy stuffed animal containing an advanced computer system that could respond to its environment in elaborate ways and even talk to its owner through a speech synthesizer. Furbies used the same microprocessor as the Apple II computer of 20 years earlier, and they had the means to talk to each other by means of an infrared link.

Communications

Panasonic (Matsushita) introduced a 900-MHz cordless telephone that used spread-spectrum technology to achieve a range of about 1.6 km (one mile), rather than just the size of the average house, without compromising privacy or conflicting with other cordless phones on the same frequency. Spread-spectrum allows the frequency to be changed many times per second in a prearranged pseudorandom sequence. The receiver is designed to rec-

Toys with built-in computers include the "Tamagotchi," virtual pets from Japan that beep for virtual food (below) and the Furby, a fuzzy stuffed animal that can respond to its environment (opposite page, with Tiger Electronics president, Roger Shiffman).

Xavier Rossi/Gamma Liaison International

ognize the sequence and follow the signal as it moves around. Would-be eavesdroppers are unable to follow the sequence and may not even be aware that a signal is present (it sounds like random noise). Channel conflicts are not a problem because if a spread-spectrum device lands on the same frequency as something else, it moves on within a fraction of a second. Spread-spectrum transmission had been used for military and experimental purposes for many years, but this was its first major civilian use.

During the year many police departments and similar agencies switched to computer-controlled "trunked" two-way radios. In a trunked system a computer automatically keeps track of who is talking to whom and assigns frequencies whenever someone presses a push-to-talk button. The receiving equipment follows the frequency assignments automatically. This enables the system to carry multiple, separate conversations without requiring users to search manually for clear channels. It also makes interception slightly more difficult.

Steve Kagan/Gamma Liaison International

Digital signal processing (DSP), the use of microprocessors to process audio, video, and radio signals, became widespread during 1998. DSP is accomplished by converting the signal into an array of numbers on which computation can be done and then converting the result back to an analog signal. For example, a sudden pop in a digitized sound wave will stand out as an excessively high or low number and can be eliminated by replacing it with the average of the numbers adjacent to it. Applications include removing pops and crackles from recordings of old phonograph records, eliminating whines and noise from the sound of a shortwave radio, and creating video special effects. More importantly, DSP is crucial to the operation of modems that transmit digital data at increasingly higher rates on telephone lines designed for the human voice.

In 1998 a number of companies were doing research and development on "soft radios," though none had reached the market. Soft radios are radio receivers that use software rather than circuitry to extract the audio, or other modulated signal, from the radio waves. In a conventional AM radio, the incoming signal (535–1,705 kHz) is converted to 455 kHz so that it can be amplified by circuits permanently tuned to that frequency. This had been standard practice since the 1930s, but by 1999 each 455-kHz cycle, lasting 2.2 milliseconds, was long enough for a computer to do appreciable work. Thus, it was possible to analyze the waveform and compute the audio signal rather than trying to extract it with a diode and a low-pass filter. This yielded much more accurate results and made it possible to extract digital data, multiple audio channels, or other signals too complex to decode with conventional radio circuits.

Digital photography

By 1998 "megapixel" digital cameras from numerous manufacturers were competing seriously with film cameras both for casual amateur snapshooting and for commercial photography. A megapixel is an array of at least $1,000 \times 1,000$ picture elements (pixels) that produces sharp prints at least half as large as this page. Older digital cameras that were 640×480 and smaller were suitable only for computer screen images and postcard-sized prints.

Digital cameras are remarkably easy to use because, like video cameras, they can adapt automatically to a wide range of light levels. The charge-coupled device (CCD) image sensor is normally much smaller than a piece of film (perhaps two millimeters [0.08 in] across), and the lens has a shorter focal length than that of a film camera, giving much greater depth of field; many digital cameras do not require focusing at all, and those that do can autofocus effectively because the digitized image is always available. Other advantages of digital photography include the ability to transmit the image by modem to a newspaper office or the like and the ability to

This digital camera made by Nikon produces sharp prints at least half the size of this page. It contains an array of 1,000 × 1,000 pixels.

Nikon Inc.

load the image directly into the computer for incorporation into a typeset document.

The full resolution of a 35-mm slide is equivalent to about $2,400 \times 3,600$ pixels (8.6 megapixels). As of 1999 digital cameras had not yet achieved this resolution economically because a large image sensor requires an unusually large, flawless wafer of silicon. Because of limits imposed by the wavelength of light, electronic image sensors cannot be miniaturized to the extent that other integrated circuits have been; each pixel must be on the order of 0.01 mm (0.0004 in) square. Thus, 8- or 10-megapixel image sensors were not feasible as of 1999, and film was not yet dead.

Even film photography, however, had become partly digital. It is much easier to make a good color enlargement by scanning the film image into a computer and manipulating it digitally than by printing on conventional photographic paper. This is so because the computer can analyze the red, green, and blue layers of color film individually, while conventional photographic processes must handle all three at once. Thus, in addition to shifting the overall color balance the way a colored filter could, the computer can correct defects such as "crossover" (different color rendition in highlights than in shadows, uncorrectable by filters) and even detect and remove dust and scratches. One Nikon scanner introduced in 1998 even locates dust and scratches by bouncing infrared light off the film.

During the year, many serious amateur photographers bought scanners and color printers to process their photographs. Hewlett-Packard marketed a low-cost system comprising camera, film and print

A system including a camera, a film and print scanner, and an inkjet printer was introduced by Hewlett-Packard. Among its advantages were the relatively low cost of each enlargement and the ability to avoid printing unwanted pictures.

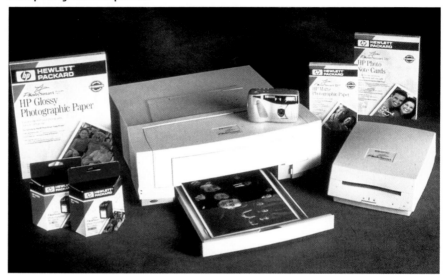

Hewlett-Packard

scanner, and inkjet printer. The cost of the equipment was offset by the relatively low cost of each enlargement and the ability to avoid printing unwanted pictures. Camera stores also set up kiosks where people could make their own prints digitally.

The look of magazine and newspaper pictures also showed the impact of digital technology. Routinely, images were sharpened (deblurred) prior to publication by increasing the difference between each pixel and its neighbors. Moderate deblurring helps overcome minor focusing errors and loss of sharpness in reproduction; stronger deblurring produces an unusual "blurry glowing edges" effect that became a familiar sight in the late 1990s. Much more sophisticated deblurring algorithms were being used in scientific work (especially astronomy), and extensive automatic analysis and correction of optical defects in images were under development.

Finally, even film cameras began incorporating extensive digital technology. The

new Nikon F5 camera used a 1,005-element array of CCD image sensors to measure the light level and coloration across the entire picture and match it to a memory bank of stored exposure information. The F5 contained five microprocessors (three 16-bit, one 8-bit, and one 4-bit) networked together—more computer power than was provided by a complete personal computer in 1989.

Video and audio

Digital television broadcasts in the U.K. and the United States began in 1998. For the first time, Britain and continental Europe had a common TV standard, although channel frequencies remained distinct. In the U.S., digital TV used the same set of 6-MHz-wide VHF and UHF channels as did conventional TV broadcasting. Temporarily, the Federal Communications Commission (FCC) allotted many TV stations a second channel on which to begin digital broadcasts without interrupting conventional analog transmissions. The FCC announced that by 2006 each station must drop back to only one channel and all broadcasts must be digital. By using a converter, one can receive digital broadcasts on conventional TV sets, but doing so sacrifices most of the improvement in picture quality that digital TV offers.

The advantage of digital television is that, by relying on computer power in the receiver, it can transmit a much more detailed picture and better sound over the same channel. The Japanese system of nondigital high-definition TV, requiring 20-MHz-wide channels, was not adopted elsewhere.

Conventional analog TV requires wide bandwidth because it retransmits the entire picture 30 times per second (25 in Britain) every time the electron beam scans the receiver's screen, even if the picture has not changed. In digital TV only the moving portion of the picture is retransmitted, and several data compression algorithms encode the picture as concisely as possible. American digital TV includes both high-definition television (HDTV) and standard-definition television (SDTV) picture formats; at first, SDTV predominated because of the lack of HDTV program material.

Flat-screen television, a dream for 30 years, became a commercial reality in 1998. Developed by the Dutch firm Philips, the approximately 10-cm (4-in)-thick TV set hangs on the wall like a picture and connects to a separate receiver unit. Its display uses ionized gas and fluorescent red, green, and blue phosphors to deliver bright colors viewable from any direction.

Flat-screen displays for desktop computers also came into wide use. Like lap-top computers, these flat screens use liquid crystal displays and are viewable only from directly in front—possibly of benefit to the user's privacy. They also offered a perceived safety advantage because, unlike cathode-ray tubes (CRTs), they do not use high voltages (which can generate X-rays) or strong magnetic fields. It was not clear that conventional cathode-ray tube displays were actually a health hazard, but many computer users, especially lawsuit-wary corporations, chose to eliminate any possible risk. Furthermore, flat screens save space, and they are easier on the eyes because their light emissions are continuous (not flickering) and because, if properly matched to the video system of the computer, they are permanently sharp and never go out of focus.

Awards

The 1998 Nobel Prize for Physics was awarded jointly to Robert B. Laughlin, Horst L. Störmer, and Daniel C. Tsui for their discovery of the "fractional quantum Hall effect," a conduction phenomenon involving apparent charges less than that of one electron. This discovery raised the prospect of overcoming a fundamental limitation on integrated circuits, the fact that it has been impossible to send a signal with less than one electron. Fractional-charge effects could allow one electron to carry more than one bit of information. (*See* SCIENTISTS OF THE YEAR: *Nobel Prizes.*)

The Institute of Electrical and Electronics Engineers Medal of Honor was awarded to Donald O. Pederson of the University of California at Berkeley for the development of SPICE (Simulation Program with Integrated Circuit Emphasis),

a software package developed in the 1960s and now incorporated into virtually all circuit-design software. The original impetus for circuit simulation was that integrated circuit designs cannot always be tried out realistically with discrete components and that making a trial IC was very expensive. With the advent of sufficiently powerful personal computers, SPICE and its derivatives became basic tools of circuit design.

—Michael A. Covington

PHOTONICS AND OPTICAL TECHNOLOGY

Telescope technical advances

Large telescopes and active control systems were the top optics news of 1998 and early 1999. Germany's Max Planck Institute for Astronomy led the active-control push by installing an "adaptive optics" system on the joint German–Spanish 3.5-m telescope in Calar Alto, Spain. (A meter is about 39.4 in.) In adaptive optics, a wave-front sensor measures atmospheric distortion (from atmospheric motion or other factors) by detecting the phase of incoming light. The sensor can then alter the mirror's shape by moving levers or other actuators to correct for the atmospheric distortion and thus produce clearer imagery.

Active control is particularly important for very large mirrors, which tend to flex under their own weight, producing distortions without any help from the atmosphere. In May 1998 the European Southern Observatory's Very Large Telescope (VLT) in Cerro Paranal, Chile, produced its "first light," using adaptive optics to provide resolution better than 0.5 arc second (the

Specially clothed technicians inspect for tiny flaws in the polished surface of one of the primary mirrors destined for the European Southern Observatory's Very Large Telescope.

Optical materials

Fused silica glass is an important optical material, but polishing it to high-precision optical standards is difficult because grinding machines leave behind tiny ridges that must be removed without altering the essential lens shape; thus the polishing process is time-consuming and imprecise, at best. The Polytechnical University of Cataluña, Terrassa, Spain, developed a laser technique that polishes lenses, including nonspherical optics, more quickly and accurately than mechanical processes can manage. The researchers used a high-power (as high as two kilowatt) carbon dioxide laser to heat the surface of the glass to about 650° C (1,200° F), and the heated glass flowed because of gravity and surface tension to fill the ridges left by the grinding machines. One difficulty with this process in the past was that thermal stresses from the laser could cause the optics to crack. The Spanish researchers avoided this by first heating the glass to 580° C (1,076° F). The research team reported measuring improvements in root-mean-square optical surface deviation from 500 nanometers (nm; 500 billionths of a meter) with traditional mechanical polishing to 1 nm with the laser technique. Polishing time was also significantly reduced, from the eight hours required for mechanical polishing to a few seconds for the laser technique. The group experi-

equivalent of distinguishing two objects that are just $1/7200$ of a degree apart). The telescope's immense primary mirror was 8.2 m in diameter and only 175 mm (6.9 in) thick and had 150 actuators for an adaptive optical control system. Its secondary mirror was also actively controlled.

In January 1999 Japan unveiled its new 8.3-m Subaru telescope Hawaii. Subaru, which also used adaptive optical techniques, had 261 actuators that controlled the shape of its primary mirror, which was 200 mm (7.9 in) thick including the aluminum coating. Its resolution was estimated at 0.2 arc second ($1/18,000$ of a degree).

A much smaller telescope with a much larger international project started a five-year mission of mapping the heavens. The Sloan Digital Sky Survey began collecting data for the immense task of producing a high-resolution map of the universe, one small piece at a time. Based at the Apache Point Observatory in New Mexico, Sloan's 2.5-m telescope used six columns of extremely sensitive 2,048 × 2,048-pixel charge-coupled device detectors to capture images of the sky in 2.5° stripes. After five years, according to Princeton University astronomer Jim Gunn, the Sloan team should have amassed data and assembled a map of the universe 100 times larger and considerably more quantitative and sensitive than any other map produced to that point. The survey's goals included obtaining imagery and distance measurements for 100 million celestial objects and spectral data for a million galaxies and 100,000 quasars.

This infrared image of the Orion Nebula was made using the new 8.3-m Subaru telescope of Japan's National Astronomical Observatory situated at the top of the volcano Mauna Kea in Hawaii.

Reuters/HO/Archive Photos

mented with lenses up to 80 sq mm (0.12 sq in) and was working on developing a method that would work on lenses up to 5,000 sq mm (7.75 sq in).

High-quality optical coatings, which can produce surface-finish problems on even the best-polished optics, was another area of research interest. The Lawrence Livermore (Calif.) National Laboratory was particularly interested in this problem because of the special needs for the National Ignition Facility in construction there. When completed, the facility would house 192 ultrahigh-energy laser beam lines that would combine at a pellet of deuterium to create a miniature nuclear explosion that scientists would be able to study for energy and military purposes. The beam lines needed ultrahigh-precision optical systems, including reflectors for the flash lamps that would pump the facility's Nd:glass (neodymium:glass) amplifiers. Silver-coated mirrors corrode over time, reducing their reflectivity and reducing the performance of an amplifier, so Livermore researchers developed a silver coating that protected the surfaces from tarnishing. Designed by Jesse Wolfe, the coating com-

prised adhesion and passivation layers on each side of the sputtered silver, as well as a layer of silicon nitride and metal oxide layers. The coating survived almost 21,000 xenon lamp flashes over four months in ordinary room conditions and maintained a 95–98% reflectivity. In addition to the laboratory's scientific application, the mirror coating technology could protect mirrors in everyday applications.

The NEC Corp. Optoelectronics and High-Frequency Device Research Laboratories developed a photonic crystal that reflected light 100–1,000 times more efficiently than normal prisms, depending on the angle of incidence and wavelength of the light. Fabrication of the crystal relied on its self-organization from alternating layers of amorphous silicon and silicon dioxide on a silicon substrate that was patterned with an array of hexagonal holes. The material should be useful in integrated optical devices, which are small optical circuits that could decrease the size of equipment needed for fiber optic telecommunications or future optical computers.

Telecommunications

As the Internet and other data communications applications have grown, communications networks have sought new ways to put more information on a single optical fiber without having to run new fibers or wires. If a communication network is a data highway, there are two ways to increase its capacity without widening the road—shrink the cars' length and increase their speed or shrink the width of the lanes so more cars fit side by side. In telecommunications terms, time division multiplexing (TDM) uses a lot of very short pulses (analogous

to a highway lane of small cars moving quickly) while wavelength division multiplexing (WDM) puts many wavelengths of light on a single fiber (lane widths are shrunk, but new lanes are added). Future telecommunications systems would likely combine these technologies.

In the WDM camp, Lucent Technologies researchers reported early in 1998 that they had sent 100 channels of data at 10 gigabits (10 billion bits) per second over a single fiber 400 km (250 mi) long, achieving the terabits (trillion bits) per second record that had been a telecommunications goal for several years. Each of the 100 channels used its own laser at a slightly different wavelength. Although it is not easy to keep each channel precisely on its assigned wavelength (each car within its narrow lane), Lucent accomplished this by using external modulation and feedback to ensure that each laser stayed within a prescribed wavelength range.

On the TDM side, researchers at the Chalmers University of Technology, Göteborg, Swed., reported that they sent one channel of information at 40 gigabits per second in a single-wavelength over a 400-km commercial fiber optic network, using soliton waves. Solitons are short waves that maintain their shape in situations where other waves break down; for example, most telecommunications laser pulses slowly flatten and spread out (an effect called dispersion) as they proceed through an optical fiber. This dispersion effect means that optical pulses—especially very fast, short pulses—must be renewed frequently in a telecommunications system, adding to the cost of the system. In 1999 one group of researchers at Japan's NTT Corp. reported achieving a transmis-

(Bottom) This illustration of a "bow-tie" laser shows how the emitted radiation travels in four controllable beams rather than in the infinite loop common to classic whispering gallery disc lasers.

sion of 40 gigabits per second over 70,000 km (43,400 mi) in a laboratory experiment, and another group achieved 40 gigabits per second error-free over 1,020 km (634 mi) in a field experiment in part of the Tokyo metropolitan loop network. The field test, considered more important because of its real-world conditions, used four repeaters and dispersion-shifted fibers. Even so, the signal experienced pulse broadening from polarization-mode dispersion. Adding in-line soliton modulation controls allowed them to extend the fiber length to 1,360 km (845 mi) without a significant increase in errors but with a slight power penalty.

Semiconductor lasers

A class of lasers known as whispering gallery disc lasers create light by sending radiation in circles until it escapes evenly through quantum mechanical tunneling. These lasers are very small but produce very little power with little directionality, characteristics that are not very efficient for most laser applications. Researchers at Lucent Technologies' Bell Laboratories, Yale University, and the Max Planck

Lucent Technologies

Institute of Physics in Germany slightly flattened the shape of a classic whispering gallery disc laser to produce a more efficient multidirectional, high-power, low-threshold "bow-tie" laser. Rather than traveling in an infinite loop constrained by total internal reflection, the radiation traveled in a bow-tie pattern and emitted in four controllable beams at 10 milliwatts each in the mid-infrared range of the electromagnetic spectrum. Continued research on the interesting structure aimed to reduce the number of beams from four to two and to reduce the wavelength from the mid-infrared to the near-infrared, around 1.5 micrometers (μm), where it would be useful for telecommunications applications.

American and Japanese researchers from Bell Laboratories, Osaka University, and the University of Utah joined to develop polymer microlasers that appear to have low or no losses. During the 1998 Conference on Lasers and Electro-Optics (CLEO), team members said that they had created optically pumped microlasers and electrically driven light-emitting diodes from soluble derivatives of poly(p-phenylenevinylene) and polyacetylene. The cylindrical devices measured 4–200 μm across on flat glass substrates and emitted 100-picosecond, 10-nanosecond, or 200-nanosecond pulses at 532 nm. (For additional information about optoelectronic applications of polymers, *see* Year in Review: MATERIALS SCIENCE AND ENGINEERING: *Polymers*.)

High-power lasers and applications

The U.S. Air Force completed several tests of its Airborne Laser Program, which sought to develop a device that could point and focus a laser from a military aircraft to a hostile target (for example, a ballistic missile). In 1998 engineers from Boeing Co., TRW Inc., and Lockheed Martin completed wind tunnel testing, experimented with a beam control demonstrator, and test-fired the multihundred-kilowatt chemical oxygen iodine laser (COIL). TRW and Lockheed Martin provided the laser and the optics, respectively, and Boeing was integrating the components.

Military and university researchers also joined forces to look for commercial applications for COIL and other high-power military-developed lasers. One effort was considering whether COIL or another large military laser, the Mid-Infrared Advanced Chemical Laser (MIRACL) could help drill oil and gas wells. The Gas Research Institute was spearheading a project to use the megawatt-class laser to drill sandstone, limestone, shale, and other minerals that oil and gas companies typically face when drilling. In 1998 researchers aimed a 15-cm (six-inch)-diameter beam from MIRACL at a sandstone sample, penetrating 6.4 cm (2.5 in) into the material in 2.5 seconds.

In an unrelated study of nonmilitary uses for large lasers, University of Illinois researchers worked with U.S. Air Force experts to cut 1.27-cm (0.5-in)-thick stainless steel plate and 9.5-mm (0.37-in)-thick Hastalloy with a 10-kw COIL, the energy of which was delivered through a 900-μm-diameter optical fiber.

At the beginning of 1998, the death of a United Airlines passenger during a bout of turbulence inspired research into compact, laser-based approaches to detecting atmospheric conditions that produce "clear-air turbulence." NASA and the U.S. Federal Aviation Authority sponsored programs aimed at producing devices that could provide seconds to minutes of warning about impending turbulence; the U.S. National Science Foundation lent a research aircraft to the effort in March and April.

The leading photonic contender in the research was light detection and ranging technology, known as Doppler lidar. In this technique, a laser beam reflects off small particles and aerosols in the air, and the light returns to a sensor. In compliance with the Doppler effect, the scattered light changes frequency as a result of the particles' motion in the air, relative to the detector. Analyzing the frequency shift of the returned, scattered light allows the determination of wind velocity at selected points along the beam path; highly variable velocities indicate the presence of turbulence. Laser light of a specific and known frequency is, therefore, crucial.

Scientists had been using carbon dioxide lasers for the task, but as the altitude of the experiments increased, the particles became tinier, and the lasers' 10-μm wavelength was too large to reflect off tiny particles. Thus, researchers at NASA's Dryden Research Center in Edwards, Calif., and the Naval Research Laboratory in Monterey, Calif., were experimenting with a Tm:YAG (thulium:yttrium-aluminum-garnet) laser that emitted a 2-μm beam, which could detect smaller particles. Paul Revey of Coherent Technologies Inc., Boulder, Colo., said the laser system could detect turbulence 10–15 km (6–9 mi) in front of the aircraft, which would provide 6–30 seconds of warning.

Awards

Four researchers who contributed to the invention of the quantum cascade laser received the 1998 Rank Prize in Optoelectronics. Sharing the prize were Federico Capasso and Rudolf Kazarinov of Bell Laboratories; Jerome Faist of the University of Neuchatel, Switz.; and Robert Suris of the Ioffe Technical Institute in St. Petersburg, Russia. The quantum cascade laser is a semiconductor device in which the thickness of its active layers determines its wavelength, which can range from the mid- to far-infrared regions (about 1–30 μm) of the electromagnetic spectrum. The name of the device comes from the way that electrons cascade through the active layers. Capasso and the other winners continued to advance quantum cascade technology toward commercialization and, in fact, produced many new results in 1998, including devices that could produce several hundred milliwatts of power and devices that emitted at more than one wavelength simultaneously. Applications for this type of device would be in gas sensing, such as pollution monitoring and medical testing.
—Stephanie A. Weiss

COMPUTERS AND COMPUTER SCIENCE

Unexpected twists and turns—both technological and legal—marked the year in computer science. Although Microsoft Corp. retained its position as the dominant purveyor of software for personal computers (PCs), many of the notable innovations in 1998 emerged from other quarters.

Pushing the envelope of top-flight performance, the U.S. Department of Energy (DOE) funded development of a "teraflops" supercomputer capable of executing 30 trillion instructions per second. In the retail market, consumers had their pick among PCs selling for under $1,000. These constituted the first wave of low-cost machines with enough heft to run serious business software applications and multimedia-intensive games.

The burgeoning home market also provided an opportunity for Apple Computer, Inc. to revive its fortunes. Under the direction of Steven Jobs, the company co-founder who was ousted in 1985 but returned as interim CEO in 1997, Apple debuted a chicly designed home computer called the iMac. Selling for approximately $1,200 and housed in a streamlined, translucent blue-and-white case, the iMac became the best-selling single computer model by year's end. Apple built on that success in early 1999 with a line of higher-powered iMacs, which cost $100 less than the initial models and were offered in an array of bold colors.

The popularity of the iMac dovetailed with that of the Internet, which continued to draw in millions of new computer users. America Online, the world's largest Internet service provider, scurried to provide better service that broadened its base by signing deals with Netscape Communications Corp., a leading maker of software to browse the Internet, and with Sun Microsystems Inc., a supplier of powerful servers that could store and deliver content to consumers' homes.

Meanwhile, Sun propelled its four-year-old programming language Java into a new area dubbed ubiquitous, or pervasive, computing. The concept was based on a wave of upcoming handheld appliances, which were

Pervasive computing

The most exciting among the computer-science innovations that began taking shape in 1998 fell under the rubric of pervasive computing. Led by Sun, the objective was to usher in a move away from stand-alone desktop PCs and toward new-age "information appliances"—downsized devices that connect to the Internet through traditional phone lines or via digital-wireless telephone systems. The first wave of such products was expected to include portable E-mail readers, but the category would ultimately encompass a bevy of "embedded computers." These would comprise everyday appliances and other machines outfitted with microprocessors but not commonly thought of as having electronic brains, including microprocessor-equipped washing machines, coffee-makers, interactive televisions, and home security systems.

In January 1999 at the annual Consumer Electronics Show in Las Vegas, Nev., South Korea's Samsung and France's Alcatel showed off telephones that used Java software technology from Sun to support long-distance voice communications, E-mail, and connections to the Internet. These telephones used "PersonalJava," a downsized implementation of Java designed to power consumer items, like smart phones, that are cost sensitive and thus contain little memory and low-power microprocessors.

Java also moved ahead in the converging worlds of television and the World Wide Web (the graphical component of the Internet). Japan's Matsushita Electric Industrial Co. Ltd. in 1998 signed a pact with Sun to further develop Java for digital consumer electronics, such as digital-TV and audio-video equipment.

expected to connect people to the Internet as easily from their car as from their kitchen.

Concerns about the year 2000, or Y2K, problem continued to bedevil programmers in the computer-science community. While experts agreed that Y2K would provide lucrative work in 1999 for consultants of all stripes, they disagreed on precisely how serious a problem Y2K would present. A number of experts expressed the view that what was largely a legitimate but manageable problem—on Jan. 1, 2000, many computers would be unable to distinguish 2000 from 1900—was being overinflated to apocalyptic proportions, fueling possible panic among computer-illiterate people.

Attention to 64-bit microprocessors reached frenzied levels in 1998, as Intel Corp. whetted the public's interest for its upcoming Merced chip. Similarly, software companies began paving a path to the 64-bit world. Microsoft reported progress on a new, 64-bit version of its Windows NT operating system (OS) to be called Windows 2000. Cost considerations touched a chord in the software world, as a free OS called Linux was adopted by numerous hobbyists and professionals alike.

The computing community also witnessed its share of legal battles, particularly as the U.S. Justice Department began its

antitrust trial against Microsoft in October. By many media accounts, Microsoft chairman Bill Gates did not win points with the public for his often combative rhetoric during the early phases of the trial. A kinder and gentler public face of computing appeared to emerge as Scott McNealy, chairman of Sun, was profiled on the television newsmagazine "60 Minutes." Some pundits predicted McNealy would emerge as the "anti-Gates," a reference to his fierce legal and market battles with his Microsoft counterpart.

Most important, such deals—including one with Sony Corp.—were likely to help Sun promulgate its Jini software architecture, which was launched in the summer of 1998 at the Telecosm Conference, a gathering of the digital world's elite in Squaw Valley, Calif. Bill Joy, vice president of research at Sun, gave the first public demonstration of Jini, which used object-oriented software techniques and Java to enable nontraditional computing devices, such as handheld computers and smart phones, to automatically communicate and share services with each other and with conventional PCs. Sun's Jini initiative sparked an intense competition for control of the technology required to enable the coming generation of Web-based services.

Microsoft mounted its own challenge to Jini with a technology called Universal Plug and Play. The software giant appeared intent on leveraging its huge installed base by folding the necessary additional capabilities into its existing operating systems, such as Windows 98. According to Microsoft's engineers, Universal Plug and Play would be able to work inside a cell phone without a huge OS. All that would be needed was a small amount of additional software on the PC to identify the phone and similar devices.

IBM Corp. began to set forth an alternate vision of pervasive computing during the year. According to its conception, a large computer, or server, would become a commonplace presence in ordinary homes. Such "basement servers" would control all aspects of a vast home network, including security systems and embedded systems such as coffeemakers and washing machines. More important, it would enable access to entertainment and the Internet

from any of dozens of flat-panel television displays located throughout the house. Entertainment producers such as the TV networks NBC and ABC were already taking note of such possibilities, as indicated by their participation in future-oriented conferences, notably "Digital Hollywood" held in early 1999 in Las Vegas.

64-bit microprocessors

During 1998 Intel continued to consolidate its hold on the hardware side of the computer-science community. At the same time, a spate of newcomers—including Rise Technology Co., of Santa Clara, Calif., and Centaur Technology Inc., a division of Integrated Device Technology Inc., Santa Clara—saw fertile opportunities at the low end of the market, which Intel had not successfully captured with its lower-priced Celeron chip.

Most notable at the high end was the emergence of 64-bit computer chips. These already existed in the form of Alpha from Compaq Computer Corp. and UltraSparc from Sun, but the most anxiously awaited was Intel's 64-bit Merced microprocessor, which was expected to power a new generation of home computers. At the

Microprocessor Forum conference held in San Jose, Calif., in October, Stephen Smith, vice president of Intel's microprocessor products group, reported that Merced's engineering team was proceeding toward the company's goal of shipping the chip in mid-2000.

Intel whetted additional interest in its 64-bit technology by revealing plans for several successors to Merced. The first, due in late 2001, would be an enhanced processor code-named McKinley. Two subsequent chips would follow—a high-powered offering due in 2002 and dubbed Madison, notable because it would be the first chip to be fabricated in Intel's next-generation 0.13-micron CMOS silicon technology, followed by a lower-cost processor code-named Deerfield.

While Intel pursued the high end of the market, startups like Rise and Centaur began nipping at its heels. These companies sensed opportunities as the market for PCs selling for around $1,000 began cresting in 1999. According to authoritative estimates, PCs selling for below $1,000 would comprise 43% of the market in 1998 and were expected to top 50% in 1999.

Rise emerged in the autumn with its first product—the low-cost mP6 central processing unit (CPU). When Rise was formed in 1993, it foresaw that low-power consumption would become very important for PCs. In addition, the company was

While expectations of a forthcoming generation of 64-bit microprocessors remained high, Intel Corp., the world's largest computer chip manufacturer, introduced its high-end 32-bit Pentium III microprocessor in 1999.

Intel Corporation

challenged to come out with an Intel-compatible design while maintaining low-power and delivering top-flight multimedia performance. A key design objective was to ensure that the mP6 could execute up to three MMX (Intel's multimedia instruction-set extensions) instructions per cycle. A second offering, the mp6 II, which added a 256-kilobyte on-chip L2 cache, was expected in late 1999. In addition, Centaur attacked the low end of the market with a processor called WinChip.

Next-generation software

While the coming of 64-bit chips like Merced garnered lots of attention, some industry analysts warned that Intel would face major challenges on the software front. Specifically, the chips would require a new class of advanced compilers to convert programmers' application software into streams of machine-code instructions that could take full advantage of the processor's architecture.

The first of those compilers came into view in mid-1998, when Hewlett-Packard Co., which helped Intel develop the instruction set used in Merced, released a research compiler called Trimaran. Trimaran was based on the pioneering Impact compiler developed by Wen-mei Hwu, a computer science professor at the University of Illinois, Urbana-Champaign, and encompassed additional research done at New York University. Such compilers were considered the key to making cutting-edge architectures such as Merced work in the real world. Trimaran was significant because it implemented speculation and predication, the two key new software features in Merced. (Predication attempts to remove

unnecessary "branch" instructions from a program, while speculation streamlines operation by executing "load" instructions as early as possible.)

A more workaday tool called VTune 3.0 was also released by Intel in 1998. It was a performance analysis program that presented programmers with a graphical view of how their software was running. In this way, they could detect "hot spots" (overused areas) in their code that could benefit from further optimization. Intel also paved a software path for its Merced microprocessor by seeding the development of a new generation of 64-bit software-development tools and operating systems.

Surprisingly, Java was not expected to play a key role when Merced hit the streets. Rather, the decade-old C++ programming language would lead, with compilers being prepared at Intel, Hewlett-Packard, and Microsoft. Two lesser known software firms—Metaware Inc., of Santa Cruz, Calif., and Edinburgh (Scot.) Portable Com-pilers Ltd.—were also developing heavy-duty, Merced-capable compilers.

On another front, a new competitor to Windows emerged in 1998 in the form of a free operating system called Linux, which was conceived by Linus Torvalds during his stint as a computer science student at the university of Helsinki. Available for downloading over the Internet, Linux attracted the attention of both programmers who

liked to write their own software and professional computer users intent on running heavy-duty applications, such as computer-aided design software. Linux also found a home as the software behind many Internet servers. As 1999 began, however, mainstream software producers did not see Linux as a serious threat to their markets.

Legal battles

Legal battles loomed large in the industry during 1998. The antitrust trial against Microsoft brought by the U.S. Justice Department and 20 (later 19) states began in October. The Justice Department contended that Microsoft used its dominant position in the software industry, particularly through its control of the Windows OS, to quash the efforts of competitors. Early in the trial, an Intel executive testi-

Linux was a Unix-based computer operating system developed by Finnish programmer Linus Torvalds and offered free over the Internet. It attracted increasing attention in 1998 from programmers and professional computer users, especially for running Internet servers.

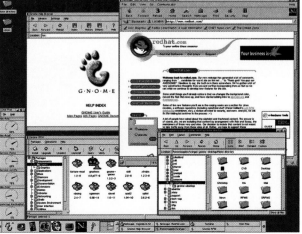

Courtesy Red Hat Software

fied that the company felt that it was prevented from entering the software market in 1995 owing to actions taken by Microsoft. However, Microsoft's lawyers vigorously defended the company's position. They disputed the Intel claim and noted the availability of other operating systems, such as Unix and Linux, as evidence that Microsoft did not maintain an unfair monopoly. The trial continued in 1999; meanwhile, Intel agreed to a settlement of a similar antitrust case in March 1999.

Separately, Sun and Microsoft traded lawsuits over Java. Sun won an early victory when a court barred Microsoft from shipping a version of Java that allegedly differed from the terms required under Sun's licensing agreement. That battle, too, was poised to continue into 1999.

Looking forward

As the millennium approached, perhaps the most ambitious project conjured up images of HAL, the archetypal computing behemoth portrayed in the 1968 movie *2001: A Space Odyssey*.

In January 1998 the DOE began an intense effort aimed at realizing by the year 2001 a 30-teraflops supercomputer—10 times the performance of the highest-powered existing systems. Called "Pathforward," the DOE effort—in partnership with the Lawrence Livermore (Calif.), Sandia (Albuquerque, N.M.), and Los Alamos (N.M.) national laboratories—was funding the development of technology that could tie together clusters of supercomputers to create machines far faster than previously possible. Pathforward, which began as a project in 1998, was an adjunct to work in process since 1995 un-

Ficara/SYGMA

Bill Gates, chairman of Microsoft Corp., defends his company's policies in the antitrust suit brought against the computer software maker by the U.S. Department of Justice in 1998. The trial, which was widely followed both within the industry and by the public, continued in 1999.

der a sister program at the DOE called the Accelerated Strategic Computing Initiative (ASCI). Under ASCI the first single-teraflops-class supercomputers were beginning to come together. A one-teraflops Intel supercomputer known as the ASCI "Red" machine had already been delivered to Sandia. The system boasted some 9,000 Pentium Pro-class CPUs.

Current-generation supercomputers in 1998 were typically designed as symmetric multiprocessors (SMP) that had 16–128 or more processors inside. However, current-generation supercomputers topped out at between 1 and 3 teraflops. One technique to increase computing power was to hook together numerous SMP boxes. The interconnects and software funded under Pathforward was aimed at this goal. Specifically, in 2001 the project directors

hoped to achieve a 30-teraflops system, and by 2004 or 2005, it was aiming for 100-teraflops performance.

—Alexander Wolfe

COMPUTER SYSTEMS AND SERVICES

As the new millennium approached, a true information society was being achieved. In just a few short years, the World Wide Web had revolutionized the information industry by changing the ways in which data providers deliver information and the way that users process it. With so much information available, the user's focus was shifting from retrieving data to transforming it into knowledge by selecting, filtering, and organizing it, and then integrating it with previous acquisitions.

The recently renovated Main Reading Room of the New York Public Library was equipped with new computers sitting on 90-year-old desks.

Libraries were creating new and expanded services and were becoming, in the words of Kevin Starr, the California state librarian, "malls for the mind and the imagination." Library automation began in the late 1960s when the labor-intensive card catalog began to be replaced by the computer-based public access catalog (PAC), and the cards that had been slipped into sleeves in the back (or front) of the book were replaced with electronic bar codes. Nearly three-fourths of the libraries in the U.S. became computerized and provided free public access to the Internet. This service became so popular that many big-city libraries had to restrict user access to the Internet to 30 minutes during busy hours.

The U.S. Library of Congress, in order to preserve its collections and to make them more available, began a multiyear project to digitize its holdings one section at a time. Underway during the year was the digitization of the African-American Odyssey collection of books, manuscripts, photographs, films, musical scores, maps, and oral histories. The hundreds of items in this collection told the story of black people's quest for full citizenship and ranged over the periods of slavery, the Civil War, World Wars I and II, the Great Depression, the New Deal, and the Civil Rights era.

U.S. systems and services

During 1998 the information industry launched many new products on CD-ROM, in print, and on the Internet. The National Technical Information Service (NTIS) made the *Statistical Abstract of the United States 1997* available in a print edition and on CD-ROM. This reference work, issued annually by the Bureau of the Census, had been the federal government's most respected statistical fact book on the social, political, and economic aspects of American life. The CD-ROM version contained more data on more subjects than did the print version and, when interfaced with the Web, allowed users to link to official government Web sites.

Encyclopædia Britannica, Inc. made its Britannica Internet Guide to the Nobel Prizes available as a free Spotlight Feature on the Web (http://www.eb.com). The Spotlight featured biographies on more than 600 recipients of the Nobel Prize. Hyperlinked tables enabled users to obtain information on all Nobel Prize winners, categorized by name, prize, and year, and to link to articles about their prizewinning concepts. A short biography of Alfred Bernard Nobel, the founder of the Nobel Prizes, was also included along with the text of the will that initiated the awards. Other Spotlight Features included Shakespeare and the Globe, Normandy 1944, Toys Through Time, Discovering Dinosaurs, and The American Presidency.

UMI (University Microfilm Inc.) reached a milestone during the year with the addition of the 1.5 millionth doctoral dissertation to its Dissertation Abstracts Database. Contained in this database were more than 90% of all Ph.D. dissertations from accredited institutions of higher learning in North America, as well as from a growing number of colleges and universities in Europe and Asia. All entries were indexed, abstracted, archived, and made available for ordering and research. UMI also announced plans to digitize its entire collection of books, newspapers, and periodicals, starting with its collection of early English literature.

The *Comprehensive Shakespeare Dictionary* on CD-ROM, published by Oryx Press in Phoenix, Ariz., contained more than 20,000 terms from Shakespeare's writings, more than 50,000 cited quotations, the names of all characters, and plot summaries of all of his plays. Users could research either very narrow or very broad topics by typing a portion of a quotation, and they would retrieve references pertaining to the phrase and the play from which it was extracted. The dictionary project resulted from a collaboration of scholars and theater specialists dedicated to making Shakespeare accessible to students and the general public.

Norman Rockwell—The Man and His Art was released on CD-ROM by Cinegram Media, Inc. Nearly 500 of the artist's paintings, including the complete series of 324 *Saturday Evening Post* cover illustrations were made available for viewing and study. The software developed for this program facilitated detailed on-screen analysis of the paintings and provided participants with insights into Rockwell's life and times, his working environment, and the influence his paintings had on society.

One hundred nine years of the *National Geographic* magazine, more than 1,200 is-

sues, were put on 30 CD-ROMs by Mindscape, Inc., of Novato, Calif. Included were all of the magazine's major articles, award-winning photographs, maps, graphics, and classic advertisements. The disc also contained a search engine and a direct link to an exclusive area on the National Geographic Web site. Users of this digital library could relive every adventure reported in the magazine and could locate specific articles, topics, and images by date, issue, subject, photograph, or writer. After an article had been selected and viewed, the program automatically highlighted related topics and contributors, enabling the user to extend the search.

Having recognized that undergraduate biology students have information needs that differ from those of graduate and professional researchers, BIOSIS published BasicBIOSIS. The 350 selected journals included in this database contained information on virtually every life-science discipline, from agriculture and biology to neuroscience and biotechnology. Approximately 300,000 records and abstracts comprised this file, which was updated monthly.

Http://www.infoplease.com, established by Information Please, was a free one-stop reference site that contained millions of up-to-date facts and figures derived from the various *Information Please* almanacs on sports, entertainment, and general knowledge together with material obtained from various encyclopedias and dictionaries.

International systems and services

UNESCO continued to implement its policy of promoting free and universal access to information resources. The organization stated that the policy was needed to help redress international imbalances in gaining such access.

The British Library produced a CD-ROM, *One Hundred Treasures,* to showcase some of the finest items in its book and manuscript collection. Spanning three millennia, the disc included the Lindisfarne Gospels, the *Diamond Sutra,* Gutenberg's 42-line Bible, the Magna Carta, the first western book printed with movable type, and many other treasures such as sacred books, illustrated manuscripts, musical scores, historical documents, maps, newspapers, stamps, and sound recordings, for a total of 100 images. Users could browse through these images, zoom in on them, read short commentaries, and listen to associated sound recordings.

The *Dangerous Substances* CD-ROM integrated information on all European Union (EU) documents related to dangerous chemical substances plus the full text of EU legislation on the classification, packaging, marketing, and the use of these dangerous preparations. Each record consisted of the item's molecular structure, data on risk and safety, and the appropriate warning symbol. More than 100,000 chemical substances were listed, and these were accessible to be searched by name and classification.

The only general lending service for blind and visually impaired people in the U.K. was provided by the National Library for the Blind (NLB). The library's updated book-production system consisted of a high-speed document duplex scanner that would scan 80 pages a minute into a computer system and an optical character recognition program that would read those images, which would then be edited, translated into Braille, and compiled into a finished book. Previously, manual transcription, translation, and production of a 500-page Braille book could have taken up to two years; the new system could produce the final product in a matter of weeks. One of the major beneficiaries of the new system was the NLB's Youth Department, which had planned to produce at least 300 new Braille titles for teenagers and young adults by 2000.

The Web site of the Scottish Office (http://www.Scotland.gov.uk) was organized into a publication section, a question and answer service, a news section, and a guide to the Scottish Office Department. The department guide was particularly valuable and useful, because it contained information about the activities of the health, education, agriculture, and development departments. News reports were updated daily. The publication section provided free access to several full text reports, and all publications were indexed both alphabetically and by department.

Information on the Chinese economy was available on a Web site organized by the country's trade ministry. The Web site (http://www.chinamarket.com.cn) contained information about more than 8,000

China's trade ministry established a Web site that contained information, in Chinese and English, about more than 8,000 industrial products.

industrial products ranging from machinery and electronics to textiles and foodstuffs. The site also included daily updated business bulletins and discussion forums.

China MOFTEC

All information was accessible in both Chinese and English.

Russian Scientific News (RSN), a database distributed by Silver Platter, claimed to be the first comprehensive source of scientific information from Russia and the countries of the former Soviet Union. RSN provided abstracts of publications, current research, institutional activities, and library holdings. The database consisted of four files: Russian Periodicals Bibliography, Current Titles and Abstracts, Directory of Russian and CIS Libraries, and the Directory of Russia and CIS R&D organizations.

Research and development

The Getty Program gave 11 grants, totaling over $700,000, as part of a five-year Electronic Cataloging Initiative designed to assist Los Angeles-area museums and art institutions in putting their art catalogs on-line. Planning grants provided support for cataloging and making an extensive inventory of their collections. Implementation grants supported the creation or expansion of such catalogs, plus the expense involved in putting them in digital format and bringing them electronically on-line.

The Institute for Scientific Information (ISI) and the American Society for Information Science (ASIS) announced the creation of annual ISI/ASIS Citation Analysis Research Grants in the amount of $3,000. These grants were designed to support the use of citation analysis in studying the generation, organization, access, and use of information, and they were to be awarded on the basis of the proposal's methodology, originality, creativity, and potential global significance. Stephen P. Harter, a professor at Indiana University's School of Library and Information Science, was the recipient of the third annual Citation Analysis Research grant for his proposal to assess the feasibility of applying citation analysis to information documents on the Web.

Assistant professor Dania Bilal at the University of Tennessee at Knoxville received a $3,250 grant from the Office of Research at her university in support of her studies of children's information-seeking behavior when using on-line search engines.

The National Science Foundations Professional Opportunities for Woman in Research and Education awarded a grant to Amanda Spink, assistant professor at the University of North Texas School of Library and Information Sciences. She received $75,000 for her project entitled "Interaction in Information Retrieval: Successive Searching by Users Over Time."

Intel Corp. awarded the University of North Carolina at Chapel Hill $2.4 million to be used, in part, to fund its Laboratory for Networking and Internet Technologies. The three-year Intel award provided the laboratory with computing equipment for a number of campus research projects that blended basic and applied research aimed at solving real-world problems.

—Harold Borko

TELECOMMUNICATIONS SYSTEMS

In the 1990s the telecommunications world was moving ahead at high speed, and by 1998 the World Wide Web (the graphic portion of the Internet) was a driving force. Internet commerce was increasing by leaps and bounds, and computer owners in nearly all parts of the world were able to communicate with each other through E-mail with the click of a mouse and at a price so small that it could almost be ignored. It was reported that traffic on the Internet was doubling each 100 days, while the amount of E-mail in the United States was 10 times greater than the amount of U.S. Postal Service mail. This made it possible for people to communicate with each other in writing within minutes, rather than days, and several round trips of memos could take place between individuals or groups within a single business day. It was not usual for a typical E-mail user to receive from 10 to 50 E-mail messages a day, and some individuals reported receiving hundreds per day.

Packet switching

What made this possible was packet switching. A conventional communication over a telephone line—be it voice or data, such as a facsimile (fax) or Internet connection—takes place over a circuit dedicated to that connection for the duration of a call. Thus, a call from Tampa, Fla., to Chicago seizes and occupies a circuit between these two cities. When one of the two parties is talking (in the case of a voice call), the other is listening, and the circuit is being utilized only 50% of the time. When the second person is talking, and the first person is listening, the same is true. Occasionally no one is talking; then the circuit efficiency is zero.

With packet switching, a computer "catches" the first word spoken by the person in Florida and converts the word to a stream of digital bits—1s and 0s. It then searches for—and seizes—a communications channel heading toward Chicago. This channel may go only as far as Atlanta. The digitized stream of bits is transmitted and then the channel is released. A small amount of "overhead" is added to the front of this bundle, or packet, of information to identify the destination and the sequence number of the packet being transmitted. Thus, the communications channel—in this case between Florida and Atlanta—is utilized almost 100% of the time. This packet of information is then transmitted in the same way to other cities along the route to Chicago. In each case, the communications channel is used almost 100%

of the time. Eventually (in this case a matter of one or two milliseconds), the word reaches the computer serving the person at the Chicago end of the conversation.

Exactly the same thing happens with each word of the conversation. Transmission of each packet to the next city along the route takes place over a communications channel that is held only long enough for the transmission to take place, so in each case the communications facilities are utilized at an almost 100% efficiency factor. Packet switching is useful in many applications, including data transmission, voice transmission over the Internet, automated teller machines, and credit-card verifications. The communications channels themselves used for packet switching, however, are no different from those used for circuit switching; it is simply a matter of assigning them to a different use.

The value of packet switching was not lost on major telecommunications companies, and several announced that they were taking major steps to make the conversion. Sprint Corp. disclosed that it had committed $2 billion for its packet switching network, and AT&T Corp. was launching a similar service.

Fiber optics

In 1998 the medium of choice for transmission of high-speed data was fiber optics, in which data, voice, or images are transmitted by the passage of light through hair-thin, transparent fibers, usually made of glass. According to a report by the U.S. Federal Communications Commission (FCC), the long-distance carriers fiber-miles in place increased by more than 16% in 1997, to a total of more than 3.4

million fiber-miles at the beginning of 1998. (A mile is about 1.61 km.) AT&T, far and away the leader in fiber-mileage, had 1,282,200 miles of fiber in place at the beginning of 1998. Local telephone companies had more than 14 million fiber-miles in place, a 14% increase over the previous year.

Although transmission over copper wire had been improved by the late 1990s, transmission over fiber was vastly superior. With a computer modem operating over copper at 2,400 bits per second, it would take approximately 2 $1/2$ days to transmit the entire print set of the *Encyclopædia Britannica*. With fiber, however, it was possible to transmit at speeds of more than one gigabit per second—that is, one billion bits per second. At such speeds transmission of the set of *Britannica* would require less than half a second.

The transmission of signals over fiber optics requires two things of the light being transmitted: it must be polarized and it must be monochromatic, that is it must be of one very pure color. There is no requirement that the color of this transmitted light (normally generated by a laser) be of any one particular color, only that it not be a mixture of several colors.

By 1998 scientists and engineers taking advantage of this requirement had developed a system by which two channels of communications, each originating on a separate strand of fiber but each with a slightly different color being used as the carrier, could be combined on a single strand of fiber. These two data streams then traveled along the fiber together, and at the receiving end they were separated by a device resembling a prism. Thus, the capacity of the fiber was doubled. Further

As the availability of wireless communication increased and prices for consumers dropped, cellular telephones turned up everywhere, including ball games and other leisure events.

advances were still in the laboratory, but it seemed clear that the capacity of a particular fiber using this technique, called dense wavelength division multiplexing, or DWDM, could be not only doubled but also expanded by a factor of at least 10.

Digital subscriber lines

Despite the advantages of fiber optics, there remained millions of kilometers of unshielded twisted pair copper wires, or UTP, in use. (One report indicated there were 120 million subscriber loops in the U.S.) These needed to be used, not only for voice but also for data transmission. Copper, however, lacked the capabilities of fiber, especially because of the addition of "load coils," a combination of resistors, inductors, and capacitors that help in the transmission of voice. Load coils limit the frequencies transmitted to approximately 3,500 Hz, thus preventing high-speed data from being transmitted.

One possible solution in transmitting data over copper pairs was to employ sophisticated coding techniques and error-checking methods called digital subscriber line (DSL) systems. These DSL systems came in many variations, notably high-bit-rate (HDSL), single-pair (SDSL), very-high-bit-rate (VDSL), and asymmetric (ADSL), which transmitted more data in one direction than in the other. HDSL, the most prevalent, was conceived in the late 1980s, and by 1998 there were more than a million lines of HDSL in service, but the system receiving the most attention was ADSL. Telephone companies hoped that such a system would allow television pictures to be transmitted satisfactorily over the lines already in place, thus allowing

them to get in the TV business. In this way, a coaxial cable plant need not be installed, and millions of dollars could be saved.

Wireless communications

In 1998 wireless telecommunications, primarily cellular telephones and personal communications services (PCS), were more prevalent, with approximately 55 million subscribers in the U.S., a 20% penetration. Some research firms predicted that by the year 2006 this would increase to 50% and 150 million subscribers. Although cellular and PCS were the dominant players, in the next few years new services based on low-Earth-orbit satellites (LEOs) were expected to become more common. These satellites (many of which would be required for a particular service) would orbit Earth at altitudes of 750–1,500 km (465–930 mi). LEO satellite constellations act as the cells of a cellular phone system, but instead of the cells staying stationary while the user roams, the users stay stationary while the cell sites move.

Iridium, a Motorola, Inc.-backed system already in operation in 1998, consisted of 66 operational satellites arranged in six polar orbital planes. Call switching from satellite to satellite was accomplished without using the ground infrastructure, a network of 12 ground stations that connected the satellites to terrestrial networks. Globalstar, a system comprising 48 LEO satellites and a global network of up to 60 ground stations, was scheduled to go into operation during 1999. This company was led by Loral Space & Communications and was a partnership of Qualcomm Inc., Air Touch Communications, Alcatel, Alenia

Aerospazio, China Telecom, France Telecom, and others. A third system, Teledesic, which was backed by Bill Gates of Microsoft Corp. and Craig McCaw of McCaw Cellular Communications, was scheduled to go into operation in 2003. Teledesic was reportedly going after the data market and billed itself as a "global, broadband Internet in the Sky."

Implementing the Telecommunications Act

In the U.S. one factor in the development of these technological advances was the Telecommunications Act of 1996. This legislation, an expansion of the Communications Act of 1934, was designed to "promote competition," which meant, essentially, that any company could get into the telephone business and any local-exchange telephone company could provide long-distance service after passing certain criteria.

A second intent of the Telecommunications Act was to provide advanced telecommunications services to primary and secondary schools. This would be done in the form of significant discounts to companies working with schools in the provision of these services and equipment. The schools would pay only a part of the charged fee, and the government would pay the rest. Initially, the support fund was to be $2,250,000,000 per year, but in mid-1998 this was cut almost in half. At year's end funds started to flow from the organi-

The Iridium low-Earth-orbit satellite system, which became operational in May 1998, consists of 66 satellites arranged in six polar orbits.

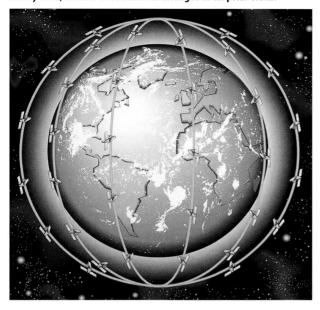

zation administering this program to the providers of the service.

Implementation of the Telecommunications Act was slow and strained, but one early result was a near frenzy of corporate mergers. AT&T (one side of the old, divested AT&T/Bell system), which had been disallowed from entering the local-exchange business, purchased Tele-Communications, Inc. (TCI), the nation's second largest cable TV firm, with plans to use TCI's coaxial cable to provide local phone service. Meanwhile, the seven regional Bell operating companies created from the other side of the divested

AT&T began to combine in order to achieve economy of scale. SBC communications Inc. (formerly southwestern Bell) had merged with Pacific Telesis Group and announced plans to acquire Ameritech Corp., whereas Bell Atlantic Corp. had merged with NYNEX Corp. and was planning to unite with long-distance provider GTE Corp.

Beyond the "Baby Bells," other mergers continued, including a massive deal between WorldCom, Inc. and MCI Communications Corp. and the purchase of LCI International, Inc. by Qwest Communications International, Inc. to create the fourth largest long-distance provider after AT&T, MCI WorldCom, and Sprint. At a smaller level, ALLTEL purchased the cellular operations spun off from Sprint and later acquired Aliant Communications, Inc., the local phone company in Lincoln, Neb. In early 1999 most of these mergers were expected to go through, pending approval by the FCC and the U.S. Justice Department.

—Robert E. Stoffels

C. Michael Armstrong (left), chairman of the telecommunications giant AT&T Corp., and John C. Malone of Tele-Communications, Inc., the U.S.'s second largest cable television provider, announce the $48 billion merger of their two companies.

ENERGY

Throughout most of 1998 demand for energy escalated in every part of the world, particularly in China and India. Asian energy consumption weakened toward midyear, owing to a serious financial crisis in that region, but experts predicted that it will again grow when the crisis subsides, perhaps more than doubling by the year 2015. In Eastern Europe and the former Soviet Union, annual energy consumption and growth were considerably behind that of Asia (1.8% compared with 4.2% in Asia), but an anticipated economic recovery in the near future may boost energy demand in these regions, analysts reported.

A follow-up to Kyoto

Environmental concerns continued to parallel the burgeoning use of energy. Debate over the economic impact of the 1997 Kyoto Protocol was widespread, particularly among industrialized nations. The Kyoto Protocol is an agreement among industrialized countries to reduce greenhouse gas emissions, which many scientists believe are contributing to global warming, by an average of 5.2% from 1990 levels by 2008–2012. As a follow-up to Kyoto, representatives from about 160 nations met in Buenos Aires, Arg., in November 1998 to hammer out details of the agreement. Although few substantive issues were resolved, support for the protocol was generally affirmed, and negotiations to make the historic agreement viable were expected to continue. Among the hot topics at the meeting were the agreement's flexibility measures, which offer countries different options for meeting emissions-reduction goals, including allowing countries to trade emissions entitlements with

Louis Goldman/Photo Researchers, Inc.

other nations, plant forests that soak up carbon dioxide (CO_2) to offset against emissions, or spend money on clean-air technologies in developing countries.

The U.S signed the Kyoto Protocol at Buenos Aires, which was seen as an important step in moving negotiations forward. Argentina voluntarily agreed to reduce emissions, also viewed as a major breakthrough, as it became the first developing country to make such a commitment. Several leading U.S. senators indicated, however, that unless countries like China and India—two of the biggest con-

tributors of greenhouse gases—sign the agreement, they will not support the treaty. The U.S. is most interested in ensuring that if it has to reduce emissions, it can do so in a cost-effective manner, whether that involves emissions trading or investing in clean technologies.

In the industrial sector, signs indicated that attitude toward the treaty may be turning more positive. The American Automobile Manufacturers Association, whose members helped fund an anti-Kyoto Protocol campaign in 1997, is dissolving and its largest member, General Motors, Inc., be-

An apartment complex in Israel uses rooftop photovoltaic modules to heat water. Originally developed for space applications, photovoltaic systems are increasingly being employed for a multitude of uses, from pumping water to powering communications equipment.

gan to work with environmental groups and joined a pro-treaty lobby association.

Clean energy

According to statistics compiled by the U.S. Department of Energy (DOE), the United

States emits about 23% of the world's greenhouse gases. Some 90% of the emissions come from energy use, and about 85% of the CO_2 released into the atmosphere is the result of fossil fuel combustion. Acknowledging the statistics, the DOE issued the 1998 report *Technology Opportunities to Reduce U.S. Greenhouse Gas Emissions,* which addressed the need to develop new clean-energy technologies. In the report, directors from 11 of the DOE's national laboratories outlined nearly 50 different technology pathways that could help reduce emissions, including the use of hybrid electric-gasoline vehicles, passive solar heating and cooling of buildings, and the use of high-efficiency lighting systems.

Even in nations where environmental concerns are strong, such as the U.S., energy is believed to be essential for economic growth. Thus, the development of cleaner forms of energy remained an important concern among scientists and environmental engineers in 1998. For example, engineers at the DOE's Sandia National Laboratories (SNL) in Albuquerque, N.M., happily announced that Solar Two, an experimental solar power plant, met all of its performance goals and set some new records, including continuous power production 24 hours a day for a week; a 1,500,000-kwh output over a 30-day period; and achievement of the design goal in parasitic electrical loads (the electricity needed to run the plant).

Located in the Mojave Desert near Barstow, Calif., Solar Two is a unique facility in that it uses molten salt to capture and store the Sun's heat. First, 1,926 Sun-tracking mirrors are used to concentrate sunlight on a receiver that sits atop a 90-m (300-ft) tower. The concentrated sun-

light heats the salt to more than 535° C (1,000° F) as it flows through the receiver. The molten salt—which can retain its heat for 12 hours after sundown—is then used to produce high-pressure steam, which powers a turbine-generator that makes electricity. The stored heat allows the plant to produce electricity at night. Solar Two can generate as much as 10 MW (megawatts; 10 million watts) of electricity, enough to

This dish/Stirling solar electric generating system is a recently developed DOE technology. A parabolic mirror array concentrates sunlight on a gas-filled receiver in the focal region. Heating and cooling of the gas turns an electrical generator.

power 10,000 homes. The plant also will be able to generate electricity after the Sun goes down, unlike traditional solar power facilities. Project managers said that this type of system will soon be ready for commercial power applications.

Interest in the use of photovoltaic solar energy systems to supplement established electrical grids continued in 1998. Better known as solar cells, photovoltaic (PV) systems convert light energy into electricity and are used every day in simple devices such as pocket calculators and wristwatches. Typically, these systems are distributed as relatively small (*i.e.,* less than 10 kw) systems on residential and commercial rooftops. Since they burn no fuel and have no moving parts, PV systems are exceptionally clean, efficient, and silent.

An interest in distributed photovoltaic systems emerged in the large government-supported programs in Japan and Europe. In the U.S., the Sacramento Municipal Utility District operated the nation's largest distributed photovoltaic program, and by the close of 1998 had installed some 400 systems. Since 1997 worldwide photovoltaic module sales have grown approximately 30% per year. Traditionally, PV systems have been used where it was very expensive to extend an electrical grid. Such applications include water pumping, telecommunication systems, and rural electrification in developing areas of the world.

A major goal in the photovoltaic industry is to increase the efficiency and reduce the cost of solar cells used in these systems. To this end, SNL scientists were busy developing a new type of photovoltaic cell—the back-contact crystalline-silicon solar cell—which offers high energy-conversion efficiency and simple, low-cost assembly into modules.

Fuel cell race

Fuel cells represent a breakthrough technology, and they are already being used in a variety of ways in schools, hospitals, airports, and office buildings. They could soon replace internal combustion engines in cars, trucks, buses, and even locomotives. Many experts believe that using fuel cells in transportation could prove to be more versatile, less expensive, and less polluting than a battery-powered electric car. Because they provide clean and quiet power, fuel cells could be a strategic part of the solution to global warming.

Fuel cells generate electricity by harnessing the chemical reaction of hydrogen and oxygen. Within the cell, hydrogen fuel is fed through channels in one of two plates, and oxygen (or air) enters through the other plate. A platinum catalyst starts a reaction that strips electrons from atoms of hydrogen, and these electrons create a useful current. The positively charged hydrogen ions that are formed pass through an electrolyte and join with the oxygen at another platinum catalyst. The two elements react, creating water and useful heat—the only emissions from the fuel cell.

Fuel cells can be made in virtually any size. Some researchers are working on making them small enough to replace batteries in portable phones and remote sensors. Others are developing larger systems to provide heat and power to homes, offices, apartment buildings, and industry. Large fuel cell systems, and systems that combine fuel cells with advanced turbines, are being developed for electric utility use. Almost any power need imaginable could be supplied by a fuel cell.

In 1998 automobile manufacturers continued to investigate the use of fuel cells to power motor vehicles. By the close of 1998, most of the major car manufacturers had some form of fuel cell development program underway.

Germany's Daimler-Benz (now called DaimlerChrysler after merging with Chrysler Corp. in November 1998) was ahead of the field. In 1994 the company unveiled NECAR I (New Electric Car), which provided convincing evidence that the principle of fueling a car with hydrogen—rather than gasoline—is feasible. Two years later, in 1996, engineers rolled out NECAR II, whose fuel cells had a gross output of 50 kw of electricity, enabling the vehicle to reach a top speed of 110 km/h (68 mph). NEBUS—the first-ever fuel cell bus—was produced by Daimler-Benz laboratories in 1997. In late 1997 came NECAR III, based on the Mercedes-Benz A-class compact car sold in Europe, and NECAR 4 was unveiled in early 1999.

General Motors (GM) and Ford Motor Co. also announced plans to release subcompact fuel cell automobiles. GM unveiled a fuel cell hybrid engine that will run on methanol, achieve near-zero emissions, and get about 34 km per liter (80 mi per gallon). They hoped to have a production-ready vehicle available by 2004. In a separate announcement, Ford officials said that the company would have a prototype fuel cell version of its advanced P2000 vehicle—operating on compressed hydrogen—ready sometime in the year 2000.

Demand for oil

The world is critically dependent on oil, and all signs in 1998 indicated that the trend will carry on in the near future. According to DOE statistics, oil production was up in 1998, and projected to increase

Increasing concern about environmental pollution and tighter emissions standards have prompted automakers to develop fuel-cell-powered vehicles. In March 1999, DaimlerChrysler unveiled NECAR 4 (below), claimed to be the first drivable fuel-cell zero-emissions passenger car.

Courtesy of DaimlerChrysler

about 50% over 1995 levels by the year 2015. Known oil reserves were expected to be adequate until the middle of the 21st century if current levels of consumption remained level. Previous studies had predicted, however, that demand for oil in industrialized countries will grow slowly, by about 1.1% annually, from 42.4 million barrels per day in 1995 to 55.3 million barrels by 2020. Oil use in developing countries was expected to rise about 3.5%, with much of the increase anticipated to come from a growing demand for automobiles.

On the other hand, the price of a barrel of oil plummeted during 1998, and gasoline prices at the pump fell, continuing a trend that began in 1986. The average price of domestic crude oil in the U.S. was $10.46 per barrel in July 1998, down 34% from its cost a year earlier. In August 1998, gas prices at the pump in the U.S. averaged $1.05 per gallon (one gallon equals 3.8 liters), 16% lower than in the previous year. The economic effects of the price drop were vast and expected to last for quite some time. It remained to be seen, however, how the low price of oil would affect the two major petroleum company mergers announced in 1998: the Exxon–Mobil merger; and the British Petroleum–Amoco union.

Representatives from the DOE and other government departments and industry executives visited China to identify business opportunities in that country's petroleum industry. Participating in what was the first-ever U.S.–China Oil and Gas Industry Forum, their goal was to explore ways the

Oil drilling platforms, such as this North Sea rig, are used to recover oil from deposits beneath the seafloor. Known oil reserves were being taxed by increasing levels of consumption in both industrialized and third world countries.

two nations could work together to develop reliable and economically feasible sources of oil and gas.

New technologies announced in 1998 should help scientists locate and utilize undiscovered sources of oil. Substantial oil reserves are known to exist, both onshore and offshore, in geologically complex settings and in deeper, smaller compartmentalized reservoirs. Ki Ha Lee of Lawrence Berkeley (Calif.) National Laboratory, another DOE facility, developed a new electromagnetic (EM) imaging method for pinpointing the locations of subsurface oil and gas reservoirs. Traditional EM visualization techniques involve transmitting signals into the ground, then gathering and computer processing the data to map out positions of underground electrical resistivity. The strength of an EM signal varies in accordance with the electrical resistivity of the material through which it passes. Oil-bearing sand, for instance, is about 10 times more electrically resistant than clay. The new imaging method also involves sending subsurface EM signals, but an additional mathematical transformation on the data allows better images to be constructed over a much wider area, significantly reducing drilling costs.

Large-scale production of a medium-density distillate liquid made from natural gas was achieved. The liquid can go directly to gasoline, diesel, or jet fuel, all of which are cleaner and more environmentally friendly than present forms of oil. It can also improve the efficiency of burning other fuels when the two are mixed. Because it is easy to transport, this oil-like liquid can make it more feasible to use stranded reserves of natural gas in remote locations such as Kazakstan.

Electricity and energy policy

Some 18–20% of the electricity used in the U.S. in 1998 was generated at nuclear power plants. Unless major changes in policy occur, however, nuclear power will decline as older plant licenses expire. Of the 101 GW (gigawatts; 101 billion watts) of nuclear capacity that were available in 1996, 52 GW, or 65 units, are expected to be retired by the year 2020. If the current U.S. nuclear power output were replaced by natural gas or coal, carbon emissions in the U.S. would increase 6–11%, translating into some 95 million to 165 million metric tons of carbon per year.

In the U.S. the issue of nuclear waste remained a serious roadblock. Interim storage was proposed as one near-term solution, however, in the longer term, approaches to reducing the toxicity of nuclear waste might be an answer. The political and regulatory climate for nuclear power plants continued to be an impediment to revitalizing the nuclear energy industry. On the other hand, advanced nuclear energy concepts offering significant benefits over existing power plant designs could mitigate some of the political and regulatory concerns. How changes in the configuration of the power industry will affect this issue remained unclear.

In China, nuclear power maintained a role in the growth of generation capacity, with new plants scheduled to begin operations each year between 2000 and 2003. Advice from nuclear engineers in France and the U.S. was sought, but the China National Nuclear Corporation was expected to take on an ever-increasing role in the design and construction of the power plants. China also has announced plans to construct

uranium-enrichment plants and a commercial plutonium-reprocessing plant, and develop a commercial fast-breeder reactor. Korea continued an aggressive position on the use of nuclear power as well, with three plants scheduled to be brought on-line from 1998 to 1999. The new facilities will generate some 2.35 GW of electricity.

The far-reaching policy initiative of restructuring, or deregulating, the U.S. electricity industry was in the forefront of energy policy issues. The initiative should affect not only nuclear energy, but the industry as a whole, as it attempts to become more cost-effective and cost-competitive. By the close of 1998, deregulation proceeded in selected states, but without any overarching new federal legislation to guide or control it. As the traditional utility industry moved from an integrated operation to separate operations for generation, transmission, and distribution, the issue of how to control a distributed system was being assessed. Significant challenges included access to information, security of financial and technical data, and managing the mass of information needed to control the electric network.

Nonregulated, for-profit companies continued to form, while power plants were increasingly bought and sold. For example, Southern California Edison in recent years has been selling off its gas plants and has held on to its capital-recovered nuclear plants. Deregulation is expected to affect research and development in the power industry as well, as this piece will likely be broken off and put into independent technical companies that will, in turn, sell their research ideas to the industry. As deregulation policies force changes throughout the industry, one unanswered question concerns who will take responsibility for the reliability of the national grid.

The U.S. government's hope is that deregulation will lower the cost of electricity in many regions of the country. As a side-effect, however, it also may force coal and nuclear power plants—which operate at much higher costs than other types of power plants—to close. If electricity prices decrease, consumption will likely go up, and the resulting demand for more electricity may mean that more natural gas and oil will have to be used to supply the electricity. Whether this increased consumption will, in the long term, spiral into higher prices and more pollution is something that was expected to be watched closely.

Studies predicted that coal generation will continue to grow rapidly but then decline in 2020 unless the Kyoto Protocol is ratified and anticipated changes occur in coal use. Gas technologies, which are inherently cleaner than coal, were expected to be increasingly used in a deregulated environment because they require less capital investment. Between 1996 and 2020, natural gas-fired electricity was expected to grow from 9% to 31% of the net electricity output of the U.S. Generation of electricity from renewable energy sources—including geothermal, solar, wind, and biomass sources—was predicted by DOE to remain fairly stable, increasing from 6.9 quadrillion to 7.7 quadrillion BTU between 1996 and 2020.

Energy and computers

Over the past 20 years a revolution has occurred in the world of technology, owing to the enormous increase in the use of computers, which continued to become

Researchers at Sandia National Laboratories developed this microscopic, mechanical lock on a chip, which can block hackers from accessing information being handled by the chip, including data on the computer's hard drive. The toothed wheel is about 200 micrometers across.

cheaper and faster. Indeed, Bill Gates, chairman and CEO of Microsoft Corp., estimated that the cost for computing went down by a factor of a million in that same period of time. That decrease was predicted to continue.

The computer revolution, in turn, has spurred the development of other high-tech silicon-based devices. At SNL, for instance, scientists continued to design and test the reliability of microelectromechanical systems (MEMS), tiny devices—invisible to the naked eye—with gears and other moving parts. MEMS are already found in many familiar devices, including computer joysticks, car air bag sensors, and inkjet printers, but their use is predicted to expand and change the electronics industry if they are proven to be reliable. Because of their extremely small

size, MEMS require very little energy to do useful tasks.

SNL scientists announced the development of two MEMS that will eventually be used in a variety of applications. One device was a microscopic mechanical lock that can be embedded in a computer chip. The researchers said that the lock will be able to block hackers from accessing whatever information that chip is handling, including data on the computer's hard drive. Another prototype MEM, developed in conjunction with scientists from the University of California, Berkeley, functions as a clock source. The pollen-grain-sized devices may one day replace quartz crystal oscillators, the traditional timing devices used in digital electronics.

—C. Paul Robinson and
Joan B. Woodard

ENVIRONMENT

World conservation attention in the past year was focused on the oceans and on a record-breaking year of climatic events and large-scale natural disasters. Hundreds of nations met in Argentina to hammer out the details of the Kyoto Protocol, which will obligate participating countries to reduce greenhouse-gas emissions in the new millennium. Human population growth projections were downgraded owing to the spread of AIDS in Africa, whereas animal habitat losses caused by climate change, land development, and wildfires continued. In a year of superlatives, the largest conservation deal was negotiated, the largest single conservation grant was awarded, and an American timber company became the first ever to be internationally certified for harvesting wood in a sustainable manner.

ISSUES AND POLICY

International Year of the Ocean

The year 1998 was proclaimed the International Year of the Ocean by the United Nations Educational, Scientific and Cultural Organization, galvanizing numerous conferences, publications, treaties, and conservation initiatives worldwide. The UN's goal was to increase public awareness of the importance of the world's oceans for human survival.

Overfishing—that is, fishing at an intensity great enough to deplete fish stocks below the level at which they will continue producing large yields—was seen as one of the biggest threats to oceans. The severity of the problem was detailed in the U.S. National Research Council's 1999 report *Sustaining Marine Fisheries,* which of-

fered some solutions for saving Earth's dwindling commercial fish populations. According to the report, roughly 84 million metric tons of fish, crustaceans, mollusks, and other marine organisms were pulled from the oceans each year during the 1990s. Additionally, another 27 million metric tons of nontarget animals were thrown back, usually dead or dying. The report concluded that the estimated 111 million metric tons of animals killed annually were perhaps more than the oceans can actually replenish in a year's time. Since roughly 20% of the animal protein consumed by people worldwide comes from fish and shellfish, the continued decline of the world's fisheries was viewed as a significant problem for Earth's growing population and the economically important fishing industry.

The report strongly urged fisheries managers to protect more coastal areas by designating them as off-limits to fishing. Less than a quarter of 1% of coastal seas are now protected. It also highly recommended giving exclusive fishing rights to individuals or communities to discourage overfishing and other destructive fishing practices. Assigning individual or group fishing rights would reduce competition for the biggest catch and encourage more economical investments in fishing equipment and technology.

As 1998 came to an end, Australia became the first country to adopt an ocean-management plan with the goal of maintaining ecosystem health, productivity, and sustainability. Additionally, 80 countries approved an accord to develop management plans for sharks, skates, and rays, and 10 nations signed an agreement to protect sea turtles.

Global climate change

The strongest El Niño event of the century continued into 1998, causing flooding, drought, and severe storms—including Hurricane Mitch, the most powerful tropical storm in 200 years—in many countries. The Worldwatch Institute disclosed that the total worldwide damage caused by weather in 1998 was $89 billion, exceeding the total for the entire decade of the 1980s. Natural catastrophes were linked to the deaths of 32,000 people and the displacement of 300,000,000 others. Experts said that the growth of populations living in low-lying areas, combined with deforestation and poorly planned development, has exposed humans to greater risks from natural disasters.

Average global surface temperature continued to rise. The World Meteorological Association reported that 1998 was the warmest year since reliable record keeping began in 1860, the second year in a row of record global temperature, and the seventh year in the 1990s with above-average temperature. Climatologists additionally reported in the journal *Nature* that three recent years—1997, 1995, and 1990—were the warmest in the past 600 years.

Most scientists believed that the observed temperature rise was being enhanced by an atmospheric accumulation of greenhouse gases—those gases, including carbon dioxide, methane, and hydrofluorocarbons (HFCs), that contribute to the greenhouse effect. International efforts to combat global warming continued as negotiators from 170 countries met in Buenos Aires, Arg., to finalize details of the 1997 Kyoto Protocol, an agreement among industrialized nations to lower greenhouse-gas emissions an average of

Residents of Tegucigalpa, Honduras, clean up wreckage caused by Hurricane Mitch in late 1998. With winds exceeding 250 km/h (155 mph), Mitch was given a Category 5 rating, the most dangerous rating for a hurricane.

5.2% below 1990 levels between 2008 and 2012.

Sixty nations signed the environmental treaty in 1997, but by the close of 1998 only a handful of countries had ratified it. The protocol takes effect once it has been ratified by at least 55 countries. Argentina and Kazakstan became the first nations to commit to voluntary emissions reductions, but other less-developed countries, including China and India, refused, arguing that nations producing most of the greenhouse gases—such as the U.S., which released approximately 20% of the world's greenhouse gases—should first reduce their emissions. Nevertheless, negotiators forged agreement on two key provisions—a mechanism for big polluters to buy the right to emit the unused portion of another nation's emission allowance, and a plan for countries to increase their allowed emissions by investing in low-emissions technologies in less-developed nations.

Population and consumption

Incorporating new data on deaths due to AIDS, the UN Population Division fore-cast a total world population of 8.9 billion by the year 2050, a 50% increase above 1998's population level of 5.9 billion but lower than estimated in the UN's Population Fund report *The State of World Population 1998*. The Population Division's estimates are used throughout the United Nations system as the basis for activities requiring population information. Lester Brown, president of the Worldwatch Institute, explained the revision by pointing out that several African nations, including Zimbabwe, Botswana, Zambia, Namibia, and Swaziland, will experience zero population growth in the future because of deaths from AIDS. The world's population was expected to stop growing in the year 2200 at just under 11 billion.

The U.S. population, which at 270 million in 1998 was the third highest in the world, after China and India, should reach 394 million by 2050, according to the U.S. Census Bureau. Sixty percent of population growth in the U.S. was due to immigration or births to immigrants, reported the Carrying Capacity Network, Washington, D.C., a private organization that specializes in demographic issues. The role of immigration in U.S. population expansion remained a controversial topic among environmental groups, however, with some, like the Sierra Club, choosing not to discuss the issue because of its harmful implications for social justice.

With gas prices in the U.S. having fallen below $1 per gallon (about 3.8 liters) by year's end, the Environmental Protection Agency reported that the top 10 most fuel-efficient cars accounted for less than 1% of all new cars purchased by Americans. For the first time, sales of new pickup trucks, sport utility vehicles, and vans exceeded car sales. Interestingly, improved technology and increased fuel efficiency in motor vehicles helped reduce each American's use of oil by 11% between 1973 and 1998, reported the U.S. Department of Energy.

Deforestation and habitat change

Sparked by severe drought caused by the 1997–98 El Niño, wildfires again burned large areas of forest. By mid-1998 fires had consumed more than 85,000 sq km (33,000 sq mi) of forest in Indonesia, Brazil, Mexico, Central America, Africa, Russia, Greece, and Canada, casting haze over vast territories for weeks. In response to some of these disasters, the World Bank approved $15 million to fight forest fires in Brazil, and the U.S. sent fire-fighting teams and more than $8 million to put out blazes in Mexico.

The extensive forest fires that torched the Amazon region in 1998 were not surprising, according to ecologist Daniel

Nepstad of the Amazonian Institute of Environmental Research, Pára, Braz. In May 1998 Nepstad reported that roughly 400,000 sq km (154,000 sq mi) of Brazilian forest were susceptible to burning. On average, approximately 15,000 sq km (5,800 sq mi) of Brazil's rain forest are destroyed each year. Limited rainfall in 1997 and increased logging in recent years contributed to the flammability of the Amazon rain forest, Nepstad said. Extraction of timber opens up the forest canopy, allowing sunlight to dry out the combustible leaf litter and other materials on the forest floor.

The spread of nonindigenous species continued to receive attention in 1998. The movement of a plant, animal, or microbe beyond its native environment is somewhat like a game of roulette. Most of the time, an organism will simply die out in its new environment. Other times, it may survive and reproduce without noticeable effects. Sometimes, however, a nonnative, or exotic, species will spread unimpeded, often with devastating ecological and economic results. In the U.S., for example, about 4,500 nonindigenous species freely breed in the wild, with some 15% of them causing great harm to native species and disruption of ecosystems. A new book, *Life Out of Bounds: Bioinvasion in a Borderless World,* describes how the spread of invasive species represents a significant threat to habitats and biological diversity around the globe.

Extinctions and recoveries

In a litmus test for the Endangered Species Act, the world's premier species-protection legislation, U.S. Secretary of the Interior Bruce Babbitt announced plans to remove

Bob Stevens/US Dept Interior, Fish & Wildlife Service

With populations on the rise, the North American grizzly bear may soon be removed from the endangered species list.

more than two dozen species of wildlife—including the gray wolf, grizzly bear, and peregrine falcon—from the endangered species list or downgrade their status from endangered to threatened. Only 11 species had been delisted since the legislation was passed in 1973. The gray wolf would be delisted only in Minnesota, where the population of some 2,200 had surpassed recovery goals.

Conservationists raised concern about the survival of other species, however. The U.S. Fish and Wildlife Service proposed listing the Australian koala as a threatened species, and the World Conservation Union added nearly 34,000 species of plants to its endangered list, more than 10% of all plants growing on Earth. Logging, farming, urban development, forest fires, and the spread of exotic species were blamed for the astoundingly large number of endangered plants.

Land and water conservation

In the largest public-private, multistate conservation deal in U.S. history, timber company Champion International Corp. agreed to sell 120,000 ha (300,000 ac) of forestland in New Hampshire, New York, and Vermont to the Conservation Fund, a nonprofit organization dedicated to the preservation of the nation's land and water resources. According to Patrick F. Noonan, chairman of the Conservation Fund, the record $76 million agreement will enhance recreation areas, protect sensitive land, and promote long-term timber production.

The largest single grant ever given to an international conservation organization was received by Conservation International (CI), Washington, D.C. The $35 million grant from Gordon Moore, cofounder of Intel Corp., will enable CI to establish the Center for Applied Biodiversity Science, which will work to identify emerging threats to biodiversity by creating research fellowships, establishing a cooperative research network, holding international conferences, and developing plans for innovative conservation strategies.

International Paper (IP) became the first American forest products company to receive "green certification"—an acknowledgement that a paper company practices sustainable forestry—from the International Organization for Standardization, based in Geneva. To qualify, IP followed guidelines prepared by the American Forest and Paper Association's Sustainable Forestry Initiative and internal procedures of best management practices.

Environment and human health

The Antarctic ozone hole grew to its greatest size ever on Sept. 19, 1998—some 27 million sq km (10 million sq mi), about 5% larger than the previous record, set in 1996. Scientists attributed the expanded thinning of the ozone layer to unusually cold temperatures in the atmosphere. The hole was first observed in 1979, and predictions are that it will grow until around 2020, when stratospheric levels of chlorine are expected to drop in response to the elimination of CFCs mandated by the 1987 Montreal Protocol.

A research team led by ecologist David Pimentel of Cornell University, Ithaca, N.Y., published a study relating human population growth and a degraded environment to the incidence of disease worldwide. The study concluded that urban crowding, widespread malnutrition, and pollution have produced conditions on Earth favorable to the emergence and spread of disease. The authors pointed out, for instance, how the construction of Egypt's Aswan High Dam contaminated bodies of freshwater in the area and led to an increase in the occurrence of *Schistosoma mansoni*—the parasitic worm that causes the snail borne disease schistosomiasis. Global warming and higher surface temperatures are also believed to increase the likelihood

of disease. In total, the researchers attributed about 40% of all deaths globally to environmental factors, mostly in less-developed countries. (*See* Feature Article: SURVIVING THE NEW MILLENNIUM.)

Citizens in less-developed countries, particularly in Asia, continue to be threatened by a group of chemicals known as persistent organic pollutants (POPs), according to investigations by Greenpeace International. POP chemicals, including industrial chemicals such as polychlorinated biphenyls (PCBs) and pesticides such as DDT, are considered among the most dangerous substances created by humans. In addition to causing a number of health problems, POPs can disrupt ecosystems by building up in the food chain, where they can reach concentrations in wildlife thousands of times higher than in the surrounding air, water, and soil. Greenpeace's study, conducted in India, Nepal, Pakistan, Bangladesh, Thailand, Vietnam, China, and the Philippines, showed that numerous POPs—banned or out of use for years in many other countries—continue to be sold, stored, and used in those nations.

Environmental awards

Environmental activist Juan Pablo Orrego was awarded a Right Livelihood Award, considered an alternative Nobel Prize, by the Swedish Riksdag (parliament) for his efforts to protect Chile's Bío-Bío River, one of the last major free-flowing rivers in the world. Orrego and his organization, Action Group for the Bío-Bío, challenged the construction of a string of dams in the Bío-Bío River valley, which resulted in government reform in the consideration of large-scale development projects.

The Royal Academy of Arts and Sciences in The Netherlands awarded the Heineken Environmental Prize to biologist Paul R. Ehrlich of Stanford University. Together with his wife, Ehrlich began publishing in the 1960s on issues of grave environmental consequence, especially human population growth and the pressures it places on the natural world. Ehrlich was credited with combining a scientist's rigorous investigation of issues with a powerful style of advocacy in writing and speaking. —Kim Alan Chapman

ENVIRONMENTAL TECHNOLOGY

With a strong push by a robust U.S. economy, American and multinational manufacturers moved ahead with new advances in environmental technologies throughout 1998, continuing a trend of environmental awareness among corporate boardrooms and investors.

Environmentally safer automobiles

The transportation sector, automobile manufacturers in particular, contributed some of the most noteworthy advances. Honda Motor Co., for instance, announced a plan to introduce a hybrid gasoline-electric vehicle into the North American, European, and Japanese markets by late 1999. The environmentally friendly roadster—engineered to meet California's stringent Ultra Low Emission Vehicle standard—will be capable of averaging 70 mi per gal (30 km per liter) of gasoline in combined city-highway driving.

Spurred by a series of technical breakthroughs in recent years, Ford Motor Co.,

Honda's gas-electric hybrid car, shown in prototype, is expected to be launched worldwide in late 1999. The two-seater is equipped with a 1.0-liter, three-cylinder engine, which gets a boost from an electric motor on acceleration.

DaimlerChrysler, and Canada's Ballard Power Systems Inc. formed a new company, Ecostar Electric Drive Systems Co., which hopes to commercialize hydrogen-based automotive fuel cells by 2004. These battery-like devices, which produce electricity directly from an electrochemical reaction between hydrogen and oxygen, may well be the successor to the internal combustion engine, automakers said. The endlessly replenishable cells can achieve efficiencies far beyond those of the best internal combustion engines and add virtually no pollution to the environment. The main difficulty with using fuel cells in passenger vehicles, according to industry experts, is in supplying the hydrogen. Although the gas can be compressed, companies are concerned about safety should a pressurized hydrogen tank be damaged in an accident.

Car manufacturers continued to make environmentally beneficial improvements in gasoline-powered vehicles. Swedish automaker Volvo announced that its top-of-

the-line Volvo S80 cars will be using American-based Engelhard Corp.'s new smog-eating PremAir catalyst coating. Tests have shown that the catalyst, when applied to a car's radiator, converts about 75% of the ozone—a key molecule in the formation of urban smog—that it contacts into harmless oxygen. Volvo said that the sedans will be the first mass-produced cars in the world to use the pollution-fighting catalyst. Meanwhile, officials at Goal Line Environmental Technologies, Knoxville, Tenn., said that their company plans to have "ultra clean" diesel engines available for the 2003 model year. The company reported that in tests its new catalyst system cut nitrogen oxide and hydrocarbon emissions from diesel engines by as much as 99%.

Eager to combat an impression that the burgeoning American market for large vehicles had sapped any interest in fuel economy, a spokesperson for the joint industry-government program Partnership for a New Generation of Vehicles pointed to the

use of lightweight materials such as honeycombed-aluminum-filler composites, graphites, and fiberglass as the basis for car exteriors in the future. The Aluminum Association, Inc. also noted that "automakers are increasingly turning to aluminum as the material of choice, a trend accounting for a 102% increase in aluminum content [per vehicle] this decade." The group reported a doubling of aluminum shipments for use in light vehicles over an eight-year period, with more than 60% of it coming from recycled aluminum made from old and new scrap. Aluminum content per vehicle in 1999 is expected to average 112.5 kg (248 lb), nearly a 9% increase over the 1996 average.

Automobiles made by the biggest American car company, General Motors Corp. (GM), will likely contain more of the lightweight metal in the future. In 1998 GM announced a multibillion-dollar arrangement to buy aluminum from Canada's Alcan Aluminum Ltd. An increased use of aluminum in cars is critical to reducing vehicle weight and increasing fuel efficiency, thereby minimizing environmental impacts. Alcan estimated that a one-ton reduction in vehicle weight would result in a 20-ton reduction in carbon dioxide emissions over the life of the vehicle. The two companies agreed on a joint research effort to "invent new ways to use aluminum in autos and to make the aluminum parts as recyclable as soda cans."

Products and practices that spare trees

Whereas auto companies received a lot of public attention for technology advances, other sectors also were moving forward. In an effort to reduce paper waste and eliminate harmful forestry practices, Imagex Technologies, Inc., Framingham, Mass., developed a "decopier" machine that removes ink and toner from standard printer and copier paper. Insert a used sheet of paper or a transparency, the company said, and the machine "spits out a clean sheet"; the paper can be reused up to four times.

United Parcel Service (UPS) made plans to improve its package production processes and pointed to eventual savings of more than $1 million annually as a result of measures that conserve energy, cut pollution, and reduce solid waste. The new packaging, combined with other steps that UPS initiated in 1998, will increase the use of postconsumer recycled materials by 22%, cut wastewater discharges by more than 15%, and use 12% less energy, UPS officials announced. The use of bleached paper in express packaging will also be eliminated, which will thereby reduce water pollution from chlorinated compounds.

In another indication that environmental technological advances were not limited to high-tech hardware, the coffee retailer Starbucks reacted to criticism from environmentalists that its double-cupping of coffee was wasteful of resources by introducing a new system that protects people's hands from the hot coffee. Working with environmental organizations and customer focus groups, Starbucks looked at 25 prototypes, conducted tests in three different markets, and approached some 45 paper-cup suppliers before settling on a single cup surrounded by a thin insulating sleeve partially made from recycled paper. The Seattle-based company said that the cardboard sleeve uses significantly less material than a second paper cup.

Pollution-fighting technologies

Phytoremediation—the use of plants to clean contaminated soil and groundwater—may be closer to commercialization as a low-cost solution to cleaning polluted environments. Researchers from the University of Georgia genetically engineered yellow poplar trees, giving the plants the ability to absorb mercury from the soil and convert the toxic metal into a comparatively inert form. The yellow poplar has large leaves, is fast-growing, and has an extensive root system, characteristics that make it suitable for remediation. Planting yellow poplar trees on a site contaminated by mercury, then, could be one method of removing the pollutant from the soil.

Phytoremediation may be a more efficient technique for cleaning up the envi-

Microscopic plants are being employed to fight pollution. At the U.S. Department of Energy's National Renewable Energy Laboratory, researchers are studying the ability of genetically engineered algae to remove metals from water.

Warren Gretz/NREL/U.S. Dept of Energy/Photo Researchers, Inc.

ronment than incineration or landfill disposal, but the method has shown mixed results at sites contaminated by heavy metals. Nickel and zinc appear most easily absorbed by plants, and early tests with copper and cadmium also have been encouraging. Lead, the single most pervasive heavy-metal pollutant found at Superfund sites (waste dumps targeted by the U.S. Environmental Protection Agency for special cleanup funds), also has been shown to be subject to phytoremediation uptake. (For more information on phytoremediation, *see* Year in Review: LIFE SCIENCES: *Botany*.)

A comparatively new remedial technology called electrokinetics is more effective for heavy-metal pollutants. In this technique electrodes are placed in the soil to deliver a low-intensity electric current. The underground electric field mobilizes contaminants and carries them to the electrodes, where they can be removed from the ground with minimal excavation. The technology, which had been commercially available in Europe and applied to copper, lead, zinc, arsenic, cadmium, chromium, and nickel contamination, has recently been licensed in the U.S.

Another technological advance offers promise for cleaning up heavy metals at abandoned mines. Contamination of land and water from abandoned mines has long been a problem. Over time, abandoned-mine wastewater becomes very acidic—pH readings of 2–3 are common. Such acidity can dissolve the heavy metals that remain within the mine, which creates a heavy-metal-laced liquid that can pollute drinking-water supplies and wreak havoc on ecosystems. A powdered-chemical mixture manufactured by Klean Earth Environmental Co., Lynnwood, Wash., can prevent this from happening by triggering a chemical reaction in soil and water that encases the heavy metals in an inert, impervious silica-based material, isolating the metals from the environment. The remaining nontoxic sludge can be left in place or removed and disposed of as a nonhazardous waste, the company said.

Researchers at the University of Illinois at Champaign-Urbana and the Illinois State Geological Survey showed that shredded automobile tires may be a huge and potentially inexpensive source of carbon for many types of air-quality-control applications. An estimated 2 billion–3 billion discarded tires are stockpiled in the U.S. alone, with more than 200 million tires added each year. Mounds of old tires present a visual blight, collect rainwater that fosters the breeding of mosquitoes, and pose fire risks that spew harmful air pollutants. Comparing the effectiveness of carbon adsorbents made from shredded tires with the performance of existing commercial products, the scientists showed that tire carbon is at least as good as and in some ways better than commercial carbons. Potential applications for tire-derived carbons include the removal of toxic pollutants from electric-utility power plants, the storage of alternative fuels, such as natural gas, in vehicles, and the removal of volatile organic compounds from industrial gas streams. In early 1999 work was under way to evaluate the product under industrial test conditions.

Energy for the future

BC International (BCI) Corp., based near Boston, announced a plan to build in Jennings, La., a $90 million production plant that can generate ethanol from sawdust, grass clippings, and other woody waste materials. The plant's technology will be based on genetically engineered *Escherichia coli* bacteria patented in 1991 by microbiologist Lonnie Ingram of the University of Florida. Traditionally, ethanol is produced by yeast fermentation, which converts plant sugars, usually from corn (maize) or molasses, into ethanol, carbon dioxide, and other by-products. With the new technology, BCI officials hope to produce ethanol much more economically, because the waste from farm crops—not the crops themselves—will be used.

Texas Utilities Electric Co. and York Research Corp., New York City, unveiled phase one of an ambitious 34,000-kw, $40 million wind-power project that will use 46 of the largest wind turbines in the U.S. The wind farm, which will be located in Big Spring, Texas, is expected to generate roughly 117 million kw-hr of electricity annually, enough to power 7,300 homes for a year. "We believe that wind energy provides a solution to the requirement of clean, renewable energy sources in Texas at affordable costs," said the chairman of York Research. The utility company said its investment was supported by 96% of its customers, who, by a 10-to-1 margin, said they would be willing to pay at least $1 more per month for electricity derived from a renewable energy source such as wind power.

An even more novel vision of windmills producing energy came from IT Power Ltd. in the United Kingdom, which announced plans to "test whether the power of the sea can provide an environmentally friendly answer to the world's energy needs." With a $1.1 million grant from the European Union, the utility company will team up with engineers from a German university, a Swedish turbine and generator manufacturer, and a British engineering firm to develop what could be the world's first full-size marine-current turbine. With visions of someday meeting up to 20% of the U.K.'s power needs, IT began exploring offshore sites in southwestern England, which appeared to provide a suitable mix of water velocity, nearness to a power grid, and safe distance from shipping channels and conservation areas. As planned, the project will use turbines 11–14 m (36–45 ft) long to produce 300 kw of electricity. IT predicted that the costs will be roughly competitive with those of wind power.

A University of Michigan study pointed to potential energy savings of up to 65% for homes equipped with Saskatchewan walls—specially designed walls built with double two-by-four studs and filled with 9 cm (3.5 in) of cellulose insulation. The walls, which have an R-value of 35, were shown to improve heat insulation by 60% and reduce electricity consumption by 40% compared with standard wall types. R-value is a number denoting the resistance a material offers in the flow of heat; the higher the R-value, the better the insulation. The initial purchase price of houses built with such walls likely would increase, but the financing could be offset by lower energy and maintenance costs, according to the study, which projects a long-term savings of more than $50,000 per home.

—Bud Ward

See also Feature Article: THE UNCERTAINTIES OF ENVIRONMENTAL FORECASTING.

FOOD AND AGRICULTURE

In 1998 droughts and floods struck areas of the world, especially Asia and Central America, that usually do not experience such abnormal weather patterns. The result was a marked increase in international trade of certain grain crops, a situation that was greatly exacerbated by economic struggles, particularly in parts of Asia.

Reports on lowering the cholesterol content in beef, administering genetically engineered vaccines via food, and the development of new fat substitutes appeared during the year, as did the first part of the U.S. Congress's in-depth review of the nation's science policy; the second part was expected to be released in 1999. The U.S. and other countries also struggled with issues associated with organic food, especially the acceptable levels of pesticide use.

As expenditures and expectations for herbal and nutritional supplements continued to increase throughout the world, scientists broadened their examination of alternative health care methods to include vitamin and herbal therapies. The effectiveness of these therapies in the treatment and prevention of chronic diseases was the focus of a number of studies that appeared during the year.

AGRICULTURE

Reduced imports by Asia contributed to a slower overall agricultural growth for the U.S. and the European Union than in recent years, although the economies of developing countries in East and Southeast Asia were expected to bounce back as their currencies appreciated in real terms against the dollar. In general, except for Indonesia and the Philippines, foreign-exchange reserves in Asian countries were at relatively healthy levels, reducing the risk of another round of sharp currency depreciations or capital flight. Global rice trade jumped 6.5 million tons to a record 25.5 million tons in 1998—4.5 million tons above the previous record. This surge in rice trade was due to crop shortfalls in Indonesia, the Philippines, and Bangladesh and throughout much of Latin America. Meanwhile, record crops in Thailand, China, and India propelled world production to a record level. Increased exports were seen from the U.S. and Vietnam, while Japan took the opportunity to reduce its burdensome stockpile by exporting rice as food aid. Global wheat trade in 1998–99 was projected at 97.7 million tons, more than 2 million tons lower than the preceding year. World agricultural production was forecast to be 588 million tons, down 23 million tons from 1997–98, with Argentina down 4 million tons and Canada down nearly one million tons.

The nonprofit humanitarian organization Bread for the World reported that, despite population increases, the proportion of starving people worldwide had dropped from one-third of the world population to one-fifth since 1970. The organization noted that the reason for the drop was due in part to economic growth, the spread of democracy, and increased government spending on social programs focusing on health, education, nutrition, and social safety needs. Famine, however, was still a significant problem in parts of the world, especially in The Sudan and North Korea.

Science policy study

Agriculture science was the first significant and organized effort by the U.S. government to discover new knowledge and apply it for the benefit of humankind. Significant funding began in 1888. By the 1930s, governmental research had reached beyond agriculture, but, since then, U.S. science policy has continued to have a major impact on agricultural research.

Since 1945 science policy in the U.S. had been driven by a powerful document entitled *Science: The Endless Frontier.* This book had been called the Bush report, after its author, Vannevar Bush, Pres. Harry S. Truman's science advisor. Written when the U.S. was embroiled in the Cold War, it focused heavily on strong federal support of science related to the military and national security. In September 1998 the U.S. House of Representatives released the first part of a new report, *Unlocking Our Future: Toward a New National Science Policy,* developed by Republican Rep. Vern Ehlers, a physicist and former college professor who serves as vice-chair of the House Science Committee. The report's purpose was to reshape the U.S. science policymaking model by moving beyond the frontiers of an earlier generation and broadening the focus of federally supported science to include high technology, education, and international science projects.

Part one of the document emphasized the need for quality science and mathematics instruction at the elementary and high-school levels. It encouraged the development of masters-of-science programs as a viable option to Ph.D. work, especially for those headed into nonacademic environments. It also suggested that the opportunity for graduate students to take at least one course in journalism or communications could be used to help educate the public about the nature and importance of their work. Some critics found the new

Courtesy of Congressman Vern Ehlers

U.S. Rep. Vern Ehlers (left), a physicist and former college professor, was at the center of attention in September 1998 when the first part of a new government report, *Unlocking Our Future: Toward a New National Science Policy,* was released. Ehlers developed the report.

report more evolutionary than revolutionary, since they felt that it merely tinkered around the edges of the current federal approach to science. For example, Rep. George Brown, the ranking Democrat on the House Science Committee, refused to support the first part of the report, stating that it was too much in favor of basic scientific research and not supportive enough of other modes of research. The report's second part was expected to be released in 1999.

El Niño and La Niña

Weather shifts had a significant impact on agriculture around the world. Weather systems shifted markedly due to the changes in temperature of the tropical Pacific Ocean triggered by El Niño (warmer water than usual) and La Niña (cooler water than usual). One result was an increase in the number of hurricanes, some of which led to disastrous agricultural losses. Powerful Hurricane Mitch, which tore through Central America in late October, destroyed significant portions of farmland in the region. According to Robert Rivera, project director at the Interamerican Agricultural Cooperation Institute in Nicaragua, rebuilding efforts would focus on agricultural products made from corn and beans, and support would be given to small farms and larger farm organizations that produced bananas, coffee, and sugar cane. These efforts, which were also to involve the introduction of new crops and soil-conservation techniques, were expected to be the basis for paying off loans used to rebuild roads, bridges, and other infrastructures.

Organic food

One of the objectives identified by the U.S. Department of Agriculture (USDA) for 1999 was the setting of standards for organic foods. Establishing a definition for organic foods involved determining the level of pesticides and bioengineered material allowed for use in products deemed "organic." Another issue was raised by Dennis Avery, a senior fellow at the Hudson Institute, Indianapolis, Ind., who said that there were certain dangers to eating only organic foods. According to Avery, people eating only organic foods were more likely to be attacked by potentially deadly *Escherichia coli* bacteria and were at increased risk from natural toxins produced by fungi, some of which cause cancer. The Food and Drug Administration reported that organic crops had higher rates of infestation by natural toxins, including aflatoxin, a very strong toxin found especially in corn, cotton seed, peanuts, and tree nuts. Whereas the Environmental Protection Agency produced a leaflet on the dangers posed by pesticide residues in the food supply, the national research councils in the U.S. and Canada said that pesticide residues posed no significant danger to consumers, including children.

One of the benefits of organic farming— namely, the reduction of atmospheric greenhouse gases, which are related to global warming—was reported by researchers at the Rodale Institute, Kutztown, Pa. The report, published in the scientific journal *Nature* on Nov. 18, 1998, concluded that regenerative agricultural management systems based on organic fertilizer can preserve carbon and nitrogen in the soil, thus reducing greenhouse-gas emissions. The report also found that organic methods could produce the same yields as conventional systems that use synthetic fertilizer. The researchers predicted that if the major corn- and soybean-growing regions of the U.S. were to adapt organic practices, the estimated annual carbon released into the atmosphere from fossil-fuel combustion could be reduced by 1–2%. The Rodale Institute experiment was conducted over 15 years and was said to be the first long-term study to quantify carbon and nitrogen balances in organically managed cropping systems. The study was done in cooperation with the USDA's Agricultural Research Service (ARS) and involved 2.5 ha (6 ac) of highly productive and intense corn-soybean systems under conventional and organic management. The organic fertilizers were either manure or a variety of legumes. The energy costs were 50% less using the organic alternative.

G. Brad Lewis/Gamma Liaison International

Organic farms, like this one in Seward, Alaska, can help reduce greenhouse gases in the atmosphere, according to a 15-year study by researchers at the Rodale Institute, Kutztown, Pa. The study found that regenerative farming systems based on organic fertilizer can preserve carbon and nitrogen in the soil.

Proposed institute for food safety research

In 1998 President Clinton directed the U.S. secretaries of Agriculture and Health and Human Services to consider the need for establishing a joint institute to address food safety research. The institute would develop a strategic plan for conducting federal food safety research and effectively coordinate all such research, including studies conducted with the private sector and academia. Clinton's Food Safety Initiative provided a proposed structure, operating principles, goals, and an implementation schedule. The key points of the initiative delivered in 1998 identified several areas in which significant knowledge gaps required a concerted interagency research effort. These included improving detection methods; understanding microbial resistance to traditional preservation technologies, as well as problems involving microbial antibiotic-drug resistance; developing prevention techniques for pathogen avoidance, reduction, and elimination; and understanding the contribution of food handling, distribution, and storage to pathogen contamination of food and developing preventions. The initiative also identified the research goal of developing data that would enhance the ability of federal agencies to conduct microbial risk assessments, including developing and validating microbial exposure models, based on probabilistic methodology, and developing and validating dose-response assessment methods for use in risk assessment.

Fat substitutes

Scientists at the ARS laboratory in Peoria, Ill., developed a fat substitute that was actually good for human health. Called Nu-Trim, the substitute was made from the soluble fiber of oats and barley. It lowered cholesterol and was specifically designed to meet the U.S. government's requirements to be labeled "heart healthy." Nu-Trim joined a growing number of fat substitutes already on the market, including Oatrim, Z-trim, and olestra, but Nu-Trim was said to transcend the basic "fake fat" label, because the oat and barley fiber in it reduced the low-density lipoprotein (or "bad") cholesterol that collects inside arteries. At high concentrations, the lipoprotein can block the flow of blood to the heart or to the brain.

One of the other existing fat substitutes, olestra, was reported to have a number of side effects, which British researchers said needed to be investigated before the product was made widely available. Their six-month study of olestra involving 76 adults was carried out in hospitals in Cambridge, Eng. Sucrose polyester, the main ingredient in olestra, is a tasteless, odorless, nonabsorbable, fatlike substance that passes undigested through the intestines, reducing the fattening effects of foods. The study's subjects, however, were found to have lower levels of vitamin E, which is fat soluble, and of other nutrients, such as carotenoids.

The FDA approved the use of the fat substitute olestra in potato chips and other snack foods despite reports that olestra had harmful side effects. Synthesized from sugar and fatty acids, olestra passes through the body undigested, but some studies indicated a risk of diarrhea and abdominal cramping.

Gamma Liaison International

Both vitamin E and carotenoids are antioxidants. Of the subjects, 30% also suffered significant bowel upsets. Olestra nonetheless was approved by the FDA.

On the horizon were some new approaches to reducing fat. The USDA recently signed a Cooperative Research and Development Agreement with a small Philadelphia food company and the ARS. The agreement outlined a plan to develop a low-fat, low-sugar milk shake in an effort to boost children's intake of calcium.

Lowering cholesterol in beef

Researchers at Kansas State University, Manhattan, reported that a process called vascular infusion performed on freshly killed grain-fed cattle lowered the cholesterol content in beef taken from the animals by 23%. The process, which involved infusion through the carotid artery with a blend of carbohydrate, sodium chloride, and phosphates, flushed out more of the animals' blood than could be extracted by

conventional methods, removing significant amounts of lipoprotein cholesterol, which is carried in the blood. The process took about two minutes. There were no effects on tenderness, flavor, or juiciness of the meat.

Genetically engineered vaccines

Researchers from the University of Maryland, College Park, and the Boyce Thompson Institute, Ithaca, N.Y., recently published a study showing that people who ate chunks of a genetically engineered potato developed defenses against a diarrhea germ. This achievement held out the possibility of vaccinating people by means of fruits and vegetables instead of needles in the future. The scientists targeted a form of *E. coli* bacterium that is a major cause of diarrhea in infants and tourists in developing countries. A particular protein in the bacterium, when taken orally, had been found to provoke a strong response from the immune system. Therefore, researchers developed a strain of potatoes with a gene added to make the potatoes manufacture that protein. In the study, 11 healthy adults ate raw chunks of the potatoes three times over three weeks. Nearly all of them developed blood antibodies targeting the bacterial protein.

Nobel Prize for farming researcher

In 1998 the Nobel Memorial Prize in Economic Science went to Amartya Sen, an Indian philosopher and economist who resided in Cambridge, Eng. He was the author of many publications, including the 1981 book *Poverty and Famines: An Essay on Entitlement and Deprivation.* The book emphasized that famines occurred because of political and economic reasons as well

as distribution problems, such as those that African nations experienced in the last decade. Sen was a former Harvard University professor who developed alternative economic indexes that also included factors beyond gross national product, such as income distribution. He emphasized the role of democracy in preventing famine, stating that democratically elected officials must pay attention to key issues such as famine or they lose their jobs. Sen pointed out that democratic forms of government never had famine and that an investigative press provided an "early warning system." Furthermore, he noted that dictators were not accountable to anyone, even when millions of people died.

—John Patrick Jordan and
Patricia Brazeel Lewis

NUTRITION

In 1998 public interest in alternative health care continued to grow. A recent review of trends in alternative medicine use in the U.S. documented substantial increases between 1990 and 1997, indicating that the American population was joining a major part of the world already extensively employing such therapies. Many of these therapies involved herbal medicine and megavitamins. Most consumers of nutritional and herbal supplements used them as alternative treatments for illnesses for which conventional medicine did not offer a cure, such as arthritis, allergies, and viral infections, or for relief from insomnia, depression, anxiety, headaches, back problems, or chronic pain. Others were looking

for a means to optimize performance, energy, or weight loss. The value of nutritional and herbal supplements for therapeutic treatment and prevention of chronic diseases underwent scientific scrutiny during the year. Significant findings regarding the effectiveness of food, nutritional, and herbal supplements were reported.

Herbal supplements

Australian researcher Alan Bensoussan and colleagues studied the effectiveness of Chinese herbal medicine for treatment of irritable bowel syndrome, a common bowel disorder for which there is no reliable medical treatment. Patients were treated with either individualized Chinese herbal formulations or placebos for 16 weeks. The Chinese herbal preparations were found to offer significant improvement in symptoms for some patients. In another study, physiologist Steven Heymsfield of Columbia University, New York City, and others evaluated the efficacy of the herbal compound *Garcinia cambogia* for body weight and fat mass loss in overweight men and women. Results showed that the compound failed to produce significant effects beyond those observed with placebos. Timothy J. Wilt, a physician at the Minneapolis (Minn.) Veterans Affairs Medical Center, and colleagues reviewed existing evidence for the efficacy of saw palmetto extract in helping men with symptoms of prostatic hyperplasia. According to their findings, the evidence generally suggested that saw palmetto extract was effective in improving urologic symptoms and flow measures.

Controlled studies using standardized experimental design were limited for many herbal supplements but were greatly needed to help consumers sort through the maze of information and claims. Credible scientific approaches to discern the benefits and risks for taking nutritional and herbal supplements are important to safeguard health.

Green tea

In the past several years, researchers have studied the effects on the human body of polyphenolic compounds, which are present in many plants and act as powerful antioxidants. In 1998 an article by Joan L. Bushman, "Green Tea and Cancer in Humans: A Review of the Literature," appeared in *Nutrition and Cancer*. Bushman examined at least 31 studies on the relationship between green-tea consumption and protection against cancer in humans. For several types of cancer—colon, rectal, stomach, and lung—there were conflicting results, with some studies showing protection and others increased risk with the intake of green tea. Bushman suggested that despite the conflicting results, the data warranted further study of the possible beneficial effects of green tea. In a large epidemiological study by researchers in Japan, the case was made for green tea's effectiveness in protecting against stomach cancer. The researchers found, however, that most associations between the intake of green tea and a decreased risk for stomach cancer occurred in individuals who had a very high tea intake (seven cups or more per day).

Keren Su/Tony Stone Images

A tea maker measures green tea in the city of Hangzhou, China. Claims that green-tea consumption could offer protection against a number of types of cancer in humans underwent scientific scrutiny during 1998 by researcher Joan L. Bushman.

Calcium studies

Although the relationship between blood pressure and calcium has attracted a great deal of interest in recent years, consistent evidence that calcium supplementation lowers blood pressure has been lacking. In a study that appeared in *The American Journal of Clinical Nutrition,* James H. Dwyer and colleagues showed that calcium supplementation reduced diastolic blood pressure in African-American adolescents, particularly those with low calcium intake. In a report published in *Hypertension,* however, F.M. Sacks and other researchers described giving calcium supplements to adult women who were habitually low consumers of calcium. The researchers found that calcium supplementation provided no changes in the women's blood pressure. Interactions with other nutrients may play a role in the observed uncertainty of the beneficial effects of calcium supplementation in lowering blood pressure.

Zinc studies

In Bangladesh, S.K. Roy and colleagues found that supplementation with zinc reduced the length of the recovery period from persistent diarrhea in malnourished children. Children between the ages of 3 and 24 months who suffered from persistent diarrhea were treated with zinc or other forms of multivitamins for two weeks. From the beginning of the study through convalescence, children receiving zinc had a shorter duration of illness than those who did not receive zinc. The researchers suggested that zinc was a beneficial therapeutic strategy for the treatment of persistent diarrhea, a high-risk child-

hood illness. In another study involving children in Bangladesh, C.P. Doherty and others provided varying levels of zinc to children with severe protein-energy malnutrition. In this case, however, high levels of zinc were associated with increased mortality.

Fish-oil supplements

A group of Greek researchers led by C.A. Gogos published a study in the Jan. 15, 1998, issue of the journal *Cancer* on the effects of dietary supplementation with fish oil—a rich source of omega-3 polyunsaturated fatty acids—and vitamin E on the immune status and survival of advanced cancer patients. Results were encouraging, with those individuals receiving the supplementation experiencing a prolonged survival and significant improvement in

immune status. Malnutrition is an important predictor of survival for patients with advanced cancer, and supplementation with fish oil and vitamin E was suggested to be effective in slowing advanced cancer. An important study involving fish-oil supplementation in diabetics also appeared in 1998. Fish-oil supplements had been used to lower serum triglyceride levels, but the effect on control of blood sugar was not known. After reviewing 26 trials, C.E. Friedberg and other researchers in The

Starving children huddle together at a Red Cross feeding center in southern Somalia. In 1998 malnourished children were the focus of a number of scientific studies. Researchers in Bangladesh, for example, searched for ways to reduce the length of the recovery period from persistent diarrhea in malnourished children between the ages of 3 and 24 months.

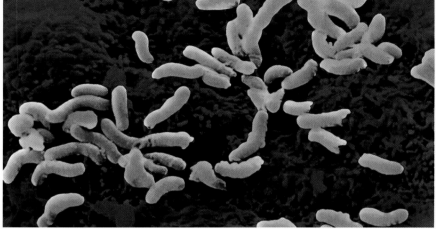

The bacterium *Helicobacter pylori,* shown in a false-color scanning electron micrograph, is a causative agent of stomach ulcers and cancer. Results of a study on the role of vitamin C as a treatment for *H. pylori* infection appeared in 1998.

CNRI/Science Photo Library/Photo Researchers, Inc.

Netherlands concluded that fish oil lowered triglyceride levels by almost 30% and did not adversely affect diabetic control of blood sugar.

Effects of soy products

Interest in the benefits of eating soy products had increased in some countries due to the favorable results observed in Asia regarding decreased incidence of cancer. Several studies examining the effects of soy products or isolated compounds in soy on blood lipid levels were published in 1998. A Japanese study involving nearly 5,000 men and women showed a relationship between lowered cholesterol levels and consumption of soy products. The compounds in soy products that had been singled out for beneficial effects were typically isoflavonoids. An intervention trial in Australia, however, failed to show any effect of isoflavonoid supplementation on lipid levels in middle-aged men who took soy supplements for eight weeks, leading researchers to conclude that the effects on blood lipids were caused by the soybean protein rather than the isolated compounds in soy or that the dose of isoflavonoids was not high enough in the Australian study.

Micronutrients

Interesting insights were gained in 1998 as to how vitamins from food or supplements may help women lower their incidence of heart disease. Researchers at Harvard University's School of Public Health drew some conclusions from a study involving more than 80,000 nurses. Overall, women who used multiple vitamin supplements had a 25% reduction in risk for heart dis-

ease. Women with higher intakes of folate and vitamin B6 from either food or supplements were found to be at lower risk, possibly due to lower levels of the amino acid homocysteine in the blood plasma. High levels of homocysteine in the blood had been implicated as an independent risk factor for some types of heart disease. In another study, C.J. Schorah and colleagues at the University of Leeds, Eng., assessed the long-term effects of small increases in folic acid on levels of plasma homocysteine. In their study, volunteers consumed breakfast cereals fortified with folic acid, which led to a decrease in plasma homocysteine by about 10%. If homocysteine levels are proven to be a causative risk factor for fatal and nonfatal heart attacks, then fortification of food with folic acid could have an impact on prevention.

Vitamin B_{12} deficiency in elderly people has been the focus of study because of its possible implications for neurological deficits or impairment of immune function. A study conducted by R.M. Russell of Holland and published in the August 1998

issue of *The American Journal of Clinical Nutrition* found that about one-fourth of 105 elderly subjects suffered mild vitamin B_{12} deficiency. This type of deficiency was usually caused by a combination of poor diet and malabsorption, which can be part of the aging process. The study raised awareness of the need to study further whether older people may protect against B_{12} deficiency by improving their diet or taking supplements.

Polish researchers coauthored a study on the role of vitamin C as a treatment for *Helicobacter pylori* infection in the stomach. *H. pylori* infection had been implicated as a causative agent for stomach ulcers and cancer. In about 30% of the subjects who received five grams of vitamin C a day for four weeks along with antacids, *H. pylori* was eradicated. In the control group, whose members received only antacids, *H. pylori* infection remained unchanged. This dosage of vitamin C was at least 80 times the amount typically recommended to prevent deficiency symptoms in adults; however, no adverse effects were documented. The researchers suggested that confirmatory studies were needed. At the Tufts University Research Center on Aging, Boston, G. Cao and colleagues studied the antioxidant capacity of the blood of older women after the women had eaten fruit or vegetables or had taken a vitamin C supplement. The total antioxidant capacity of the women's blood increased by about 10–30% four hours after consumption of strawberries or spinach and by about 45% after consumption of 1.25 grams of vitamin C. The study showed that food or vitamin C supplements can be useful in improving antioxidant capacity, which may protect against age-related diseases.

Awards

Robert E. Olson, emeritus professor of medicine at the State University of New York, Stony Brook, was awarded the Conrad A. Elvehjem Award for Public Service in Nutrition in 1998, given in recognition of specific and distinguished service to the public through the science of nutrition. Olson was known for his service as a researcher, administrator of a clinical research center in Thailand, and consultant to government agencies. His work in Thailand included study of anemia and malnutrition in children and had a positive impact on the management of protein-calorie malnutrition throughout the Third World.

Peter J. Reeds, professor in the department of pediatrics at the Baylor College of Medicine, Houston, Texas, received the Osborne and Mendel Award in recognition of outstanding recent basic research in nutrition. Reeds was recognized for his sig-

nal contributions to the understanding of the intersections of protein and energy metabolism as they relate to the nutritional regulation of the growth process. The research of Reeds advanced the knowledge of dietary amino acid requirements based on biology and intermediary metabolism.

Simin Nikbin Meydani, professor of nutrition and immunology at the Tufts University School of Nutrition Science and Policy, Boston, was awarded the Lederle Award in Human Nutrition, given in recognition of recent investigative contributions of significance to the basic understanding of human nutrition. Meydani had contributed significantly to enhancing the understanding of the dynamic interrelationships that exist among diet, age, and immunity.

—Marla Reicks

Among notable award winners in the field of nutrition was Peter J. Reeds, who received the Osborne and Mendel Award for basic research.

Courtesy of Peter J. Reeds, Ph.D.

LIFE SCIENCES

The unveiling of complete DNA sequences for the bacteria that cause tuberculosis (*Mycobacterium tuberculosis*), chlamydia (*Chlamydia trachomatis*), and syphilis (*Treponema pallidum*) were important advances in the life sciences during the past year, but the announcement that scientists had completely sequenced the genome of the nematode worm *Caenorhabditis elegans* made headlines everywhere. Knowledge of the genes of the highly studied nematode will increase understanding of the genetic underpinnings of human diseases. In botany, researchers pressed on with work to develop new varieties of genetically engineered crops, while ecologists demonstrated that a common fishing practice has contributed to the decline of marine fisheries worldwide. In microbiology, scientists continued to study one of the latest weapons in the war on cancer— viruses that replicate in cancer cells and kill them without harming normal tissue. Molecular biologists worked out the three-dimensional structure of the potassium ion (K⁺) channel, a critical molecular mechanism in the cells of all organisms from bacteria to human beings. In zoology, the discovery of coelacanths in Indonesia represented only the second-known population of these fish, despite more than a half-century of searching.

BOTANY

Transgenic plants

Research involving the development and application of transgenic plants continued an important trend in biotechnology during 1998. A transgenic plant is a genetically

Leonard Lee Rue III/Photo Researchers, Inc.

A plant disease caused by the fungus *Endothia parasitica* has killed virtually all native American chestnut trees in the United States and Canada. Scientists are now hoping to produce genetically modified chestnut trees capable of resisting fungal diseases.

modified plant containing genes transferred from another organism with desirable characteristics. In recent years such genetic manipulation has resulted in an assortment of commercial crop plants with many beneficial traits, including increased resistance to insects and diseases, greater tolerance of chemical herbicides, better ripening characteristics, and improved nutritional quality and taste. Several recently created transgenic plants approached commercialization in the past year.

Scientists from the Center for Plant Breeding and Reproduction Research, Wageningen, Neth., successfully used genetic engineering to create a transgenic sugar beet plant whose sugar tastes sweet but that the body cannot digest. The mod-

ified sugar beet incorporates a gene taken from the Jerusalem artichoke; expression of the gene converts the sucrose normally produced by the sugar beet into fructans, indigestible forms of the fruit sugar, fructose. Fructans taste less sweet than sucrose but may have several health benefits, including the ability to lower cholesterol.

American chestnut trees might one day be saved from the devastating fungus blight that has driven the trees to near extinction, thanks to researchers from the State University of New York (SUNY) College of Environmental Science and Forestry, Syracuse, N.Y. In 1998 the SUNY team reported that they had successfully transferred fungus-resistant frog genes into chestnut tree cells, hoping to

create hybrid trees capable of tolerating fungal diseases. Later, the scientists grew dozens of transgenic shoots in sterile petri dishes under fluorescent light. The next challenge, according to the scientists, was to successfully grow the shoots into saplings. They expected to plant transgenic saplings for testing by late 1999.

The U.S. Department of Agriculture (USDA) released three new lines of transgenic tomatoes into the commercial market. The genetically engineered fruits contain 10–25 times more beta-carotene than regular tomatoes. Beta-carotene is found in high concentrations in dark-green leafy vegetables and orange and yellow fruits and vegetables. It is the most biologically available of the several related carotenoid plant pigments that act as a precursor to vitamin A. The human body converts beta-carotene into vitamin A, an essential nutrient that aids vision, bone growth, tooth development, and reproduction. High-beta-carotene cherry and beefsteak tomatoes will also be released into the market.

Another genetically improved crop offered by the USDA was a worm-resistant carrot made by crossing a wild Brazilian carrot with a commercial American carrot variety. Field trials indicated that the hybrid carrot was remarkably resistant to root-knot nematodes, which every year cause significant crop losses. The new carrot should offer welcome relief to California carrot growers, who in 1998 produced about 70% of American fresh-market carrots.

Plant-microbe interactions

Interactions between plants and microbes—particularly bacteria and fungi—

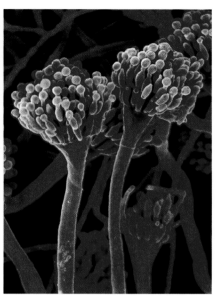

Aflatoxin contamination is a serious problem faced by the U.S. peanut industry. In 1998 USDA scientists reported on a way to use benign fungi to reduce aflatoxin contamination of peanut plants (above left) caused by noxious strains of *Aspergillus* fungi (above, in a microscopic view).

play vital roles in the health and functioning of ecosystems. For example, an interesting ecological pact exists between leguminous plants, such as peas, clover, and alfalfa, and soil bacteria in the genus *Rhizobium*, which live within the roots of the plants. In this alliance, the bacterial cells obtain food from the host plants and in exchange convert atmospheric nitrogen gas into a form that plants can use. The dynamics of such interactions have provided scientists with important information for a wide range of research endeavors. In 1998 investigators made use of plant-microbe interactions in several positive applications, including the prevention of plant disease and the regulation of plant growth.

In recent years, increased restrictions on the use of chemical pesticides has encouraged scientific research on the development, production, and application of environmentally friendly biological control methods. Soil-borne fungal diseases have been a constant problem in the agricultural industry. Fungi such as *Pythium* and *Rhizoctonia,* for instance, are the main culprits in a crop disease known as damping-off, which kills both germinating seeds and young seedlings. To eliminate these pathogens, farmers have traditionally fumigated soils with chemical fungicides such as methyl bromide. Research in the 1990s indicated that methyl bromide is a significant ozone-depleting substance, and in 1998 the U.S. Congress approved a plan to phase out agricultural use of the chemical by 2005. Fortunately, other studies have shown that certain soil-dwelling fungi, most notably *Gliocladium virens,* can suppress damping-off. *Gliocladium* kills pathogens by engulfing them, releasing enzymes that destroy the organisms. In

1998 USDA scientists approved the use of *G. virens* on crops.

Investigators discovered that competition between microbes also may be helpful in tipping the scales against plant diseases. This was demonstrated by USDA researchers working with *Aspergillus ssp.,* a fungus known to attack peanut plants. When peanut plants become infected by *A. parasiticus* or *A. flavus,* a harmful chemical called aflatoxin is produced, rendering the peanuts unmarketable.

Benign strains of *Aspergillus* that do not produce the poison had previously been identified and isolated. When researchers inoculated peanut plants with both non-toxic and poison-producing strains of *A. parasiticus,* a competition between the two occurred, dramatically reducing aflatoxin contamination.

Natural competition between related microbes is helping fruit growers control one of the most damaging diseases of apple and pear trees—fire blight. The causal organism is the bacterium *Erwinia amylovora,* which is carried to tree blossoms by wind, rain, and insects. In the 1980s scientists discovered that a related bacterium, *Pseudomonas fluorescens,* outcompetes the fire blight organism for nutrients when the two species are placed on the same blossoms, keeping the numbers of *Erwinia* low enough to avoid severe infection.

In 1998 researchers from Utah State University, Logan, reported on a new method—employing the services of a honeybee—to apply this protective microbe to fruit trees. First, the beneficial bacteria are combined with pollen. The mixture is then placed in a pollen insert attached to the entrance of a beehive. As bees exit the hive,

they inadvertently pick up the bacteria, subsequently transferring the microbes to the flowers they visit. The technique may be an effective, low-cost method for inoculating fruit trees since honeybees are already used in orchards for pollination.

USDA scientists issued a report showing that an interaction between poinsettia plants and the bacteria-like phytoplasmas that live within them is responsible for the bushy, free-branching look of the festive poinsettia. The researchers came to this conclusion after conducting a series of plant-grafting experiments and DNA analyses on the phytoplasmas. Although they had not determined exactly how phytoplasmas influence the bushiness of poinsettias, it was believed that the microbes act to disrupt a plant's hormonal balance, causing it to grow outward, rather than upward like a tree.

Plant diversity and conservation

Our supply of food and fabric—and even the quality of the air—is dependent on a diverse plant ecology. Researchers had long suspected that ecosystems containing a broad diversity of plants are healthier and generally better able to adapt to fluctuating environmental conditions than less diverse communities. This idea was further supported by an elaborate series of experiments directed by ecologist G. David Tilman of the University of Minnesota, Minneapolis-St. Paul.

In 1993 Tilman set up hundreds of experimental garden plots in the Cedar Creek Natural History Area, some 48 km (30 mi) north of the Twin Cities. Each plot was thoroughly plowed and completely cleared of weeds. He then sowed the plots with native prairie plants, varying the number of species per plot and choosing species at random. In other experiments, differing amounts of nitrogen—an essential plant nutrient—were applied to the plots, or elevated carbon dioxide levels were introduced to mimic rising levels of the gas in the atmosphere. Measurements were made periodically over a five-year-period to see how the variations would affect plant productivity and nutrient ecology.

The study showed a number of interesting results. First, Tilman clearly demonstrated that species diversity does influence the health of ecosystems. A lack of plant diversity significantly worsens the impact of drought on an ecosystem, Tilman said, because reduced variety means that there is less of a chance that one or more species will be drought-resistant. The experiments also showed that as nitrogen levels in the soil increase, the number of plant species decreases. Nitrogen is a critical nutrient but, like many of the nutrients used by organisms, too much is harmful. This observation was a matter of importance since farming and the burning of fossil fuels have loaded the biosphere with excess nitrogen. The loss

of species allows opportunistic plants to proliferate wildly in the high-nitrogen soil, crowding out other plants. The study should provide scientists with valuable information for developing and improving strategies for achieving sustainable agriculture.

Phytoremediation

In recent years phytoremediation—the use of plants to clean up hazardous substances in the soil—has emerged as a less expensive and perhaps more successful alternative to traditional methods of environmental cleanup. Some plants have demonstrated an ability to absorb harmful contaminants from soils through their root systems; they either store the chemicals within their tissues or metabolize them into less-toxic compounds. In 1998 at least 24 companies in the U.S. shared a $16 million–$30 million market for their phytoremediation services. Industry experts projected that by 2005 the market would grow to $370 million.

Environmental engineers continued a massive phytoremediation effort in rural Oregon to clean up a toxic waste spill that had occurred more than a decade earlier. In 1984 a tanker truck carrying hundreds of gallons of the industrial solvent trichloroethane crashed on an icy road, spilling the chemical—a suspected carcinogen—all over the pavement and surrounding soil. Gradually, the chemical percolated into the ground and made its way into local water supplies. In 1997, after years of ineffective conventional cleanup methods, poplar trees were planted at the site of the spill in an attempt to extract the contaminant from the ground. By that time scientists had learned that poplar trees were very good at cleaning up pollutants.

The overall effectiveness of the effort was still being evaluated at the close of 1998, but laboratory simulations indicated that the poplars will be able to reduce trichloroethane concentrations in the soil by as much as 97%.

While cleanup efforts continued in Oregon, scientists from the University of Georgia reported that genetically engineered poplar trees may be effective at cleaning up heavy-metal contaminants such as mercury. The scientists, led by forest biotechnologist Scott Merkle, fitted poplar trees with genes borrowed from mercury-resistant bacteria. It was shown that the transgenic poplars were 10 times more effective at absorbing and metabolizing mercury than control trees.

Vegetables are not only good to eat—they can also help remove toxic industrial chemicals from the ground, according to research conducted at the University of California, Berkeley. There, investigators discovered that many kinds of vegetables, including broccoli, spinach, lettuce, cucumber, and tomato, are able to extract hexavalent chromium—a toxic form of the element chromium and a potent carcinogen—from the soil and convert it into a harmless form of chromium. Several aquatic plants, including water hyacinth, cattail, and salt marsh bullrush, also demonstrated this ability.

Medicinal plants

The rapidly growing interest in botanical medicinals continued in 1998. In 1997 worldwide sales of drugs derived from medicinal plants topped $16 billion, with Europe (46%) and Asia (33%) accounting for the bulk of the market. U.S. sales ac-

The annual wormwood plant has long been used to make absinthe and other beverages. Scientists from the USDA are studying medicinal qualities of the plant—including its self-made pesticide, artemisinin, which could be exploited to develop antimalaria drugs.

counted for approximately 18% of the total, but revenues had grown in that country about 10–15% in the previous two years, with sales projected to grow at the same or greater rate over the next several years.

In response to the increased interest in medicinal plants among U.S. consumers, the USDA Agricultural Research Service (ARS) established the Natural Products Utilization Research Unit in Oxford, Miss., to learn more about how plants manufacture beneficial compounds and how to better extract them. In 1998 scientists continued to study the aromatic plant known as annual wormwood (*Artemisia annua*) for its medicinal qualities. For years scientists had known that the plant—which has been used since ancient times to make absinthe and flavored wines—produces a chemical in its leaves that has amazing insect-fighting properties. ARS scientists were interested in how this useful compound, artemisinin, might be exploited on a large-scale basis as a commercial insecticide and as a potential malaria-fighting drug for people.

Plants, soil, and the greenhouse effect

Many scientists suspect that the phenomenon known as the greenhouse effect—in which the Sun's heat is trapped near Earth's surface and prevented from radiating out into space due to the presence of so-called greenhouse gases in the atmosphere—has been accentuated over the past century due to human activities. A study by USDA soil scientist Donald C. Reicosky showed how modern farming practices play a significant role in production and consumption of greenhouse gases, specifically carbon dioxide (CO_2).

The Minnesota-based scientist examined the influence of different tillage methods on CO_2 levels in the soil. Reicosky discovered that when land is plowed, CO_2 is forcefully released from the soil. As much as 290 kg per ha (about 260 lb per ac) per hour may be released immediately after tillage. Over time, even more carbon may be lost because tilling oxygenates the soil, rapidly increasing the process of decomposition, a chemical reaction that releases CO_2 as a by-product.

On the other hand, certain practices, such as conservation tillage, can both reduce carbon loss and increase the amount of carbon stored in the soil. Conventional tillage tends to produce a barren and smooth soil surface that encourages run-off and erosion problems. Conservation tillage, on the other hand, disturbs less soil and leaves part of the field surface covered with dead roots and crop residue. In Reicosky's study, conservation tillage reduced carbon losses in the soil by as much as four-fifths.

Research and education

According to the U.S. National Academy of Sciences (NAS), plant science research in the United States "is not keeping pace

Studies revealed that conservation tillage practices such as used in this cotton field, in which soils are minimally tilled and left with crop residues, can help retain carbon in the soil.

Long-term studies in the Amazon Basin showed that forest-clearing practices that leave enormous lengths of forest edge can have negative effects on rain forest ecology as deep as 500 m (1,640 ft) from the forest edge.

Antonio Ribeiro/Gamma Liaison International

with research in other fields of biology." The NAS strongly recommended that scientists pay more attention to the fundamental aspects of plant biology, including molecular processes, cell biology, organismal processes, ecology and population biology, and interactions between plants and other species. Additionally, the NAS suggested that more plant science research needs to incorporate a global perspective.

A report from the Botanical Society of America underscored the need for professional botanists to become more active in educating the public. The following summary statement from the report deals with the need for improvements in botany education in public and private grade schools, high schools, and universities: "The common call for more effective teaching is one that every botanist can and must answer. Teaching students about plant biology is as critical to the future of the field as is research, and must take its proper place as an equally laudatory endeavor for botanists. Equally vital are activities that communicate the excitement of plant biol-

ogy to students and teachers involved in K–12 education and the general public."

—Michael J. Pelczar, Jr., and
Rita M. Pelczar

ECOLOGY

Fragmented forests

In the late 1970s Thomas Lovejoy of the Smithsonian Institution, Washington, D.C., engineered a unique natural experiment to study the ecological effects of tropical rain forest clearing. At the time, population expansion in the Amazon Basin was resulting in high rates of deforestation. Brazilian law required that some forest be left intact; thus, clearing practices tended to leave isolated forest fragments of varying size. Lovejoy had wondered what kinds of ecological changes, if any, would occur in the forest patches over time.

Working with the National Institute for Amazonian Research in Manaus, Braz., Lovejoy ensured that deforestation in an

area north of Manaus would leave neat forest patches of 1, 10, or 100 hectares. (A hectare is about 2.5 acres.) In 1998 he met with other ecologists to assess the results of two decades of monitoring these patches. Several important questions were to be answered. First, would the theory of island biogeography—which explained why small oceanic islands have fewer species than larger ones and why islands distant from the mainland have fewer species than closer ones—apply to these forest "islands" surrounded by a "sea" of cattle pastures? If so, how large and how near to source areas would forest fragments need to be in order to retain most of their species?

As expected under the island biogeographic model, many species, including palms, bees, butterflies, beetles, termites, birds, and primates, declined in the forest fragments. Primates disappeared, for example, because forest patches were too small to accommodate their typically large home ranges. The model failed for some animal groups, however. Unlike true islands, where "unusable" ocean surrounds land, species can use the land surrounding forest islands to different degrees. Some animals, including leaf-cutter ants, flourished in the disturbed habitats around forest fragments. An increase in the number of frog species was unexpected. Many types of frogs, originally thought to be highly dependent on microhabitats within the forest, actually thrived in farm ponds outside forest fragments.

A second question concerned the edges of the fragments. On average, roughly 21,000 sq km (8,100 sq mi) of Amazonian rain forest are cleared each year for development. Although clearing leaves behind

Conservation biologists demonstrated in 1998 that the effects of bottom trawling (right) on coastal seabeds are as devastating as clear-cutting forests. Bottom trawling rips up the seafloor, destroying the delicate habitats of corals, starfish, and other marine invertebrates (bottom).

very little forest as islands, it creates enormous lengths of forest edge. Because vegetation growing along the edge of a forest is more vulnerable to damage caused by soil erosion, high winds, driving rains, and other environmental factors compared to plants in the forest's interior, Lovejoy asked whether he might see any differences in species composition between the two kinds of environments. If so, how far into a forest patch would such "edge effects" penetrate?

Studies of plant communities within forest fragments confirmed that ecological changes occurred along forest edges. Wind-damaged trees were observed as far as 500 m (1,640 ft) into a forest patch from its edge. In total, researchers concluded that about 10% of the plant biomass in the forest edges they studied was lost within two to four years of forest clearing.

Plowing the oceans

Marine conservationists reported in 1998 that years of commercial bottom trawling for fish and shellfish has destroyed vital ocean habitats in the same way that clear-cutting has ravaged the world's forests. In bottom trawling, huge nets and dredges are dragged along coastal seabeds. Les Watling of the Darling Marine Center in Walpole, Maine, and Elliott Norse of the Marine Conservation Biology Institute, Redmond, Wash., estimated that roughly 15 million sq km (6 million sq mi) of the world's seafloor is plowed annually by bottom trawling, twice the area of the continental United States and about 150 times greater than the total area of forest cleared each year.

The damage caused by trawling is immense. Some equipment, such as otter trawls, act like giant plows and create vis-

ible furrows on the seafloor. A wide range of invertebrates share this environment, including corals, brachiopods, mollusks, sponges, sea urchins, and various worms. A few fish species benefit when the naturally complex habitat is simplified, but, in general, when the ocean floor is ripped up, habitats are destroyed and food chains are disrupted. Recovery of the seafloor can take more than a century. Many animals, such as deep-sea corals, are slow-growing and long-lived, and therefore slow to repopulate after an area has been

disturbed. Bottom trawling can also disrupt an ecosystem by stirring up nitrogen-rich sediments on the seafloor, according to Lawrence Mayer, a biogeochemist at the

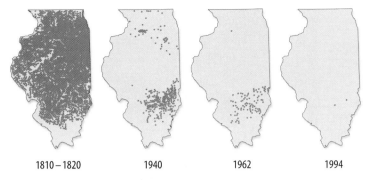

1810–1820   1940   1962   1994

(Photograph) John Shaw/Tom Stack & Associates

Maps (left) show Illinois prairies during 1810–1820 and the distributions of greater prairie chickens (below) in 1940, 1962, and 1994. In 1998 biologists from the Illinois Natural History Survey showed that the rapid decline of greater prairie chickens in Illinois was the result of diminished genetic variability due to inbreeding.

Darling Center. Resuspension of such sediments can spark population explosions of the noxious dinoflagellates responsible for red tides, leading to massive fish kills and an upsetting of marine food chains.

Inbreeding and extinction

Cultural taboos against marrying close relatives exist for good genetic reasons. Such inbreeding leads to decreased genetic variability among offspring and, therefore, to a greater chance for the expression of deleterious recessive genes that can reduce survival and fertility. Avoidance of inbreeding is not limited to human beings. Many plants and animals also shun matings with genetically similar kin. Nevertheless, inbreeding does happen in nature, particularly within small isolated populations where there are a limited number of mates from which to choose.

Some conservation geneticists have theorized that in small inbreeding populations the probability of extinction increases over time because reduced genetic variation makes the population more susceptible to disease, climatic fluctuations, and random demographic events, such as skewed sex ratios. Others have argued that, whereas inbreeding and decreased genetic diversity may be inevitable in small populations, it does not necessarily translate into an increased likelihood for extinction. The debate has raged for more than a decade. Is a reduction in genetic variation a cause or a consequence of decreasing population size? The answer has a bearing on how conservationists manage wildlife populations that are teetering on the brink of extinction.

In 1998 Ronald Westemeier from the Illinois Natural History Survey and colleagues published one of the first well-documented studies of how formerly large populations are driven to extinction. As part of an experimental conservation-management program, the scientists monitored greater prairie chicken populations in Illinois for 35 years, observing a rapid decline in the endangered birds as open prairies were lost to cities and farmland. At the same time, populations in Kansas, Minnesota, Missouri, and Nebraska were still numerous and widespread. By the 1970s the Illinois birds became isolated from other populations, and in 1994 fewer than 50 birds remained. As the numbers of birds declined, so too did the fertility and genetic variation of their offspring. Were the losses in fertility and variation the cause of the population decline or just an effect?

The Westemeier study demonstrated that a loss of genetic diversity exacerbated the population decline of Illinois prairie chickens. Despite strong efforts in the 1960s and 1970s to increase the area and quality of the chickens' habitat and to control their natural predators, populations continued to diminish, suggesting that the downward spiral was caused by isolation. Moreover, beginning in 1992, prairie chickens were brought in from neighboring states in an attempt to increase numbers and enhance genetic diversity and fitness within the population. The impact of this simple experiment was dramatic. Hatching-success rate increased and the birds' numbers have slowly climbed upward ever since. No major environmental or climatic events could have accounted for the increased hatching rates, according to the researchers. Rather, the study demonstrated that the importation of individuals from healthy populations elsewhere can work as a genetic-management technique.

Designing reserves

Though habitat loss is a major threat to biodiversity, it has been estimated that only about 5% of the planet's land is protected in one way or another from habitat destruction. Moreover, the allocation of nature reserves around the world is poor. Reserves larger than 100,000 sq km (38,600 sq mi) are frequently located in high mountains, frigid tundras, or dry deserts, areas that are geologically interesting but not particularly rich in species. The plants and animals most vulnerable to extinction from loss of habitat—that is, those with the smallest geographical ranges—are not distributed randomly around the globe. Rather, most rare endemic species occur only in a few "hot spots" around the world. If nations were to set up more nature reserves in these special places, might they save a greater fraction of species? Several teams of scientists

addressed this issue in 1998, pointing to the challenges involved.

Research conducted by Amanda Lombard and colleagues of the University of Cape Town dealt with preserving vegetation on the Algulhas Plain of southern Africa, a hot spot for plants. There, plant diversity is extraordinarily high—an area of 1,500 sq km (580 sq mi) contains some 1,700 species. Whereas most of the state forests and nature reserves in the region are coastal, most of its 99 endemic plants live inland. Lombard's work involved the use of a computer to determine where new nature reserves should be situated in order to protect the maximum number of species at a minimum cost.

One aspect of the Lombard analysis was purely a matter of biogeography. The computer selected sets of reserve locations according to species composition, aiming to capture as many total species or as many rare species as possible. Naively applied, however, this may not be a practical method. For example, selected locations may not even be available to be set aside as reserves. In addition, if selected locations are too small, the process can lead to a "Noah's Ark" effect, whereby species are protected in a collection of widely scattered reserves that may in the long run be too small to allow a species to persist.

On the other hand, when additional factors are considered along with biogeographical ones, computers are needed to sort out the complex relationships. If, for instance, a species is already protected by reserves, it does not need to be added again, and every species should be represented more than once as insurance against disasters. Additionally, some areas are unsuitable, alien weeds overrun others, and some

selected sites are in mostly agricultural or urban areas. Whenever possible, computers also should add areas adjacent to existing reserves. Computer algorithms are excellent for sorting out these kinds of constraints.

Amy Ando of Resources for the Future, Washington, D.C., and colleagues examined the problem of efficiently establishing nature reserves in a country as economically diverse as the United States. Their work was critical of a previous study, which equated efficiency with the minimum number of U.S. counties needed to achieve a given coverage of endangered species. If land prices were broadly similar, this would be reasonable, Ando concluded. The analysis, however, included counties in California, Florida, and Hawaii, areas with some of the highest-priced land in the country. Ando's suggested technique was a modification of the earlier approach, maximizing the species protected for a given cost. In other words, in selecting sites to provide coverage for endangered species, land prices must be taken into account. Expensive land purchases can rapidly diminish limited resources and bring about a lower total coverage than if the same resources were used elsewhere.　　　—Stuart L. Pimm

MICROBIOLOGY

Endosymbiosis

In the 1970s American biologist Lynn Margulis advanced a promising new hypothesis about the evolutionary origin of eukaryotic cells—cells containing a nucleus and other specialized internal structures (organelles). Dubbed the endosymbiont hypothesis, it postulated that the two major eukaryotic organelles—plastids, the sites of photosynthesis in plants, and mitochondria, the sites of energy production in plants and animals—originated as free-living bacteria that had become engulfed by larger bacteria, with which they formed a symbiotic relationship. These organelles emerged as remnants of the ancient endosymbioses (*endo* for "internal") when many of the engulfed partners' genes were transferred to the nuclei of the host bacteria, the nascent eukaryotic cells.

Margulis's endosymbiont hypothesis has been modified over the years, but its basic elements are widely accepted by biologists. A more thoroughly articulated hypothesis of eukaryotic origins was offered in 1998 by William Martin of the Technical University of Braunschweig, Germany, and Miklós Müller of Rockefeller University, New York City. According to their hydrogen hypothesis, eukaryotic life may have begun as a result of an endosymbiotic association between a free-living eubacterium (true bacterium) and a methanogen, an archaebacterium that consumes hydrogen and carbon dioxide and gives off methane as a waste product.

The beauty of the model was that it offered explanations for the origins of the three different types of eukaryotic cells: those that possess mitochondria and generate energy-rich adenosine triphosphate (ATP) molecules aerobically (with the consumption of oxygen); those that contain hydrogenosomes, odd mitochondria-sized organelles that manufacture ATP anaerobically (without oxygen) and release hydrogen as a by-product; and those eukaryotes, such as certain protists, that lack both mitochondria and hydrogenosomes and obtain energy parasitically by living inside other cells.

Hydrogenosomes have been known to scientists for many years, but their evolutionary origin has largely remained a mystery. It is thought that hydrogenosomes, like mitochondria and plastids, arose as a result of an ancient endosymbiotic association between bacteria. For many years it had been assumed that the three kinds of cellular-power plants arose independently. In 1996 and 1997, however, scientists presented evidence suggesting that mitochondria and hydrogenosomes evolved from a common precursor organelle. The hydrogen hypothesis is also consistent with the idea that these cell structures share a common evolutionary history.

Martin and Müller speculated that the ancient eubacterium was engulfed by the methanogen. The eubacterium could generate ATP both aerobically and through hydrogen-evolving anaerobic respiration, whereas the methanogen could live only anaerobically in the presence of hydrogen, which it needed for making ATP. Originally, both organisms would have shared an anaerobic environment, where the eubacterium began to provide hydrogen for the methanogen. Once the associated organisms became separated from an environmental source of hydrogen, the methanogen would

Typical prokaryotic (left) and eukaryotic (right) cells are compared. Eukaryotes are single- or many-celled organisms whose cells possess a nucleus and other specialized cell structures. Prokaryotes are single-celled organisms, such as bacteria, that lack a nuclear envelope and most of the components of eukaryotic cells.

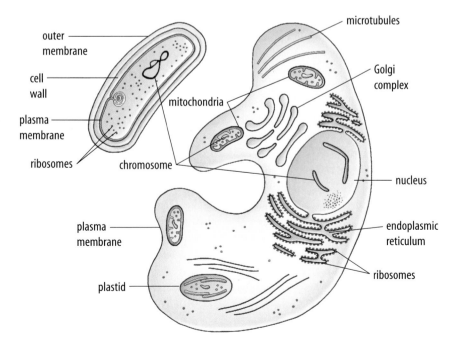

According to the hydrogen hypothesis, the three types of eukaryotic cells observed today originated as a result of an ancient symbiosis between a hydrogen-producing bacterium and a methanogen host. The host's dependence on hydrogen produced by the symbiont may have been the selective pressure that forged the common ancestor of eukaryotic cells.

have been entirely dependent on the eubacterium, and the selective advantage for the association would have been strengthened. The fact that methanogens and hydrogen-producing bacteria engage in many fascinating symbioses on Earth today provides strong support for this kind of early association.

As oxygen became more abundant in Earth's atmosphere, the eubacterium endosymbiont could have switched over to the more efficient, aerobic means of ATP production. This shift would have placed the endosymbiont on the path to becoming a mitochondrion. Alternatively, methanogen host cells that continued living in anaerobic environments provided an opportunity for their endosymbionts to lose the capacity for aerobic respiration—a matter of losing one or more genes—and become hydrogenosomes. Lastly, the methanogen-eubacterium associations that eventually became parasitic eukaryotes lacking any ATP-generating organelles would have transferred the genes for ATP production to the host nucleus and shed their endosymbionts.

Further support for the view that mitochondria and hydrogenosomes descended from a common precursor organelle was provided during the year by a team of researchers from The Netherlands studying an anaerobic eukaryote, the ciliate protist *Nyctotherus ovalis*. Although most protists require oxygen to make ATP, two main groups possess hydrogenosomes and ex-

Evolution of Eubacterium-Methanogen Association

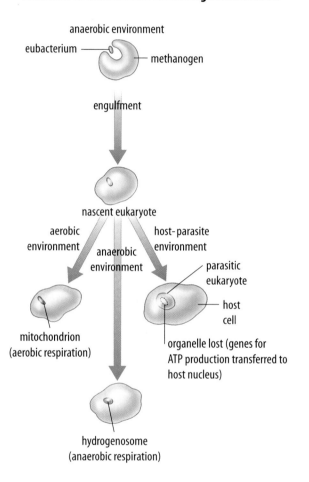

hibit anaerobic metabolism: parasitic species that inhabit the oxygen-free gastrointestinal tracts of humans and other animals (*N. ovalis* lives in cockroach intestines) and free-living species that live deep within certain marine and freshwater sediments.

Ribosomal RNA sequence data from *N. ovalis* revealed numerous characteristics that would be expected of a bacterial endosymbiont that had degenerated into a hydrogenosome. Moreover, the gene encod-

ing this protist's ribosomal RNA is clearly related to ribosomal RNA genes from the mitochondria of aerobic protists. The scientists may have also discovered a gene encoding a hydrogenase, the enzyme that couples hydrogen production to the synthesis of ATP. Did the gene encoding this hydrogenase come from the common ancestor of mitochondria and hydrogenosomes, or was it acquired later by gene transfer between cells? The answer remained to be determined.

In a related development, DNA studies of the bacterium *Rickettsia prowazekii* by Charles Kurland and co-workers at the University of Uppsala, Sweden, hinted that the organism may be the closest living relative to the ancient endosymbiotic bacterium that became the mitochondrion. *R. prowazekii* is an obligate intracellular pathogen and the cause of the louse-borne disease typhus. DNA sequencing revealed many similarities between the bacterium's DNA and the DNA of modern-day mitochondria, particularly in genes involved in energy production. A gene-by-gene comparison of the mitochondrial genome with the *R. prowazekii* genome also suggested that both evolved through similar evolutionary processes.

Researchers had long speculated that genes must have been transferred from the endosymbiont to the nucleus of the host cell during mitochondrial evolution. Over

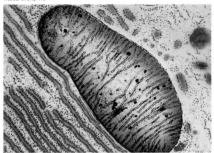

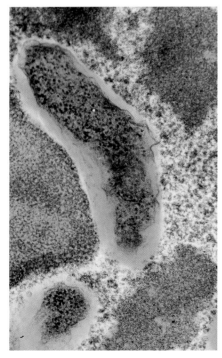

The bacterium shown above lives inside the cell nucleus of a eukaryotic organism. Although not yet proven, the notion that the mitochondrion (top) is the relic of an ancient bacterium that began living within a host cell is supported by compelling evidence. DNA research in 1998 on the bacterium *Rickettsia prowazekii*—which also depends on a host cell—revealed many similarities to the DNA of modern-day mitochondria.

time, the endosymbiont probably became more and more dependent on the host. Its shrinking genome diminished its metabolic capacity until it could no longer survive except within the host cell. Eventually, this process would have created the modern mitochondrion.

The DNA analysis of *R. prowazekii* supported this notion. As this bacterium—which depends upon a host cell for reproduction—evolved, it lost many of the genes necessary for independent reproduction, including those needed to make the building blocks of DNA and protein. Whereas all of the other 17 bacterial genomes that had been completely sequenced as of the end of 1998 have little extraneous DNA, about 25% of the *R. prowazekii* genome consists of noncoding, or junk, DNA. Scientists believed that the junk DNA is likely to be an evolutionary vestige of genes needed to be a free-living cell.

Symbiotic relationships of mycorrhizal fungi

A proclivity to engage in symbiotic relationships is not limited to single-celled organisms. A variety of fungi, for example, live on and within the roots of certain plants, forming an association with them called mycorrhiza. Mycorrhizal fungi are abundant in the soils of most ecosystems, where they form symbioses with approximately 80% of all terrestrial plants. The many species of mycorrhizal fungi differ in the way they colonize plant roots and the types of plants they colonize. In pine trees, for instance, the fungi form an extensive sheath around the outside of the root with only a little penetration into the root tissue itself. In other species, such as

orchids, the fungal mycelium is embedded in the root tissue.

The ecological relationship between mycorrhizal fungi and plants is known as mutualism, an association in which both organisms derive benefits. In the mycorrhizal relationship, the fungi obtain nutrients from the plants and, in turn, help nourish the plant by acting as extensions of the plant root system and increasing the uptake of essential nutrients.

Mycorrhizal fungi not only are important for the overall health of plants but also play a key role in the maintenance of plant diversity. In a recent study conducted by researchers at the Botanical Institute of the University of Basel, Switz., and the University of Guelph, Ont., it was shown that 8 out of 11 European grassland plants, grown under greenhouse conditions, were almost completely dependent on the presence of mycorrhizal fungi isolated from the plants' habitat. Moreover, when the researchers increased the different types of the fungi available to the plants, the structure and composition of the greenhouse plant community increased.

The researchers also enlarged the scale of their experiments by performing the same work on outdoor field plots simulating North American plant communities. As in their greenhouse studies, both plant diversity and plant productivity increased with increasing mycorrhizal fungi species richness. The lowest plant biodiversity and productivity were found in those plots without mycorrhizal fungi or with only a few species. Plant biodiversity and productivity were highest in plots containing 8 or 14 different species of mycorrhizal fungi. In addition, increasing the species richness of mycorrhizal fungi was shown to improve the plants' uptake of phosphorus from the soil. The scientists suggested that a diversity of mycorrhizal fungi in the soil raises the likelihood for the presence of at least one type that is very effective in boosting the ability of plants to exploit soil phosphorus. Taken together, these experiments clearly showed that conservation of the fungal gene pool is needed to maintain plant biodiversity.

Viruses that attack cancer cells

Biomedical scientists continued to experiment with a revolutionary new type of cancer therapy that uses viruses to selectively kill cancer cells without adversely affecting normal cells. In 1998 the most highly developed of these oncolytic (cancer-cell-killing) viruses was a genetically altered adenovirus called ONYX-015, which had been shown in a 1996 study to shrink human tumors by at least 50% in more than one-third of the patients studied. Several other similar viruses were in clinical trials.

Among the most recent entries in the field was a reovirus that is harmless to noncancerous cells. In order to replicate inside cells, the virus requires a cellular protein known as Ras. In normal cells, the activity of an enzyme called PKR prevents the reproduction of the virus; Ras, however, acts to block PKR activity. Because the overproduction of Ras in cells stimulates cancer-cell proliferation, it is logical that the virus would replicate readily in tumors that have an overactive Ras gene. This category includes nearly one-third of all known cancers including colon, pancreatic, brain, and lung cancers.

Following this line of reasoning, Patrick Lee and colleagues of the University of Calgary, Alta., transplanted cancerous human brain cells into immune-deficient mice in order to induce tumor formation. After tumors began to appear, the team introduced the reovirus. The tumors shrank or disappeared in 65–80% of the mice tested. The results encouraged future testing of this virus in humans.

Biological clocks

It has long been known that animals, including humans, possess genetically controlled biological clocks that govern the biologic cycles (circadian rhythms) of their metabolic activities. The rhythmical activities usually covered by the human biological clock include sleeping and waking, body temperature, cell division, and the secreting activity of endocrine glands. The alternation of night and day has been shown to be an important factor in regulating biologic rhythms.

Scientists have also discovered biological clocks in plants, fungi, and certain bacteria. In the cyanobacterium *Synechococcus,* for example, the circadian clock controls metabolic processes such as nitrogen fixation and amino acid uptake. Because biological cycles are found in many organisms, scientists have long wondered whether circadian clocks arose only once during evolution or evolved independently in different lineages. In 1998 a group of Japanese researchers led by Masahiro Ishiura and Takao Kondo of Nagoya University analyzed the circadian clock of *Synechococcus,* providing evidence for an independent evolutionary origin.

The *Synechococcus* clock consists of at least three genes known as *kaiA, kaiB,* and *kaiC* (*kai* is the Japanese word for "cycle"). The genes code for proteins (KaiA, KaiB, and KaiC) that act to increase or decrease their own expression to generate a cyclic expression system. Early in the cycle, the *kai* genes begin to produce messenger RNA that is translated into protein. The KaiA protein increases the expression of both the *kaiB* and *kaiC* genes. After a delay, the KaiC protein turns the genes off. Eventually, the KaiC protein concentration in the cell diminishes such that it can no longer repress *kai* gene expression, thus allowing the *kai* genes to switch back on and renew the cycle.

The cyclic and self-regulatory nature of the system is similar to the fruit-fly clock, in which proteins turn off genes. Despite the cyclic nature of their autoregulation, however, the proteins that make up the two clocks are completely different. These results suggested that biological clocks in organisms arose multiple times, recreating a similar design each time.

DNA replication "factories" in bacteria

For years, scientists assumed that bacteria lack intracellular organization because their small size enables relatively rapid diffusion of proteins through the cytoplasm. An application of fluorescent microscopy by researchers at the Massachusetts Institute of Technology (MIT) revealed, however, that many proteins in bacteria have distinct intracellular locations.

Bacterial reproduction depends on the faithful replication of DNA through the action of DNA polymerase, an enzyme that catalyzes the synthesis of the molecule. Because of the enormous length of the DNA molecule, scientists generally thought that chromosome replication was

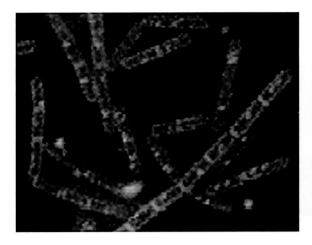

Katherine P. Lemon and Alan D. Grossman from "Localization of Bacterial DNA Polymerase: Evidence for a Factory Model of Replication"/ MIT Department of Biology

Using fluorescent probes, scientists identified discrete DNA "replication factories" (far left, bright areas) inside bacterial cells. Slow-growing cells (left, top) possess one or two replication factories, whereas rapidly growing cells (left, bottom) have more. The research supported the view that the replication machinery is located in fixed positions in bacterial cells and that the DNA template is pulled through to emerge as two daughter chromosomes.

carried out by mobile polymerases that moved along the DNA. MIT scientists Katherine Lemon and Alan Grossman revised this notion after studying actively growing cells. Using fluorescent microscopy techniques to observe the subcellular locations of DNA polymerase, the scientists found that slow-growing cells have one or two replication "factories" near their center. Rapidly growing cells have as many as four replication factories going at once, again anchored near the center of the cell.

The correlation between growth rate and the number of replication factories fit the view that the sites were actively replicating DNA. The results suggested that the replication machinery remains at a relatively fixed location and that the chromosomal DNA is threaded through to emerge as two daughter chromosomes.

—Lawrence J. Shimkets

MOLECULAR BIOLOGY AND GENETICS

Molecular biologists made numerous strides in 1998 in the determination of the three-dimensional structure of important proteins. Two such structures are described, along with some of the advances that accompanied researchers' increasing knowledge of the genomes of bacteria, yeasts, and multicellular organisms. Indeed, one of the really powerful emerging technologies

in molecular biology will wed information from genome sequencing projects and determinations of protein structure.

Structure of a potassium ion channel

A particularly exciting new protein structure, determined at Rockefeller University, New York City, by a group led by Roderick MacKinnon, is that of the potassium ion (K^+) channel. All cells, from bacterial to human, have to pump K^+ ions from the extracellular environment into the cell; at the same time, they have to pump sodium ions (Na^+) out. Many of the biochemical reactions in cells require K^+ and are strongly inhibited by Na^+. All cells are bounded by lipid membranes, which cannot be crossed by either K^+ or Na^+ ions. Ion-selective pumps consist of proteins—molecules comprising long chains of amino acids folded into highly specific three-dimensional configurations—that span the membrane and form channels through it. These channels include pores through which ions can be pumped. The nature of these channels and the way in which they can be selective for one ion over another has been a major scientific puzzle for more than 50 years. Detailed knowledge of the structure of the K^+ channel goes a long way toward answering such questions as how the channel can selectively transport 10,000 K^+ ions for every Na^+ ion and how a single channel can

transport 100 million K^+ ions per second.

Previous work on K^+ channel proteins from a variety of sources showed that generally they comprise pairs of membrane-spanning (transmembrane) alpha helices connected by a short stretch of amino acids containing a "selectivity filter." (Alpha helices are characteristic structural elements of proteins in which the amino-acid chain winds like a screw thread.) This filter is located on the outer surface of the membrane. Molecular genetic experiments indicated that the amino acids comprising the filter are critical for selective pumping, whereas those of the two transmembrane helices are much less important. The strong similarity seen among all K^+ channel proteins that had been investigated meant that a structure determined for one might shed light on all.

This was the approach of MacKinnon and co-workers when they set out to determine the structure of a K^+ channel protein from a bacterium. For numerous technical reasons, it was preferable to study a bacterial channel protein than to attempt to crystallize channel proteins from flies or human beings. The importance of K^+ channels to bacteria is underlined by the fact that the well-studied bacterium *Escherichia coli* has no less than three different systems for K^+ transport, each one active under different environmental conditions. Nevertheless, for reasons to do with the stability of the protein and the

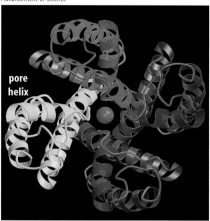

quality of X-ray diffraction data obtainable, the choice was made to study the KcsA K$^+$ channel protein from the bacterium *Streptomyces lividus.*

Membrane proteins have always presented special challenges to crystallographers. Usually when such proteins are separated from the membrane, they precipitate and so cannot be crystallized from solution. In the 1980s the German biochemists Hartmut Michel and Johann Deisenhofer designed new detergent molecules that allowed the gentle extraction of membrane proteins and, in some favorable cases, their crystallization. They applied these techniques to bacterial proteins called photosynthetic reaction centers, the results of which were honored with the 1988 Nobel Prize for Chemistry (shared with Robert Huber). The same techniques, with additional refinements, were used by the MacKinnon group.

What picture did the research team get of the KcsA channel protein? The active protein is made up of four subunits, each consisting of two alpha helices that span the membrane, connected by a short helix called the pore helix. Each subunit can be considered to have an inner helix, which defines one of the four walls of the channel, and an outer helix, which does not contribute to ion transport but stabilizes the rest of the structure (*see* Figure 1). MacKinnon referred to the channel architecture as an inverted tepee, with the wide part of the structure, containing the selectivity filter, on the outside of the membrane.

Ion flow through the channel can be pictured as involving three K$^+$ ions at any given time (*see* Figure 2). The larger part of the channel cavity, downstream of the selectivity filter, is aqueous and contains a

Figure 1: Computer models of the KcsA K$^+$ channel protein depict top and side views (top and center, respectively) of the protein's four subunits, each comprising an inner and an outer helix. In the top view, a potassium ion rests in the selectivity filter. The inverted teepee configuration can be seen in a model showing only the inner and pore helices (bottom).

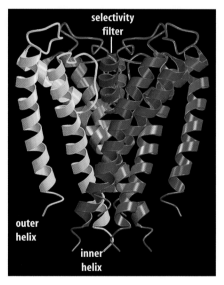

hydrated K$^+$ ion—one surrounded by water molecules. The amino acids that comprise the inner helices, facing the cavity, are hydrophobic, or water-repelling. Thus, to escape this unfavorable environment, the hydrated ion moves toward the inner surface of the membrane. The other two ions are upstream in the narrower selectivity filter; they are not hydrated, and in this environment the small size difference between K$^+$ and Na$^+$ becomes critical. The slightly larger K$^+$ ion is just the right size, whereas the Na$^+$ ion is too small to make cooperative contacts with all four subunits of the channel protein. The channel protein's very-high throughput is managed by having two ions in the filter at one time. Their electric charges repel one another and have the effect of kicking the lower ion into the aqueous cavity and thence to the inner surface of the membrane.

A gated mechanosensitive ion channel

The mechanism described above is of a high-throughput selective ion channel, one that allows K$^+$ to pass, but not Na$^+$. There are many classes of ion channels in nature and many ways to open and close channels in response to external information. For example, the conduction of a nerve impulse re-

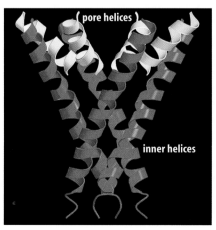

Ion Flow Through Potassium Ion Channel

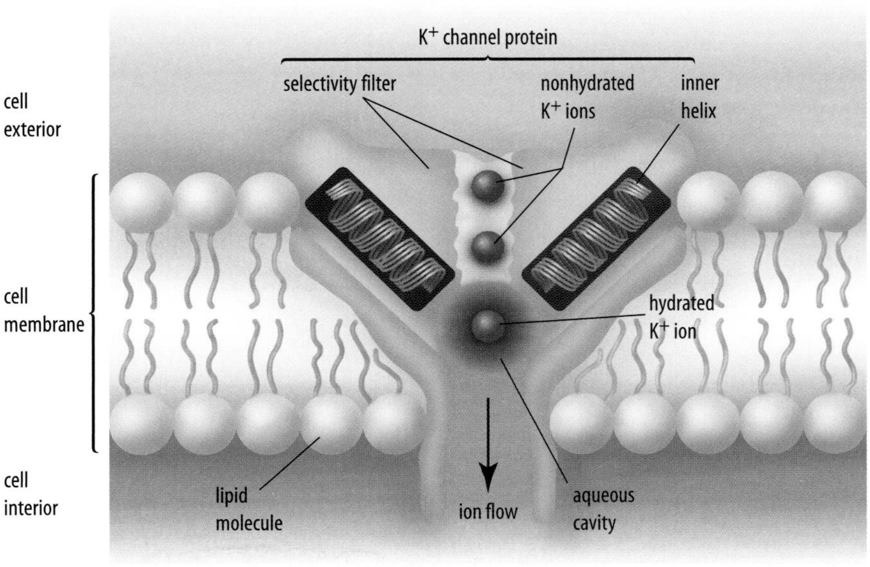

Figure 2: Ion flow through the KcsA K⁺ channel can be pictured as involving three potassium ions at any given time. One is hydrated and lies in an aqueous cavity downstream of the selectivity filter. Two other ions, which are not hydrated, are in the selectivity filter.

quires the rapid opening and closing of K⁺ ion channels; such channels possess a "gate" for controlling ion flow. Another example of a gated channel is found in bacteria, which have a way to adjust their internal osmotic pressure when faced with environments of either high or low pressure. Their adjustment mechanism consists of a relatively nonspecific mechanosensitive channel protein— one that opens in response to mechanical (stretching) pressure and admits any of a number of ions.

A group led by Douglas Rees at the California Institute of Technology, Pasadena, took advantage of the tremendous pool of information from bacterial genome projects in its structural determination of the mechanosensitive channel protein called MscL. After searching through genome data from a wide range of bacteria and cyanobacteria to find proteins with similar amino-acid sequences, Rees's group found a number of candidate organisms that express the MscL channel protein. The researchers then made numerous attempts to crystallize MscL— nine different versions of the protein, 24,000 crystallization conditions. Eventually they settled on the MscL from *Mycobacterium tuberculosis,* not because the organism is of interest for being the cause of tuberculosis but because its MscL gave the best crystals for X-ray analysis.

The structure that the group uncovered shows some similarities, as well as crucial differences, with respect to the KcsA K⁺ ion channel. The MscL protein has five subunits, rather than four, although each subunit has two transmembrane helices (called TM1 and TM2 by Rees) that correspond to the inner and outer helices of the KcsA channel (*see* Figure 3). Another difference from the K⁺ ion structure is that the MscL protein has the ends of its subunits extending down beyond the inner cell membrane into the cell cytoplasm. In the figure the channel is shown in a closed state. There are hydrophilic (water-attracting) amino acids lining the cavity through the membrane, but at the cytoplasmic end where the extending subunits are constricted, there are hydrophobic amino acids that prevent the passage of ions. Rees's group proposed that tensile force applied to the membrane in which the MscL channel is embedded causes its transmembrane helices to move apart. As they do, so do their cytoplasmic extensions, opening the channel between the inside and the outside of the cell.

Genome sequencing

Determination of the complete sequence of nucleotides in bacterial chromosomes accelerated in the past year. Many of those sequences were obtained by academic groups and other public institutions, but some were done by private industry, which made its data available to clients only by subscription. There was hope, as yet unrealized, that genome information will provide new targets in disease-causing microorganisms for new antibiotic drugs.

Several years of experience have produced tacit agreement on the optimal strategy for sequencing DNA, but not much on the best way to do the next step, which is called annotation. Annotation means, first, determining the positions in a DNA sequence that signal the beginning and end of transcription (the "start" and "stop"

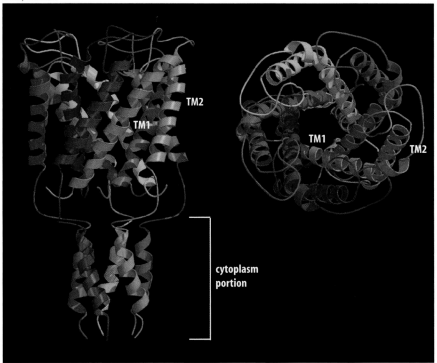

Figure 3: Side and top views of the mechanosensitive MscL ion channel protein are modeled. The MscL protein has five subunits, each made of two alpha helices (TM1 and TM2) that span the cell membrane. The end of each subunit extends down beyond the inner cell membrane into the cytoplasm.

codons), which correspond to the beginning and end of the proteins encoded by the sequence, and, next, determining the functions of the proteins so identified. The assignment of function depends on finding similar sequences of amino acids in proteins of known function in other organisms. For each newly sequenced bacterial genome, the function of at least half of the proteins can be assigned with confidence this way—based on similarity. The real challenge is to figure out what the remaining proteins do.

The size of a bacterial chromosome varies from less than 600,000 base pairs (bonded pairs of bases in the nucleotides that make up DNA) for the simplest organism (*Mycoplasma*) to as many as nine million base pairs for the most complex (*Myxococcus xanthus*). As of early 1999, the largest bacterial sequence in the public domain was that of *E. coli,* which runs from four million to five million base pairs, depending on the strain. Fungi have larger genomes. In 1996 the sequencing of all the DNA in the yeast *Saccharomyces cerevisiae* was completed by a worldwide consortium; the project took several years and eventually established the order of 12 million base pairs.

In this context, the achievement of the *Caenorhabditis elegans* Sequencing Consortium was impressive. In 1998 it pub-

lished an account of its determination of 97 million base pairs for the genome, comprising six chromosomes, of this tiny nematode worm—the first complete sequence for any multicellular organism. The consortium consisted primarily of a sequencing center at Washington University, St. Louis, Mo., headed by Robert Waterston, and the Sanger Centre in Hinxton, Eng., near Cambridge, headed by John Sulston. (Previously, Sulston, with the English molecular biologist Sydney Brenner, had described the fate of all the cells in the nematode body during its development from an embryo to an adult of 959 cells.) This monumental achievement was noteworthy in being a truly worldwide collaboration among the sequencers and the nematode research community. The latter scientists were responsible for providing the sequences of individual genes as well as the physical map positions of those genes. The actual sequencing effort required about 10 years.

A typical bacterial genome contains 4,000–5,000 protein-coding genes in four million to five million base pairs. The nematode has about 20,000 protein-coding genes in 97 million base pairs. Put another way, the nematode devotes five times more DNA for each gene than does the bacteria. Where is all this extra DNA? Some of it is in introns—intervening sequences averaging five per gene—that interrupt the coding regions of genes and need to be spliced out of the messenger RNA transcript each time the gene is transcribed. Some of it is in repeated DNA—sequences of unknown function that are tandemly repeated many times or inverted. Together, tandemly repeated and inverted DNA make up 6.1 million base pairs of the nematode DNA, more than most bacterial chromosomes. This peculiar DNA is not distributed uniformly throughout the nematode's six chromosomes. Rather, it is most abundant near the ends of the chromosomes and much less so near their centers.

Based on their amino-acid sequence, many proteins that are found encoded in sequenced genomes can be placed in functional families. For example, the most abundant family of proteins in *E. coli* are ones devoted to the transport of substances from the environment into the cell, including ions (for example, K$^+$ ions), sugars, amino acids, and sources of nitrogen, sulfur, and phosphorus. The second most abundant class of proteins in the bacterium are those that regulate expression of genes by controlling their transcription. In the multicellular nematode, however, the hierarchy of abundance puts first the family of receptor proteins that span the cell membrane and respond to external signals from ions, hormones, or other cells. The next most abundant are protein kinases, enzymes that respond to signals from receptor proteins and transmit them by promoting biochemical reactions in a signaling cascade. At the end of such a cascade, there is usually a transcription factor that enhances the expression of target genes. Indeed, the nematode has 240 proteins with one type of transcription factor domain, 130 with a second type, and 90 with a third. These domains, called zinc fingers because they bind zinc ions, are virtually absent from bacterial transcription systems.

Comparison of the proteins encoded by the yeast genome with those of the nematode led to further conclusions. On the one hand, all of the enzymes that catalyze core metabolism, the basic biochemical conversions that produce energy in the form of adenosine triphosphate (ATP) by oxidizing carbohydrates to carbon dioxide and water, are similar in the two organisms. On the other hand, most of the signaling and other regulatory proteins in the nematode have no related counterparts in yeast. These findings are important because they deal with fundamental features that relate multicellular and unicellular organisms and also distinguish them from each other. They have vast implications for the more complex, ongoing Human Genome Project, which is intent on sequencing the three billion base pairs contained in the 23 chromosomes of humans. They indicate that human core metabolism can probably be modeled accurately using data from both yeast and nematode, whereas the signaling and regulation aspect of human cells can be modeled on the worm. (For additional information on the sequencing of the *C. elegans* genome, see *Zoology* below.)

—Robert Haselkorn

ZOOLOGY

Female choice in tree frogs

Evolutionary biologists have long wondered why female animals choose particular mates. In many bird species, for example, females tend to prefer the most colorful, ornately plumaged, or most outlandish-looking males in the population. Some scientists have hypothesized that

Studies on the gray tree frog (left) supported the "good genes" hypothesis, which states that females choose mates by looking for traits that advertise the presence of favorable genes. Researchers showed that female frogs prefer males that emit calls of long duration and that long-call males almost always produce higher-quality offspring than short-call males.

Courtesy of Carl Gerhardt

such exaggerated traits are advertisements for the presence of "good genes" and that females mate with these kinds of males in order to confer greater fitness to offspring.

In 1998 Allison Welch, Raymond Semlitsch, and Carl Gerhardt of the University of Missouri, Columbia, published research that got to the heart of the good-genes hypothesis. The study organism was the gray tree frog, *Hyla versicolor,* a species whose reproductive biology and behavioral ecology had previously been documented by the scientists. During the earlier studies they had learned that females strongly prefer males who produce calls of long duration (more pulses per call). Neither long-call nor short-call males provide any parental care for eggs or offspring; moreover, long-call males do not fertilize more eggs than males with short-duration calls. Indeed, it was clear to the scientists that female gray tree frogs do not receive any direct benefits from choosing long-call males. Based on these and other observations, they hypothesized that the benefits of a female's mate-choice would only be revealed by looking for evidence of increased fitness in offspring.

To test the hypothesis, the scientists produced maternal half-siblings by mating females with short-call males and long-call males. The creation of half-siblings enabled the investigators to control for maternal effects; the only differences in offspring would come from the fathers. Offspring fitness was evaluated by measuring several key variables, including larval growth, larval period, metamorphic mass, larval survival, and postmetamorphic growth. All these variables had been found to influence lifetime reproductive success. The researchers discovered that males with long

In many animal species, successful males—those that produce the most offspring—are often bigger or more brilliantly colored or tend to advertise themselves with more vigorous displays. How and why female animals choose their mates and how mating preferences have evolved remain hotly debated topics in evolutionary biology.

calls almost always produced better-quality offspring than males with short calls. The results of the experiment provided further support for the idea that female choice is not a whimsical event but an earnest effort to look after future offspring.

Worm genome project

In December 1998 researchers from the Washington University Genome Sequencing Center, St. Louis, Mo., and the Sanger Centre, Cambridge, Eng., announced in the journal *Science* that they had finished sequencing the genome of the nematode worm *Caenorhabditis elegans*, marking the first time scientists have spelled out the complete genetic blueprint for a multicellular organism. Compared with bacteria and yeast—single-celled organisms whose genomic sequences had been completed earlier in the 1990s—*C. elegans* is a com-

plex organism and similar to humans in that it has a nervous system, digests food, and reproduces sexually with sperm and eggs.

The project began as a pilot study in 1989 after scientists made a nearly complete gene map of the worm's chromosomes, a prerequisite to sequencing the genome of an organism. Initially, the investigators proposed to sequence about 3% of the animal's genome by 1993. The task, however, proved to be much more complex than expected. By 1992 they were sequencing approximately one million base pairs per year, but at that rate it would have taken until 2086 to complete the project. (Base pairs are the bonded pairs of bases in the nucleotides that make up double-stranded DNA.) With ingenuity and improved technology, the investigators were able to speed up their work such that more than 99% of the genome had been deciphered by 1998. In total, the *C. elegans*

Cottonwood leaf beetles are among the approximately 350,000 different species of beetle that exist on Earth today. Scientists in 1998 attributed the tremendous diversity of beetles to a concurrent radiation of flowering plants during the past 125 million years.

genome consists of 97 million base pairs and nearly 20,000 genes. By comparison, the genome of the yeast *Saccharomyces cerevisiae* contains fewer than 7,000 genes.

Aside from the hope that it gave promoters of the Human Genome Project, the elucidation of the *C. elegans* genome is significant in its own right. For instance, the additional genes within the worm, compared with yeast, should help researchers learn more about how multicellular animals differ from single-celled eukaryotes like yeast. Moreover, the worm's genome should offer insight into human biology. By comparing worm and human DNA se-

A magnified image of the roundworm *Caenorhabditis elegans* is shown below. Scientists in the U.S. and Great Britain finished sequencing the genome of the highly studied animal, uncovering nearly 20,000 genes.

quences, for instance, scientists will be able to identify related genes and then use the worm to examine their function. From these kinds of studies, conclusions can be drawn about the genetic causes of human disease. (For additional information on the sequencing of the *C. elegans* genome, see *Molecular Biology and Genetics,* above.)

Beetle-mania

Scientists have named nearly 350,000 kinds of beetles, approximately one-fifth of all known species on Earth. Entomologist Terry L. Erwin of the Smithsonian Institution, Washington, D.C., once counted more than 650 beetle species in a single tree in Peru. The remarkable diversity of beetles even prompted British evolutionary biologist J.B.S. Haldane to wonder whether the Creator has "an inordinate fondness for beetles."

Why are there so many beetles? An intriguing look at this question, coupling molecular, morphological, and fossil data, suggested that the evolutionary diversification of beetles was associated with a concurrent radiation of flowering plants, or angiosperms. The compelling new evidence was reported by Brian D. Farrell of the Museum of Comparative Zoology at Harvard University.

Farrell used DNA sequence data and anatomical observations to construct an evolutionary tree, or phylogeny, of plant-eating beetles. Since herbivorous forms make up more than 50% of all known beetle species, Farrell believed that they would provide a wealth of clues about beetle evolution. According to his phylogeny, the most primitive beetle lineages are conifer- and cycad-feeding beetles in the superfam-

ilies Chrysomeloidea and Curculionoidea. Eventually, these groups diversified and gave rise on five separate occasions to angiosperm-feeding beetle lineages. The phylogeny was also supported by fossil evidence, which had indicated that gymnosperm-feeding beetles evolved about 200 million years ago and diversified rapidly as the variety of flowering plants blossomed over the past 125 million years.

From the family tree, Farrell could see which groups of beetles had continued to feed on the primitive gymnosperms and which had begun to feed on the more recently evolved flowering plants. In each case, groups of beetles that fed on flowering plants were more diverse than their gymnosperm-feeding counterparts, reflecting the rapid diversification of angiosperms. Evolutionary biologists were enthusiastic about Farrell's work because it provided further support for the notion that diversity generates diversity.

Evolution of cichlids

The amazing variety of Central American cichlid fish for years has attracted attention from scientists and hobbyists alike. More than 100 different kinds live in Central America alone, exhibiting considerable morphological, ecological, and behavioral differentiation. Even within the same habitat, diversity can be quite high. Among so-called heroine cichlids, for instance, species come in a variety of sizes and shapes and exhibit a number of different feeding modes, including fish-eating, plant-eating, invertebrate-picking, and gravel-sifting. Biologists have long believed that Central American cichlids originated in South America, evolving later into the array of species observed today. Regrettably, uncertainties regarding the evolutionary relationships of neotropical cichlids and questions arising from the complex geological history of the area have complicated interpretations of the biological history of these fish.

In 1998 Andrew Martin of the University of Colorado, Boulder, and Eldredge Bermingham of the Smithsonian Tropical Research Institute in Panama published the results of a DNA study that shed some light on the evolutionary history of the enigmatic cichlids. By sequencing the mitochondrial cytochrome *b* gene in 21 different species of cichlids, Martin and Bermingham tested various hypotheses regarding the time of origin and pattern of diversification of Central American cichlids.

Overall, their analysis indicated that Central American heroine cichlids are genetically well differentiated and probably diversified in a brief period of time, perhaps beginning 15 million to 18 million years ago. This estimate was concordant with the discovery of fossil cichlids in Miocene Epoch (23.7 million to 5.3 million years ago) deposits on the island of Hispaniola in the West Indies. One hypothesis for the great diversity of heroine cichlids in Central America, according to the researchers, was that the area might have been colonized by multiple cichlid genera after the rise of the Isthmus of Panama during the late Pliocene Epoch (5.3 million to 1.6 million years ago). Alternatively, a single lineage or a few closely related lineages may have entered the area before the Pliocene emergence of the isthmus. The wide distribution exhibited by heroines suggested earlier colonization, although further research was

necessary to establish the source cichlid lineages.

Additionally, the researchers used the DNA-based family tree to formulate hypotheses about the evolution of feeding adaptations in Central American cichlids. This work suggested that the diverse feeding modes of modern-day cichlids may have evolved independently from an ancestor with a more generalized feeding adaptation. Interestingly, the pattern accorded well with previous studies on the evolution of feeding adaptations in African cichlids.

Overall, Martin and Bermingham's study revealed that a thorough taxonomic revision of Central American cichlids is needed. In some cases, the taxonomic relationships elucidated by the DNA analyses did not agree with species groupings based on traditional anatomical methods. Ideally, a classification reflects evolutionary relationships whenever possible.

Conservation of a living fossil

A dead coelacanth, *Latimeria chalumnae*, was spotted by a marine biologist in an Indonesian fish market, offering conservationists and evolutionary biologists some hope that the enigmatic fish may not be as rare as once thought. Until 1938, when a trawler scooped up a live specimen in the Indian Ocean near the southern coast of Africa, coelacanths were known only from the fossil record. Most scientists had assumed that the lobe-finned fish had become extinct some 70 million to 80 million years ago, but the discovery proved that a relic population had survived. Since then, hundreds of other coelacanths have been caught, mostly in the waters off the Comoro Islands, Africa, where a coelacanth was net-

ted in 1952. The extraordinary finding of a coelacanth taken from Indonesian waters—some 9,700 km (6,000 mi) away from what was thought to be the fish's only location—led scientists to conclude that a second coelacanth population exists. Mark V. Erdmann and Roy L. Caldwell of the University of California, Berkeley, and M. Kasim Moosa of the Indonesian Institute of Sciences, Jakarta, announced the newly found population of Indonesian coelacanths in the journal *Nature*.

The coelacanth is often called a living fossil because it closely resembles its fossil predecessors. Evolutionary biologists have been excited about the prospects of studying modern-day coelacanths because the fish are the last living example of the crossopterygians, a primitive group of bony fish whose fleshy limblike fins may have been the precursors of arms and legs in terrestrial vertebrates.

Although the discovery of another coelacanth population was considered to be a fortuitous event, concerns were expressed about the conservation of the species. Since 1987 marine biologist Hans Fricke and his colleagues from the Max Planck Institute for Animal Behavior, Seewiesen, Ger., had been tracking coelacanths near the Comoro Islands. Between 1987 and 1991, the team identified a stable population of as many as 650 fish. By 1994 the population in their census area had dropped 30%. Writing in the August 1998 issue of *Conservation Biology,* the researchers estimated that as few as 300 coelacanths remain in the Comoro Islands region. The decline was attributed to increased fishing pressure, not because the coelacanth was a highly sought-after species but as a result of accidental by-catch in deepwater fishnets. An alternative explanation for the decline of coelacanths in African waters is that the fish may have migrated to a new area. In 1996 the coelacanth was listed as an endangered species by the Convention on International Trade in Endangered Species (CITES).

Growing up hyena

A study of the spotted hyena, *Crocuta crocuta*, provided some interesting insight into the behavioral development of young animals. The research, published in the journal *BioScience* by Kay E. Holekamp and

Gerald & Buff Corsi/Focus on Nature, Inc.

Zoologists showed that hyena behavioral development is partitioned into discrete stages that are molded by the ecological and social demands imposed by the environment.

Laura Smale of Michigan State University, East Lansing, suggested that juvenile animals are more than just imperfect adults with imperfect behaviors. Rather, many juvenile behaviors represent adaptations to specific selection pressures, which change as young animals grow into adulthood.

The spotted hyena, a large carnivore native to most of sub-Saharan Africa, is a fascinating species characterized by females with very masculine traits. Females are socially dominant over males and much more aggressive. The scientists found that postnatal development in spotted hyenas occurs in five distinct phases. During each phase, the young carnivores confront a different suite of social and ecological challenges imposed by the surrounding environment. The first phase occurs immediately after birth, when an infant hyena spends its first few weeks of life in a natal den shared with one or two siblings. One of the primary hurdles young hyenas must overcome during this time is the establishment of rank within the litter. Hence, from birth, siblings engage in exceptionally intense fighting, facilitated by the presence of fully erupted teeth, wide-open eyes, and the ability to move about freely.

The second phase of development, according to Holekamp and Smale, takes place within a communal den, where cubs are raised for about eight months. The change in environment represents a completely different social world for juveniles, compelling them to adapt in different ways. Instead of contending with siblings for food and rank, they are forced to compete with a host of unrelated clan members. In this stage of life, juveniles gather information about other clan members, begin establishing social rank within the larger group, en-

gage in play behavior, and develop essential motor skills.

Another big change in life occurs during the third stage of hyena development, when juveniles move out of the den and begin to explore the clan's home range. It is at this time that young hyenas acquire critical life skills such as learning how to obtain food, water, and shelter. Such skills are important for the fourth stage of life, when developing hyenas are cut off from the maternal milk supply and pressured to find their own solid food, acquired mostly by scavenging. In the final stage, adulthood, males and females become sexually mature. In this period, females learn to be sexually unresponsive to males of their own clan, forcing males to leave the natal clan in order to breed. Males wander into the home ranges of neighboring clans and eventually become integrated into one.

Through examination of the spotted hyena's five developmental stages, Holekamp and Smale were able to observe the adoption of particular behaviors as well as the abandonment of a behavior when its importance became diminished or even maladaptive. The scientists concluded that individual behaviors in juveniles are merely temporary adaptations to specific selection pressures. The research also suggested that the rate at which a young hyena progresses through life is related to energy availability, which is determined by social rank of the mother.

—Charles Lydeard

See also Feature Articles: FORENSICS ON THE WILD SIDE; SURVIVING THE NEW MILLENNIUM; THE UNCERTAINTIES OF ENVIRONMENTAL FORECASTING; WITNESSING THE BIRTH OF THE MICROSCOPE (Photo Essay).

MATERIALS SCIENCE AND ENGINEERING

Significant advances in the science and engineering of materials during 1998 included the development of ceramic technology for automotive gas-turbine engine applications, environmentally driven improvements in the steelmaking process, and new applications of polymeric materials in data-storage systems and flat-panel displays.

CERAMICS

The past year saw completion of a major effort to develop technology for ceramic automotive gas turbines. A simple gas-turbine engine consists of three main parts: a compressor, a combustor, and a power turbine. The engines run on an open cycle, in which compressed air is mixed with fuel and combusted. Power is produced when the heated combustion gas is allowed to expand through a turbine. Gas turbines offer many advantages—increased fuel economy, operation with a wide range of fuels, reduced emissions, and a smooth, quiet ride.

The material in a modern gas turbine must survive temperatures in excess of 1,100° C (2,000° F), high thermal stresses caused by rapid temperature fluctuations, high mechanical stresses, oxidation, and other factors. Ceramic materials—in particular, silicon carbide and silicon nitride—have emerged as substitutes for metallic parts in such systems because of their ability to withstand these tremendous operational demands.

In recent years, the U.S. Department of Energy (DOE) has funded programs to develop ceramic-based automotive gas-turbine engines. In the Advanced Turbine Technology Applications Project (ATTAP) initiated in 1987, work focused on developing a primary power unit coupled to a

HVTE-TS Key Ceramic Technologies

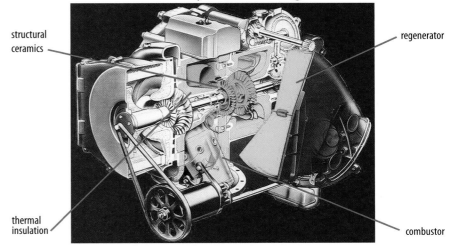

structural ceramics

regenerator

thermal insulation

combustor

Rolls-Royce Allison developed this automotive gas-turbine engine for the U.S. Department of Energy's Hybrid Vehicle Turbine Engine Technology Support (HVTE-TS) effort, which was initiated to evaluate the feasibility of ceramic engine components.

Courtesy of Rolls-Royce Allison

conventional transmission and power train. Focus of the DOE's more recent Hybrid Vehicle Turbine Engine Technology Support (HVTE-TS) effort was on the development of a hybrid electric-gas turbine engine, in which a ceramic turbine drives a high-speed alternator for electric power generation.

The major objectives of the ATTAP and HVTE-TS programs were to demonstrate the feasibility of ceramic engine components. To that purpose, Rolls-Royce Allison, Indianapolis, Ind., prime contractor for both efforts, used an automotive turbine test bed specially designed for operation up to 1,370° C (2,500° F). This permitted evaluation of the key ceramic components—which included a combustor, a gasifier turbine rotor and scroll, a regenerator system, and thermal insulation—under realistic conditions. For example, analysis showed that silicon carbide rotors would not sur-

vive transient start-up–acceleration cycles. Silicon carbide has a high stiffness, high coefficient of thermal expansion, and relatively low strength, making the material susceptible to cracking under rigorous transient conditions. Silicon nitride thus became the material of choice for the rotors.

Efforts to develop the ceramic engine components for the test bed were aimed at methods applicable to high-volume, low-cost production of near-net-shape articles. AlliedSignal Ceramic Components, Torrance, Calif., for instance, gelcast turbine rotors and combustor bodies of their in-situ-reinforced and toughened AS800 silicon nitride material. (In in-situ reinforcement, the material microstructure is modified during the sintering process to provide desired properties.) Designed to function under temperatures as high as 1,400° C (2,550° F), AS800 has a high thermal conductivity and the capability to absorb high thermal shocks without damage.

Carborundum Co., Niagara Falls, N.Y., slipcast gasifier scrolls of sintered alpha silicon carbide. Improved processing yielded significant enhancement of the material's density and strength, and scroll assemblies were delivered for engine evaluation. A two-piece combustor of the same material was also supplied.

Kyocera Industrial Ceramics Corp., Vancouver, Wash., worked on the gasifier rotors, scrolls, and combustor liners. The rotors were fabricated of slipcast SN253, a new high-strength silicon nitride. The green bodies were then hot isostatically pressed to achieve full density and strength. The processed rotors required little machining and were evaluated at speeds as high as 80,000 revolutions per minute. Kyocera's SN252, a toughened material best-suited for static turbine parts, was used for the gasifier scrolls and combustor

liners, which were drain-cast and then sintered. Thin, void-free, undistorted walls were achieved, and parts were delivered for testing.

In an automotive gas turbine, an exhaust-heat recovery system is needed to achieve maximum fuel efficiency. Corning Inc., Corning, N.Y., developed ceramic heat-regenerator materials for use in the Rolls-Royce Allison test-bed program. The structures were fabricated of extruded lithium aluminosilicate (LAS) and magnesium aluminosilicate (MAS). LAS had better strength and temperature capability, but MAS could be made more cheaply. Corning's effort led to a reduction in price for LAS, leaving it more price-competitive with MAS. Final selection for use would be based on specific engine needs versus cost.

Significant accomplishments were achieved in the automotive gas-turbine test-bed program. Establishment of component durability in the test bed was a ma-

jor issue. Using a cooled metallic combustor, the all-ceramic gasifier section was run at peak design conditions of 1,370° C and full gasifier speed. This configuration also completed a 300-hour cyclic durability test that included cycles to peak conditions. The SN252 silicon nitride inlet scroll assembly and the SN253 silicon nitride turbine rotor showed no physical or structural damage after testing. The MAS heat regenerator survived the 300-hour test with little evidence of surface pitting or cracking, and the injection-molded ceramic insulation also performed very well. In addition, a 20-blade SN252 silicon nitride rotor successfully completed a 1,000-hour durability test, demonstrating capability for extended life.

A major program objective was demonstration of ceramic combustor operation at the rotor inlet temperature of 1,370° C. A two-piece alpha silicon carbide combustor was tested and performed admirably for two hours under full gasifer operating conditions, including four start-stop cycles, showing the efficacy of ceramic combustors for this important application.

Testing culminated with the "all-ceramic" engine, which added a two-stage silicon nitride power turbine to the combustor and gasifier sections. The engine performed successfully to a rotor inlet temperature of 1,460° C (2,660° F), achieving 73 hp at 92% full engine speed.

—Allan P. Katz

METALS

In 1998 steelmakers contemplated the technological and political challenges that the industry faced due to the 1997 Kyoto Protocol, an environmental agreement

Ceramic engine parts, such as the scroll, rotor, and other components shown below, have emerged as replacements for metallic parts in gas-turbine engines because of their ability to withstand rigorous operational demands, including high mechanical stresses, rapid temperature changes, and oxidation.

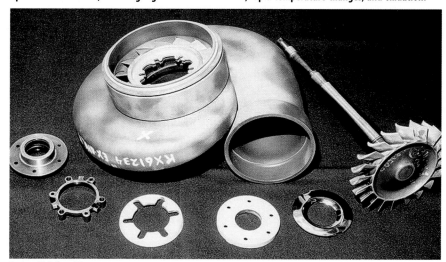

Courtesy of Rolls-Royce Allison

among nations to limit and cut back the production of greenhouse gases. In recent years, scientists have placed some of the blame for global warming trends on the accumulation of human-released greenhouse gases—primarily carbon dioxide (CO_2), methane, and hydrofluorocarbons—in the atmosphere. The Kyoto Protocol set emissions-reduction targets and timetables for industrialized countries but placed no meaningful restrictions on developing nations such as Indonesia, China, and India. The United States signed the agreement at a November 1998 climate-change conference in Buenos Aires, Arg., and it was expected that the U.S. Senate will debate its ratification in 1999. Under the pact, greenhouse-gas emissions must be reduced

an average of 5.2% from 1990 levels by 2008–2012. (*See* Year in Review: ENVIRONMENT.)

Restrictions on CO_2 emissions pose significant challenges to the steel industry. In every step of steelmaking, CO_2 is produced, either directly in the process or indirectly through the use of various energy sources such as electricity, fuel oil, or natural gas. For instance, in the blast furnace, CO_2 gas is given off as a by-product when metallurgical coke, which is mostly carbon, is used to chemically reduce iron ore to a carbon-saturated liquid iron (or hot metal, as it is called in the industry). Carbon is employed because it is a cheap and relatively easy-to-use reducing agent for iron oxide ores.

In light of the stringent CO_2 emissions-reduction requirements set forth in the Kyoto Protocol, the U.S. steel industry is searching for ways to reduce carbon emissions by cutting energy use and modifying the steelmaking process.

In the next step of the process, steel is made from the hot metal in a basic oxygen furnace by combusting the carbon in the melt with pure oxygen, a practice that releases carbon monoxide (CO) gas. The postcombustion of CO to CO_2 releases large amounts of heat, which can be returned to the melt in the furnace or harnessed to preheat feedstocks. Capturing this heat and reusing it in another stage of the process actually reduces overall CO_2 production by replacing an equivalent amount of electricity

John D. Cunningham/Visuals Unlimited

The use of recycled scrap iron as feedstock for electric-arc furnaces saves time and cuts energy consumption, but steelmakers are concerned about the rising prices and overall availability of quality scrap.

that otherwise would have been produced through the burning of fossil fuels. Nevertheless, there are other sources of CO_2 in steelmaking, including the use of heat-treatment furnaces, which operate on fuel oil or natural gas, and electric-arc furnaces and rolling mills, which require large amounts of electricity. Accountability for the CO_2 discharged into the atmosphere through the production of electricity is pushed off to the power producers, however, and usually is not attributed to the steel mills directly.

The concern within the U.S. steel industry over CO_2 emissions is obvious. If the country is required to make drastic cuts in CO_2 emissions, then the steel industry will either have to make significant, expensive process changes or reduce overall production. American steelmakers have called for negotiated voluntary agreements with the government to target emissions reductions. Such agreements could be similar to successful ones in Holland and Denmark, although those countries have much smaller steel capacity. Over the past 30 years, the American steel industry has spent more than $50 billion on technology improvements (with over $7 billion of this total spent directly on environmental controls) designed to cut industry costs through energy savings and changes in the steelmaking process.

These savings directly relate to cuts of greenhouse-gas emissions and have been driven, to a large extent, by high energy prices and the need to lower production costs.

Recent studies have indicated that cost-effective methods of cutting energy usage and carbon emissions, such as improved preheating of feedstocks, more efficient furnaces, and switching to thin strip casting, could be used more widely in the industry. Other research has called for the use of recycled scrap as a feedstock to electric-arc furnaces, which eliminates the need for the blast furnace and the basic oxygen furnace. The steel industry has been very successful in its recycling efforts, including adding scrap metal to basic oxygen furnaces, but the use of scrap introduces quality-control problems because of the difficulty in controlling the chemical content of the incoming scrap. Additionally, as this alternative has become increasingly used in the past decade or so, the availability and price of quality scrap metal has become a concern. Another alternative is the use in electric-arc furnaces of direct-reduced iron, which has a low carbon content and thus releases much less CO_2 than conventional sources of iron. Reduced-carbon combustion, however, requires more electricity to keep the melt hot, so it may be a false economy, depending on the fuel used to produce the electricity.

While reductions in carbon emissions may be achieved through greater energy efficiency and the use of recycled scrap, the fact remains that a large part of steel production must come from iron ore. As noted, the most efficient and least expensive method of reducing iron ores uses carbon. The only way to curtail production of CO_2 in the reduction process is to use biomass (organic refuse, typically derived from plants) as a coking agent in the blast furnace, rather than coal. When coal is used to make metallurgical-grade coke, carbon previously buried in the Earth is released into the atmosphere, with no possibility of it returning to its source. On the other hand, if plants, whose carbon comes from the atmosphere, were used to make coke, the net effect on the carbon cycle would be minimal. In 1998 a Brazilian company was working on a process that uses eucalyptus trees, which have a very low ash content, as the source of coke. While the economics of such a technique may only be advantageous in a tropical climate, where forests regenerate more quickly, it does suggest some long-term solutions for the steel industry's carbon-emission problems.

—Matthew John M. Krane

POLYMERS

The escalating demand to store colossal amounts of digital information, have faster access to it, and display it in convenient and cost-effective ways will one day reach the limitations of current technologies. During the past year, materials scientists provided several examples of the potential for polymers to contribute to these growing technological needs.

Holographic memory is an appealing method for electronic data storage because it can potentially store a terabyte (1,000 gigabytes, or one trillion bytes) of data—the

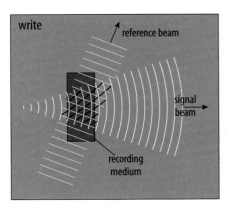

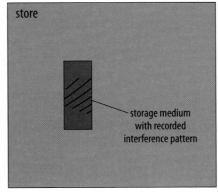

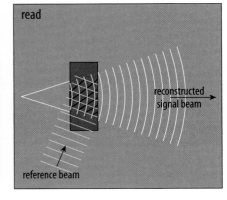

equivalent of 213 digital video disks (DVDs)—on a sugar-cube-sized block of medium. Moreover, such systems can access information at rates in excess of 1,000 megabits (one gigabit, or one billion bits) per second, 100 times faster than current DVD drives. In a holographic memory system, information is stored as interference patterns throughout the entire volume of the medium. The patterns, taking the form of diffraction gratings, are created when two laser beams originating from the same laser source, a reference beam and a signal beam, interfere with each other on a photosensitive substrate, altering the optical properties of that substance, such as the refractive index. Multiple holograms can be recorded on the same substrate simply by changing the angle of the recording beams slightly. To read the hologram, a laser is shone at it using a different wavelength so that the written hologram is not destroyed; the hologram then diffracts the light in a pattern that holds the stored data.

Although a few different materials have been used for recording holographic memories, such as thin crystals of lithium niobate, all have had serious limitations, including low exposure sensitivities, instability, and poor diffraction efficiency. In 1998 German researchers presented an amorphous polymer with read-write capabilities and moderate diffraction efficiency. The material is a copolymer (a polymer made of two distinct component polymers) that combines two rigid azobenzene side groups that align perpendicular to the polarization of the incident light. The side chains work cooperatively to form small domains, possessing a high degree of orientation. The rigidity of the side groups stabilizes reorientation. The result is a diffraction grating formed by a change of refractive index between exposed and unexposed polymer of as much as 13%, depending on the relative amount of each polymer. The diffraction efficiency of the copolymer was found to increase significantly as the temperature neared its glass-transition temperature.

Advances also were made in alternatives to the liquid-crystal display (LCD), the dominant flat-panel display technology. Although LCDs are currently the best means to produce high-quality portable displays, they are limited in brightness, energy efficiency, angle of viewing, workable temperature range, and their ability to produce clear video images.

In recent years, polymeric light-emitting diodes (LEDs) have generated considerable attention as promising alternatives to LCDs. An LED is a semiconducting device that converts an electric current into visible or infrared light by means of electroluminescence. The electroluminescence of conjugated polymers, which contain a system of alternating double bonds, has appealed to scientists because thin-film LED devices made from these materials can easily be fabricated over large areas by spin-casting from solution. With the exception of amorphous and crystalline silicon, which are relatively unstable and exhibit low efficiencies when used for LED devices, large-area processing has proved difficult for inorganic materials. Conjugated polymers are attractive because alterations in chemical structure can be used to control the emitted color; they also are relatively stable, and, unlike their molecular organic counterparts, they do not have the tendency to recrystallize. The elasticity of these polymers even may be exploited to make flexible displays.

In 1998 a team of scientists from the Cavendish Laboratory at the University of Cambridge reported the construction of an all-polymer, integrated semiconductor device using a conjugated polymer transistor to drive a polymer LED. The LED was fashioned from a thin film of poly[2-methoxy-5(2´-ethyl-hexyloxy)-*p*-phenylenevinylene] (MEH-PPV), which was deposited directly from solution and sandwiched between thin layers of gold and a semitransparent layer of calcium-silver (Ca-Ag). The Ca-Ag layer injects electrons into the conduction band of the MEH-PPV, the lowest energy level normally unoccupied by electrons. Light was generated when the electrons combined with holes (a positive-charge carrier involving missing electrons created by the gold layer) in the valence band, the highest energy level normally occupied by electrons. This process produced visible light, the color of which was determined by the energy difference between the conduction and valence bands.

The LED was driven by a polymer transistor using poly(hexylthiophene) (P3HT). P3HT possesses a conjugated backbone in which electrons are delocalized along the polymer chain. Electrons can move easily along the polymer chain as they are added to or removed from double bonds, while a framework of single bonds maintains the

Cavendish Laboratory, University of Cambridge/Science Magazine

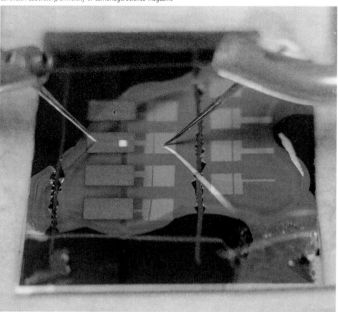

The conjugated polymer LED device developed at the Cavendish Laboratory is shown with one of its four "pixels" switched on. The MEH-PPV layer (orange) is only partially overlaid in order to make the underlying (blue) P3HT layer visible.

structural integrity of the polymer. P3HT acted as a switching device to turn the LED on and off, depending on the current permitted to pass through the material. The current was varied by the presence of an applied field in the transistor, which facilitated or impeded the flow of charge carriers. The material was considered "on" or "off" when it was conducting or nonconducting, respectively. The device's performance approached that of inorganic amorphous silicon transistors and represented a step toward all-polymer optoelectronic integrated circuits such as active-matrix polymer LED displays.

Another flat-panel display technology that has been pursued is the field-emission

display (FED). Often called "thin CRTs," these displays employ a vacuum into which is sealed red, green, and blue phosphors, similar to those that produce color in cathode ray tubes (CRTs). Unlike the CRT, however, which uses a large vacuum tube and excites phosphors by firing electrons from a comparatively great distance, FEDs use a semiconductor process to strip electrons from the surface of microscopic cold cathode "microtip" emitters. Typically, the cathode emitters require electric fields on the order of 10 million volts per cm to promote electron emission. As in a CRT, when electrons strike the phosphors, colored light is produced. The result is a relatively lightweight, thin display with a full viewing angle. Because of their emissive nature, FED displays require no backlight, generate little heat, and are resistant to extreme temperatures.

In the first demonstration of using polymers as field-emission cathodes, researchers at the University of Liverpool, Eng., used thin films of poly(3-octylthiophene) (P3OT) as a planar electron emitter. The films of P3OT deposited on silicon emitted electrons into a vacuum at "ultralow" electric fields of 1,000 volts per cm. The demonstration of low power consumption and inexpensive processing opened up the possibility of cost-effective cathode materials for a new generation of flat-panel FEDs.

—David E. Collins

MATHEMATICS

Mathematics in 1998 saw the resolution, at last, of Johannes Kepler's simple-sounding conjecture about sphere packing; an explanation for the "small world" phenomenon; a mathematical theory for origami, the Japanese art of paper folding; and a new approach to paradoxes in mathematical game theory. The quadrennial International Congress of Mathematicians was held in Berlin, with awarding of prizes to distinguished young mathematicians.

Kepler's conundrum

How do you stack spheres to take up the least amount of space? The problem has vexed mathematicians for centuries. In 1611 German mathematician and astronomer Johannes Kepler, best known for his work on planetary orbits, conjectured that the densest way to pack spheres in infinite space is the face-centered cubic packing technique, a method commonly used by grocers to stack oranges and other fruits. In face-centered packing, spheres are stacked in a square-based pyramid, with each layer positioned so that spheres rest on the "holes" of the layer below. (Packing with spheres in each layer in a hexagonal grid is equally dense.) In the 19th century, the German mathematician Carl Friedrich Gauss concluded that face-centered packing is the tightest way to stack spheres in a regular lattice, but this left open the question of whether

Solving a problem that has stymied mathematicians for more than 300 years, Thomas Hales of the University of Michigan proved that face-centered cubic packing (bottom)—a method commonly used to stack fruits in supermarkets—represents the tightest way to pack spheres in infinite space.

an irregular stacking of spheres might still be denser.

In 1998 Thomas Hales of the University of Michigan announced a proof of Kepler's famous conjecture, for which he made use of a variety of computational techniques to ensure the accuracy of his calculations and verify his results. The method involved classifying the possible kinds of star-shaped gaps between spheres and solving an enormous optimization problem for each kind. Previous claims of success in proving the Kepler conjecture had arisen over the years, but the arguments were not able to hold up under close scrutiny. Hence, it was expected that it will be some time before experts pronounce an opinion on the correctness of Hales's proof.

Making the world smaller

Today Earth has six billion people, yet modern folklore says that any person is connected to any other person through a relatively short chain of acquaintances. This claim was investigated by psychologist Stanley Milgram in the 1960s, concretized in the play and film *Six Degrees of*

Separation by John Guare, and popularized in a recent campus game of trying to trace connections of actors to the actor Kevin Bacon through joint appearances in films.

In the Kevin Bacon game, an actor's "Bacon number" is the smallest number of links from the actor to Bacon. Bacon himself gets a Bacon number of zero, actors who have appeared in a film with Bacon get a Bacon number of one, actors who have appeared in a film with someone who has worked with Bacon get a Bacon number of two, and so on. Those who cannot be linked to Bacon at all get a Bacon number of infinity. Mathematicians are fond of a similar game of determining the Erdos number of a mathematician, in which the relationship is joint authorship of a paper. The goal is to determine the smallest number of links to the late Hungarian mathematician Paul Erdos, with whom hundreds of mathematicians have written papers. Steven Strogatz of Cornell University, Ithaca, N.Y., and his graduate student Duncan Watts theorized that such "small worlds" are probably common in many types of networks, and in 1998 they demonstrated that even a tiny amount of random rewiring in a network can dramatically shorten the number of links required to get from one point to another.

Graph theory is the branch of mathematics that studies structures (graphs) involving interconnections. A graph consists of a set of vertices, together with links be-

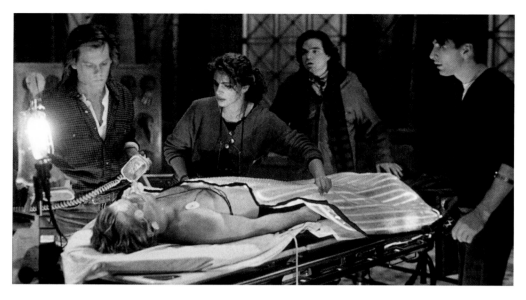

In the table below, an average of 3.65 links exists between Kevin Bacon (right, at far left, in a scene from the movie _Flatliners_) and any other Hollywood actor. Mathematicians in 1998 showed that introducing just a few random connections in a regular network of links creates the kind of "small-world" networks that operate in such pastimes as the Kevin Bacon game.

Examples of Small-World Networks				
	characteristic path length		clustering coefficient	
network	actual	random	actual	random
movie actors	3.65	2.99	0.79	0.00027
power grid	18.7	12.4	0.080	0.005
worm neurons	2.65	2.25	0.28	0.05

tween some pairs of them. Some graphs are "regular" in that each vertex has the same small number of links to neighboring points; others are "sparse" in that there are only a few links relative to the total number of vertices. Strogatz and Watts proved the unexpected result that introducing a few random connections into a regular graph can greatly decrease the average path length between two vertices. They called graphs with a small average path length "small-world networks." The neural circuitry of the nematode worm _Caenorhabditis elegans,_ the power grid of the western U.S., and the network of Hollywood actors associated with Kevin Bacon are all examples of small-world networks, the researchers said.

Small-world networks are important in the spread of disease, the diffusion of trade goods, and the transmission of information, such as marketing over the Internet. Hence, in a real sense, the random acquaintanceships that a person makes on a round-the-globe trip do indeed make the world smaller.

Origami is logical

Origami is the Japanese art of folding shapes from a square of paper. This centuries-old practice involves several skills: devising a pattern and sequence of creases to create a shape, discerning from crease lines the order of folding, and predicting properties of the folded object from crease patterns. In 1996 Barry Hayes of Placeware Inc., Mountain View, Calif., and Marshall Bern of the Xerox Palo Alto (Calif.) Research Center asked, given a pattern of creases on a flat piece of paper, whether the paper can be folded along those creases to form a flat origami shape. The question of whether a pattern can be folded flat, as is the case for a road map, turns out to be NP-complete (the symbol _NP_ stands for "nondeterministic polynomial time"), meaning that there is no known algorithm (step-by-step procedure) for answering the question that has a number of steps that is a polynomial in the number of creases.

In 1998 Hayes and Bern translated logical expressions into crease patterns and

showed that the flat-folding problem is equivalent to the NP-hard problem called "not-all-true 3-SAT." This problem states: Given a sentence in propositional logic consisting of three-variable clauses, in each of which not all three variables can be assigned _true,_ determine if there is a truth-assignment that makes the sentence true. Despite the apparently discouraging nature of this result about flat-foldability, most origami does not involve the very large number of creases that would defeat efforts to determine if the pattern can be folded flat. The work by Hayes and Bern has led to increased interest in devising a mathematical theory for origami.

How to avoid losing at "Chicken"

The game of "Chicken" presents difficulties for game theorists. In the game, two daredevils drive toward each other; the first one to swerve, or "chicken out," loses. If both swerve, both gain (they live), but neither gains as much in prestige as if the other had chickened out. If neither swerves, both lose (they die). Again, each player has strong incentive not to chicken out, but if both pursue that strategy, both experience disaster.

Game theory, in which rationality decides what course is best, is not well-suited to deal with a game like Chicken. In Chicken, acting rationally gets one killed; thus, the best strategy is to act irrationally. Such "rationality paradoxes" instead are at the heart of drama theory, according to

Nigel Howard of ISCO Ltd., Birmingham, Eng., who advises international organizations and government bodies on issues involving conflict and negotiation. Unlike game theory, drama theory takes into account the values, beliefs, and emotions of players as a game or situation unfolds. In a paper published in 1998 in the *Journal of the Operational Research Society,* Howard showed how it is possible to take the "credibility paradoxes" at the root of games like Chicken and transform the games into others free of paradox.

Milestones

More than 4,000 participants gathered in Berlin for the 1998 International Congress of Mathematicians. Fields Medals, often called the Nobel Prizes of mathematics, were handed out during the opening session. The 1998 recipients were Richard E. Borcherds of the University of California, Berkeley; William T. Gowers of University of Cambridge; Maxim Kontsevich of the Institut des Hautes Études Scientifiques, Bures-sûr-Yvette, France; and Curtis T. McMullen of Harvard University.

Borcherds, who completed his award-winning work as Royal Society Research Professor at Cambridge, established an explanation for an apparent coincidence among an elliptic modular function, the Monster simple group, and string theory in physics. The theory of elliptic curves, exploited by Andrew Wiles of Princeton University in his proof of Fermat's last theorem, includes one particular elliptic modular function, the so-called *j*-function, which arises in studying surfaces created by rolling a plane into a punctured sphere. While reading a book on the subject of el-

liptic modular functions, John McKay of Concordia University, Montreal, noticed that the third coefficient in the expansion of the *j*-function as an infinite series is 196,884. He knew that the numbers 1 and 196,883, which sum to the 196,884 of the modular function, also appear in connection with the Monster simple group, an object in group theory. Borcherds suspected that the relationship between these two very different branches of mathematics had to be more than coincidence.

A group is a finite or an infinite collection of objects, with an operation between pairs of them that obeys a few simple rules. Examples include the integers, under the operation of addition, and the symmetries of a geometric object (the different ways to rotate and flip it about so that it ends up looking the same), under the operation of applying one rotation or flip after another. Simple groups are the prime building blocks of all groups; just as any positive integer can be factored uniquely as a product of primes, any finite group can be decomposed uniquely into a kind of product of finite simple groups. Curiously, whereas there are a number of infinite families of simple groups, there are also 26 known one-of-a-kind "sporadic" simple groups, the largest of which is the Monster, which has more than 8×10^{53} members. The Monster "lives"—that is, it describes the symmetries of some kind of object—in 196,883 dimensions, but it also lives in still higher dimensions, where it describes the symmetries of still other, scarcely imaginable objects.

The connection between finite groups and modular functions seemed so preposterous that John Horton Conway (then of Cambridge, now at Princeton) dubbed the theory "monstrous moonshine." Borcherds,

however, proved that every coefficient of the modular function is a sum of numbers in the list of dimensions in which the Monster lives. This relationship, Borcherds discovered, has a connection to string theory in 26 dimensions. String theory, a leading theory of the physics of matter, asserts that all matter is composed of tiny loops of one-dimensional strings. Some spatial dimensions, such as the three dimensions that we experience, may be extended, whereas others are all curled up and, hence, imperceptible to us. The Monster turns out to be the group of symmetries of one particular string theory, of 26 of these curled-up dimensions, whose surfaces inherently involve the modular function.

Gowers received his Fields Medal for proving important results in the field of functional analysis. Kontsevich earned his prize for contributions to mathematical string theory. He showed that two models for quantum gravity are, in fact, the same and invented a new way to characterize knots. McMullen's work involved characterization of the boundary of the Mandelbrot set, a set that arises in connection with some chaotic phenomena.

A special silver medal was awarded to Wiles for his proof of Fermat's last theorem (he was over the age limit of 40 for a Fields Medal). Peter W. Shor of AT&T Research Labs in Florham Park, N.J., received the Nevanlinna Prize, given for significant mathematical contribution to computer science. Shor pioneered the invention of algorithms for yet-to-be-built quantum computers, which will use quantized states of atoms to store data. The algorithms would be significantly faster than algorithms used on current silicon-based computers.

—Paul J. Campbell

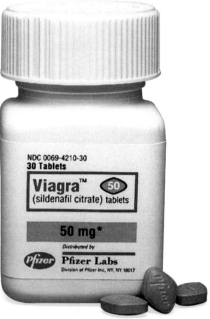

Pfizer/AP/Wide World

MEDICAL SCIENCES

In 1998 medical researchers made advances on a number of fronts, introducing exciting new procedures in the field of transplant medicine and using genetic engineering techniques in the battle against heart disease. The approval of the first oral drug for male impotence, Viagra, also brought new hope to millions of men who suffer from this condition. In the field of dentistry, a newly developed cavity vaccine raised hopes of reducing not only the number of dental infections but also infections of other types, including those that cause sore throat and the common cold. Veterinary research witnessed advances in the treatment of anemia and Addison's disease in dogs. The first behavioral drugs for dogs were also approved during the year.

GENERAL MEDICINE

When it comes to progress in medical science, it is often difficult to separate realistic hope from overblown hype. The task was particularly daunting in 1998, a year in which the headlines were dominated by reports of amazing advances in fights against a wide range of disorders. From the sensation over the anti-impotence pill Viagra to the furor surrounding a dramatic new cancer "cure," drug development fueled many heated medical debates during the year. Even what seemed to be a clear cause for celebration—the approval of the first drug to prevent breast cancer, tamoxifen—was greeted with controversy.

Other volatile issues centered less on medical science than on medical ethics. Touching on questions left unanswered from previous years, 1998 witnessed the intensification of ethical concerns over euthanasia, cloning, and sex selection.

Impotence

If there were any doubts about whether sex really sells, the blockbuster performance of Viagra (sildenafil), the first oral drug for male impotence, laid them to rest in 1998. After its approval by the U.S. Food and Drug Administration (FDA) in March, Viagra flew out of pharmacies at a record pace. More than three million prescriptions were written in the U.S. during the first five months, and the drug was expected to chalk up $1 billion in worldwide sales in its first year alone.

Viagra's influence extended far beyond its financial prowess; it also pushed the topic of impotence out of the bedroom and into the public forum. Viagra became the topic of comedy routines and water-cooler discussions, and even a distinguished public figure, former U.S. senator Bob Dole, revealed that he was taking the drug.

Often lost among the hype, however, were some of the drug's potentially serious side effects. While Pfizer, Inc., Viagra's manufacturer, had warned men with heart or blood-pressure problems against using Viagra, it appeared that many were ignoring that caution. As of mid-November the FDA had received reports of 130 deaths among patients taking the drug, many from heart attacks, although there was no proof that the new medication itself caused the deaths. The U.S. Federal Aviation Administration (FAA) had a different worry—the drug's effect on vision. Viagra can impair a user's ability to distinguish between blue and green, a skill essential to piloting a plane. To address that concern, the FAA issued an advisory cautioning pilots not to fly a plane for at least six hours after taking Viagra. The risks

may not end there. In September a study published in *The New England Journal of Medicine* showed that Viagra may also cause fatal lung complications.

Still, Viagra remained a high-profile drug, garnering even more attention in October when the Nobel Prize for Physiology or Medicine was awarded. The work of the 1998 honorees, Robert Furchgott, Louis Ignarro, and Ferid Murad, laid the groundwork for the development of Viagra. The three U.S. scientists discovered that the body uses a chemical called nitric oxide to regulate the diameter of blood vessels. Viagra promotes an erection by enhancing the effect of nitric oxide on blood vessels in the penis.

Furchgott, an emeritus professor of pharmacology at the State University of New York Health Science Center, Brooklyn, was cited for his work on the effect of drugs on blood vessels. Murad, chairman of the department of integrative biology, pharmacology, and physiology at the University of Texas Medical School,

Houston, was recognized for his 1977 discovery that nitroglycerin and other compounds long used by doctors to relax blood vessels release nitric oxide, which relaxes smooth muscle cells. Ignarro, a professor of pharmacology at the University of California, Los Angeles, School of Medicine, was cited for his contributions to the chemical understanding of nitric oxide in the body.

The Nobel committee said the nitric oxide findings "elicited an avalanche of research activities in many different laboratories around the world. This was the first discovery that a gas can act as a signal molecule in the organism." Scientists were particularly amazed that nitric oxide, a common air pollutant, could exert such important functions in humans. "Nitric oxide was known to be produced in bacteria, but this simple molecule was not expected to be important in higher animals," the Nobel committee said. In addition to its role in regulating blood flow, nitric oxide also has been found to act as a signal molecule in the nervous system and as a weapon against infections. (*See* SCIENTISTS OF THE YEAR: *Nobel Prizes.*)

Cancer

The hopes of cancer patients and their families around the world soared in May when a front-page article in the *New York Times* trumpeted a powerful new breed of drugs that appeared to wipe out many different kinds of tumors in mice. The "antiangiogenesis" drugs, which were designed to inhibit the growth of blood vessels feeding cancer tumors, had been developed by Judah Folkman at Boston's Children's Hospital.

While Folkman downplayed the importance of his team's mouse tests, the *New York Times* article set off a media frenzy by quoting Nobel laureate James Watson as saying that "Judah (Folkman) is going to cure cancer in two years." Watson later denied making the statement, but the hype machine was already on a roll. Reports on the antiangiogenesis drugs made the covers of newsmagazines and topped network television newscasts, spurring thousands of desperate cancer patients to contact Folkman and other doctors pleading for the "cure." The problem was that the new drugs, dubbed angiostatin and endostatin, had never been tested in humans, and the manufacturer, EntreMed, did not have sufficient quantities on hand to conduct such tests even if researchers had wanted to.

Over time the inflated hopes for the antiangiogenesis drugs subsided. In November researchers from the U.S. National Cancer Institute issued a statement saying that their tests of one of the drugs, endostatin, failed to produce the dramatic shrinkage of tumors in mice that Folkman's lab had reported. Folkman countered that the drug may have lost its potency during shipment, and new tests were scheduled to begin in January 1999.

In contrast, years of waiting finally came to an end in 1998 for millions of women searching for a way to reduce their odds of getting breast cancer. In October the FDA approved the first drug to prevent breast cancer in high-risk women, such as those with a family history of the disease. Although the drug, tamoxifen (Nolvadex), had been used to treat cancer for more than two decades, its potential as a preventive agent remained unproven until September, when a study of 13,000 high-risk women published in the *Journal of the National Cancer Institute* found that tamoxifen re-

A woman receives a mammogram to check for breast cancer. A 1998 study found that women at high risk of breast cancer could reduce their chances of developing the disease by taking the drug tamoxifen.

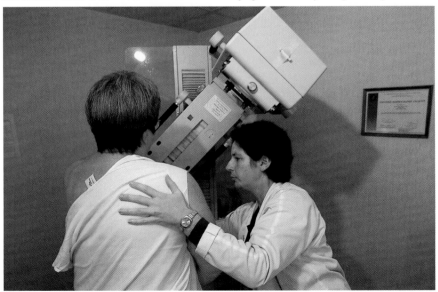

duced the women's chances of getting breast cancer by more than 40%. Approval of tamoxifen, however, came quickly under attack by some consumer groups because of the drug's potential for serious side effects, including blood clots in the lungs and increased risk of endometrial cancer. Questions were also raised about the drug's long-term effects, the types of breast cancer that it helps prevent, and the possibility that it could promote the growth of more aggressive forms of breast cancer in some women.

Doctors looking for ways to help women who were already battling breast cancer also received a new pharmaceutical weapon in 1998. In September the FDA approved Herceptin (trastuzumab), a genetically engineered compound, for treatment of advanced breast cancer. The drug is a monoclonal antibody specifically designed to attack cancer cells that overproduce a protein called HER-2, a circumstance that occurs in 25–30% of women with advanced breast cancer.

As for other types of cancer, the emphasis remained on figuring out prevention strategies and getting people to stick to them. A study of more than 29,000 men in Finland found that those who took daily vitamin E supplements were 32% less likely to develop prostate cancer than those who did not. Reporting in the *Journal of the National Cancer Institute,* researchers said that the dose amount of vitamin E used in the study, 50 mg per day, is more than people usually get in their daily diets but can easily be obtained through over-the-counter vitamin pills.

Despite years of warnings about lung cancer and other health risks, U.S. health authorities reported disturbing trends in smoking among teenagers. In October the Centers for Disease Control and Prevention released a report showing that the rate at which young people took up smoking rose 50% from 1988 to 1996. Health officials estimated that, if current trends continued, about five million American youths will eventually die from smoking-related causes.

Young people in the U.S. are taking up smoking at an alarming rate. According to health officials, as many as five million American youths may die prematurely as a result of their tobacco use.

Blair Seitz/Photo Researchers, Inc.

"We're losing ground in the battle to protect our children," U.S. Health and Human Services Secretary Donna Shalala warned. Reducing youth smoking was a key component of a settlement reached in November between 46 states and major tobacco companies. In addition to paying the states $206 billion, the tobacco manufacturers agreed to curtail marketing campaigns that appeal to children and to spend $1.7 billion on antismoking advertising and studies of youth smoking.

AIDS and other infectious diseases

While still lacking a vaccine or a cure, medical science continued to make inroads against AIDS in 1998. In October the U.S. National Center for Health Statistics credited wider access to new drug "cocktails" for dropping the nation's AIDS death rate to its lowest level since 1987, the first year that mortality records were kept on the disease. The rate of infection with the AIDS-causing human immunodeficiency virus (HIV), however, remained stable at about 40,000 Americans per year, prompting concerns that intravenous drug users, homosexual men, and other high-risk groups may be getting complacent about the risk of HIV infection.

HIV was not the only blood-borne virus to grab headlines in 1998. In March U.S. Surgeon General David Satcher announced plans to notify blood recipients about the possible risk of hepatitis C. It was estimated that about one million Americans may have been infected with hepatitis C through blood transfusions before a donor screening test became available in July 1992, but less than 250,000 of those people were aware of their situation. Hepatitis C can lead to chronic liver disease and is a driving force behind the increasing demand for liver transplants. Until 1998 no effective drug therapy was available for people with hepatitis C. In November, however, two studies published in *The New England Journal of Medicine* reported encouraging results with a strategy that combined the new antiviral drug ribavirin with an older drug, interferon.

Also in November, the American Academy of Pediatrics began urging doctors to start giving children a new oral vaccine

The left ventricular assist device (below), which is used to temporarily support the pumping action of the heart in patients with severe heart failure, may allow some people to avoid heart transplants. (Right) A patient poses with one of the devices.

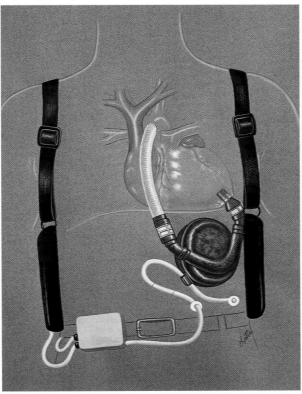

to protect against one of the world's most common, yet deadly, infectious agents: rotavirus. While most parents have never heard of rotavirus, the disease agent sends about 500,000 U.S. children to the doctor and kills about 870,000 children worldwide each year, according to the U.S. National Institutes of Health (NIH). The virus can cause severe diarrhea, which in turn can lead to fatal dehydration. The oral, three-dose vaccine, called RotaShield, can prevent about 80% of serious rotavirus infections, said

(Above) Howell/Liaison Agency/Gamma Liaison International; (right) Paul S. Howell/Gamma Liaison International

NIH researchers, who labored for more than 20 years to create the much-needed vaccine. The manufacturer of RotaShield, Wyeth-Ayerst, also announced plans to work with the World Health Organization to provide the vaccine to developing nations, where the need is most dire.

Diabetes

Most people with noninsulin-dependent, or type II, diabetes know that the best way to avoid the disease's debilitating complications is to closely control their blood sugar levels. In September, however, a long-awaited British study of 5,000 type II diabetics added something else to the list: controlling blood pressure.

The landmark results, published in the medical journal *The Lancet,* showed that type II diabetics who took medication to lower high blood pressure were 24% less likely to develop complications like kidney failure or blindness and were 32% less likely to die over the 20-year course of the study. Researchers emphasized that their findings did not mean that controlling blood sugar was unimportant—just that type II diabetics would be wise to watch both their blood pressure and their blood sugar.

Heart disease

Building on encouraging early results, researchers reported continued progress in using genetic engineering techniques to

fight heart disease. In a study published in February in the journal *Circulation,* German scientists presented an update on their efforts to use a genetically engineered growth factor, fibroblast growth factor-1, to stimulate blood vessel growth in patients with heart disease. Three years after administering treatment, the researchers found that the 20 patients who had received the engineered growth factor had two to three times more blood flow to their hearts than untreated patients.

In 1998 two other studies published in *Circulation* showed that "treatment" with electronic pumps called left ventricular assist devices may allow some people with congestive heart failure to avoid heart transplants. Usually, the devices are used as a stop-gap measure to keep patients with severe heart failure alive while awaiting a donated heart. Researchers found that placing patients on the devices appears to help heart tissue recover by giving it a break from its normal pumping routine. According to researchers, when five patients with severe heart disease were weaned off left ventricular assist devices, their heart function had improved so much that they did not need heart transplants.

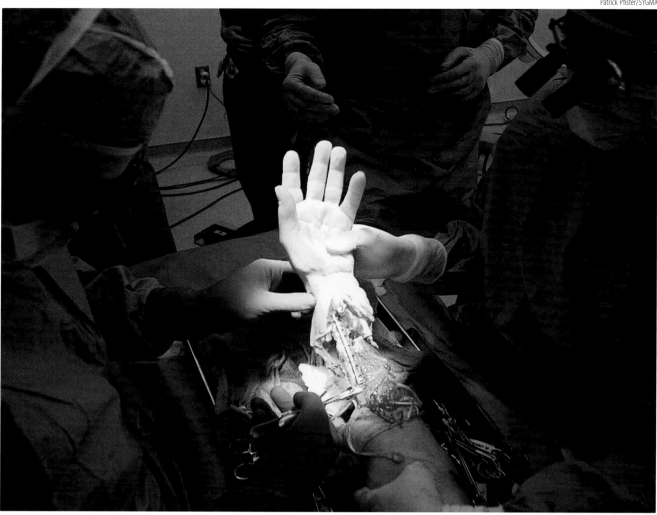

Transplants

The field of transplant medicine attracted widespread public attention throughout 1998. In February Health and Human Services Secretary Donna Shalala set off a storm of controversy when she ordered the nation's organ allocation system to be revamped to give the sickest patients preference regardless of where they lived. That action prompted outcries from transplant centers in less populous states, which feared they would be driven out of business because most of their donated organs would go to patients at larger centers. Some states, like Wisconsin, passed "me-first" laws aimed at keeping all donated organs within the state. An 11th-hour decision by a federal court blocked the new nationwide rules from taking effect on October 1, and the issue of the best way to distribute organs remained unresolved as 1998 drew to a close.

In late September an international medical team in Lyon, France, upstaged plans by surgeons in Louisville, Ky., to perform the world's first successful hand transplant. In the 13-hour-long operation at Lyon's Edouard Herriot hospital, the surgeons attached the right hand and forearm from a dead donor to the arm of 48-year-old Clint Hallam. The patient reportedly could move his new hand three months after the operation, but doctors said it would be about two years before they could tell whether the operation was a complete success. In 1964 a similar transplant attempt in Ecuador failed when the recipient's body rejected the limb.

The drama of the Lyon transplant was not limited to the operation itself. Hallam originally had been portrayed to the media

Doctors in Louisville, Ky., give amputee Matthew Scott a new hand in January 1999. The procedure marked the first hand transplant in the U.S. and the second in the world.

as an Australian businessman who had lost his hand while working at a building site. It was later revealed that he had actually lost his limb while using a power saw in a New Zealand jail, where he had been locked up for fraud.

In January 1999 the Kentucky team performed the first hand transplant in the U.S., replacing the left hand of Matthew Scott, a New Jersey man, injured in a firecracker accident. Both the U.S. operation, performed at Louisville Jewish Hospital, and the Lyon procedure spurred concerns about the risk of transplanting nonessential organs such as a hand. Patients receiving any sort of transplant usually must take powerful, antirejection drugs that increase the risk of infection, cancer, and death.

In an advance that may eventually help reduce the need for many kinds of transplants, researchers at the University of Wisconsin, Madison, announced in November that they had successfully grown human stem cells in a laboratory. Stem cells are embryonic cells that can develop into virtually any kind of cell in the human body, depending on the type of growth factors to which they are exposed. Theoretically, stem cells could be used to grow new heart cells to repair failing hearts, new liver cells to treat livers damaged by hepatitis, or new bone marrow cells to help cancer patients who would otherwise need traditional bone marrow transplants.

Neurological disorders

Exercise is often touted as a way to keep the heart healthy and the muscles strong, but 1998 provided some of the best evidence to date that it may be a good strategy for keeping the mind healthy as well. In a study presented at the American Academy of Neurology's annual meeting in May, researchers from Case Western Reserve University in Cleveland, Ohio, examined the exercise habits of about 400 older people. The researchers found that those who had exercised on a regular basis between the ages of 20 and 59 were less likely to develop Alzheimer's disease than those who had been physically inactive or who had exercised sporadically.

Another study, published in October in the journal *Stroke,* showed that Harvard University alumni who spent a half hour a day in vigorous physical activity had a 24% lower risk of stroke than those who did not. The protective effect appeared to increase with the amount of activity, researchers said, noting that people who exercised for one hour a day five days a week suffered 50% fewer strokes.

Reproduction

Just as the ethical controversy over the November 1997 birth of the McCaughey septuplets had begun to die down, the December 1998 birth of the Chukwu octuplets in Houston, Texas, reignited the debate over whether fertility treatments needed closer regulation. The babies born to Nkem Chukwu and her husband, Iyke Louis Udobi, were the world's first octuplets to be delivered alive and ranged in weight from 0.29 kg (10.3 oz) to 0.74 kg (1 lb 11 oz). Although the smallest baby died within a week, doctors at St. Luke's Episcopal Hospital in early January gave the remaining seven a more than 90% chance of surviving.

While the Chukwu octuplets may have been the most dramatic example, the number of multiple births continued to skyrocket in 1998 due to the increased use of fertility drugs and treatments. Procedures that employed fertility drugs, such as the gonadotropins used by Chukwu, led to twins 20% of the time and to triplets or more 5% of the time. With each additional baby came a greater risk of miscarriage and increased health risks to mother and children, not to mention a higher cost to society. For example, the hospital bill for the octuplets was expected to run more than $2 million.

Despite all the concerns over multiple births and other thorny ethical issues like frozen embryos and donated eggs, the U.S. had no nationwide laws or regulations governing fertility clinics as of 1998. "We can identify the ethical issues, but we can't seem to solve them," commented George Annas, a medical ethicist at Boston University.

Another ethically charged technology—cloning—also refused to stand still in 1998. Following up on the 1997 report that a team of Scottish scientists had produced Dolly the sheep, the first clone of an adult mammal, researchers at the University of Hawaii, Manoa, used the same method to clone 22 mice in July. A team from Japan's Kinki University repeated the feat in December by creating eight identical calves from a single cow.

Those experiments, however, represented just the tip of the ethical iceberg. In November scientists from the University of Massachusetts, Amherst, announced that they had created embryos that combined cow and human genes. The work involved placing genetic material from a human skin cell into the egg cell of a cow, a technique the researchers said could help grow organs for human transplants.

Cloning of humans appeared to be inching closer to reality. In December a group at Kyunghee University Hospital in Seoul, S.Kor., announced that it had cloned a human embryo. According to the researchers, they took a nonreproductive cell from a woman in her 30s, removed the cell's genetic material, and then inserted it into one of the woman's eggs. They claimed that the cell divided and grew into a four-cell embryo in the test tube before they halted the experiment for ethical reasons. Experts from the Roslin Institute in Scotland, where Dolly was cloned, challenged the

South Korean claim, saying the researchers did not provide sufficient scientific evidence that the "cloned" human embryo was genuine and viable.

While cloning technology remained primarily a curiosity of the research lab, other 1998 advances in reproductive medicine had immediate and far-reaching implications for people's everyday lives. In September researchers at the Genetics & IVF Institute in Fairfax, Va., reported impressive results with their technique to select the sex of a child. In a study published in the journal *Human Reproduction,* the Virginia team said that its method, which involved using a sperm-sorting technique followed by artificial insemination, was 93% accurate when a female baby was desired. Figures for male babies were not released.

Critics decried the sex-selection technique as an ethical minefield, saying that it should only be considered in cases in which the family carried a genetic disease that was limited to one sex or the other. In addition to that use, however, the Genetics & IVF Institute said that it was offering its sex-selection procedure to parents who wanted to choose a certain sex of child to "balance" their families.

In another move that stirred controversy, the FDA in September approved the first "emergency" contraception kit in the U.S. Using the PREVEN kit could prevent unintended pregnancy if started within 72 hours after sex. Although the kit consisted of nothing more than a specific combination of birth control pills and similar pills that had been prescribed for European women for years, many U.S. women and doctors were unaware of the contraception strategy until the FDA gave its stamp of approval.

Euthanasia

Just when much of the public had begun to tune out Jack Kevorkian's campaign to assist patients who wanted to die, the Detroit pathologist took his work to a dramatic new level: actively killing, or "euthanizing," a patient and recording the death on a videotape that was later aired on national television. The video, broadcast on the TV newsmagazine "60 Minutes" in December, showed Kevorkian administering a lethal injection to Thomas Youk, a 52-year-old man suffering from Lou Gehrig's disease. While the Youk case represented Kevorkian's first involvement in euthanasia, the doctor acknowledged having used a homemade "suicide machine" to assist at least 130 other patients in end-

ing their lives, the first being Alzheimer's disease patient Janet Adkins in 1990.

Critics contended that Kevorkian's venture into euthanasia was nothing more than a ghoulish publicity stunt aimed at forcing a "right-to-die" showdown in the courts. Voters in his home state of Michigan had one month earlier rejected a measure to legalize physician-assisted suicide; however, Kevorkian's supporters, including Youk's family, argued that euthanasia was merely a natural outgrowth of the doctor's desire to help chronically and terminally ill patients end their suffering. Whatever the

Jack Kevorkian, shown below at a court appearance in May 1998, crossed from passive to active euthanasia when he gave a man a lethal injection and recorded the act on videotape.

AP/Wide World Photos

case, Kevorkian was arrested for murder after the euthanasia videotape aired and remained free on bail awaiting trial at the end of 1998.

Awards

In September seven scientists received Albert Lasker Medical Research Awards, often referred to as the American Nobels because so many of the winners had gone on to win Nobel Prizes.

Chosen to receive the awards for clinical medicine were Alfred Knudson, Jr., former president of the Fox Chase Cancer Center in Philadelphia, Peter Nowell of the University of Pennsylvania School of Medicine in Philadelphia, and Janet Rowley of the University of Chicago Medical Center. All were honored for their work on how genetic abnormalities can trigger cancer. Knudson's work led to the idea of tumor suppressor genes, while Nowell and Rowley proved that leukemia could be caused by genetic mutations.

Awards for basic medical science went to Yoshio Masui of the University of Toronto, Lee Hartwell, director of the Fred Hutchinson Cancer Research Center in Seattle, Wash., and Paul Nurse, director-general of the Imperial Cancer Research Fund in London. All were honored for their work on the biochemical machinery that drives cell division. Hartwell and Nurse identified a series of genes involved in regulating cell division in yeast, while Masui discovered a factor that stimulates cell division in frog eggs.

Daniel E. Koshland, Jr., of the University of California, Berkeley, received a separate Lasker award for lifetime achievement in medical research. Koshland was honored for his work on enzyme regulation and cell-signaling systems, as well as for his work as the former editor-in-chief of the journal *Science*.

—Rebecca Kolberg

DENTISTRY

The National Institute of Dental Research (NIDR) marked its 50th anniversary in 1998. The institute came into being on June 24, 1948, when U.S. Pres. Harry Truman signed the National Dental Research Act into law. At that time tooth decay was a serious problem, and most Americans could expect to lose most of their teeth by the age of 45. In 1998, however, fewer than 10% of Americans were in this category, due in part to the efforts of the NIDR. The institute's first major public-health contribution centered on the addition of fluoride to drinking water, which greatly reduced the number of dental caries (cavities) among children and adults. Among important innovations that resulted from NIDR-sponsored research were the high-speed drill, panoramic X-rays, and the development of dental sealants and new restorative materials.

As the NIDR turned 50, it changed its name to the National Institute of Dental and Craniofacial Research. The name change reflected an increased emphasis on research into the genetic, behavioral, and environmental factors that influence the intricate relationships between disease and disorders of the craniofacial complex. Research in the late 1990s encompassed such areas as arthritis, diabetes, oral and pharyngeal cancers, osteoporosis, temporomandibular (jaw) disorders, and the relationship between oral and systemic diseases. Programs supported by the institute also focused on the genomes (genetic blueprints) of the major pathogens responsible for dental caries, periodontal (gum) disease, and oral candidiasis as well as on gene technology transfer and studies in molecular epidemiology to identify the genes involved in oral diseases and disorders, such as cleft lip and palate, periodontal disease, and oral cancers. Other research included growing bone and other craniofacial tissues, such as cartilage, tooth pulp, periodontal ligaments, and salivary glands, and working with enamel-forming proteins that may one day be used to fill decayed teeth.

Caries vaccine

Julian Ma, an immunologist at Guy's Hospital, London, who had been working on a caries vaccine for 15 years, succeeded in creating a vaccine made from plants. The major cause of caries is a bacterium, *Streptococcus mutans*. Ma created antibodies against the bacterium in his laboratory with the idea that he could apply them directly to the teeth. The process of raising antibodies in animals and then collecting them was expensive, however, so Ma learned how to transfer genes for the antibodies into the DNA of tobacco plants. As the tobacco plants grow, they produce not only their own proteins but also Ma's antibodies.

Growing the antibodies in this manner is cheap. Ma also discovered that the plants were very efficient in their production of the antibodies, which suggested that the plants would be able to produce more complex and superior antibodies. The antibody synthesized by Ma comes in two different forms, one that circulates in the bloodstream and a second that is similar to secretions found in saliva. The second form has a special protein chain that wraps around the antibody, protecting it from being destroyed by enzymes in saliva. The extracted antibodies from the plants were mixed into a solution and applied to the teeth of volunteers whose mouths had been cleared of bacteria with antibiotics. Following a succession of applications over several weeks, the volunteers' mouths remained free of *S. mutans*. The application method was still being perfected.

Implications for this technique go beyond dentistry. Mucosal surfaces could be similarly treated with antibodies against other infectious agents, including those responsible for the common cold, sore throat, and chest and urinary-tract infections.

Dental studies

Chronic dental infections may increase the risk for heart attack. At the February 1998 annual meeting of the American Association for the Advancement of Science in Philadelphia, Mark Herzberg of the University of Minnesota, Minneapolis, presented results possibly linking the chronic infection of gum disease to heart disease. Herzberg and his research team studied the effects of the oral bacterium *Streptococcus sanguis* in the bloodstream of rabbits. This bacterium, normally present in the mouth and thought to be harmless, contains a collagen-like protein that causes clotting of blood platelets. After introducing *S. sanguis* bacteria into the blood of the experimental animals, the researchers detected increases in the heart rate and blood pressure of animals, changes

similar to those that occur during a heart attack. Moreover, *S. sanguis* may cause chronic inflammation of blood vessels by stimulating the aggregation of white blood cells, forming artery blockages that cut off the blood supply of the heart.

Previous studies had shown that people with poor oral health are at higher risk for heart disease. Although *S. sanguis* was not thought to be pathogenic, it does mimic collagen, a human protein necessary for clotting. The bacterium, which mimics collagen so that the immune system will not attack it, gains entry into the human bloodstream via food.

Studies at the State University of New York, Buffalo (SUNY Buffalo), linked a bacterium common in periodontal disease to atherosclerotic deposits in coronary arteries. Frank Scannapieco, a dental professor at SUNY Buffalo, speculated that dental infections may also be linked to respiratory disease. The relationship between oral health and general physical health strengthens the necessity for good personal oral hygiene and regular checkups.

Another study at SUNY Buffalo, conducted by Jean Wactawski-Wende, showed a link between dental problems and osteoporosis. Wactawski-Wende's research involved the analysis of 2,500 postmenopausal women. Women who suffered from periodontal disease or had experienced tooth loss were found to be at a higher risk for hip fractures.

Sleep apnea

A team of researchers at the University of California, Los Angeles, School of Dentistry, led by Arthur H. Friedlander, discovered why snoring can damage arter-

ies and sometimes kill. Persons with sleep apnea—a disorder marked by irregular breathing and snorting, which generally affects overweight, middle-aged men—were studied. X-rays of the necks of men who had sleep apnea were compared with a group of men who did not have the disorder. Of the men with sleep apnea, 21% had hardened blockages (atheromas) in the carotid artery, as opposed to only 2.5% of the control volunteers. These results showed that an increased risk for stroke in the sleep apnea group was due to problems in the neck, not in another part of the body. Calcium deposits, fat, platelets, and other soft tissue blocked the artery. Air cannot flow in or out of the nose or mouth in a person who suffers from sleep apnea. The tongue falls back into the throat, blocking the airway; blood pressure increases; and oxygen is not taken in, allowing carbon dioxide to build to dangerous levels in the blood, which further increases risk of stroke. The study indicated that persons with sleep apnea have a greater prevalence of calcified carotid-artery atheromas than healthy, age-matched persons.

Fluoride concerns

As bottled water, which is free from most contaminants, gained popularity, dentists were becoming concerned that the product was undercutting the positive benefits of fluoridation. Fluoride added to tap water helps build stronger teeth in children and helps prevent tooth decay in adults. With bottled-water consumption at an all-time high, many parents are unknowingly depriving their children of fluoride, and dentists are seeing more cavities than they did in the 1980s.

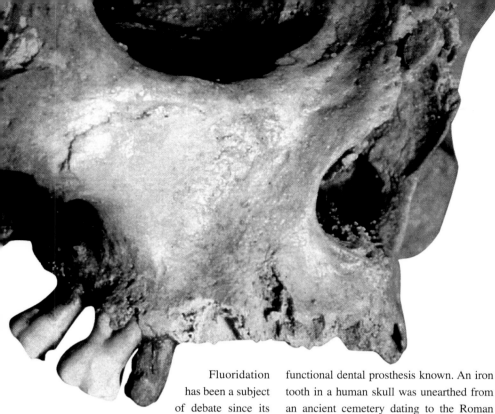

(Left and below) Crubezy E., Murail P., Girard L., Bernadou J.P.

Fluoridation has been a subject of debate since its introduction into water supplies in the U.S. beginning in 1945. Public health experts agree, however, that fluoride consumption from tap water in prescribed levels benefits the developing teeth of children.

In studies compiled by the American Dental Association, fluoride was found to prevent upwards of 50% of dental caries in children and adults who live in communities with fluoride in the water system. Other statistics showed that an estimated one-half of U.S. children were celebrating their 18th birthday without ever having had a cavity. Dentists noted that tooth decay was resurfacing among young patients who live in fluoridated communities, probably as a result of the use of bottled water without fluoride. Some bottlers were responding by producing water with added fluoride. Because it was unclear whether children could get enough fluoride from toothpaste or other dental products, parents were advised to consult with their dentists and pediatricians to ensure that their children received the proper amount.

Discovery of ancient false tooth

In early 1998 Louis Girard of the University of Bordeaux, France, reported the oldest functional dental prosthesis known. An iron tooth in a human skull was unearthed from an ancient cemetery dating to the Roman Empire at Chantambre. When a person of that period lost a tooth, there was little to be done. Wealthy people could have a replacement made of ivory, horn, or wood kept in place by threads; however, the false tooth was nonfunctional and merely cosmetic. The tooth Girard found was incredi-

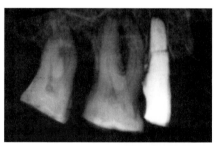

Made of iron, the dark tooth in the human skull pictured at top dates to the Roman Empire and is the oldest functional dental prosthesis known. An X-ray of the false tooth is shown above.

bly precise in its form, complete with roots that fit snugly into the socket of the jawbone, the bone having grown around the roots. This type of dental treatment is unique for the period. Dentists today do not ordinarily implant false teeth directly into the jawbone. How the ancient artist created the tooth or prevented infection will perhaps never be known.

New products

A gel was developed in Sweden that painlessly dissolves tooth decay. A commercial company claims that the gel, called Carisolv, eliminates the need for injections and drilling. The formula for the gel is kept in two vials; when mixed, the ingredients create the substance that dissolves the decay. The components of the formula include three amino acids—glutamine, leucine, and lysine—which interact with a weak solution of sodium hypochlorite. The amino acids act as a buffer to prevent damage to healthy tissue. The gel works best on teeth that have not been previously restored. The company planned to market the product outside Sweden in 1999.

A company in California developed a high-powered device that eliminates the need for anesthetic and traditional drilling. Approved for use on adults by the Food and Drug Administration (FDA), the Millennium device pumps a jet of water. A laser beam fragments the jet, turning it into minuscule elliptical water droplets. These droplets explode as they impact the enamel surface of the tooth, grinding down the surface. The device does not work well for drilling large areas, such as are needed in preparing a crown. Continued development was promised by the manufacturer.

The FDA approved the first prescription medication to treat periodontal disease. The drug, called Periostat, was developed by a group in Newtown, Pa. It contains an antibiotic, doxycycline, which slows the progression of the disease by attacking the bacteria that cause it. The FDA also approved PerioChip, a tiny piece of biodegradable material designed to reduce bacteria below the gum line and improve gum health. Inserted into an infected area (periodontal pocket) after deep cleaning, the chip releases chlorhexidine and is absorbed within 10 days. None of the new products, however, eliminates the need for seeing a dentist regularly.   —Ron Sims

VETERINARY MEDICINE

The 100-year anniversary of the change in name from the United States Veterinary Medical Association (USVMA) to the American Veterinary Medical Association (AVMA) was celebrated in 1998. The USVMA was started in 1863 with 38 charter members when the profession's primary focus was the health care of horses. The name change in 1898 provided new visibility for the association and occurred at a time of rapid growth in the number of veterinarians as well as in interest in a national organization representing veterinary medicine. In the late 1990s, AVMA membership exceeded 60,000 veterinarians, and the organization's focus encompassed biomedical research and public-health protection as well as the health care of animals.

New disaster-response programs of the AVMA and the American Veterinary Medical Foundation (AVMF) were used effectively in recent years to help animals injured or endangered by flooding, hurricanes, and brush fires. In an effort to enhance veterinary medicine's involvement in disaster relief and recovery, the AVMA and the AVMF signed a formal statement of understanding with the American Red Cross in January 1998. The agreement outlined collaborative efforts by these organizations to plan for coordination of all disaster-site, animal-related relief efforts, to emphasize incorporation of veterinary

oversight of all animal care and welfare operations in American Red Cross disaster plans, and to develop joint training programs. At the signing, Elizabeth Dole, president of the American Red Cross, noted that "by ensuring the care and safety of animals in times of disasters, the veterinary associations will help us ensure the mental and physical well-being of their owners."

While injured animals were a concern in disasters, specially trained dogs had important roles in assisting with disaster recovery. For example, 74 dogs were involved in the disaster response to the bombing of the Alfred P. Murrah Federal Building in Oklahoma City, Okla., in 1995; 46 of the dogs were used to search for victims, 14 for patrol of the site, 12 for explosive detection, and 2 for search and patrol. Results of a survey of the handlers of these dogs was published in the April 1998 issue of the *Journal of the American Veterinary Medical Association.* The survey sought information on any injuries or illnesses of these dogs that were associated with the high-risk environment of the bomb site. Twenty injuries occurred in 19 of the dogs. Eighteen of these injuries involved the footpads, which raised the question of need for paw protection for dogs used in this type of disaster. Some of the handlers noted, however, that use of the currently available types of paw-protection boots could reduce a dog's agility, which may endanger the animal's safety while searching rubble. Teaching avoidance of dangerous surfaces when training disaster-response dogs was suggested as an alternative to use of boots.

In 1998 more than 1,800 dogs were used in U.S. Department of Defense installa-

tions worldwide. These dogs were trained in security patrol and in explosive and drug detection. Twenty-five of these dogs had been assigned to duty in the Persian Gulf War; the health of these dogs was being monitored by the Armed Forces Institute of Pathology in a special study that included a similar group of military dogs not deployed in the war. The study will continue through the life of these dogs, including the period of their retirement from active duty. Since the Persian Gulf War military dogs were exposed to the same environment as military personnel, health differences between the two groups of dogs may improve understanding of health problems of Persian Gulf War veterans.

Prion disease diagnoses

In a study published in *Veterinary Record* in May 1998, a research team from the U.S. Department of Agriculture's Agricultural Research Service and Washington State University's College of Veterinary Medicine reported the development of a new test for scrapie, a fatal, degenerative neurologic disease of sheep. The test arose from the discovery that lymphoid nodules on the back side of the nictitating membrane, or third eyelid, accumulate scrapie prion proteins (PrP), which are a marker for the disease and perhaps the causative agent. The lymphoid tissue removed from the third eyelid by biopsy under local anesthetic was subjected to an immunohistochemistry test, which used a monoclonal antibody specific for scrapie PrP with an immunostaining procedure to produce a microscopically visible, red staining of the antibody-bound scrapie PrP. With this test, scrapie PrP could be iden-

Gary Payne/Gamma Liaison International

Specially trained dogs are being used increasingly to assist disaster-response teams. During 1998 veterinary research focused on the dangers that such dogs face and on finding ways to protect them.

tified in infected sheep well before clinical signs of the disease were seen. Diagnosis of scrapie previously required examination of brain tissue of dead sheep. When commercially available, the new test will reduce the cost of eradicating the disease by limiting destruction of sheep in infected herds to those testing positive for the infection. There is no cure or treatment for this disease. Since prions are also involved in bovine spongiform encephalopathy (BSE, or "mad cow" disease), research was initiated to determine whether the new scrapie test could be adapted for use as a BSE test. Adaptation may not be possible because BSE prions appear to be less sen-

sitive to the immunohistochemistry test, and they do not accumulate in lymph tissue, as do scrapie prions.

In recent years, BSE, also a neurodegenerative disease, has been a major problem in the U.K. Control programs resulted in a decline in the number of cases from a peak of 1,000 per week in early 1993 to

about 100 new cases per week in 1998. The decline was expected to continue. As of early 1999, no cases of BSE had been identified in cattle in the U.S. A relationship between the occurrence of BSE and the new variant Creutzfeldt-Jakob disease (nvCJD) in humans was suspected but had not been proven. Neither vaccines for prevention of these diseases nor treatments were available for cattle or people.

A live-animal test that distinguishes normal cattle from cattle infected with BSE prior to processing the cattle for food remained a critical need. It had been proposed that elevation in the concentration of a group of proteins named 14-3-3 in cerebrospinal fluid could serve as such a test. A report in *Veterinary Record,* however, concluded that the 14-3-3 levels in normal cattle were not significantly different from those in cattle in the early symptomatic stages of the disease. Thus, 14-3-3 levels did not represent a suitable live-animal diagnostic test for BSE. In another study, clinical signs for two groups of cows were

Dr. Linda A. Detwiler at USDA/APHIS/Vet Services

A sheep infected with scrapie is shown at right. Researchers reported the development of a new test for scrapie that could identify infected sheep before clinical signs of the disease became visible. Research was under way to determine if the new test could be adapted to check for "mad cow" disease.

compared. Although both groups were suspected to be infected with BSE, only one of the groups was subsequently confirmed to actually be infected. It was concluded that careful assessment of a series of clinical signs, including more frequent locomotor problems, could be used to reliably identify cows with BSE, but unfortunately only in the later stages of the disease, when clinical signs have appeared.

Therapeutic advances

In January 1998 the Food and Drug Administration (FDA) approved a product, Oxyglobin, derived from cow's blood for use in the treatment of anemia in dogs. Oxyglobin is a polymerized hemoglobin-based oxygen-carrying fluid that increases the body's total hemoglobin concentration and thus the oxygen content in tissues. Because of the limited availability of blood through animal blood banks and the difficulties in maintaining a readily available source of whole blood for emergency use within a veterinary practice, Oxyglobin is a much needed product. Oxyglobin does not require refrigeration and has a shelf life of two years. In contrast, whole blood must be refrigerated and has a shelf life of only one month. Oxyglobin does not require crossmatching with blood from the recipient, which is a major advantage, since dogs have eight blood types. Because the life span of Oxyglobin after administration is about one week, the underlying cause of the dog's anemia—if the anemia continues—needs to be identified and corrected through use of other therapeutic procedures.

Addison's disease affects nearly 100,000 dogs in the U.S. alone, most often middle-aged female dogs. The disease results from a deficiency of glucocorticoid and/or mineralocorticoid hormone production by the adrenal cortex. In 1998 the FDA approved a new drug, desoxycorticosterone pivalate (Percorten-V), for treatment of Addison's disease in dogs. Percorten-V was the first drug approved to treat this disease in dogs.

In early 1999 the FDA also announced the approval of the first behavioral drugs for dogs, clomipramine (Clomicalm) and the combination of selegiline and L-deprenyl (Anipryl). Clomicalm was intended for use in controlling separation anxiety, which some dogs experience when separated from their owners. The anxiety may be exhibited through excessive barking, destruction of household furnishings, and inappropriate defecation.

By 1998 improved health care and nutrition had extended the life spans of dogs and cats to the extent that veterinarians were noting diseases of the "aged" with increasing frequency. Anipryl was intended for use in dogs to control clinical signs associated with age-related deterioration of the nervous system, or cognitive dysfunction syndrome (CDS). In a presentation at the American Animal Hospital Association meeting in March 1998, the occurrence of CDS was described in geriatric dogs and cats, and its similarities with Alzheimer's disease in humans were noted. Clinical signs of CDS in pets include a gradual decline in activity and interaction with owners, altered wake/sleep cycles, loss of house training, disorientation in the home environment, and compulsive behavior.

Awards to veterinarians

The 1998 Dubai Equine Award was shared by two equine virologists, Jenny Mumford of the Animal Health Trust in the U.K. and Michael Studdert of the University of Melbourne, Australia. The award, which was given at the Eighth International Conference on Equine Infectious Diseases, recognized Mumford for her research on the diagnosis and control of equine influenza and Studdert for his research on typing of the equine herpesvirus.

The World Small Animal Veterinary Association's 1998 Waltham International Award for scientific achievement was presented to Gustavo Aguirre, Caspary professor of ophthalmology at Cornell University's James A. Baker Institute for Animal Health in Ithaca, N.Y. Aguirre was recognized for his contributions to the understanding of inherited eye diseases in dogs.

—John M. Bowen
See also Feature Article: SURVIVING THE NEW MILLENNIUM.

PHYSICS

Experiments aimed at the control of light were a major focus of physics research in the past year. Scientists brought light waves essentially to a standstill in small regions of material, observed molecule-like behavior from light trapped in microscopic boxes, and created an artificial structure called a photonic crystal that selectively blocks certain wavelengths of light, analogous to the control of electrons in a transistor. Nuclear scientists used a new determination of the half-life of a radioactive isotope to improve their understanding of how elements are synthesized in exploding stars. In another highlight of the year, particle physicists working in Japan reported the most convincing evidence to date that the subatomic particle called the neutrino has mass.

ATOMIC, MOLECULAR, AND OPTICAL PHYSICS

Photonic molecules

Scientists in the past year connected a pair of microscopic boxes and injected each box with light in such a way as to make the whole arrangement act like an artificial molecule. In addition to providing a test bed for the nature of chemical bonds in naturally occurring molecules, this work may allow researchers to produce laser light in colors previously hard to obtain.

Ordinary molecules, such as oxygen molecules (O_2) in air, are made up of atoms held together by chemical bonds. In such molecules it is not possible to alter the fundamental properties of the atoms themselves or the bonds holding them together. The negatively charged electrons in each atom have well-defined energy states that cannot be changed to any desired value. Because chemical bonds are dictated by the outermost electrons in each atom, it is the energy levels of these electrons that determine the properties of the bonds.

In artificial molecules made by a German-U.S.-Russian collaboration, the particle-like quantum packets of light called photons take the place of electrons, and nanometer-scale boxes take the place of the overall atom. The "atoms" in the artificial molecules are simply blocks of gallium arsenide material with dimensions comparable to a wavelength of light, the distance between crest to crest in a light wave. (The wavelength of yellow light is about 575 nanometers, in which one nanometer is a billionth of a meter.) The shape and dimensions of each block determine the en-

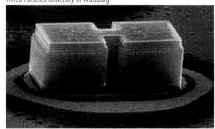

Alfred Forschel/University of Würzburg

ergies of the photons that are allowed to exist within it. The researchers called these structures photonic dots because they are similar to artificial microscopic boxes called quantum dots, which contain electrons whose energies are similarly constrained by the dimensions of the box.

Led by Alfred Forchel of the University of Würzburg, Ger., and Thomas Reinecke of the U.S. Naval Research Laboratory, the researchers first constructed an array of photonic dots. At the center of each dot was an ultrathin indium gallium arsenide layer, which served as a "quantum well." Shining light into the quantum well caused electric charges to combine and produce photons having specific energies allowed by the dimensions of the photonic dot. Finally, the researchers etched away material in the array so that pairs of photonic dots became connected by a bridge.

In isolation, the photons in each dot had specific energy levels dictated largely by the geometric conditions inside their box. Two identical photonic dots would have an identical set of allowed energy states. When the dots were connected to each other by a bridge, however, the photons then occupied a single, larger space, which constituted a different environment. The researchers noted that the photon energies were split. The photons in each dot no longer had identical energies; instead, one

Researchers created an artificial molecule fabricated of microscopic blocks of gallium arsenide material connected by a narrow bridge. Photons trapped within the structure behaved similarly to the electrons of atoms that are bonded to form a molecule.

dot's photons had a set of slightly higher energies than before, whereas those in the other dot had a slightly lower set of energies. A similar splitting occurs to the electrons in two atoms when they are connected to form a molecule.

By changing the size and shape of the dots and the length and width of the bridge, scientists can modify the nature of the "bonds" in a photonic molecule. In addition to allowing scientists to test ideas about chemical bonds, such modifications may allow researchers to create laser photons having colors—that is, energies—that are usually difficult to attain.

Localization of light

Confirming a theoretical prediction made in the 1980s, a Dutch-Italian team trapped light waves in small regions of material and managed to bring them essentially to a standstill. Controlling light in this fashion may give scientists a new way to design low-power lasers and optical memory devices.

Like a ball bearing fired into a forest full of trees, a light beam aimed at a material made of highly reflective objects follows a straight line until it ricochets from an object. The average distance that an object travels before it ricochets, or scatters, from an obstacle is known as its mean free path.

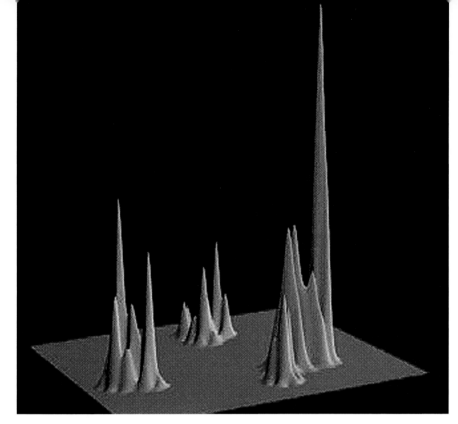

The intensity distribution for light in a material such as milk, in which the light wave has a mean free path much larger than its wavelength, is shown below. Because the peaks overlap, the light can diffuse, or escape, from the material. By contrast, in materials that restrict the mean free path to a distance comparable to the wavelength, Anderson localization can occur. The light becomes localized in separate peaks (right) and is prevented from leaving.

(Right and below) Diederik Wiersma/European Lab for Non-Linear Spectroscopy

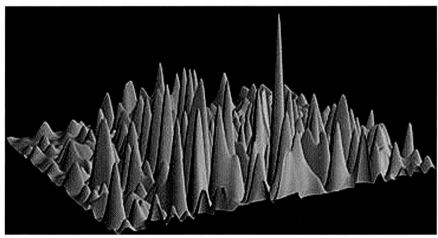

In most materials a light wave has a mean free path that is much larger than its wavelength. This is the case in milk, for example, which contains tiny particles dispersed fairly uniformly throughout the liquid. When white light (made of all visible colors added together) enters a glass of milk, all of its colors get scattered equally by the particles, and they all eventually escape, giving milk its white appearance.

If, however, light is restricted to a mean free path comparable to its wavelength, it essentially has a much greater probability of becoming trapped inside a material. This is known as Anderson localization, named after Princeton University physicist Philip Anderson, who first predicted a similar phenomenon for electrons in the late 1950s. He and Sajeev John of the University of Toronto showed independently in the 1980s that, under the right conditions, Anderson localization would also occur for light waves.

Demonstrating Anderson localization for near-visible light for the first time, Diederik S. Wiersma of the European Laboratory for Non-Linear Spectroscopy, Florence, Italy, Ad Lagendijk of the Van der Waals-Zeeman Institute of the University of Amsterdam, and their colleagues first prepared a finely ground powder of the semiconductor gallium arsenide. This material was an appropriate choice because it did not absorb the near-infrared light used in the experiment but, instead, scattered the light waves dramatically as they traveled through the material.

When light entered the gallium arsenide powder, a given light wave had a relatively high probability of following a closed path, by which it would return to a point that it had traversed earlier. In turn, there was also a relatively high probability for another light wave to be traveling the same closed path but in the opposite direction. The combination, or interference, of the two waves following opposite paths resulted in a phenomenon known as a standing wave, in which the position of the peaks of the waves did not travel but stayed fixed.

Standing waves occur widely in nature and everyday life. For example, if a person ties one end of a rope to a wall and then shakes the rope, the action produces a wave traveling toward the wall and a second wave reflected from the wall. When the original wave combines with its reflection, a standing wave can form.

Similarly, the standing wave of light remained fixed inside the gallium arsenide powder; it did not escape. Moreover, because of the powder's gallium arsenide composition, the light was not absorbed.

In addition to providing a striking demonstration, Anderson localization of light waves may prove applicable to the creation of many new types of optical devices. Moreover, the powders used in the experiments are easier to fashion into useful devices than the inflexible crystals that are often employed for optical devices.

When molecules collide

Many chemical reactions result from high-energy collisions between a molecule and another chemical species. Advancing the studies of such reactions, researchers demonstrated a tool for viewing collisions between a single molecule and a target atom. With the new tool, they could determine the way in which the alignment of a single molecule with respect to its target influences the outcome of a collision between the two.

Their advance follows from a decade of work by researchers in Germany and the U.S. to develop a new technique called COLTRIMS (cold target recoil ion momentum spectroscopy). In the technique, the researchers collide a photon or an ion (an electrically charged atom or molecule) with a low-temperature supersonic jet of target atoms or molecules. The products of the collision are then collected in a weak electric field, which directs them to time- and position-sensitive detectors. By recording the positions of the particles and the times that they take to fly to the detectors, the researchers can determine the momen-

tum—mass multiplied by velocity—of each collision product. With these momentum values, they then can reconstruct the details of the collision itself.

Whereas previous COLTRIMS experiments had explored the breakup processes involving photons or single-atom ions colliding with cold atoms, researchers at Lawrence Berkeley National Laboratory, Kansas State University, and the University of Frankfurt, Ger., extended the technique to studies of molecules colliding with atoms. In their experiment, a beam of helium hydride ions (HeH^+) struck a cold helium gas jet. During the collision, the HeH^+ captured an electron from a helium target atom. This turned the helium atom into an He^+ ion, which recoiled from the collision. In addition, it transformed the HeH^+ ion into a neutral HeH molecule, which, being unstable, rapidly broke up into hydrogen and helium atoms. These neutral fragments from the HeH molecule traveled on to their own time- and position-sensitive detectors where each impact was recorded. While they were doing so, the slower He^+ ion was collected, and its momentum components likewise were measured using the COLTRIMS technique. Thus the motion of each of the three products—the He^+ recoil ion from the target and the He and H from the neutralized HeH^+ molecule—was recorded for every collision.

From an analysis of their data, the researchers deduced that the collision was most likely to produce neutral HeH in its lowest-energy (ground) state when the long axis of the HeH^+ ion approaching the He target was oriented perpendicular to the plane formed by the direction of the incoming beam and the direction of the scattered HeH product. In subsequent studies,

the researchers determined that the likelihood for HeH^+ to ensnare an electron successfully during the collision depended strongly on which end (He or H) was facing the He target as it approached.

In addition to this example, physicists believed that COLTRIMS, combined with the ability to image single molecular fragments produced in a collision, will serve as a valuable tool for addressing many outstanding questions about breakup processes and high-energy chemical reactions at the molecular scale.

Triple photoionization of lithium

A Japanese-U.S. collaboration produced and detected a very rare process known as triple photoionization, in which a single colliding photon removes three electrons from an atom. In their experiment they observed this process for the very first time in lithium, the third lightest atom, which only has three electrons. Further studies of this process in the relatively simple lithium atom promises to offer clear-cut insights into the interplay between trios of charged particles in many environments such as stars.

At the Photon Factory, a synchrotron radiation facility in Tsukuba, Japan, a very bright beam of photons in the extreme ultraviolet (EUV) range encountered a beam of lithium atoms. A detector then recorded triple photoionization events by collecting lithium ions having an electrical charge of +3, an indicator that all three electrons of lithium had been removed. The researchers found that triple photoionization was about 17,000 times less likely to occur than single ionization, in which only one electron is removed by a photon. Nonetheless, the

The Photon Factory, a synchrotron radiation facility in Tsukuba, Japan, is shown in an aerial view. A bright beam of extreme ultraviolet light supplied by the facility was used to create a very rare process called triple photoionization in the element lithium.

Institute of Matls Structure Science-KEK

very intense beam of photons caused enough triple photoionization events to occur, and the use of very efficient, low-noise detectors in the experiment made it possible to observe the process.

In the most simplified picture of the process, an EUV photon deposits all of its energy into one of the lithium atom's electrons, which then shares its energy with the other two. Nevertheless, physicists still do not fully understand the cooperative behavior that ensues among the three electrons, enabling them all to leave the atom. Because the triple photoionization process occurred more frequently than estimated by theory, new theoretical developments are needed to accommodate the observations.

Studying triple photoionization in lithium is one of the best ways of elucidating how the three electrons interact in the absence of outside disturbances, since the photon disappears after striking the atom, removing itself from the scene. Triple photoionization has been observed before in heavier atoms, such as neon, but those processes are typically more difficult to analyze because they involve complicated rearrangements of other electrons in the atom. Lithium, on the other hand, is the most straightforward system in which this process can occur.

Awards

In 1998 the Frederick Ives Medal/Quinn Endowment, the highest award of the Optical Society of America, went to Arthur Ashkin, a 40-year veteran of Bell Laboratories (now part of Lucent Technologies) for "his pioneering work on the manipulation of particles with light." During his time at Bell Labs from 1952 to 1992, Ashkin invented or co-invented many tools and techniques—for example, "optical tweezers," in which lasers are used to trap and manipulate molecular-sized objects such as single DNA molecules and muscle proteins.

Mark G. Raizen of the University of Texas at Austin won the American Physical Society's 1999 I.I. Rabi Prize in Atomic, Molecular, and Optical Physics. Studying the border between quantum and classical physics, Raizen investigated how atoms—like all particles that obey the rules of quantum mechanics—display wavelike interference effects that often suppress the kind of chaotic behavior that appears in macroscopic, everyday systems. (An example of the latter is a collection of colliding billiard balls, which follow trajectories that can quickly become unpredictable even though their equations of motion are perfectly known.)

—Ben P. Stein

ELEMENTARY-PARTICLE PHYSICS

Over the past decade, physicists have become increasingly confident of the validity of the standard model of elementary particles. In the standard model, all matter is composed of elementary particles called quarks and leptons. Those particles interact through fundamental interactions, or forces—the strong interaction (experienced between quarks, but not by leptons) and the electroweak interaction, a unified interpretation of the electromagnetic and weak interactions. The fundamental interactions are understood in quantum field theory to be mediated—that is, carried—by field quanta. The most familiar field quantum is the photon, the carrier of the electromagnetic interaction. Radiation of photons by oscillating electric charges or currents constitutes light, radio waves, X-rays, and other forms of electromagnetic radiation. The quanta of the weak interaction are the W and Z intermediate vector bosons, particles having large rest masses (more than 80 times that of the proton). When produced as physical objects, the intermediate vector bosons spontaneously decay. The quantum of the strong interaction is the gluon, which, like the photon, is massless. Conspicuous by its absence from the standard model is the force of gravity. Although weaker by far than the other fundamental interactions, gravity affects all particles with mass and must be part of any totally comprehensive theory.

The quarks and leptons comprise three generations, with each generation containing four particles: a quark of electrical charge $+^2/_3 e$ (in which e is the magnitude of the electrical charge of an electron), a quark of charge $-^1/_3 e$, a charged lepton with a charge of $-1e$, and a neutral neu-trino. Thus, there are three quarks with charge $+^2/_3 e$ (named the up, charm, and top [or truth] quarks); three quarks with charge $-^1/_3 e$ (the down, strange, and bottom [or beauty] quarks); three charged leptons (the electron, the mu meson [or muon], and the tau lepton); and three neutral leptons, the three neutrinos (the electron, muon, and tau neutrinos). Familiar matter, of which virtually the entire universe is comprised, is made up of only the first-generation particles—the up and down quarks (the constituents of protons and neutrons) and the electron. The other, heavier quarks and charged leptons spontaneously decay, ultimately, into these first-generation particles through the weak interaction. For each of these particles, there is a corresponding antiparticle—a particle with the same mass but opposite electric charge and the opposite quantum property of "lepton number" or "baryon number."

Neutrino masses

The most important new result in elementary-particle physics in 1998 was the observation by a Japanese-U.S. collaboration, using a new detector facility in Japan, of the strongest evidence to date for a finite (nonzero) rest mass for neutrinos. Previous research had set upper limits on the masses of neutrinos. For example, the rest mass of the electron neutrino was determined to be less than about a millionth of the mass of an electron, and theoretical physicists had felt that the rest mass could indeed be zero, like that of the photon. Because neutrinos interact so very weakly with other matter, direct experiments with them have been extremely difficult, and their study has progressed slowly.

Each of the three types, or flavors, of neutrinos is closely associated with the production of its charged lepton namesake. For example, in some cases the process of beta decay—the radioactive decay of nuclei—produces an electron neutrino together with an anti-electron, or positron; in other cases it produces an electron antineutrino and an electron. If, however, neutrinos have a finite rest mass, their flavor states may not correspond unequivocally to specific mass states. Rather, physicists theorize that every neutrino has some share in

Model of Elementary Particles

three generations of matter (fermions)			force carriers (gauge bosons)	
I	II	III		

key R = red G = green B = blue

electric charge	color charge
symbol	
name	
mass	

	I	II	III		
quarks	$+^2/_3$ · · · R,G,B *u* up 2–8 MeV	$+^2/_3$ · · · R,G,B *c* charm 1–1.6 GeV	$+^2/_3$ · · · R,G,B *t* top/truth 176±6 GeV	0 · · · 0 γ photon 0	electromagnetism
	$-^1/_3$ · · · R,G,B *d* down 5–15 MeV	$-^1/_3$ · · · R,G,B *s* strange 100–300 MeV	$-^1/_3$ · · · R,G,B *b* bottom/beauty 4.1–4.5 GeV	0 · · · R,G,B *g* gluon 0	strong interaction
leptons	0 · · · 0 ν*e* electron neutrino less than 7 eV	0 · · · 0 νμ muon neutrino less than 170 keV	0 · · · 0 ντ tau neutrino less than 31 MeV	±1 · · · 0 W$^\pm$ W boson 80.400±0.075 GeV	weak interactions
	−1 · · · 0 *e* electron 0.511 MeV	−1 · · · 0 μ muon 105.658 MeV	−1 · · · 0 τ tau less than 24 MeV	0 · · · 0 z^0 Z boson 91.187 GeV	

The known elementary particles can be grouped into a "periodic table" of quarks, leptons, and the force carriers (field quanta or gauge bosons) that mediate the basic interactions between particles. Quarks and leptons form three generations, each containing two quarks, a neutral neutrino, and a charged lepton.

the three generations, with each flavor an admixture of the three mass states and each mass state an admixture of the three flavors. Moreover, as a neutrino propagates through space, these states shift phases relative to each other such that the initial flavor of a neutrino may change.

In the case of the production and nuclear-interaction processes of neutrinos, the specific flavor states are the critical parameters. For example, the nuclear processes by which the Sun "burns" hydrogen to form helium produce only electron neutrinos, whereas the decay of pi mesons (or pions, produced in the interaction of energetic cosmic-ray protons in Earth's upper atmosphere) produces only muon neutrinos (and muon antineutrinos) together with negative (and positive) muons.

On the other hand, in the case of the propagation of neutrinos through space, the mass states of the neutrinos are the relevant parameters. If an electron neutrino emitted from the Sun is an admixture of mass states, it may arrive at Earth with those mass states in a different phase combination than when it started and thus may now be a muon neutrino or a tau neutrino. Physicists refer to this identity-changing process as neutrino mixing or neutrino oscillation—the latter term because, over a sufficient propagation distance, the relative phases of the mass states could shift through one or more full cycles to reconstitute the electron neutrino.

The Super-Kamiokande result

During the 1980s physicists built a large experimental detector facility, called Kamiokande, in a zinc mine near the Japanese village of Kamioka to look for

Technicians on a rubber raft inspect the interior of the Super-Kamiokande detector tank during water-filling operations. Some of the 13,000 photomultiplier tubes are seen lining the tank wall. Ultimately, 50,000 tons of ultrapure water were needed for complete filling.

(Above and opposite page) Institute for Cosmic Ray Research/The University of Tokyo

evidence of the spontaneous decay of the proton. Although the experiment failed to detect proton decay, it was able to detect the interaction of neutrinos coming from the Sun. In order to further these proton-decay and neutrino studies, researchers built a larger detector called Super-Kamiokande. It is, in essence, a huge tank filled with 50,000 tons of water and lined with 13,000 photomultiplier tubes. The photomultiplier tubes are designed to detect so-called Cherenkov radiation—light given off by high-energy (high-velocity) charged particles moving through the water at velocities greater than the velocity of light in water.

The result that excited the physics world in 1998 came from the study of muon neutrinos emerging from the decay of cosmic-ray–produced pions in the atmosphere. In the Super-Kamiokande detector, an incoming muon neutrino interacts with an atomic nucleus within a water molecule or the surrounding rock to produce a muon. The muon travels in almost the same direction as the incident neutrino while giving off Cherenkov radiation, thus signaling both the presence and the direction of the neutrino. In observing muon neutrinos in this way, the Super-Kamiokande researchers found that the rate of detection depended on the distance through the Earth that the neutrinos traveled to the detector. Specifically, the detection rate was significantly lower for neutrinos coming upward through the Earth than for neutrinos coming downward. Because the probability is very small that a neutrino will interact with matter in its passage through Earth, the result strongly suggested that some of the muon neutrinos had oscillated to other flavors. Super-Kamiokande also observed electron neutrino interactions but found their rate of detection to be the same in all

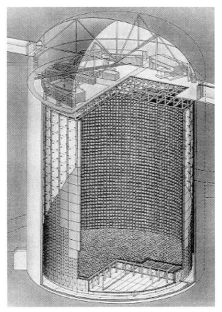

A schematic of the immense Super-Kamiokande tank is shown above. At right, workers prepare to install individual photomultiplier tubes, which are designed to detect light, called Cherenkov radiation, given off by high-energy charged particles moving through the water in the tank.

directions. This suggested that the shortfall in the Earth-traversing muon neutrinos was due primarily to their oscillation to tau neutrinos rather than to electron neutrinos.

The Super-Kamiokande result was the strongest evidence to date for neutrino mass and the latest finding in what has been a lively field of experimentation. For many years several different experiments have reported an apparent shortage of electron neutrinos coming from the Sun compared with theoretical expectations. Although neutrino oscillations were strongly suggested as the reason for the deficit, it could not be excluded that physicists' understanding of the interior dynamics of the Sun, and hence the prediction of the neutrino flux, was in error. In the mid-1990s a particle-accelerator–based experiment at the Los Alamos National Laboratory in New Mexico observed signs of transformation from muon neutrinos to electron neutrinos, providing yet another line of evidence for neutrino oscillations.

Theorists have found it difficult to reconcile the results of these different kinds of experiments with the known set of parameters—the three neutrino masses and their couplings to the three flavors. Some have suggested the existence of a fourth, "sterile" neutrino that so far has escaped detection. Although the sterile-neutrino concept would introduce enough new parameters to make all the experimental results compatible, it is aesthetically unattractive to many physicists.

Many experiments with neutrinos at reactors and at particle accelerators have been conducted since the first experimental detection of electron neutrinos by the American physicists Frederick Reines (*see* SCIENTISTS OF THE YEAR: *Obituaries*) and Clyde Cowan at a nuclear reactor in the 1950s. Not surprisingly, a large number of new experiments are being planned around the world to extend the study of neutrino phenomena. In three cases, at the KEK laboratory in Japan, CERN in Switzerland, and the Fermi National Accelerator Laboratory (Fermilab) in the U.S., there are plans to produce a muon neutrino beam from a proton accelerator and direct it

through the Earth over distances greater than 700 km (430 mi) to a neutrino detector. Other experiments are planned at Fermilab to repeat the Los Alamos experiment, and still others in France and California are aimed at studying electron neutrinos—and seeking evidence for oscillations—from nuclear reactors.

CP nonconservation and B mesons

Neutrino physics is not the first place in which particle physicists have encountered oscillation, or mixing, phenomena. A much better understood situation involves the neutral K meson (or kaon). This particle is composed of a down quark and a strange antiquark; its antiparticle is composed of down antiquark and a strange quark. Although produced as pure states of either one or the other of these particles, the kaons' flavor states mix, or oscillate, in their propagation through space. Kaons have different ways of decaying into other particles—pions, muons, electrons, and neutrinos. These decay states, however, do not correspond to either of the neutral kaons described above but to admixtures of both, in analogy with the neutrino mass states. In order to understand these decays, it is necessary that both the conservation of parity (the left-right symmetry of the laws of physics) and charge symmetry (the symmetry of the laws governing the interchange of a particle and its antiparticle) be violated—a circumstance known as CP nonconservation. Although much has been learned about the parameters describing the complex neutral kaon system and its decays, further study of the systematics and parameters of CP nonconservation remains a major focus of experimental programs at the large particle accelerators.

Until recently, the kaon system was the only known example of CP nonconservation observed in particle physics. In 1998, however, the B-meson system, the corresponding neutral meson system composed of heavier quarks, showed evidence (as was theoretically expected) of similar oscillations in experiments at the CERN Large Electron-Positron accelerator facility and at the Stanford Linear Accelerator Center in California. The B mesons are composed of a down quark and a bottom antiquark or a down antiquark and a bottom quark. New facilities were being built at Stanford, at the KEK laboratory, and at Cornell University, Ithaca, N.Y., to explicitly study CP-violating interactions in the B-meson system.

Antimatter

One specific reason for seeking a better understanding of CP nonconservation is the apparent asymmetry of matter and antimatter in the universe. All big bang models of the beginning of the universe presume that equal quantities of matter and antimatter were formed as the universe cooled and the present-day elementary particles condensed out. (Antimatter, when brought together with matter, results in the annihilation of both, ultimately leaving only electromagnetic energy and neutrinos.) Nevertheless, as well as scientists can observe, the universe is made of matter. Excellent upper limits have been placed on the existence of antimatter by observations of cosmic ray particles and cosmic gamma rays and by other astronomical measurements. In 1998 a major new space experiment seeking to extend these limits was being prepared for flight on the future

International Space Station (see Feature Article: THE INTERNATIONAL SPACE STATION) by an international team headed by Samuel C.C. Ting of the Massachusetts Institute of Technology.

One possibility for explaining this apparent lack of antimatter in the universe would be the spontaneous decay of antiprotons and antineutrons, with a lifetime shorter than the present age of the universe (12 billion–15 billion years), through CP-nonconserving processes. An experimental lower limit has been placed on the antiproton decay lifetime of the order of a million years, much too short to be definitive for this problem. The lifetime of the proton, as determined from Kamiokande measurements and an experiment in the U.S., is at least 10^{32} years, many orders of magnitude greater than the age of the universe. The hope is that a more complete understanding of the role of CP nonconservation in the kaon and B-meson systems might lead to a better understanding of matter-antimatter asymmetry as well as the specific particle physics phenomena.

—Lawrence W. Jones

NUCLEAR PHYSICS

Measuring a radioactive half-life

The violent explosions of stars, called supernovas, produce and distribute all the heavier elements in the universe. The details of this process, however, are still not well understood. One clue to the dynamics is the abundances of the various radioactive elements produced. Earth-orbiting space telescopes have detected gamma rays from a number of short-lived ra-

Samples of titanium-44 were prepared at a heavy-ion accelerator (above) at Michigan State University in an improved determination of the half-life of the radioactive isotope. This study and three others agreed that the isotope has a half-life of 59 years, give or take a year.

dioactive isotopes produced by supernovas. One of the isotopes is titanium-44, whose gamma rays have been observed from the supernova remnant Cassiopeia A. Several models of the supernova process have been developed over the years, each one predicting the formation of a different amount of ^{44}Ti. If the amounts could be measured, it would be easier to decide which models are more realistic and hence closer to providing the full explanation of the explosive process.

The supernova remnant known as Cassiopeia A was produced from a star that exploded in 1680, and all but a small fraction of its radioactivity has died away. To deduce how much ^{44}Ti was present initially, an accurate determination of its half-life is needed. Previous experiments had

bracketed this isotope's half-life in the range of 40–60 years, which was not accurate enough to deduce the initial abundance of ^{44}Ti. Consequently, it had not been possible to say which theoretical model was better.

During the past year, four separate laboratories carried out improved experiments to measure the half-life of ^{44}Ti. Measuring a radioactive half-life of a few days is relatively easy, but for half-lives of many years the process is surprisingly difficult. Waiting many years for the radioactivity to diminish substantially is just not practical. Moreover, long-term drifts in a detector's sensitivity make it difficult to compare data taken years apart. To overcome this problem, all the research groups followed a similar strategy—they prepared radioac-

tive sources using two different isotopes, one using the ^{44}Ti to be measured, and another using an isotope with a known half-life. By comparing the decay rates of the sources, the effects of an uncertain detector sensitivity could be separated out.

One group, led by researchers at the University of Notre Dame, made the radioactive samples using the heavy-ion accelerator at Michigan State University, East Lansing. This accelerator is capable not only of producing the isotopes by colliding large nuclei but also of separating out the desired isotopes and depositing them in measured amounts on collection foils, allowing the ratio of ^{44}Ti to the other isotope to be determined with high precision. The relative radioactivity levels were used to infer half-life; the higher the radioactivity level of the atoms collected, the shorter their half-life.

The other three research groups used sources prepared several years earlier in the heavy-ion accelerator at Argonne (Ill.) National Laboratory. The source preparation was similar to the one used by the first group, but a different calibration isotope was included on the foil. The relative numbers of the two isotopes were not required. Instead, the scientists measured the decrease of radioactivity over a three-year period. Although the level of ^{44}Ti radioactivity diminished by only a small amount, it was measured accurately by comparing it with the known isotope's rate of decay.

All of the experiments agreed that ^{44}Ti has a half-life of 59 years, give or take a year. The mass of the ejected ^{44}Ti from Cassiopeia A, inferred from the half-life measurement and expressed as a percentage of the mass of the Sun, was 0.02%. The mass measurement disagreed with one

Max Planck Institut Fur Physik und Astrophysik/Science Photo Library/ Photo Researchers, Inc.

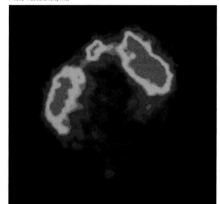

The new half-life value of titanium-44 allowed researchers to estimate the mass of the isotope ejected from the exploding star that formed Cassiopeia A (above). The result disagreed with one supernova model but supported another.

supernova model, which treated the supernova's explosion as a piston acting on the outer envelope of the star to create the isotopes. On the other hand, the value did agree with predictions of a less-simplistic model, which had previously been used to explain the production rate of another radioactive isotope, nickel-56. The consistency between the two isotopes demonstrated that the basic nucleosynthesis processes that occur in the envelope explosion are probably adequately understood, even if the driving forces of the explosion itself may not be.

Short-range correlations in a nucleus

Paradoxically, although the nuclear force in an atom is very strong, its strength is normally hidden from view within nuclei. Scientists' basic understanding of nuclear properties comes from the shell model of the nucleus, in which individual nucleons (the constituent protons and neutrons of the nucleus) travel freely through the nucleus without colliding with other nucleons. An experiment reported in 1998 provided convincing evidence that the force between nucleons in a nucleus remains strong, producing what are called short-range correlations.

The nucleons in the nucleus carry momentum, and these momenta are affected when two nucleons move close together. Each nucleon "feels" the other's strong force and briefly recoils from it. The recoil gives both nucleons high momenta for the small fraction of time that they are close together. According to the law of conservation of momentum, the two momenta should be equal and opposite in direction. An important part of the experiment, then, was to observe pairs of nucleons in the nucleus and to see whether they can be present with large equal and opposite momenta. In order to measure the momenta of the nucleons, the particles had to be taken out of the nucleus. This was accomplished by bombarding nuclei with high-energy electrons. In some of the resulting collisions, electrons transferred energy and momentum to the nucleons, which then escaped. During the experiment the scientists measured the energy and momentum of the scattered electrons and looked for accompanying pairs of nucleons with high momentum.

Although two nucleons may be seen emerging from a nucleus with high momentum, it does not necessarily mean that they started with the short-range correlation. Nucleons can gain energy and momentum in other ways. For instance, if an electron hits a nucleon, the nucleon could recoil and hit another nucleon, sharing momentum and energy with it. The process is just like a billiard ball hitting another ball and passing on some of its momentum and energy. In this case, however, both balls would have some component of momentum in the direction of the original momentum. Because it is impossible to start with one moving ball and one stationary ball and end up with both balls moving in opposite directions, the ejected nucleons' direction of motion was the key to proving the existence of the short-range correlations.

The experiment was conducted by a team of researchers led by Gerco Onderwater of the National Institute for Nuclear and High-Energy Physics in The Netherlands. Using a beam of 584-MeV (million-electron-volt) electrons, the experimenters bombarded a target containing oxygen, which is mostly the isotope oxygen-16. They collected events in which the electron scattered with a large loss of en-

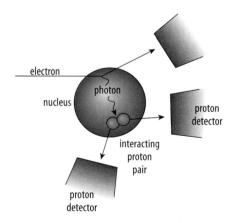

In recent studies of nuclear short-range correlations, physicists looked for events in which a high-energy electron scattering from a nucleus resulted in the ejection of two protons with high equal and opposite momenta.

ergy and momentum and two protons were simultaneously ejected, leaving a nucleus of carbon-14. To minimize the disturbing effects of multiple collisions that deflect the protons, the scientists focused on those events in which the ^{14}C remainder was left with little or no excitation energy. With this criterion included, the proton-emission directions showed the signature of short-range correlations, favoring emission in opposite directions. The behavior was particularly clear for those events in which the ^{14}C ended up in its ground state with no excitation energy at all. After the momentum imparted by the electrons was subtracted, the sum of the two proton momenta was found to be very small, even though individual momenta were substantial. This implied that the two protons started out with large equal and opposite momenta.

The quantitative interpretation of the experiment used theoretical calculations to compute the momentum distribution of the protons. The theory had to treat both the short-range strong force between the two protons and the somewhat milder forces associated with the rest of the nucleus, which hold protons in their shell-model orbits. Using current knowledge about the nucleon-nucleon force and the shell-model orbits in carbon-12, the theory explained the data quite well. One can conclude that the strong force is present and that present-day theoretical techniques can describe its effects.

Magnetic bands

Spectroscopic bands—groups of photons of closely spaced frequency—are a prominent feature not only in molecular spectroscopy but also in nuclear spectroscopy.

Photons are produced by oscillating electric charge and currents, and their character depends on the shape and conformation of the source. The most common emission in molecular physics is called dipole radiation, which is produced when the charge center in a molecule moves back and forth or is off center in a rotating object. The very energetic photons that make up nuclear gamma radiation also can be classified in a similar way.

Since the charge in nuclei is normally quite evenly distributed, dipole bands are extremely rare. Most bands seen in nuclei arise from the rotations of deformed nuclei. For instance, the rotation of a football-shaped charge distribution gives rise to an emission pattern called quadrupole radiation. Quadrupole bands have been known for a long time and are common in nuclei in mass ranges that are far away in mass from the most stable, spherical nuclei (those having so-called magic numbers of protons or neutrons). Recently, however, investigators found bands that have a completely different character from the well-known electric dipole or quadrupole bands. They were first observed in isotopes of lead, and in 1998 they were found in tin isotopes as well. Both of these nuclei have a magic number of protons.

To study magnetic bands, a nucleus is created and given a high rotational velocity. This can be done together by producing the nuclei in a heavy-ion accelerator, where collisions between smaller nuclei caused them to fuse together. Since the collisions are mostly off center, the combined system is formed with a high spin. In the case of the 1998 experiments on tin

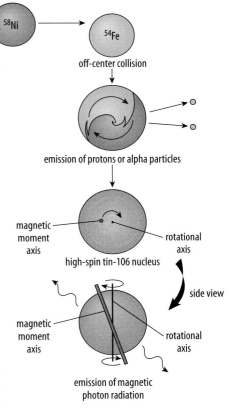

In the tilted-axis cranking model, the emission of magnetic photon radiation observed from high-spin tin-106 nuclei is explained by assuming that the axis of the magnetic moment of the nucleus is not aligned with its rotational axis. As the nucleus rotates, the magnetic field fluctuates, resulting in photon emission.

isotopes, the accelerator bombarded iron-54 nuclei with nickel-58 nuclei. The two nuclei fused together, emitting several protons or alpha particles to become a tin isotope. Bombarding energy was carefully selected so that the tin nucleus stopped emitting particles at that point, although it still had enough energy to emit gamma rays. The gamma rays from the band were difficult to distinguish from background radiations produced by other reactions taking place at the same time. This problem was solved by means of a large array of high-precision detectors placed around the target. With many detectors, the experimenters were able to record the cascade of gamma rays within the band as well as other gamma rays characteristic of the individual isotopes, allowing them to suppress the background of gamma rays coming from competing reactions. They found a band of photons in tin-106 with half the frequency of the normal quadrupole band as well as a different distribution of gamma rays. Its gamma rays, in fact, seemed to arise from an oscillating magnetic moment rather than an oscillating charge.

When this phenomenon was first observed in lead isotopes, it was quite unexpected. The nucleons in a nucleus, like the electrons in a superconductor, like to be paired together with opposite momentum and spin orientations. This configuration has no net magnetic moment; in fact, nuclei with even numbers of protons and neutrons are not magnetic in their ground states. At high excitation energy, however, the nucleons can uncouple from each other—this is apparently how the magnetic moment arises. The mere existence of a magnetic moment, however, is not enough to get magnetic photon radiation. The moment must oscillate in some way, with the frequency of oscillation corresponding to the photon frequency.

Exactly where in the magnetic band the magnetic oscillation comes from remains unclear. One possibility is that the rotational axis is not aligned with the axis of the magnetic moment. If that occurs, the magnetic poles are off center, and the magnetic field fluctuates as the nucleus rotates. One theory, called the tilted-axis cranking model, explains the bands in this way. Whereas the measured strength of the magnetic band turned out to be much larger than calculated from the tilted-axis theory, the theory was successful in predicting that the effect would be observed in tin isotopes.   —George F. Bertsch

CONDENSED-MATTER PHYSICS

A molecular pencil

Over the past 50 years, the never-ending demand for smaller and faster computing devices has motivated a great deal of fundamental research in condensed-matter physics. In 1998 important breakthroughs occurred in this ongoing quest for the small and the fast. Two of them involved the carbon nanotube, a carbon molecule that forms in the shape of a hollow tube. Discovered in 1991, carbon nanotubes are the only molecules known to assume such a shape and are the thinnest tubular structures known, with outer diameters of the order of a nanometer (nm; one billionth of a meter). A carbon nanotube's wall may be as thin as a single atom of carbon, in which case the molecule is referred to as single-walled, or it may be multiwalled, consisting of several layers. Both types conduct electricity and exhibit either metallic or semiconducting behavior, depending on the precise arrangement of carbon atoms.

Despite their Lilliputian dimensions, carbon nanotubes are extremely strong and durable. In 1998 Hongjie Dai and Nathan Franklin of Stanford University, together with Jie Han of the NASA Ames Research Center, Moffett Field, Calif., took advantage of the remarkable properties of carbon nanotubes by demonstrating that the molecules can be used as amazingly durable pencils. Lithography is the art of inscribing patterns on a flat plate. It is central to the manufacture of all electronic devices, silicon being the plate material of chief interest.

Researchers used a carbon nanotube "pencil" and techniques developed for the scanning tunneling microscope to write on the surface of a silicon crystal in lines only 10 nanometers wide. Scale units are in micrometers.

American Institute of Physics

In lithographic terms, the quest for the small and the fast has translated into the search for a pencil that can draw ultrafine patterns on silicon.

A benchmark lithographic task is to write a line of silicon oxide, an insulator, on the surface of a silicon crystal. Silicon oxidizes spontaneously when exposed to oxygen. Hence, if an oxide line is to remain distinct in the presence of air, the silicon surface must be given a protective layer. It is convenient to do this prior to writing—by doping, or passivating, the entire surface with a thin layer of hydrogen. Since unprotected regions oxidize in air, writing can be done by selectively removing hydrogen atoms. In the early 1990s it was discovered that hydrogen removal can be accomplished with a sharp metallic tip positioned above the passivated surface. Because such a tip can be just a few atoms wide, a small voltage applied between it and the silicon produces a large electric field—comparable to that experienced by an electron orbiting the nucleus of an atom. The hydrogen atoms lying directly under the tip are pulled right off the surface, forming a tiny hydrogen-deprived region. Fine oxide lines can be drawn in this manner simply by scanning the tip across the surface.

Unfortunately, tips made of metal wear out rather rapidly. Wear is caused by mechanical forces between the tip and the surface, as well as by the electric fields required to remove the hydrogen. The Stanford and NASA scientists showed that carbon nanotubes of the conducting multiwalled variety also can be used to "write" on a silicon substrate, and without the wear. They obtained their best results with nanotubes that had their ends "capped" with a dome of carbon atoms. When one uses an ordinary pencil, carbon atoms are deposited on the paper. By contrast, the capped-tube molecular pencil never needs sharpening because it never loses carbon atoms, even when dragged directly over a passivated surface. The researchers wrote words whose individual letters were made of lines only 10 nm wide. By means of scanning techniques developed for the scanning tunneling microscope, the writing was done at speeds of the order of a millimeter (0.04 in) per second.

A conventional pencil draws a line when it is dragged over the writing surface. When a nanotube pencil is used in this manner, the letters are rounded where the line changes direction. The researchers concluded that nanotubes suffer a significant amount of bending when used this way. To eliminate the effect, the scientists used an ingenious refinement of the conventional

The molecular structure of a single-walled carbon nanotube, capped on the end, is depicted in a computer model. Each vertex in the structure represents a carbon atom.

approach. As it was scanned, the nanotube was also vibrated up and down, with the domed tip of the pencil spending most of its time well above the surface. This allowed it to contact the material in a sequence of brief taps, eliminating the bending problem. The tap marks were not isolated from each other, however; the high oscillation frequency of the pencil caused the marks to overlap, forming a continuous line.

The surface of any real silicon crystal contains irregularities. Strong as it is, even a nanotube will break if it encounters a large obstacle. Breakage was avoided by using sophisticated feedback techniques. Like a low-flying missile, the nanotube sensed the terrain underneath and adjusted its height so as to avoid running into the microscopic obstacles. Although a number of problems must be overcome in applying the molecular carbon pencil to mass production, nanotube lithography represents an exciting landmark in the ancient art of writing.

A molecular transistor

The idea of building an electronic device from a single molecule was first proposed in the 1970s. Converting this dream into reality has proved to be a daunting task. Not the least of the challenges has been the difficulty of making electrical contact to a molecule. In 1998 researchers at Delft University of Technology, The Netherlands, used a carbon nanotube to demonstrate the first working room-temperature electronic device constructed from a single molecule. Since its operation closely resembles that of a field-effect transistor (FET), researchers Sander Tans, Alwin Verschueren, and Cees Dekker gave it the name TUBE-FET. The basic characteristic of a FET is that the current flowing through it can be switched off by the application of a voltage, termed a gate voltage.

To make their TUBEFET, the researchers deposited two platinum electrodes onto a thin, insulating layer of silicon oxide on a silicon substrate. A nanotube was then laid across these electrodes—like a bridge between two footings—making electrical contact with them. Current was passed along the molecule by applying a voltage between the electrodes. The controlling gate voltage was applied between the silicon substrate and the nanotube. The researchers found that gate voltages on the order of a few volts were sufficient to change the nanotube from its natural state—a semiconductor—into an insulator. In the insulating state, the current flow was completely switched off; that is, the TUBEFET achieved classic transistor switching action via modification of the electrical properties of a single molecule.

Fabrication of the transistors turned out to be relatively straightforward, encouraging the hope that integration of many devices into a circuit—using molecular self-assembly techniques—might prove possible. One significant problem is that the nanotube used in fabrication must be semiconducting for the device to work.

American Institute of Physics

Physicists built the first working room-temperature electronic device made from a single molecule. It comprised a nanotube laid across a pair of platinum electrodes that were deposited on a silicon substrate. A voltage between the nanotube and the substrate controlled current flow through the nanotube.

Even a small deviation from the optimum tube diameter is known to result in a metallic tube—and no transistor action. At present, it is impossible to produce semiconducting carbon nanotubes in a controlled manner.

Controlling the motion of photons

The fundamental limits for semiconductor-based electronics are rapidly being approached. Faced with this fact, researchers have been turning their attention to the possibility of processing digital information using light. Unlike the electron, the quantum of light—the photon—has neither mass nor charge. It therefore provides an ideally simple vehicle for moving digital information from one location to another. Indeed, photons are already in extensive use for the transmission of data by means of optical fibers. In building active photon devices, however, it is not sufficient simply to move photons from place to place. One must also achieve a fine control over their movement inside real materials.

One reason for the dominance of electron-based computing devices is that the motion of electrons is relatively easy to control. Indeed, in an important sense, semiconducting materials perform this feat themselves—with no assistance from condensed-matter physicists. Inside a semiconductor, electrons with a certain range of energies move around freely, whereas the motion of electrons with energies lying outside that range is blocked. The selective blockage of electron motion is fundamental to the operation of the transistor. Researchers have long sought materials that could exert an analogous control over the motion of photons. Their goal was to block—that is, reflect—photons of certain wavelengths, while transmitting others. The wavelength used for optical-fiber data transmission is about a micrometer (one millionth of a meter), in the infrared portion of the spectrum. Unfortunately, no naturally occurring materials selectively reflect such photons. Research effort has therefore been focused on artificial structures.

After a decade-long quest, photon control was demonstrated in 1998 by James Fleming and Shawn-Yu Lin of Sandia National Laboratories, Albuquerque, N.M., with specially engineered microstructures christened photonic crystals. The idea behind photonic crystals rests on the same phenomenon that is responsible for the color of objects as diverse as a compact disc and a butterfly wing. Both objects are colored, but the colors are not produced by light-absorbing paint or dyes. Rather, they arise from periodic structures whose repeat distance is comparable to the wavelength of light. The phenomenon of wave interference ensures that wavelengths that match this structural periodicity are selec-

A photonic crystal that selectively reflects infrared photons in the wavelength range of 1.5 micrometers was constructed from an array of stacked polysilicon bars, each of the order of 0.1 micrometer in width. The lattice reflected as much as 99% of the light that fell on it.

tively reflected, producing the color perceived by the eye.

In a similar way, the Sandia scientists' photonic crystal blocks the passage of infrared photons. Using advanced silicon-processing techniques developed for micromechanical and integrated-circuit systems, the researchers were able to lay down an array of polysilicon bars, much as one would stack logs on a woodpile. The width of each bar was of the order of 0.1 micrometer, the distance between them being chosen to match the wavelength of the infrared photons. The three-dimensional lattice reflected as much as 99% of the incident light energy. A key feature of the technology was that it used silicon-processing techniques—methods that are well suited for implementation by mass production.

Like semiconductor crystals, the photonic crystal will require additional processing to turn it into a useful device. This could be done, for example, by introducing imperfections into selected locations. Any imperfection destroys the periodicity and therefore the photon-blocking property of the region in which it resides. If an ap-

propriate dopant—an impurity deliberately added to a semiconductor for the purpose of modifying its electrical conductivity—was distributed along a line, photons could travel along that line but would be prevented from wandering elsewhere in the crystal. In this manner, a photon guide could be produced. Alternatively, by doping a specific crystal location, that region could be converted into a tiny optical cavity, or the core of a light-emitting diode. Although the practical importance of the photonic crystal remained to be determined, the demonstration of photon control by a three-dimensional material opened up a new route for building useful devices. In principle, the photonic crystal could play the same role for photon devices that semiconductors play for conventional electronics.

The achievement of ever-finer control over the motion of the irreducible quanta that inhabit condensed matter is one of the major success stories of physics. The building blocks discussed above—the carbon nanotube and polysilicon bar—are both invisible to the naked eye. Success in assembling them into demonstration devices opened a new chapter in this ongoing story.

—David E. Farrell

See also Feature Article: Expecting the Unexpected.

371

PSYCHOLOGY

Among the major thinkers within psychology during the past century were individuals originally trained in other fields: physicians William James, Sigmund Freud, and Henry Murray; philosopher Kurt Lewin; biologist Jean Piaget; artist Erik Erikson; writer B.F. Skinner; and linguist Noam Chomsky, to mention but a few. With the next millennium approaching, the future of psychology might well be predicted by remembering how psychology has been infused by ideas and methods from other disciplines.

Evolutionary psychology

Ever since it was formulated by Charles Darwin, the theory of evolution has been applied to people. By the late 1990s, psychologists had placed human beings and their behavior in an evolutionary context. As articulated by David Buss in his 1999 book *Evolutionary Psychology: The New Science of the Mind,* what distinguishes evolutionary psychology from such related fields as sociobiology is an explicit interest in the mechanisms—biological or psychological—selected for in the course of evolution and producing behavior.

An exciting report in 1998 by Kathleen Stern and Martha McClintock at the University of Chicago showed that humans have pheromones—airborne chemicals released by one individual and influencing others of the same species. Pheromones are well documented among other species, but their existence in people had proved elusive. Stern and McClintock collected compounds secreted in the armpits of women during the late follicular stage of menstruation and exposed other women to these by swabbing their upper lips (where the com-

pounds could be inhaled). Menstrual cycle timing of these other women was thereby affected. These particular pheromones may create menstrual synchrony among women who live in close proximity to one another. Synchrony presumably confers a selection advantage because women living together tend to conceive at the same time and thus are available to help one another with child rearing.

The application of evolutionary ideas to psychology is criticized when explanations are circular. For example, a theorist may begin with a well-known fact about human behavior—such as that males are more aggressive than females—and then suggest why this fact provides an evolutionary advantage. If, however, the starting fact is the only evidence for the explanation, nothing has been explained. Accordingly, evolutionary psychology will become an established field when evolutionary explanations are able to fail—when evidence can count against hypotheses. An example is provided by a 1998 study by S. Michael Kalick at the University of Massachusetts, Boston, and his colleagues that addressed a popular theory about the evolutionary role of facial attractiveness. Supposedly, attractiveness signifies long-term health, and it makes evolutionary sense to be drawn sexually to healthy individuals as prospective parents. As the research showed, however, attractiveness as judged from photographs taken in late adolescence had no relationship to measures of health throughout adulthood.

Biological psychology

Shortly after taking office, former U.S. president George Bush declared the 1990s

the "Decade of the Brain," and psychologists have drawn on new methods to understand the neurological basis of behavior. The interdisciplinary field of cognitive neuroscience, for example, relies on neuroimaging technology (medical imaging techniques applied to the nervous system, particularly the brain) to determine which areas of the brain are active during complex mental activities such as learning, memory, and judgment.

Edward Smith, Andrea Patalano, and John Jonides at the University of Michigan used neuroimaging to study how people categorize concepts. They found that different mental circuitry is involved when people categorize by using rules (this is Disease X because it shows symptoms A, B, and C) versus judging similarity (this is Disease X because it is similar to another example of Disease X). The goal of cognitive neuroscience is not to replace traditional cognitive theorizing but rather to ground it in what is known about the brain. Distinctions drawn between different types of mental activity can only be sustained if they make neurological sense, and distinctions drawn between different brain structures can only remain relevant if they can be related to different psychological processes. Cognitive neuroscience intends to provide a fuller account of both cognition and neurological structure and function.

An important 1998 book was Elliott Valenstein's *Blaming the Brain: The Truth About Drugs and Mental Health,* a criticism of biological explanations of psychological disorders. Most of these explanations point to neurotransmitter activity, either too much or too little, as the cause of the disorders. Schizophrenia is explained as a result of excess dopamine activity, for example, and depression may be attributed to insufficient serotonin activity. The most frequently cited support for neurotransmitter explanations is the effectiveness of such psychiatric medications as Thorazine (for schizophrenia) and Prozac (for depression), which presumably target the neurotransmitters in question. According to Valenstein, however, there is no good evidence that these are the only or even the most important biological consequences of those drugs or even that the disorders in the first place were caused by neurotransmitter abnormalities. Valenstein himself is a biological psychologist, and his book does not dismiss mental "illness" as a myth but rather calls for an expanded view of how biology is involved, along with psychological and social factors, in the genesis of psychological disorder and its most effective treatment.

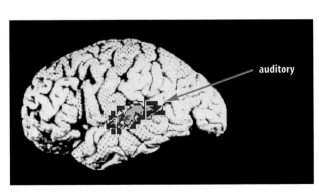

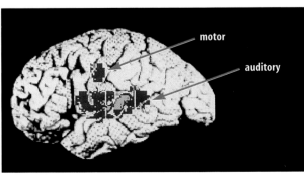

Health psychology

Health psychologists continued their interest in the psychological context of physical well-being, and their research took place on several fronts, including the workings of the immune system. The interdisciplinary field of psychoneuroimmunology explores the mutual influences among psychological characteristics, the nervous system, and the immune system. Steven Maier and Linda Watkins at the University of Colorado, Boulder, began to study the ways in which these influences take place and proposed that much of what has been identified as "sickness" (fever, for example) should be regarded as adaptive behavior. Janice Kiecolt-Glaser and her colleagues at Ohio State University explored the implications of this research in regard to how patients recover from surgery. Their data document multiple ways in which psychological factors influence wound recovery. Some of these pathways play out on a microscopic level: stress influences the

Positron emission tomography, a neuroimaging technique, reveals a human brain's active areas when a person is listening to words (top) and when both listening to words and repeating them.

production of glucocorticoids, which suppress cytokine production, which in turn slows healing. Other pathways loop outside the body through behavior: stress influences such habits as sleeping, smoking, and drinking, which interfere with the production of growth hormone and ultimately the regeneration of damaged tissue.

This latter point about behavior deserves emphasis in light of findings that positive and negative mental states are associated, respectively, with good and bad health. There is a temptation to interpret these findings solely in terms of biological mechanisms, but the role of behavior also deserves attention. Christopher Peterson and his colleagues at the University of Michigan reported a 50-year study demonstrating that individuals who catastrophized as young adults (explained the causes of bad events with pervasive causes—those that would affect everything in that person's life) did not live as long as those who viewed bad events in more circumscribed terms. Catastrophizers increased their risk of untimely death chiefly through accidents, which were often the product of lifestyle.

The cognitive psychology of surveys

One of the important juxtapositions of traditionally separate fields of psychological inquiry was achieved by Norbert Schwarz and his colleagues at the Survey Research Center in Ann Arbor, Mich. Within the context of cognitive psychology, they studied the ways in which people respond to survey questions.

Although it had long been recognized that the wording of questions influences

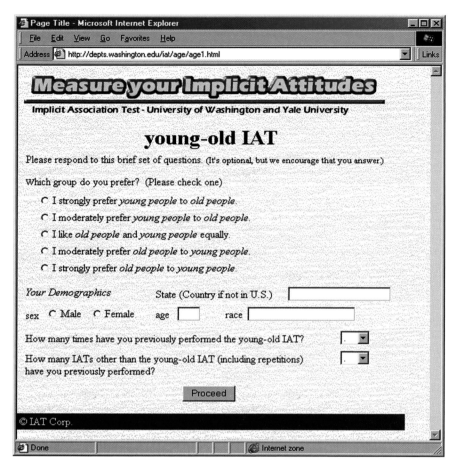

how people respond to them, many psychologists seemed to regard this phenomenon as a nuisance that could be overcome by objective questions that tapped a person's real opinions. Schwarz and colleagues maintained, however, that there are no "objective" questions in the sense that responses to them would be unshaped by whatever else the person was thinking while answering.

For example, the researchers determined that the degree to which reported marital satisfaction relates to general life satisfaction depends on the order in which someone is asked about them. Similar effects were demonstrated with respect to political opinions; during the 1996 U.S. presidental campaigns, survey-based evaluations of Bob Dole were more negative if the respondents had been previously asked about Colin Powell.

Psychology and the Internet

No topic is more current than the Internet, and psychologists were beginning to grapple with the possibilities that it affords. In 1998 the American Psychological Association (APA) launched its first electronic journal, *Prevention and Treatment*. Researchers submit articles for review over the Internet, editors obtain reviews the same way, and the eventual products become accessible to the entire psychological community with a few keystrokes. Electronic journals have the obvious potential to greatly reduce publication lags and costs and to allow psychological knowledge to be disseminated more effectively than ever before.

Anthony Greenwald of the University of Washington and his colleagues placed on

the Internet a version of the Implicit Association Test (IAT), a strategy for measuring implicit (nonconscious) attitudes. Respondents sit at a keyboard and push keys to categorize as quickly as possible presented words as good or bad, Black or White, male or female, and so on; they also categorize as quickly as possible combinations of those words. The robust finding was that certain combinations are responded to most quickly by a given individual, presumably because they represent that person's assumed associations; for example, the test may indicate for a given respondent that black females are good and white males are bad, even if that person consciously disavows those associations. To date, thousands of people have logged on and completed the task. Whether this strategy taps what is meant by an attitude is debatable, but the more important point is that the Internet can exponentially increase the number of research partici-

pants. Psychology is often characterized as the study of college sophomores; perhaps someday it will be described as the study of people with mouse pads.

Internet users are not a random cross-section of the population, of course, and a study reported in 1998 by Robert Kraut and his colleagues at Carnegie Mellon University, Pittsburgh, Pa., suggests that people who use the Internet may suffer adverse effects. In a longitudinal study (repeated observations over time) in which originally "off-line" families were provided with Internet access, the investigators traced over a two-year period the psychological and social impacts of Internet use. Greater use of the Internet was associated, on average, with decreased family interaction, a shrinking of one's social circle, and increased depression and loneliness. These effects may be a function of the novelty of the Internet, but they deserve further scrutiny.

Positive psychology

In his role as the 1998 APA president, Martin Seligman of the University of Pennsylvania called for psychology to be as focused on strength as on weakness, as interested in building the best things in life as in repairing the worst, and as concerned with making the lives of normal people fulfilling as with healing pathology. He dubbed this approach "positive psychology," in which representative topics included hope, creativity, optimism, happiness, courage, emotional intelligence, genius, future-mindeness, interpersonal skills, and honesty. What is right about people, he maintained, is not simply the absence of what is wrong, and he added that psychologists interested in promoting human potential needed to pose different questions from those predecessors who had assumed a disease model of human nature.

Positive psychology differs from the humanistic psychology of the 1960s and '70s and from the positive-thinking movement in its reliance on empirical research to understand the human condition. Humanists were skeptical about the scientific method and what it could yield, yet they were unable to offer an alternative other than the insight that people were good. In contrast, positive psychologists see both strength and weakness as authentic and as amenable to scientific understanding.

Notable people

Several major psychologists died during the past year. Of the many contributions made by Sigmund Koch of Boston University, the most enduring was his six-volume edited series *Psychology: A Study of a Science,* published between 1959 and 1963. Koch invited every important theorist of the time to articulate basic assumptions and practices. The series was and continues to be an intellectual tour de force unifying psychology and legitimizing new developments.

Amos Tversky of Hebrew University of Jerusalem and Stanford University had a career marked by brilliant contributions to a variety of fields in which judgment and decision are significant factors. His work with Daniel Kahneman on judgment heuristics, *i.e.,* cognitive shortcuts taken by decision makers, is particularly well known and reshaped psychology's view of human nature—people are neither strictly rational nor strictly irrational but rather a blend.

Bärbel Inhelder began her career as Jean Piaget's volunteer research assistant, became his collaborator on classic studies of cognitive development, and finally succeeded him as the chairman of genetic (developmental) and experimental psychology at the University of Geneva. Where Piaget emphasized structural knowledge (knowing what), Inhelder stressed functional knowledge (knowing how). Inhelder was concerned more with processes than structures, and her dynamic emphasis foreshadowed much of contemporary cognitive and developmental psychology.

The 1998 American Psychological Foundation (APF) Gold Medal Award for Life Achievement in the Science of Psychology went to Mary Ainsworth, honoring her investigations of attachment between young children and their caregivers. She devised a laboratory technique—the "strange situation test"—for classifying patterns of attachment (secure, insecure, and ambivalent) by observing how a child responds to a brief separation from a care-giver. Her research strategy and theorizing sparked great and ongoing interest in attachment across all manner of human relationships. Attachment has become a central topic of investigation not only by developmental psychologists but also by social, clinical, and organizational psychologists.

The 1998 APF Gold Medal Award for enduring contributions to psychology in the public interest was given to Wilbert McKeachie. Best known for his contributions to the teaching of psychology, McKeachie for 50 years conducted research into the psychology of teaching and learning and was able to convey his findings in ways that shaped how teachers teach and how students learn. In 1951 he wrote *Teaching Tips: Strategies, Research, and Theory for College and University Teachers,* a book both provocative and practical and in its 10th edition in 1999. He was also a pioneer in establishing volunteer social service as part of the undergraduate psychology curriculum.

Chris Argyris received the 1998 APF Gold Medal for Life Achievement in the Application of Psychology. Throughout his career Argyris championed the idea that the most convincing test of a psychological theory is how well it can be applied to settings outside the laboratory. In particular, he focused on interventions in the context of complex organizations. In his blending of theory and practice, in his concern for both individual potential and organizational effectiveness, and in his willingness to challenge and change the status quo, Argyris helped stamp psychology with a character that is certain to serve it well in the years to come.

—Christopher Peterson and
Martin E.P. Seligman

SCIENCE POLICY

Throughout the 1990s, a persistent dilemma in most of the world's scientifically-significant countries has been how to strike an appropriate balance between support for so-called curiosity-driven research, which requires a substantial degree of individual and institutional autonomy, and the imperative to fund more focused, top-down programs and provide incentives to facilitate research directly related to specific socioeconomic outcomes. This theme has manifested itself in very different ways in different national settings.

INTERNATIONAL

Europe

For over a decade, U.K. university researchers have labored under constrained budgets imposed by the Conservative Party governments of former prime ministers Margaret Thatcher and John Major, which emphasized the wealth-creation aspects of scientific research. During those years, many academic facilities deteriorated for lack of adequate maintenance, while British scientists were denied the state-of-the-art instrumentation to which their colleagues in continental Europe and the United States often enjoyed access. The Labour government of Prime Minister Tony Blair, elected in May 1997, pledged to "modernize" Britain, explicitly recognizing that support for the country's science base was integral to that goal. In July 1998 the government announced that its $2.2 billion research budget would be increased by 15% to $2.7 billion over the next three years, including $1,750,000,000 in new funds—*i.e.,* funds for new programs. A novel feature of this

Anna Clopet/Black Star

Claude Allègre, France's minister of research and education, in 1998 announced extensive reforms in the French university research system.

plan was a proposed partnership between the British government and the Wellcome Trust, the world's largest private supporter of biomedical research, which agreed to provide $640 million of the new money.

Of these new funds, $480 million each from the government and the Wellcome Trust will go into an infrastructure program to construct new academic laboratories and modernize aging facilities. The Blair government also plans to devote $650 million in additional funds to support research in high-priority areas through its seven research councils. In addition, the government and Wellcome Trust announced plans to finance a new synchrotron radiation facility to be used primarily by the country's university scientists.

While emphasizing the importance of modernizing the U.K.'s science base, Blair did not neglect the knowledge-transfer and wealth-creation themes favored by his predecessors. His government also announced a new $82.5 million scheme to provide venture capital for start-up businesses created on the basis of university research results.

In France research scientists experienced a sense of relief a year earlier than their British counterparts when Socialist Prime Minister Lionel Jospin, who came to power in June 1997, appointed the eminent geochemist Claude Allègre as minister of research and education. French scientists had complained that successive conservative governments had never really understood the importance of basic research, having focused almost entirely on socioeconomic outcomes. Indeed, according to the scientists, those governments had displayed their ignorance by placing oversight for research priorities and funding in the hands of ministers who lacked scientific backgrounds.

Allègre seemed at first to justify the high hopes of French scientists. Within weeks of his appointment, he released funds for basic research in the laboratories of the National Council for Scientific Research (CNRS) that had been frozen by the previous government, while announcing that the creation of a significant number of new positions for younger scientists would be assigned a high priority. These moves, he stated, were among the first he would make in a determined effort to improve the international status of French science, while coupling French science more closely with wealth creation.

Despite these demonstrations of commitment by the Jospin government, some members of the French research community expressed unease at Allègre's brusque, often iconoclastic, manner and were skeptical about his stated intention to reform the archaic French university research system and make it contribute more to the country's research enterprise. The university system in the U.S., as he often pointed out, was critically important in American research. He opined that the French system should move in that direction but, as critics noted, the centralized, government-controlled French university system is very different from the decentralized, diverse American system.

During 1998 unease and skepticism about Allègre gradually intensified, breaking into open revolt during the last months of the year. In July, at a meeting presided over by Jospin and attended by several ministers, Allègre announced three goals for the next four years: to double the impact of French scientific publications; to triple the number of international patents held by French inventors; and to create 400 new high-technology start-up firms in the country. Skeptics pointed out that many factors beyond the control of either the French government or its research scientists determined international citation rates. They acknowledged, however, that much more could be done to encourage and facilitate knowledge transfer to potentially productive, wealth-creating ends.

Allègre also said that thenceforth increased emphasis would be placed on peer review in allocating research funds, as opposed to the traditional formula system, which relied on factors such as the size of the scientific and support staff and past numbers of publications to determine funding for CNRS laboratories. At the same time Allègre announced that these laboratories themselves would be subject to more rigorous evaluation. In October the Ministry of Research and Education announced further organizational reforms for CNRS. CNRS laboratories, in addition to being subject to rigorous external evaluation and to funding decisions based on peer review, would now be obliged to seek partners from laboratories in universities, industry, or other ministries for all their research projects. Research scientists regarded the latter provision, intended to provide a boost to universities, as an attempt to limit their autonomy and transfer authority to set research priorities from the CNRS to Allègre's ministry. They revolted.

Leaders of CNRS's national committee, which consists of 800 scientists from all research disciplines, took the unprecedented step of calling for a meeting of the entire committee on their own initiative. The meeting was held on December 14 in Paris, in which a succession of speakers denounced the government's plans. The bureaucratized, archaic university system, they pointed out, was ill equipped to assume any substantially

larger share of responsibility for the country's research activities. Rather than increase the research capabilities of French universities, implementation of the government's mandatory partnership plan threatened to eviscerate the capabilities of the CNRS laboratories. Two days later it was reported that the senior administration of the ministry's research department, consisting of seven directors, had resigned en masse, suggesting a deep-seated opposition to Allègre's reforms within the government itself.

Japan

Despite, or in part because of, the country's eight-year recession and continuing uncertainty about the stability of its banking sector, the financial outlook for Japan's research enterprise remained positive in 1998. Total national expenditures for research and development (R&D) were estimated to have been $13.7 billion for Japanese fiscal year (JFY) 1997, which

Physicist Akito Arima, shown meeting with a group of schoolchildren, was the first scientist in 50 years to be named head of the Japanese Ministry of Education, Science, Sports, and Culture.

Kyodo News International

377

ended on March 31, 1998. These investments amounted to an increase of 4.4% over the previous fiscal year and were 3.12% of the country's gross domestic product (GDP), compared with 3.0% in JFY 1996.

Of the country's total JFY 1997 R&D expenditures, 79.4% were accounted for by private industry, 20.4% by government, and the remainder by foreign sources. That the government's share was down from its 21% level during the previous year disappointed leaders of the Japanese research community, who had long pointed out that government contributions in the U.S. and the major Western European countries were typically on the order of 30% or more. They argued that since universities and public research facilities rely primarily on government funding, the continuing vitality of the country's research enterprise required larger government investments. Such increases were a central feature of the government's Basic Science and Technology Plan, adopted in July 1996.

JFY 1998 brought a substantial bonanza. The government's initial budget for the year allocated approximately $2,640,000,000 for R&D, only slightly more than in the previous year. The government later submitted a succession of three supplementary budgets (the latest in November 1998) designed to stimulate the country's troubled economy. The public-works components of these budgets included significant amounts earmarked for "the infrastructure for promoting science and technology," so that the total government JFY 1998 allocation for R&D amounted to an estimated $3.6 billion, about $1 billion more than in the previous year.

The government's proposal for substantially increased research funding could be considered a personal triumph for Akito Arima, who became head of the Ministry of Science, Education, Sports, and Culture (Monbusho) on July 30, following his election to the upper house of the Diet (parliament) on July 12. Arima, a physicist and former president of the University of Tokyo and of the Institute of Physical and Chemical Research (RIKEN), has long been one of the most vigorous and visible advocates for increased funds for university research. As the first scientist to lead Monbusho in 50 years, Arima was no doubt responsible for the inclusion of funds for science infrastructure in the government's supplementary budgets. Yet only about 2% of the approximately $60 billion annual budget of his ministry is devoted to research; the bulk supports the Japanese primary and secondary education system. Arima's stated goals include increasing Monbusho's share of the government's research budget and reforming primary and secondary education, which he regards as overly focused on rote memorization with too little attention paid to stimulating and nurturing creativity.

India

India's announcement that it had tested three nuclear weapons on May 11, 1998, and two more on May 13, together with Pakistan's retaliatory tests on May 28 and 30, may have constituted the year's most widely publicized science story from Asia. Because India had tested a nuclear device in 1974, the only surprises were that preparations for the test eluded international satellite inspection and, more significantly, that the government of Prime Minister A.T. Vajpayee may have risked international

Soldiers stand guard over a crater at the Shakti-1 site near Pokaran, where India detonated an underground nuclear device on May 11, 1998.

(Below left and right) Agence France Presse/Corbis

Despite international condemnations, Indian Prime Minister Atal Bihari Vajpayee's authorization of underground nuclear testing in 1998 drew considerable public support at home.

approbation in order to secure domestic political advantage. Nor did informed observers doubt that Pakistan had long since become a closet nuclear state.

In view of the serious geopolitical implications of the Indian and Pakistani actions, Western scientists were dismayed at the widespread support the tests received from scientists in those countries with whom they had long-standing ties. In an impassioned letter published in the July 10, 1998, edition of *Science,* G. Padmanaban, director of the elite Indian Institute of Science in Bangalore, complained that, "there have been few occasions when progress made in India has been depicted by the Western media without bias or sarcasm. . . . India has many, many problems, but we are tired of being depicted in the West as having negative qualities. Given this treatment, one clutches at any 'victory' that makes one feel like an entity to be counted."

Despite Padmanaban's plea for understanding, Japan and several Western European nations suspended cooperative science projects pending a review of their potential military implications. The U.S. government, obligated by law to impose sanctions on new nuclear powers, suspended several cooperative projects involving U.S. and Indian institutions, including nondefense institutions—most obviously those (such as Padmanaban's Indian Institute of Science) that receive a sizable fraction of their financial support from India's Department of Atomic Energy. Indian and Pakistani nationals working at U.S. government facilities such as the National Institute of Standards and Technology in Gaithersburg, Md., were asked to leave the country, and several Indian scientists intending to participate in scientific meetings in the U.S. were denied entry visas.

UNITED STATES

President Clinton at the AAAS

No doubt the symbolic high point for U.S. science policy in 1998 occurred in Philadelphia on February 13 when Pres. Bill Clinton addressed the 150th anniversary meeting of the American Association for the Advancement of Science (AAAS). The president used the occasion to highlight the revolutionary progress that had taken place in many fields of basic and applied science since Pres. Harry Truman addressed the AAAS on Sept. 13, 1948, at its 100th birthday celebration. Clinton also spoke glowingly about the world that might exist, based largely on further advances in science and technology, when a U.S. president addressed the bicentennial meeting of the organization in 2048.

Clinton's punch line, however (at least as far as his scientific audience was concerned), was his announcement that his administration had proposed to Congress the creation of "a 21st Century Research Fund, part of our gift to America in the millennium—providing for the first time a strong, stable, multiyear source of funding for research that will enable you to engage in long-term planning as never before." The proposed research fund, according to administration spokespersons, would be "revenue neutral," since it would be largely derived from the increased taxes on tobacco that the administration had proposed as part of its proposal to regulate that industry. By providing a long-term reserve, the fund would offer a measure of stability to the budgets of the government's principal research agencies, relieving those agencies of the need to request at least a fraction of their annual appropriations from Congress.

Research funding

The 21st Century Research Fund died a quiet death when Congress declined to enact the administration's proposed tobacco legislation. Nevertheless, the fiscal record for U.S. R&D during 1998 was positive, as were the prospects for 1999—at least for federal expenditures. Total national expenditures in 1998 are estimated at $220.6 billion, an increase of 7.3% over the $205.6 billion level in 1997. These R&D

Dirck Halstead/Gamma Liaison International

investments represented 2.6% GDP, the highest level this ratio has reached since 1992, and less than half a percentage point below the record high of 2.9% achieved in 1964. The impressive increase in national R&D expenditures during 1998 was attribut-

U.S. Pres. Bill Clinton (right) appears before the 150th anniversary meeting of the American Association for the Advancement of Science in 1998.

able primarily to private industry, which invested a record $143.7 billion in R&D—an increase of 7.7% over 1997. The federal contribution to total R&D expenditures in 1998 was $66.6 billion, representing an increase of less than 1% over 1997. Thus, the increasing dominance of private-sector R&D, evident from the beginning of the decade, persisted during 1998. The industrial share was estimated at approxamately 65% and the federal share at about 30%—the lowest share in percentage terms since the 1950s. The remaining 5% of expenditures were accounted for by other sources, including state and local governments, nonprofit organizations, and academic institutions.

With the passage on Oct. 20 of an approximately $520 billion omnibus appropriations act for fiscal year 1999 (which began on Oct. 1, 1998), Congress provided the government's research agencies with what *Physics Today* called "the best allocations in more than a decade." Total R&D appropriations for the fiscal year were $80.2 billion—$4.1 billion, or 5.3%, above their fiscal year (FY) 1998 level. Among the principal research agencies, the National Institutes of Health (NIH) fared best, receiving $15.6 billion—$2 billion more than in FY 1998 and the largest per-

centage increase (nearly 15%) in its history. The recently beleaguered Department of Energy (DOE) received a $714 million increase, 11.4% over its FY 1998 level, while the National Science Foundation's (NSF's) research account reached $2.8 billion, 8.4% above the previous year.

Prospects for federal research funding were not entirely positive, however, since several actions were held hostage to nonscientific considerations. The National Oceanic and Atmospheric Administration (NOAA), within the Department of Commerce, received $2,160,000,000 for FY 1999, or 8.2% more than in FY 1998, but its appropriations will continue only until June 15, 1999, rather than until September 30. Apparently, this unusual deadline was intended to pressure NOAA's parent department into conceding its disagreement with Congress over the proposed use of sampling in the year 2000 population census. The Clinton administration also had proposed expenditures of $110 million per year for R&D to support the Next Generation Internet Initiative, to be financed from the budgets of several agencies, including the Department of Defense, the DOE, the National Aeronautics and Space Administration (NASA), NIH, the National Institute for Standards and Technology (NIST) within the Department of Commerce, and the NSF. Influential members of Congress from smaller states contended that the end result of this initiative would be to channel increasing largess to the already well-endowed states, while widening the in-

formation technology gap between the "haves" and "have nots." In the event, the Next Generation Internet Initiative was funded for $67 million in FY 1999 and for up to $75 million in FY 2000.

New science adviser

Clinton took the occasion of his February 13 address to the AAAS to announce the retirement of Jack Gibbons as his science adviser and director of the White House Office of Science and Technology Policy (OSTP). The president also announced that Gibbons, who had served in those capacities since the beginning of his administration in 1993, would be succeeded by Neal Lane, a physicist who had been director of the NSF since 1993. Lane's nomination was confirmed by the Senate on July 31. The new presidential science adviser spent most of his professional career before coming to the NSF at Rice University, Houston, Texas. During his tenure at the NSF, he was noted more as a conciliator than as an innovator, a management style that no doubt helped the agency weather the dark days of 1994–95 when it appeared entirely possible that Congress would overturn its long-standing record of bipartisan support for basic research by eviscerating the NSF's budget. That Lane managed not only to weather that storm but also to preside over healthy increases for the agency's annual budgets could be regarded as fitting tributes to the virtues of quiet conciliation and patient negotiation.

Lane's successor as director of the NSF was Rita Colwell, a University of Maryland microbiologist, an exuberant innovator and iconoclast, and the first woman to head the agency since it was created in 1950.

Toward a new national science policy?

In July 1945, during the last full month of World War II, Vannevar Bush, a former dean of engineering at the Massachusetts Institute of Technology who had served as Pres. Franklin Roosevelt's de facto science adviser since 1940, submitted a report to President Truman entitled *Science—the Endless Frontier*. The Bush report made the then-bold and innovative recommendation that the federal government had not only the authority but also the responsibility to support basic research outside of government, primarily in universities. Because federal support for academic research became an important, enduring component of relations between science and government, *Science—the Endless Frontier* itself has often (and in the view of many critics mistakenly) been referred to as the foundation document for U.S. science policy. Particularly since the end of the Cold War there have been repeated calls for a new science policy framework to replace the Bush paradigm.

On Sept. 24, 1998, a new congressional report, *Unlocking Our Future: Toward a New National Science Policy,* was released as the latest contender to supplant *Science—the Endless Frontier*. The report was prepared by a special task force of the House of Representatives Committee on Science that was chaired by Rep. Vernon Ehlers, a Republican congressman from Michigan who received a Ph.D. in physics from the University of California, Berkeley, and taught at Calvin College, Grand Rapids, Mich., before entering politics. The charge to his task force was to outline "a framework for an updated national science policy

that can serve as a policy guide to the Committee, Congress and the Nation." Despite the sweep of this charge, Ehlers made it clear that his ambitions for the report were more modest. He stated on more than one occasion that Congress itself was his principal intended audience, noting that only a small minority of its members grasp the rudiments of science policy or understand the importance of science to the nation. In a July 21 interview with *Science,* Ehlers suggested that his report would be only a first step in an ongoing process in which Congress would focus more actively on science policy, perhaps reviewing it every five years.

Consisting of 51 pages of text, including four pages of summary recommendations, in addition to a four-page list of sources, the Ehlers report groups its findings under four major headings: Ensuring the Flow of New Ideas, The Private Sector's Role in the Scientific Enterprise, Ensuring that Technical Decisions Made by Government Bodies Are Founded in Sound Science, and Sustaining the Research Enterprise—the Importance of Education. Those familiar with successive government pronouncements on science policy noted that although the first, second, and fourth of these sets of findings rehearsed long-familiar themes and broke little new ground, they were cast in terms that might capture the attention of Ehlers's primary audience—congressmen with little or no knowledge of, or interest in, science policy. These three sets of findings deal with issues in the category that science-policy scholars refer to as "policy-for-science"; that is, how best to allocate resources to science-related activities, including education. In contrast, the fourth

group of findings—"Ensuring that Technical Decisions Made by Government Bodies Are Founded in Sound Science"—deals with issues in the science-for-policy category: how to ensure that scientific findings are used as effective tools of governance. By incorporating such science-for-policy considerations into its study, the Ehlers report went beyond the 1945 Bush report and many other subsequent government science-policy studies. If that aspect of the report comes to be taken seriously, the Ehlers report might yet qualify as something of an enduring classic.

Even friendly critics of the report noted that it failed to encompass important areas of science, including those related to health, agriculture, and, notably, national defense. The explanation for this deficiency was as simple as it was unfortunate: the Ehlers task force was established by the House Science Committee, which does not have jurisdiction over science in agencies and bureaus within the Department of Agriculture, the Department of Defense, and the Department of Health and Human Services. Had the Ehlers task force made any recommendations that could have been construed as being under the jurisdiction of congressional committees overseeing those agencies, its report would have been subject to approval by those committees before being released.

The report did make passing reference to the problem of scattered congressional oversight for federal science policy. It recommended that the House of Representatives should make it a practice to schedule joint hearings between two committees and work toward joint authorization bills on issues involving two or more federal agencies and, therefore, two or more congressional committees. It remains to be seen whether Congress will take even this modest step toward rectifying the problem of scattered legislative oversight authority, which many observers regard as among the most serious barriers to a more effective, coordinated U.S. science policy.

Science at the State Department

Midway in its four pages of recommendations, the Ehlers report notes the growing importance of international considerations to U.S. science. It proposes that "Mechanisms that promote coordination between various Executive Branch Departments for international scientific projects must be developed. *The State Department should strengthen its contingent of science advisors within its Bureau of Oceans and International Environmental and Scientific Affairs and draw on expertise in other agencies* [emphasis added]."

This relatively low-key statement encapsulated the mounting frustration of the principal federal R&D agencies, including the White House Office of Science and Technology Policy (OSTP), at the short shrift given to science and technology by the Department of State. Beginning in 1948, a succession of reports has argued persuasively that because of the importance of the international aspects of science to the U.S. enterprise, science should be accorded higher visibility in the State Department. While some of the earlier of these reports resulted in an apparent upgrading of the status of science within the department, including the appointment of larger numbers of science and technology counselors in U.S. embassies abroad, the effectiveness of many of these actions

waned over the years. A 1992 report by the Carnegie Commission on Science, Technology, and Government dealt in great detail with the importance of science as an instrument of U.S. foreign policy, noted the deficiencies of the State Department in making effective use of that instrument, and included explicit recommendations to improve its capabilities. Yet, as former secretary of energy James Watkins emphasized in his 1998 testimony before the Ehlers task force, the situation has, if anything, deteriorated since 1992.

The State Department has been laboring under serious financial constraints since the 104th Congress, elected in November 1994, began to subject its annual budgets to severe reductions. One of its responses has been to reduce the number of so-called nonessential personnel in U.S. embassies abroad, including science and technology counselor positions (relabeled environment, science and technology, or EST, counselors) in several scientifically significant countries, including Germany, India, and the U.K. The State Department's Bureau of Oceans and International Environmental and Scientific Affairs (OES) also began slowly and methodically reassigning its Washington, D.C.–based staff from its scientific section to its environmental affairs section, perhaps in response to the high priority that Vice Pres. Al Gore has assigned to environmental policy. Private dissatisfaction with the State Department's attitude toward science became far more public in July 1997, when the then-head of the OES announced a reorganization of the bureau that effectively abolished its science section. The resultant outcry from the federal R&D agencies led to an April 1998 request to the president

of the National Academy of Sciences (NAS) from a principal aide to Secretary of State Madeline Albright for recommendations on "how the department might better carry out its responsibilities to that end [of using science as an effective instrument of foreign policy], within its resource constraints." The letter to the NAS president suggested that "we may not be doing as much in the science, technology, and health area as we can."

The final report from the NAS to the State Department, with its recommendations, was anticipated in the spring of 1999. Meanwhile, several critics have noted that whereas there are manifest deficiencies in the department's understanding of the importance of the international aspects of science, it cannot bear the entire responsibility for integrating science into U.S. foreign policy or, reciprocally, integrating the international dimensions of science into the formulation and implementation of U.S. science policy. Accomplishing those tasks, as the Ehlers report suggests, must involve the principal operational R&D agencies of the federal government and, most importantly, the OSTP.

Considerable lip service has been paid to the centrality of science to what is often referred to as the borderless, knowledge-based society of the 21st century. One of the principal challenges to U.S. science on the threshold of this new century is to assure that not only the Department of State and the operating agencies of the federal government but also the U.S. scientific community itself understand the importance of the international dimensions of science to the continuing health and vitality of the U.S. enterprise.

—William A. Blanpied

(Left) Early in the linkup of the first two elements of the International Space Station, *Endeavour* astronauts used the shuttle's robot arm to maneuver Unity into an upright position in the cargo bay for coupling with the shuttle's docking system. Later, they used the arm again to grapple Zarya and position it for mating with Unity (below). Once the two elements were joined and serviced, *Endeavour*'s crew released the nascent space station (bottom).

SPACE EXPLORATION

Highlights of the past year in space exploration included the return to space of 77-year-old John Glenn, the first American to orbit Earth, and the joining of the first two elements of the International Space Station (ISS). The Lunar Prospector probe detected the presence of water in the Moon's south polar region, and the Galileo probe revealed a deep and salty ocean on Jupiter's moon Callisto. A test model for a potential "Internet-in-the-sky" constellation of small communications satellites was launched in February 1998.

MANNED SPACE MISSIONS

Assembly of the International Space Station started in 1998, more than 14 years after the program was initiated as Space Station Freedom by U.S. Pres. Ronald Reagan in 1984. The first two elements of the ISS, launched by the Russian Space Agency and the U.S. National Aeronautics and Space Administration (NASA), were joined to form the cornerstone for a spacecraft that will be the largest—more than

100 m (330 ft) wide—and most complex—more than 30 modules and major components—ever built.

The program started with the launch by Russia on November 20 of Zarya ("Dawn"), formerly called the Functional Cargo Block. Zarya was derived from designs used earlier in the Soviet Union's Salyut and *Mir* space station programs. Launched atop a Russian Proton booster rocket, it was equipped with its own solar power arrays and attitude-control system for operating in space. Although it was built in Russia, Zarya is considered a U.S. element because it was built under contract to Boeing Co., NASA's prime contractor for the ISS.

The first U.S.-built element was a connecting node, dubbed Unity, that provided six berthing ports to join several modules and supply a docking point for the space shuttle. In addition, Unity was equipped with attachment points on its top for the long truss that will carry solar power arrays, thermal radiators, and other equipment. Unity was launched on December 4 aboard the space shuttle *Endeavour*

(STS-88). On December 6 it grappled Zarya with its robot arm and positioned Zarya above the shuttle's payload bay. *Endeavour*'s crew had already positioned Unity upright in the bay so that the docking ports of the two modules faced each other across a gap of approximately one meter (about 3.3 ft). After checking alignments and solving a problem involving use of the robot arm, the crew fired thrusters to drive the shuttle upward and gently force Unity into Zarya. Docking clamps then grasped the two and formed a rigid connection.

The *Endeavour* crew then engaged in a series of three space walks to join electrical connectors between Zarya and Unity so that Unity, which had no solar arrays, could draw power from Zarya rather than from *Endeavour.* The crews also installed handrails and other aids that astronauts would use in later assembly missions. Once the two modules were joined and operating as one, the crew opened the docking hatch and entered to set up equipment and check systems. The interiors showed a stark contrast as the crew moved from the large Unity to the narrow confines of Zarya.

Further work on the ISS was in some jeopardy because of the economic and political crisis in Russia. The ISS started as a U.S. project with the European Space Agency, the National Space Development Agency of Japan, and the Canadian Space Agency soon signing on as international partners. When NASA's efforts ran into rising costs, the U.S. government decided to invite the former Soviet Union to be a partner and supply expertise gained from years of operating the Salyut and *Mir* space stations. What became the ISS was soon re-

NASA

Enjoying their pressurized, "shirtsleeve" environment aboard Zarya, astronaut Nancy J. Currie and cosmonaut Sergei K. Krikalev use rechargeable power tools to install equipment, while mission commander Robert D. Cabana (background) travels along the module's rail network. The crew members entered Zarya through the shuttle's docking hatch and Unity's connecting module.

designed to include two Russian elements, Zarya and a service module built from the never-launched *Mir 2* station. These were in the so-called critical path, meaning that their presence was essential to the success of the ISS. Deteriorating conditions in Russia caused work on both Zarya and the service module to be delayed, thus pushing the entire program back and requiring more cash from the United States. Conditions became bad enough that in 1998 NASA started designing an Interim Control Module based on the propulsion module for a classified U.S. Navy satellite. This module would take the place of the Russian service module to reboost the orbit and provide attitude control during as-

sembly. Meanwhile, the service module was scheduled for launch in July 1999. Also in 1999 the STS-96 mission (*Discovery*) was to carry a crew and equipment to outfit the interior of Unity and Zarya, and STS-92 (*Atlantis*) was to bring the Z-1 truss, a major structure to which the large solar-array trusses and other elements would be attached. In 1999 and 2000, other shuttle flights were scheduled to supply the first solar-array module (STS-97, *Endeavour*), the U.S. Laboratory Module (STS-98, *Discovery*), and the Italian-built Leonardo supply module (STS-100, *Endeavour*).

The assembly of Unity and Zarya marked a new phase in the ISS program.

The previous phase was completed with the last two U.S. space shuttle missions to Russia's aging *Mir* station. *Endeavour* (STS-89, Jan. 22–31, 1998) made the eighth docking with *Mir,* and *Discovery* (STS-91, June 2–12, 1998) made the ninth and last docking with the Russian station. *Endeavour* replaced an astronaut who had been aboard since the previous mission *Mir* shuttle and carried experiments in protein crystal growth (for pharmaceutical studies) and low-stress soil mechanics (to understand how soil behaves when it liquefies during earthquakes). *Discovery* picked up the last U.S. crewman and delivered more supplies to the Russian crew staying aboard *Mir. Discovery* also carried a forerunner of an ISS experiment, the Alpha Magnetic Spectrometer, designed to measure very-high-energy cosmic rays. (For additional information on the ISS, *see* Feature Article: THE INTERNATIONAL SPACE STATION.)

Operations aboard *Mir* continued, with the crew conducting several space walks to help repair the facility. In 1998 Russia launched two spacecrafts to *Mir,* Soyuz TM-27 on January 29 and TM-28 on August 13. Soyuz TM-26 (launched in 1997) returned to Earth on Feb. 19, 1998, carrying two cosmonauts who had been aboard *Mir* since 1997. A similar pattern was followed when TM-27 returned with three cosmonauts on August 25. Cosmonauts on the final manned launch to *Mir,* Soyuz TM-28 in February 1999 completed the experiments. As 1999 progressed, Russia was still looking for funding to keep *Mir* alive.

The most controversial space mission in many years took place in 1998 when *Discovery* (STS-95, October 29–November 7) carried retiring U.S. Sen. John Glenn on his first mission since he became the first American to orbit Earth (Friendship 7, Feb. 20, 1962). Many space analysts claimed that the assignment, for which Glenn had campaigned openly, was a political payoff with little scientific value, especially since much of the biomedical data about Glenn would not be available for wide analysis because of privacy regulations. NASA claimed that the mission would contribute to research on the aging process—Glenn was 77. Although Glenn's presence was the main news story, the primary purpose of the flight was to carry the Spacehab module, which contained an array of materials- and life-sciences experiments. One experiment, for example, was designed to study the formation of aerogel, a highly effective, transparent insulator whose uses are limited by its bluish tint. Scientists hoped that studying its formation in space, without gravity's effects, would lead to an improved product on Earth.

Spacehab, a commercial module leased to NASA for a variety of flights, was expected to host a number of science missions, as NASA retired its complex and more capable Spacelab in anticipation of expanded operations on the ISS. Space

Jim Borgman/King Features Syndicate

shuttle *Columbia* flew the last Spacelab mission, Neurolab (STS-90, April 17–May 3), which comprised a range of experiments on how nervous systems react and adapt to the effects of space travel. In addition to seven people, the crew consisted of mice and rats (some pregnant), swordtail fish, snails, crickets, and cricket eggs. Scientists believed that the results might also have applications to neurological disorders such as Parkinson's disease.

SPACE PROBES

Water was the headline subject in planetary exploration, as evidence mounted for its existence on the Moon and Mars and in liquid form on Europa, one of the large, Galilean moons of Jupiter. For extended manned space expeditions, water is a precious resource. Beyond the obvious implications for the presence of extraterrestrial life, water can be electrolyzed into oxygen and hydrogen, which can then be burned as rocket propellants. Free oxygen can also be used in life-support systems. Thus, water ice on the Moon or Mars can be viewed as energy reserves, and on both Mars and Europa water is viewed as a potential home for life under extreme conditions. (Such "extremophiles" are found on Earth in hot

springs, undersea volcanic vents, and Arctic regions.)

Lunar Prospector, the third of the Discovery-class interplanetary missions, revealed the presence of water in the Moon's south polar region. The probe was launched on Jan. 6, 1998, by an Athena II vehicle and entered lunar orbit on January 11; the final mapping orbit, 100 km

Lunar Prospector data led NASA scientists to propose the existence of vast amounts of water ice at the Moon's poles. The finding confirmed results returned by an earlier spacecraft, Clementine, which had visited the Moon in 1994 and sent back images such as the one above, of the north lunar pole.

Courtesy of Clementine Project, BMDO, NRL, LLNL/Astronomy Picture of the Day

(62 mi) high, was achieved January 16. Because the Moon's surface had already been well mapped and was virtually static, Lunar Prospector carried no cameras.

Instead, the probe was equipped with a gamma-ray spectrometer, a magnetometer, an electron reflectometer, a neutron spectrometer, and an alpha-particle spectrometer to assay the chemistry of the surface. The major find, announced March 5, consisted of strong evidence for subsurface ice in areas protected from sunlight.

In September 1998 NASA announced that the Moon may contain up to six billion metric tons of water ice in the north and south polar regions, more than a tenfold increase over previous estimates. Although the exact form of the water ice remained unknown, scientists concluded that the data indicated it may be in discrete, confined, near-pure water ice deposits under about 40 cm (16 in) of lunar soil. The ice most likely was delivered evenly across the Moon by countless comet impacts but survived only in the permanently shadowed craters at the poles. If borne out by observations as low as nine kilometers (six miles) from the surface, planned for late 1999, this would become a major resource for interplanetary missions.

A gravity experiment aboard the spacecraft discovered seven previously unknown mass concentrations, lava-filled craters on the lunar surface that can affect a satellite's speed. Other data indicated that the Moon has a small, iron-rich core approximately 220–450 km (135–280 mi) wide. Lunar Prospector's magnetometer and electron reflectometer detected magnetized rocks on the Moon's upper surface that form the two smallest known magnetospheres in the solar system.

Mars Global Surveyor, which reached Mars in September 1997, continued to work its way into a mapping orbit around the planet, although efforts were hampered by a solar array that apparently was not fully locked. Engineers feared that it could fold up under aerodynamic pressures. Aerobraking was suspended once for that reason and once because of other equipment problems; it was then resumed in September 1998. The satellite achieved its final mapping orbit around Mars in early 1999.

During the braking phase of the Mars probe, scientists managed to use its cameras and scientific instruments to make some striking discoveries. One surprise was that Phobos, the larger of Mars's two moons, appeared to be covered "hip deep" in dust. This was determined by the thermal emission spectrometer, which showed that temperatures drop rapidly from –4° C (25° F) on the side facing the Sun to –112° C (–170° F) on the side facing away from the Sun. The rapid drop was explained by the increased surface area of a fine powder as opposed to the monolithic surface of a single, massive object. Mars Global Surveyor also revealed small boulders that had slowly rolled downhill, even in Phobos's gravity, which was only 0.001 times Earth's gravity.

Other images from the probe showed giant plates of solidified volcanic lava on Mars. Close-up views of Elysium Basin revealed the first evidence of these huge plates, which measured hundreds of kilometers across. The find indicates that Mars had volcanic activity as recently as many millions of years ago, although it is dormant now. New discoveries were also made at the north pole. Sand dunes apparently were being formed and moved across the planet as recently as July or August 1998. Some dunes appeared to be coated with thin, late-winter frost. The polar ice cap appeared to be 1,200 km (750 mi) wide and up to 3 km (1.8 mi) thick. Large areas of the cap are smooth to within a few meters over expanses several kilometers wide, but the cap is also cut by canyons and troughs that plunge as deep as one kilometer (0.62 mi) beneath the surface, unlike anything on Earth. Remnants of a much larger ice cap are seen in the form of large mounds about one kilometer high and dozens of kilometers across. Although measuring less than half of the Greenland ice cap and about 4% of the Antarctic ice sheet, the total volume of north polar ice is a significant 1.2 million cu km (300,000 cu mi).

Japan became only the third nation (after Russia and the U.S.) to reach for Mars with the July 4, 1998, launch of Nozomi ("Hope"). Its mission was to measure the interaction between the solar wind and upper atmosphere of Mars. Later in 1998 Nozomi made two flybys of the Moon, on September 24 and December 18, to reshape its trajectory for arrival in Mars's orbit in October 1999. Unfortunately, a mid-

This three-dimensional computer-generated image of the Martian north polar ice cap is based on elevation measurements made by NASA's Mars Global Surveyor spacecraft.

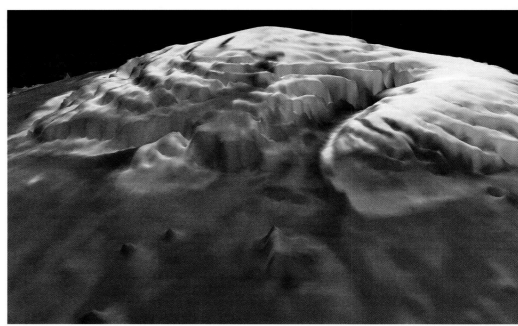

Courtesy of MOLA Team, MGS Project, NASA, Image: Greg Shirah/Astronomy Picture of the Day

course correction at the time of the second flyby was incorrect, and Japan rescheduled the Mars rendezvous for 2003.

NASA launched two new Mars missions, the Mars Climate Orbiter, on Dec. 11, 1998, scheduled to arrive on Sept. 23, 1999, and the Mars Polar Lander, on Jan. 3, 1999, scheduled to touch down in the south polar region on Dec. 3, 1999. During its descent, the lander was to release two Deep Space 2 microprobes that were designed to make hard landings and penetrate the surface. They would then send back data about conditions beneath the surface for up to 50 hours.

The Galileo spacecraft completed its primary mission to explore Jupiter on Dec. 7, 1997, two years after its arrival, and then started an extended mission to explore the planet's four Galilean moons—Io, Ganymede, Callisto, and particularly Europa. Evidence of water ice on Europa had been revealed during earlier Galileo flybys of the moon. Spacecraft images taken from an altitude of 200 km (124 mi)

had revealed massive ice rafts that apparently were moving across Europa's face, much as crustal plates move on Earth. The implication is that these ice plates must be floating on something liquid. During 1998 Galileo provided additional images that revealed more details of ice structures on Europa, such as Astypalaea Linea, a strike-slip fault similar to the San Andreas Fault and estimated to be 810 km (503 mi) long.

Galileo's magnetometer indicated that electrical currents flow in a shell near Callisto's surface, causing changes observed in Jupiter's magnetic field in the vicinity of Callisto. The implication is that Callisto has a deep, extremely salty ocean. Galileo's camera showed dozens of volcanic vents on Io, which is heated by constant tidal distortions from Jupiter. One vent, Pillan Patera, may have a temperature of 2,000 K (3,140° F), one of the hottest lava spots in the solar system. Even Ganymede, the largest of Jupiter's moons, may have icy volcanic flows. Galileo revealed impact craters with unusual

pedestals, dark ejecta halos, and a crater chain possibly caused by a comet impact.

The Cassini mission to put a spacecraft in orbit around Saturn and drop a probe into the atmosphere of Saturn's moon Titan continued smoothly after its Oct. 15, 1997, launch. It flew past Venus for a gravity assist on April 26, 1998, and is set to do the same with Earth on Aug. 18, 1999.

On Feb. 17, 1998, Voyager 1 overtook Pioneer 10 as the man-made object that had traveled farthest from Earth; both were then 10.4 billion km (6.5 billion mi) from the Sun and moving in opposite directions. The Ulysses International Solar Polar Mission probe crossed the orbit of Jupiter on April 17 and started arcing back to make a third pass over the Sun. Giotto, Europe's successful 1986 Comet Halley flyby probe, in hibernation since a 1992 comet flyby, was expected to fly past Earth about July 1, 1999. At that time, engineers will try to reactivate it.

The Near Earth Asteroid Rendezvous (NEAR) mission missed its goal in late 1998 but will get a second chance in 2000. NEAR flew past Earth on Jan. 23, 1998, to reshape its trajectory toward the asteroid Eros and then was to fire its rockets on Dec. 20, 1998, for the final approach to Eros and go into orbit on Jan. 10, 1999. Because the preset safety limit had been exceeded, the onboard computer aborted

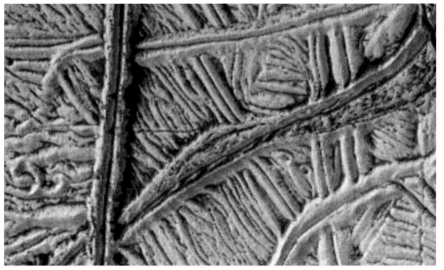

High-resolution photographs taken in 1998 by the Galileo spacecraft revealed more details about the intricate system of ridges and cracks that criss-cross the icy surface of Jupiter's moon Europa. In the photograph, the distance between parallel ridges is typically one kilometer (0.62 miles).

Courtesy of Galileo Project, JPL, NASA/Astronomy Picture of the Day

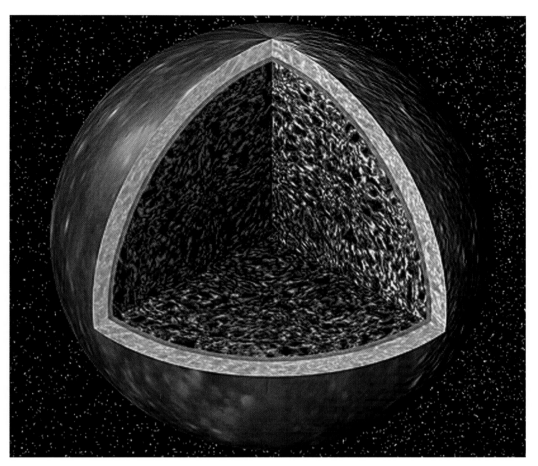

Courtesy of JPL, NASA/Astronomy Picture of the Day

Magnetic measurements made by Galileo suggest the presence of a subsurface water ocean on Callisto. In this cutaway model, the moon's outer layer comprises an icy shell (whitish band) 200 km (125 mi) thick. The hypothetical ocean (thin blue band) lies just below it.

tail of Comet Wild-2 in January 2004 and return to Earth in 2006 with gas and dust samples obtained during the encounter.

In June 1998 NASA formed an Astrobiology Institute to investigate the possibilities of life existing beyond Earth. Unlike the search for extraterrestrial intelligence, the Astrobiology Institute planned to study the extreme conditions under which life exists on Earth and then compare them with conditions on Mars, ice-covered Europa, methane-shrouded Titan, and even asteroids and meteors. The institute would also be concerned with planetary protection methods to ensure that alien life is not accidentally released on Earth.

Relatively few space-science probes were launched during 1998. Sweden's Astrid 2, launched December 10, carried an electron spectrometer, a magnetometer, and an ultraviolet imager to support auroral research. The spacecraft's orbit was to take it about 1,000 km (620 mi) above the aurora borealis to study the region where Earth's environment is directly affected by space. Launched April 1, the Transition Region and Coronal Explorer (TRACE) provided stunning, detailed views of activities in the solar atmosphere. Its extreme ultraviolet telescopes were designed to study the solar chromosphere and lower

the rendezvous firing. NEAR did, however, take pictures of Eros as it passed by the asteroid. On Jan. 3, 1999, a burn was completed that will allow NEAR to catch up with Eros in mid-February 2000 and orbit the asteroid for a year. The probe was equipped with a laser rangefinder so that scientists can make precise maps of the asteroid's surface.

The first test of ion propulsion for interplanetary missions got under way with Deep Space 1, launched Oct. 24, 1998. The probe was designed to test a dozen new space technologies, including autonomous navigation and superminiature cameras and electronics. Its most prominent feature was a low-thrust, high-efficiency ion engine. The engine employs electrostatic repulsion by ionizing xenon gas and repelling it through a grid with an electrical charge of 1,280 volts. An electron gun discharges the electrons stripped from the xenon atoms so that the spacecraft does not build up a massive static

charge that would stop the engine. Although the exhaust travels faster than 100,000 km/h (62,000 mph), the quantity of gas used is so small that the thrust is less than 90 millinewtons (about as much force as the weight of a sheet of paper). The ion engine, however, can run for hundreds or thousands of hours, as opposed to chemical engines, which consume their propellants in a few minutes. The engine quit a few minutes after starting its first "burn" on November 11, but engineers described this as a normal start-up problem and were able to coax it to life on November 24.

Deep Space 1 was scheduled to fly within 5–10 km (3–6 mi) of asteroid 1992 KD in July in a test of its autonomous navigation system. Later, the probe would fly past comets Wilson-Harrington and Borrelly. Deep Space 1 was followed by Stardust, the fourth of NASA's Discovery-class missions. Launched on Feb. 7, 1999, the Stardust craft was to fly through the

A telescope on board the TRACE satellite took this dramatic picture of the limb of the Sun in extreme ultraviolet light. The graceful arcs are blasts of intensely hot plasma suspended in twisting loops of the Sun's magnetic field.

corona at a resolution of one second of arc. That resolution is sufficient to monitor the plasma entrapped by the thin bundles of twisted magnetic lines of force that are presumed to dominate the transition region and contribute to coronal heating. A third solar probe, Spartan 201, made its fifth flight aboard a space shuttle in November 1998. Spartan 201 consisted of two coronagraphs, white light and ultraviolet. It was deployed by the shuttle for two days of observations and then recovered. Images from Spartan 201 were expected to help recalibrate instruments on the Solar and Heliospheric Observatory (SOHO) probe as they were returned to use following a temporary loss of contact with SOHO in mid-1998.

The Submillimeter Wave Astronomy Satellite, launched Dec. 5, 1998, carried dual heterodyne radiometers and a spectrometer to study star-forming interstellar clouds. The instruments measure emissions from water vapor, molecular oxygen, isotopic carbon monoxide, and atomic carbon.

NASA and prime contractor TRW completed the third of four "Great Observatories for Space Astrophysics." The first two were the Hubble Space Telescope and the Compton Gamma Ray Observatory, launched in 1990 and 1991, respectively. The third, the Advanced X-ray Astrophysics Facility, was formally renamed the Chandra X-ray Observatory for Indian-American Nobel laureate Subrahmanyan Chandrasekhar. It was scheduled to be launched in mid-to-late 1999 by the space shuttle *Columbia* under Eileen Collins, the first woman to command a shuttle mission. It then would be boosted into a higher orbit for a better view of the universe.

The observatory was built around a special set of mirrors that reflect X-rays in the range of 0.1–10 keV (thousands of electron volts). Like conventional telescopes, the assembly has parabolic primary and hyperbolic secondary mirrors. Their surfaces, however, must be almost parallel to the incoming X-rays in order to focus them by means of grazing incidence reflection (the same effect that makes light glare off a windshield at a shallow angle). Thus, the mirrors resemble slightly tapered tubes rather than conventional mirrors. Four sets of mirrors, nested within each other, are used to capture more X-rays and make a brighter image than a single mirror set could accomplish. Behind the mirrors are transmission gratings that can be swung into the X-ray path to diffract the X-rays, much like a prism spreading light into its colors. At the focal plane are two specialized X-ray cameras and spectrometers on a mechanism that will swing the appropriate instrument into position. Chandra complemented the Hubble Space Telescope's infrared-through-visible views of the universe. Unlike Hubble, however, Chandra's orbit was too high for the space shuttle to reach for servicing missions. Meanwhile, Hubble, entering its 10th year of life in 1999, will get an emergency servicing call in late 1999 by *Columbia* to replace failing attitude-sensing gyroscopes.

Europe's Infrared Space Observatory was turned off on May 16, 1998, when it ran out of the liquid helium that was needed to keep the telescope mirrors and instruments sufficiently cool to do their work. NASA was planning a Space Infrared Telescope Facility, the last of the four Great Observatories, for launch in 2001.

APPLICATIONS SATELLITES

Of the Earth-observation satellites launched during 1998, the largest was France's Satellite Probatoire d'Observation de la Terre (SPOT) 4 remote-sensing satellite, lofted into space on March 23. It carried multispectral cameras to monitor vegetation at a resolution of one kilometer and other cameras to provide resolution of 10–20 m (33–66 ft). Also on board was a laser transmitter to relay data through the planned Artemis satellite network. NASA delayed the launch of its SPOT-like satellite, Landsat 7, from late 1998 to April 1999. Continuing a series started in 1972, Landsat 7 introduced the new Enhanced Thematic Mapper Plus (ETM Plus) with finer resolution and more channels (colors) than the thematic mappers carried on earlier Landsats.

The U.S. Navy's Geosat Follow On, launched February 10, carried a radio altimeter and a water vapor radiometer to measure sea levels and glacial heights. An important environmental-studies satellite

was the Student Nitric Oxide Explorer (SNOE), launched February 26. Designed and built largely by students at the University of Colorado, Boulder, SNOE carried instruments to monitor stratospheric ozone, auroral ultraviolet emissions, and solar X-ray output.

Two South American nations launched Earth-science satellites in 1998. Brazil's SCD-2, sent up October 22, relayed data from environmental stations on the ground. Argentina's SAC-2 microsatellite, launched December 14, carried a Global Positioning System (GPS) receiver, a magnetometer, and a charge-coupled device (CCD) camera for whale tracking and other photographic observations. On July 10 Russia launched its RESURS-O natural-resources-sensing satellite. It also deployed several environmental microsatellites: Australia's WESTPAC, Israel's TECHSAT 1B, Thailand's TMSAT, Germany's SAFIR 2, and Chile's FASAT-B. They performed a range of duties, including monitoring ozone levels, natural resources, and vegetation.

In October 1998 NASA selected Francisco P.J. Valero of the Scripps Institution of Oceanography, La Jolla, Calif., to lead development of Triana, an Earth-observation mission initiated by U.S. Vice Pres. Al Gore. Triana will carry the Earth Polychromatic Imaging Camera, an advanced radiometer, and a small, next-generation space-weather monitoring instrument. (Triana is the name of the sailor on Columbus's voyage who first saw the New World.) The satellite will be placed in a "halo" orbit abound L-1, a gravitational balance point between the Earth and the Sun that is about 1.5 million km (932,000 mi) away from Earth. In this position, it will monitor the solar wind full time, and its camera will provide continuous color images of the sunlit side of Earth. The launch was scheduled for December 2000.

An important satellite, Clark, was canceled by NASA in the wake of the failure of the Lewis satellite in 1997. Lewis and Clark were to demonstrate a number of new technologies, including advanced miniature sensors. An investigation into the loss of Lewis after its August 1997 launch revealed a number of problems that led NASA to cancel the second satellite.

Earth was also being observed by SED-SAT-1, a mini-spacecraft developed by the Students for the Exploration and Development of Space at the University of Alabama in Huntsville. Its mission was to take images of Earth for distribution through the World Wide Web from the University of Arizona and to relay amateur radio communications.

The Tropical Rainfall Measuring Mission (TRMM) spacecraft, launched in 1997, completed its first year of operations with a number of significant achievements. It reduced uncertainties in global rainfall measurements by a factor of two, from approximately 50% to 25%, and provided strong clues (through the first spaceborne rain radar) that raindrops are significantly smaller when first formed than scientists had believed. It also revealed that lightning occurs more often in storms over land than over sea, apparently from enhanced convection over land. A surprise observed by TRMM was a set of massive chimney clouds 17 km (56,000 ft or 10.5 mi) high in Hurricane Bonnie in August 1998.

A detailed look at Earth was planned for September 1999, when *Endeavour* (STS-101) carries out the Shuttle Radar Topography Mission. This was to be a joint NASA–U.S. Department of Defense mission to obtain digital elevation data across much of Earth's surface. It would be the fourth shuttle mission to carry synthetic aperture radar, which produces high-resolution radar images comparable to those that would require a much larger antenna. Technologies for future satellites were being tested in Mightysat 1, which was placed in orbit on Dec. 15, 1998. The technologies included advanced gallium-arsenide solar cells, low-shock ejection mechanisms, debris detectors, and composite structures.

A flurry of launches of small communications satellites, including Iridium, Globalstar, and Orbcomm, took place during 1998. Iridium satellites were placed in low-Earth orbits inclined to the Equator. Each satellite acted as a relay station for Iridium cellular phones on Earth. As one satellite set below the horizon, it handed off the relay function to another satellite in view of the user and assumed relay duties for other users beyond the horizon. To the caller on the ground, this operation was seamless and invisible. The count for networked Iridium satellites grew to a total of 66, with launches ranging from as few as 2 satellites on one rocket to as many as 7 (most involved 5). This clustering ensured that the satellites were placed in orbits with the same inclination so that they could provide global coverage. Iridium satellites operated in orbits about 780 km (480 mi) high and inclined 86° to the Equator.

Eight Globalstar satellites were orbited in two Delta 2 launches (future Globalstars will use Russian launches). Globalstar, also designed for specialized cell phones, operated in an orbit about 1,400 km (870 mi) high and inclined 52° to the Equator. A total of 20 Orbcomm satellites were orbited. Orbcomm provides worldwide voice and data links for fixed or mobile industrial sites such as oil rigs, cargo trucks, and ships. These satellites were placed in orbits about 820 km (510 mi) high and inclined 108° to the Equator.

A significant newcomer to this competitive arena was the Teledesic 1 (also called the Broadband Advanced Technology Satellite), launched Feb. 25, 1998. It was a test model for a potential "Internet-in-the-sky" constellation that would consist of 288 minisatellites. Its orbit ranged in altitude from 535 to 580 km (330 to 360 mi), and its inclination to the Equator was 97.7°.

Also during the year, 36 conventional geostationary communications satellites were orbited for international consortia, industrial and less-developed nations, and government agencies. These included two advanced Intelsats. One of the most remarkable achievements was the salvage of

ASIASAT 3, launched in 1997 into a useless orbit. Hughes Aircraft purchased it from the insurer and used the craft's onboard propulsion to maneuver it toward the Moon and then exploited the Moon's gravity to reshape the orbit for insertion into a partially useful Earth orbit.

LAUNCH VEHICLES

Sea Launch, an ambitious U.S.-led venture to launch Ukrainian Zenit rockets from a Norwegian-developed launch platform at sea, made its maiden voyage in March 1999 after completion of its launch platform (converted from a floating offshore petroleum platform) and control ship. Sea Launch used a Zenit 3 launch vehicle, a three-stage rocket that can place up to 5,000 kg (11,000 lb) in geostationary transfer orbit. The Zenit booster and its dummy-satellite payload were prepared aboard the control ship at Sea Launch's

operations base in Long Beach, Calif., and then transferred to the floating, remote-controlled launch platform. The ship then sailed to the central Pacific Ocean, where the rocket was erected, loaded with propellant, and successfully launched. Should several launches a year be booked, Sea Launch planned to develop the option of carrying three Zenits in the control ship and reloading the platform at sea.

In October 1998 the U.S. Air Force selected Boeing Co. to supply 19 new Delta IV launch vehicles and Lockheed Martin Corp. to supply 9 Atlas 2AS vehicles for the Evolved Expendable Launch Vehicle program. The air force in 1997 had de-

William G. Hartenstein/Double H

Sea Launch's rocket is readied for liftoff from its launch platform, while its control ship cruises nearby. The successful flight of the rocket in March 1999 marked the first commercial launch from a floating platform at sea.

cided to select two contractors rather than one and then purchase quantities that provided the best value. On July 7 Russia tried a new approach, launching two German satellites, Tubsat N and N1, from a converted ballistic missile fired from a submarine.

A number of private launch endeavors were undertaken by companies and individuals who believed that they could take advantage of advanced materials and electronics and dispense with bureaucracies in order to develop cheaper, more innovative launch vehicles than those provided by national governments. One of the most interesting was Rotary Rocket Co.'s Roton, a craft using a helicopter landing scheme. Roton resembled the DC-X vertical launch/vertical landing test vehicle flown earlier in the 1990s. It was to be propelled by a ring of engines consuming kerosene in a tank at the bottom of the craft and liquid oxygen in a tank at the top. A two-person crew compartment and a small payload bay would be located between the tanks. The Roton would ascend to orbit like a conventional rocket, discharge its cargo (weighing up to one metric ton), and return to Earth on a short, ballistic reentry trajectory. The final phases of descent would be controlled by deployment of four helicopter blades attached to a rotor at the top of the craft. The blades would rotate freely and provide lift, like a helicopter landing in autorotation, or "windmill mode." Each Roton was to be recycled for its next flight in a day or two. During the past year, Rotary Rocket tested the engine system and started assembling the prototype vehicle. The first atmospheric test flights of the rotors were planned for mid-1999.

Another entrant, Kistler Aerospace Corp., put its plans on hold when an initial stock offering failed to raise the anticipated cash. Meanwhile, NASA pushed ahead with a number of launch programs. It selected four companies and three of its own centers to develop new space transportation concepts under the Future X program. Proposals ranged from Boeing's plan to fly an unmanned Advanced Technology Vehicle, which would test new technologies in orbit and reentry, to Marshall Space Flight Center's plan to use an electrodynamic tether, a bare wire cutting through Earth's magnetic field, to propel spacecraft without using fuel.

The X-33, a subscale test model of a proposed VentureStar Reusable Launch Vehicle that would ascend to orbit as a single unit and then fly back to Earth, moved ahead with testing of its rocket engines and heat shield and assembly of its first flight hardware. No boosters or tanks would be shed along the way. One of the innovative elements of the X-33 was the linear aerospike engine, which comprised two lines of burners firing along a wedge between them. The outer "wall" of the engine is formed by shock waves from the vehicle's high-speed flight. A 2.8-second firing in October 1998 at NASA's Stennis Space Center, Bay St. Louis, Miss., initiated tests that were expected to lead to full-scale testing of the engines. A section of the X-33's heat shield was flight tested aboard an F-15B jet fighter flying at 1.4 times the speed of sound. The heat shield consisted of metallic tiles and soft Advanced Flexible Reusable Surface Insulation tiles. The X-33's liquid oxygen tank, a complex, two-body structure, was completed, and assembly of the flight ve-

hicle was begun. The first test flight of the X-33 was scheduled for mid-2000.

NASA also moved to ensure complete testing for the X-34, a smaller reusable launcher that would be carried aloft by a Lockheed L-1011 jetliner. NASA began buying parts to make a second vehicle in case the first was seriously damaged. The X-34 is a single-engine winged rocket, 17.8 m (58.4 ft) long and spanning 8.5 m (27.9 ft). It was designed to fly as fast as eight times the speed of sound and reach altitudes up to 76 km (250,000 ft) and was also to demonstrate low-cost reusability, autonomous landing, subsonic flights through inclement weather, safe abort conditions, and landing in strong crosswinds. The first flight was scheduled to take place by 2000.

Several launch failures dotted the calendar during the year, including an attempt by amateurs to launch a satellite by "rockoon"—a combination of a booster rocket and a balloon that would lift the rocket to a high altitude before ignition. It also was the first attempt by amateurs to launch any satellite. Participants said that the failure was due to a problem in the balloon system. More spectacular failures occurred with the losses in August of a Titan 4 carrying a classified spy satellite and a Delta III launch vehicle, on its first flight, carrying a Galaxy X communications satellite. The Delta III comprised six large solid-fuel rocket boosters surrounding a liquid-propellant Delta II core and topped by an oxygen-hydrogen third stage and a nose cone 4 m (13 ft) wide for large satellites.

—Dave Dooling

See also Feature Article: YOU ARE HERE: NAVIGATION IN THE 21ST CENTURY.

TRANSPORTATION

During the past year, significant civil infrastructure improvements were made across all modes of transportation. The use of advanced technologies to improve traffic operations and safety increased in many countries. Multimodal integration was a common factor in the transportation networks of major metropolitan areas. The resulting facilities exhibited sophisticated telecommunications, new construction techniques and materials, and the partnering of public and private service providers. A heightened awareness of the effects of transportation on global climatic changes surfaced as an international issue among numerous countries. Creating balance between economic growth and the environment, while providing equitable access to all users, was seen as the means toward sustaining an effective integrated transportation system.

TEA-21

The U.S. Congress passed a bipartisan, $200 billion transportation bill in 1998. This legislation was entitled the Transportation Equity Act for the 21st Century (TEA-21). Cited as a historic piece of legislation, the bill increased spending from the Highway Trust Fund and guaranteed the linking of revenue into the Highway Account to highway transportation. TEA-21 was distinguished by a "firewall" that financially separated transportation investments from other existing discretionary funding categories such as defense and domestic programs.

In addition to the funding enhancements, TEA-21 provided considerable flexibility for state and local transportation providers. Innovative financing techniques

were encouraged, environmental protection was maintained, and the ability to transfer money between programs helped gain bipartisan support for the bill. An average of $27 billion was authorized for annual expenditure. Significant improvements in transportation infrastructure and technology were envisioned as the authorized funds are supplemented with other public and private dollars.

A few examples of the programs funded by TEA-21 included improvements to the Interstate Highway System, intelligent transportation systems (ITS), replacement and rehabilitation of deficient bridges, air quality mitigation, public transit financing, safety improvement projects, and innovative approaches to motor carrier safety. Approximately 4,000 lives are expected to be saved due to the improvements anticipated on existing roadways.

Intelligent transportation systems

The application of advanced technologies to surface transportation facilities continued during the past year. Intelligent transportation systems use electronic communication networks to improve traffic flow and safety in rural and urban areas. Recent ITS projects included deployment initiatives in various cities throughout the world, installation of video-based adaptive traffic signal systems, integrated traveler information applications, freeway traffic management centers, weather advisory systems, and continued development of "smart" vehicles. Full integration among the various modes of travel continued to evolve. Computer architectures that will permit individual components to work cooperatively as future systems are con-

structed were being developed in many parts of the world.

Four ITS metropolitan model deployment initiatives took place in the United States during the year. Seattle, Wash.; San Antonio, Texas; Phoenix, Ariz.; and the New York City metropolitan area had been selected as participants in major urban area projects jointly sponsored by the Federal Highway Administration and the Federal Transit Administration. Travelers in those areas, using various electronic devices, received traffic condition updates, transit arrival information, parking availability notices, and other related transportation information. Formal evaluations were underway to determine the effectiveness of these efforts.

The Seattle initiative, Smart Trek, is a partnership with 25 public agencies and provides traveler information updates. The real-time information was provided online, at kiosks, and through the use of personal digital devices. Variable message signs and highway-advisory radio broadcasts were used throughout the region. Transit vehicles were monitored via automatic vehicle locators. "Mayday" devices using the 9-1-1 systems and Global Positioning System (GPS) equipment were used to reduce emergency response time. The Seattle freeway traffic management system used closed-circuit television cameras and highway detection sensors to provide surveillance on the freeways.

TransGuide in San Antonio included a telecommunications system that provided two-way video conferencing between emergency medical personnel in a trauma center and ambulance paramedics. Approximately 20,000 drivers placed on their vehicles "traffic tag" sensors that transmit signals to the operations center in order to calculate average traffic flow along the freeways and other major streets in the urban area. TransGuide also uses fiber optics, sensors, and video cameras to monitor changes in traffic conditions and then respond to specific incidents with preprogrammed scenarios.

Phoenix established a partnership, AZTech, that includes public and private companies, cities, and state, county, transit, and emergency services agencies. Their network was supported by road sensors, cameras, and computers that communicate via 13 operations centers in the urbanized area. A "peer-to-peer permissive control" allows the sharing of the field equipment among the partners. GPS was used on more than 80 buses to track their progress; travel-time information was available at kiosks and an Internet site.

The iTravel model deployment served New York City, Long Island, the lower Hudson River valley, southwest Connecticut, and northern and central New Jersey. Traveler information includes accidents and other incidents on the roads, weather, special events, and construction-related activities. iTravel information was provided free via telephone and the Internet. Regional transit trip information consisted of route guidance, schedules, rates, and arrival-time information. A subscription-based customized Personalized Traveler System was available for daily commuters who desired real-time travel information that was sent directly to them via telephone, E-mail, fax, or pager as travel conditions changed.

One of the largest ITS traffic signal systems in North America was built in Oakland County, Michigan. The goal of the Road Commission for Oakland County (RCOC) was to ease traffic congestion and improve safety. Using an overhead machine-vision technology to provide vehicle detection, FAST-TRAC (Faster and Safer Travel Through Routing and Advanced Controls) was established as the advanced traffic management system. Cameras were used at intersections to detect the presence of vehicles. The information was fed to a computer controller, SCATS (The Sydney Coordinated Adaptive Traffic System), which processed the detector data used to regulate the traffic signals. Approximately 350 traffic signals were equipped with SCATS; RCOC planned to include all of the county's 1,100 signals in the future.

Orlando, Fla., installed a Surveillance and Motorist Information System (SMIS) along Interstate 4. It was designed to provide real-time traffic information to the Metro Orlando computerized signal system so that signals could be timed immediately to handle traffic diverted from I-4 incidents. Since I-4 accommodated both heavy commuter and heavy tourist traffic, roadside variable message signs were set up to provide additional motorist information. The experimental signs used a "flip-disk" technology that displayed freeway exit numbers and names of specific tourist destinations.

Salt Lake City, Utah, the site of the 2002 Winter Olympics, began incorporating an $80 million Advanced Traffic Management System into a $1.75 billion design-and-build project on 27 km (1 km is about 0.62 mi) of Interstate 15. To expedite the overall project, the designers worked directly with the highway builders during the construction process. Three traffic control centers were designed to coordinate 550 traffic signals by means of information from incident detection devices and from remote cameras on freeways and arterial streets. The Utah Department of Transportation also planned to use freeway traffic management computer software during the Olympic events; the software was introduced during the 1996 Olympic Games in Atlanta, Ga.

Many toll roadways converted during the year to electronic toll collection (ETC) technologies, which used vehicle tags to debit tolls remotely. South Americans were increasingly buying tags for use on several ETC roadways in Argentina and Brazil. By 1999 the Acceso Norte highway in Buenos Aires had ETC equipment on more than 100 lanes with 150,000 transponders. The first Brazilian ETC system, on the Rio-Niterói Bridge, linked the cities of Niterói and Rio de Janeiro. Besides providing a convenience to motorists, the vehicle tags improved traffic flow operations and safety.

The 5th World Congress on ITS was held in Seoul, S. Kor., in October 1998. With vehicle ownership increasing by one million vehicles per year in the past 10 years, ITS deployment was being coordinated throughout South Korea. A National ITS Master Plan included traffic management systems, traveler information, commercial vehicle services, and the development of an advanced vehicle-highway system. A total of $3.4 billion was budgeted for the plan. Funding comes from the central government, local agencies, and the private sector. The Olympic Expressway in Seoul was monitored by image-detecting, closed-circuit TV cameras placed along the freeway. Variable message signs were controlled from a traffic management center that operated 24 hours a day, every day of the year.

To demonstrate the benefits of ITS to commercial vehicle operations, the Federal Highway Administration's Office of Motor Carriers and the Office of Technology Applications, plus numerous private partners, developed a semi with a trailer filled with computers that ran truck-routing software applications, video clips, and in-vehicle and other safety related technologies. The truck served as a classroom on wheels and toured the U.S. in 1998. A unique feature was a full-sized tractor-cab simulator that contained a suite of technologies for demonstrations of various mobile communications applications. Examples included collision-avoidance instrumentation, breath alcohol detection, transponders for a weigh-station bypass, and an onboard computer to record road speed and mileage.

Road transport

In October 1989 the Loma Prieta earthquake caused the collapse of the double-deck Cypress Freeway in Oakland, Calif. Reconstruction included the rerouting of the I-880 expressway to San Francisco. The project's budget was $1.1 billion for a new right-of-way, relocation of a railroad and utilities, and related traffic management strategies. Completed in 1998, the rebuilt Cypress Freeway incorporated the latest technology and standards for seismic design. The project improved railroad facilities and trucking depots and provided access to the port of Oakland and community businesses.

A privately financed toll road, E-470, being built around Denver, Colo., was designed to provide improved access to the Denver International Airport. The new road was equipped with an ETC over its 48-km length. It was four lanes in width and was designed to be expanded to eight in the future; space was also provided for additional public transit service.

Australia's National Highway 1, in the state of New South Wales, was being reconstructed through difficult terrain and with sensitivity to the surrounding natural environment. The $76 million improvement was a bypass to existing winding roads and provided a four-lane roadway divided by a median strip. The highway traversed pastureland, mountains, rain forest, and swamps. Because of the terrain in the area some cuts were as deep as 49 m (1 m

To demonstrate the benefits of intelligent transportation systems, U.S. federal agencies and private industry developed a semi (right) fitted with equipment (above) that included collision-avoidance instrumentation and a computer to record road speed and mileage.

(Above and right) Courtesy of FHWA Technology Truck Project

is about 3.28 ft), and some embankments were 24 m high.

In Perth, Australia, a new road tunnel was being constructed using a "top-down" method that minimizes the need to take existing land. The land above the tunnel was to be sold to the private sector for future development. The tunneling excavation began after the walls and a concrete roof slab were in place. The wall panels were 80 cm thick (31.5 in) and as much as 30 m high by 6 m long. Approximately seven panels per week were installed using an innovative 100-m-long conveyor suspended from a monorail attached to the ceiling of the tunnel. The conveyor loaded trucks with soil that was to be removed from the tunnel while the flooring was being prepared immediately behind the trucks. The resulting roadway was 23 m wide and was laid as 14.75-m-long floor blocks of poured reinforced concrete.

Construction progressed on the Denmark and Sweden tunnel-bridge link to the point where the high-bridge pylons were erected and the bridge deck elements were being placed. The crossing was approximately 16 km in length and was a combination of a four-lane roadway and a dual track-electrified

railway between the two countries. The construction consisted of a 3,500-m immersed tube tunnel that emerged onto a constructed island in the Øresund that also supported the approaching bridge. Each of the 20 tube tunnel units was 176 m long and weighed approximately 57,000 metric tons. On the high-bridge section two 204-m-high reinforced concrete pylons supported a single crossbeam and bridge girders. When completed, the pylons would be Sweden's highest construction.

On April 5, 1998, the world's longest suspension bridge was opened in Japan. Connecting the islands of Shikoku and Honshu, the Akashi Kaikyo Bridge had a main span that was 1,991 m long and two side spans of 960 m each. The bridge deck was constructed over a 14-m-deep and 35.5-m-wide truss girder system suspended above sea level. Two steel towers rising 298 m above sea level supported the

The first cars to cross the newly completed Great Belt East Bridge arrive at Denmark's Zealand Island in June 1998. At 1,624 m it was the world's second longest suspension bridge.

Opening in April 1998, the longest suspension bridge in the world, the Akashi Kaikyo, connected the Japanese islands of Honshu and Shikoku. Its main span was 1,991 m long, and each of its two side spans measured 960 m.

Rossi Xavier/Gamma Liaison International

main cables; the shipping lane clearance was 65 m in water 110 m deep. The main cables' strands were fabricated of 127 galvanized wires, each 5.23 mm (0.206 in) in diameter. To provide aerodynamic stability, the bridge deck was designed and constructed using vertical plates at the bottom center of the highway deck. The complex construction took 10 years to complete and reportedly was accomplished with few injuries to workers and no deaths.

Air transport

Gardenmoen Airport, north of Oslo, contained a 137,000-sq m terminal (1 sq m is about 10.8 sq ft), a train station, and a 350-room hotel. Due to environmental considerations, this facility took almost 25 years from conception to completion. Norway's state bank provided NKr 10 billion in 30-year loans and another NKr 1 billion in equity capital to finance the project. Two parallel, independent runways accommodated approximately 80 flights per hour. The terminal was designed to handle up to 17 million passengers per year via 64 check-in counters. The new airport was expected to increase competition for travelers, provide additional European routes, and enhance international service.

The largest offshore airport complex in the world was under construction in the suburbs of Seoul. Inchon International Airport (IIA) was designed to serve the region's international traffic, and Kimpo International Airport would support domestic travel. At more than $5 billion, the development was referred to as a "pentaport" because it also included a seaport, a business center, a telecommunications facility, and a recreation complex. Because

of the airport's offshore location, noise problems were expected to be minimized. Construction costs for land preparation were also low because two adjacent islands were connected by using excavation from the island mountains and sand dredged from the sea. An approximately 16-km dike surrounded the entire project. IIA was expected initially to handle 27 million passengers per year with provisions to accommodate 100 million by 2020. Parallel runways would provide for 170,000 flights per year in the first phase of operation. The airport's transportation center would contain terminals for intercity trains, intra-airport transit, and people-mover systems. Financial support was provided by a combination of government, capital markets, and private investments. An airport expressway and railroad were being financed privately.

Hong Kong International Airport, one of the world's largest infrastructure projects at approximately $20 billion, included related roadways, bridges, railroads, and tunnels. Approximately 75% of the airport site consisted of land reclaimed from the sea. The total area of the airport island was

1,248 ha (3,082 ac), which was the result of connecting Chek Lap Kok island to Lam Chau island. The terminal was eight stories high and contained 288 check-in counters to initially serve 35 million passengers and 2.5 million metric tons of air cargo per year. Rail transportation was designed to handle nearly 40% of the total number of air passengers.

In the U.S. a new approach was being taken to building a midfield terminal complex at the Detroit Metropolitan Airport in Romulus, Mich. Northwest Airlines was the project manager and was supervising the design and construction of the terminal and was responsible for any cost overruns. The county would maintain oversight, approve all design elements, and lease the concession space. When construction was completed, Northwest would occupy the new, 85-gate, $958 million midfield terminal; the existing terminal would serve other carriers. One noted characteristic of the new terminal was that the planned people mover would be inside the new terminal, riding on a cushion of air and running along one side of the building. Passengers on this elevated train would be able to see their gates as they moved through the terminal. A fourth parallel runway was planned as the airport redevelopment continued into 2001.

Rail transport

In preparation for the 2002 Winter Games in Salt Lake City, a 40-km light-rail transit line (TRAX) was being completed. The system would consist of two lines, one between downtown Salt Lake City and the town of Sandy and the other from the airport to the University of Utah. The 24-km downtown connector was estimated to cost more than $300 million and the university line $400 million. The Utah Transit Authority was projecting 14,000 riders daily on the downtown line and 10,000 riders for the university line. During the competition, the Olympic athletes would be housed at the university. The downtown connector began operation as a test track, having received 8 of the 23 light-rail vehicles in the summer of 1998. Total TRAX daily ridership was projected to reach 34,000 by 2020.

The first design-build-operate-maintain transit project in the U.S. was under construction by a public-private partnership between New Jersey Transit and a consortium company, the 21st Century Rail Corp. The consortium would operate and maintain the system for 15 years; New Jersey Transit would retain ownership of the resulting project. Upon completion of all phases, the system line would be 33 km long with 32 stations and serve approximately 100,000 riders daily. Estimated total cost was $1.1 billion to cover all aspects from design through maintenance. The line would begin in Bayonne, N.J.,

and extend through Jersey City, N.J., to Hoboken, N.J., in the initial phase. Later phases, to be completed by 2010, would extend the project to Lombardi on the New Jersey Turnpike in Bergen County, N.J.

Ground was broken during the past year for a 32-km intermodal road and rail route to connect the ports of Los Angeles and Long Beach, Calif., to downtown Los Angeles. At a cost of $2 billion the Alameda Corridor would provide a common connector for several railroad lines and also eliminate 200 railroad at-grade crossings. Projected cargo traffic in 2001 was estimated at 200 million metric tons for the ports each year. Street traffic flow would move unimpeded, and the land-bound trains (from port-to-downtown) would be able to travel at 64 km/h (40 mph) through the corridor. One-half of the track corridor was being constructed in a trench 15 m wide and 9 m deep and would accommodate two tracks.

Rail competition in the U.S. increased during the year, as CSX and Norfolk Southern railroads acquired Conrail. The transaction was valued at more than $20 billion. Benefits to users included rate reductions, operating efficiencies, and reduced highway pavement damage as a result of truck traffic shifting to rail transport. Norfolk Southern planned to operate 6,000 Conrail route miles for a total of 20,400 miles; CSX gained 3,600 miles for a total of 22,100 route miles.

Railroad derailments decreased in North America owing to the application of new technologies to detect potential derailments and vehicle and track structure improvements. The overheating of wheel bearings and broken rails were the principal causes of derailments. Remote sensing

of the condition of the wheel bearings detected when rapid heating was taking place. To detect rail flaws, ultrasonic applications were being used in combination with electronic sensors. Rail flaws can be caused by wheel "flats" and out-of-round wheels that produce undesirable dynamic vibrations. As train car weights increase, rail damage also increases. Automated Truck Performance Measurement Systems used sensors on the rail to measure lateral and vertical forces as the wheels negotiate a horizontal rail curve. The measurements reveal the "signature" of each train truck and identify bad performers. Once identified via a tag reader on each car, a dispatcher down the line can remove the poor performers from the system and minimize additional future damage or potential rail failure.

Marine transport

Freeport on Grand Bahama island has been used primarily as a cruise ship and island supply port for many years. A joint venture between Hutchison Port Holdings and the Grand Bahama Development Co. called the Freeport Container Port completed an 18-ha (45-ac) addition to the harbor and supplied it with four container cranes. The port's deep harbor was also expanding due to mining of natural limestone in the harbor area. It was anticipated that much of the new freight business would be transshipment container cargoes that would link east-west and north-south routes.

During the past year, the 300-m-long, 6,000-TEU (20-foot-equivalent unit) *Regina Maersk* arrived in the New York City harbor. Such large vessels drew attention to the need for deeper channels at U.S. ports. Some containers must be unloaded before reaching a major port because some channels are too shallow. The New York harbor's main channel was 14 m deep, and the main channel at Norfolk, Va., was 15 m, compared with 18 m at Halifax, N.S. Some west coast U.S. ports, however, had main channel depths near 24 m. The problem facing many ports was funding the dredging of ship channels. In the U.S. the federal government provided the harbor access channels; ports were responsible for terminal infrastructure and dredging their berths. Since the 1986 Water Resources Act, ports shared 60% of the improvement costs for channels more than 14 m deep. The increasing number of large ships seemed certain to cause harbors to seek the means to deepen their channels.

A major Asian alliance pursued during the year created a "large slot-exchange" agreement in the Pacific trade. The three lines included the China Ocean Shipping Co. (COSCO), Japanese carrier "K" Line, and Taiwan's Yangming Marine Transport. All partners operated independently but exchanged harbor slots. The arrangement was a noticeable strategic change for COSCO from state control to a more co-operative policy. While competition continued to be maintained, the partnership was seen as an opportunity for further mutual development among the three carriers.

Sustainable transportation

The significant funding provided in TEA-21 was expected to support the construction and rehabilitation of the surface transportation infrastructure across the U.S. Environmental issues, however, remained a critical concern in sustaining a safe and efficient transportation system.

The U.S. was not alone in its concern for providing sustainable transportation. More than 150 nations convened in Kyoto, Japan, to address transportation issues as they were related to environmental impacts, economic growth, and equity among the global community.

Although transportation was not the only contributor to global climate changes, it was responsible for approximately one-third of the primary sources. With gasoline prices relatively low, the public's concern for higher fuel economy waned. Additionally, the Federal Highway Administration reported that the U.S. contributed to the environment a disproportionate share of greenhouse gases and motor vehicle emissions. Steps toward sustaining a responsible transportation system consequently included both future technology advances and changes in transportation preferences.

The application of ITS technologies continued to demonstrate benefits by reducing travel time and enhancing traffic safety. Additional vehicle-fuels research and engine technology seemed certain to produce lower emission rates in the next-generation vehicle fleet. Improvements to public transportation, additional provisions for pedestrians and bicyclists, regional land planning, and growth management strategies also were expected to contribute to maintaining a safe and efficient global transportation system.

—John M. Mason

See also Feature Article: YOU ARE HERE: NAVIGATION IN THE 21ST CENTURY.

One of the world's largest containerships, the 300-m-long 6,000-TEU (20-foot-equivalent unit) *Regina Maersk,* **passes through New Jersey on its way to the New York City harbor in July 1998. Many ports had channels too shallow to accommodate vessels of that size.**

SCIENTISTS OF THE YEAR

NOBEL PRIZES

The 1998 Nobel Prizes were announced in Stockholm and Oslo on October 8–16. In the fields of chemistry, physics, and physiology or medicine, the awards recognized a notable diversity of individual achievements, including the use of quantum mechanics to study and model chemical processes at the molecular level, the discovery that under certain conditions electrons in semiconductors can act like a fluid and behave as if they had fractional electric charges, and the groundbreaking finding that the simple compound nitric oxide—perhaps more familiar as a common air pollutant—is also a regulator of critical life processes in the human body. The following article describes the prizewinners and their work in detail.

NOBEL PRIZE FOR CHEMISTRY

"As we approach the end of the 1990s, we are seeing the result of an enormous theoretical and computational development, and the consequences are revolutionizing the whole of chemistry." So stated the Royal Swedish Academy of Sciences in its award of the 1998 Nobel Prize for Chemistry to "the two most prominent figures in this process," Walter Kohn and John A. Pople. Kohn, an Austrian-born American physicist at the University of California, Santa Barbara, and Pople, a British citizen and mathematical chemist at Northwestern University, Evanston, Ill., were widely acknowledged pioneers in devising computational methods to study the properties of interactions of molecules.

The development of quantum mechanics in physics in the early 1900s offered chemists the potential for a deep new mathematical understanding of their science. Nevertheless, describing the quantum mechanics of large molecules, which are very complex systems, involved what appeared to be impossibly difficult computations. Chemists remained stymied until the 1960s, when computers for solving these complex equations became available. Quantum chemistry, the application of quantum mechanics to chemical problems, emerged as a new branch of chemistry. "Quantum chemistry is used nowadays in practically all branches of chemistry, always with the aim of increasing our knowledge of the inner structure of matter," the Swedish Academy said. "The sci-

entific work of Walter Kohn and John Pople has been crucial for the development of this new field of research."

Kohn and Pople made contributions as closely related as the two faces of a coin. The Swedish Academy cited Kohn for development of the density-functional theory in the 1960s. It simplified the mathematical description of bonding between atoms that make up molecules. Pople was cited for having developed computational methods, based on quantum mechanics, which he packaged in 1970 in the computer program Gaussian. Gaussian later became the basic tool used by thousands of scientists worldwide for modeling and studying molecules and chemical reactions.

Before Kohn's and Pople's work, chemists thought that a description of the quantum

Sharing the 1998 Nobel Prize for Chemistry were John A. Pople (left) and Walter Kohn (top).

(Top) Phil Klein/AP/Wide World Photos;
(left) AP/Wide World Photos

mechanics of molecules required precise knowledge of the motion of every electron in every atom in a molecule. In 1964 Kohn showed that it is sufficient only to know the average number of electrons at any one point in space—*i.e.,* the electron density. For determining that information Kohn introduced a computational method that became known as the density-functional theory. Years of additional research, however, were needed before chemists were able to apply the theory to large-scale studies of molecules. By the late 1990s the theory had become widely used as the basis for solving many problems in chemistry—for example, calculating the geometrical structure of large molecules such as enzymes and mapping the course of chemical reactions.

Pople's research in the 1960s led to the discovery of a new approach for analyzing the electronic structure of molecules, based on the fundamental laws of quantum mechanics. He put the approach, called theoretical model chemistry, into a computer program that allowed chemists to create computer models of chemical reactions that were difficult or impossible to run in a laboratory. One use of such information was, in the development of new drugs, to determine how a molecule would react inside the body. In the early 1990s Pople incorporated Kohn's density-functional theory into the program, making possible the analysis of more complex molecules. The original program, Gaussian 70, was updated and improved over the years. Its commercial version, marketed by Gaussian Inc., Pittsburgh, Pa., was one of the most widely used quantum chemistry programs.

Kohn was born on March 9, 1923, in Vienna and received a Ph.D. in physics from Harvard University in 1948. He de-

veloped his density-functional theory while at the University of California, San Diego (1960–79). In 1979 he became founding director of the Institute for Theoretical Physics at the University of California, Santa Barbara, where he later served as a professor (1984–91). Pople was born in Burnham-on-Sea, Somerset, Eng., on Oct. 31, 1925. He received a Ph.D. in mathematics in 1951 from the University of Cambridge. He became a professor at Carnegie Mellon University, Pittsburgh, in 1964 and a professor at Northwestern in 1993.

NOBEL PRIZE FOR PHYSICS

The 1998 Nobel Prize for Physics was awarded to three scientists, a German and two Americans, who discovered that electrons in semiconductors placed in very strong magnetic fields at extremely low temperatures demonstrate bizarre behavior. Under such conditions electrons condense to form a quantum fluid similar to the quantum fluids that occur in superconductivity and liquid helium. Electrons in the fluid act, seemingly impossibly, as if they have only a fraction of a whole electron charge. "What makes these fluids particularly important for researchers is that events in a drop of quantum fluid can afford more profound insights into the general inner structure and dynamics of matter," stated the Royal Swedish Academy of Sciences in its prize announcement. "The contributions of the three laureates have thus led to yet another breakthrough in our understanding of quantum physics and to the development of new theoretical concepts of significance in many branches of modern physics."

The prize was shared by Horst L. Störmer of Columbia University, New York City, Daniel C. Tsui of Princeton University, and Robert B. Laughlin of Stanford University. Störmer was born on April 6, 1949, in Frankfurt am Main, Ger., and received a Ph.D. in physics in 1977 from the University of Stuttgart. Tsui, a naturalized U.S. citizen, was born in Henan, China, on Feb. 28, 1939, and earned a Ph.D. in physics in 1967 from the University of Chicago. Laughlin, born on Nov. 1, 1950, in Visalia, Calif., received his Ph.D. in physics in 1979 from the Massachusetts Institute of Technology.

Störmer and Tsui were cited for the discovery in 1982 of a new aspect of a phenomenon first demonstrated in an 1879 experiment by Edwin H. Hall, a U.S. physicist. Hall found that when a conductor carrying an electric current is placed in a magnetic field that is perpendicular to the current flow, an electric field is created that is perpendicular to both the current and the magnetic field. This phenomenon, called the Hall effect, occurs because the magnetic field deflects the flow of electrons toward one side of the current-carrying material. The electric field gives rise to a voltage, called the Hall voltage, and the ratio of this voltage to the current is called the Hall resistance. The Hall effect, which occurs in both conductors and semiconductors, later became a standard measurement tool in physics laboratories around the world.

In 1980 the German physicist Klaus von Klitzing discovered a variation of the Hall effect, which came to be called the integer quantum Hall effect. For moderate applied magnetic fields, the Hall resistance changes smoothly with changes in the strength of the field. Klitzing, however, used high-

(Below) Mike Derer/AP/Wide World Photos; (right) AP/Wide World Photos; (bottom) Archive Photos

Winning the 1998 Nobel Prize for Physics were Horst L. Störmer (right), Daniel C. Tsui (far right), and Robert B. Laughlin (bottom).

magnetic fields and temperatures near absolute zero to study the Hall effect in a semiconductor device in which electron motion was confined to two dimensions. Under those conditions he found that varying the magnetic field causes the Hall resistance to change not smoothly but rather in discrete steps, a behavior physicists described as being quantized. Klitzing won the 1985 Nobel Prize for Physics for his work.

In 1982 Störmer and Tsui, then at Bell Laboratories, Murray Hill, N.J., carried out a similar experiment using even lower temperatures and stronger fields. To their surprise they found more steps in the Hall resistance, some of them lying between Klitzing's integer steps. Whereas the integer quantum Hall effect could be understood in terms of the behavior of individual electrons, the new effect suggested that the involved particles had fractional electric charges—one-third, one-fifth, or one-seventh that of an electron. The finding mystified and excited physicists, who searched for an explanation.

A year later Laughlin, at Bell Labs and then Lawrence Livermore National Laboratory, Livermore, Calif., in the early 1980s, solved the mystery with a theoretical explanation. He proposed that the low temperature and intense magnetic field made the electrons condense into a new kind of quantum fluid. Earlier researchers had observed other quantum fluids at very low temperatures in liquid helium and in superconductor materials. Laughlin's quantum fluid exhibited many bizarre properties, including one in which the participating electrons behaved as fractionally charged "quasiparticles." Laughlin showed that such quasiparticles had exactly the right electric charges to explain Störmer and Tsui's findings.

The Swedish Academy stated that the laureates' work in 1982–83 represented "an indirect demonstration of the new quantum fluid and its fractionally charged quasiparticles." Verification came only in the late 1990s thanks to "astonishing developments in microelectronics" that made it possible to obtain more direct evidence for the existence of quasiparticles.

NOBEL PRIZE FOR PHYSIOLOGY OR MEDICINE

Three American scientists, Robert F. Furchgott of the State University of New York (SUNY) Health Science Center in Brooklyn, Ferid Murad of the University of Texas Medical School in Houston, and Louis J. Ignarro of the University of California School of Medicine in Los Angeles, won the 1998 Nobel Prize for Physiology or Medicine for discovering that a gas, nitric oxide (NO), acts as a signaling molecule in the cardiovascular system. Their work, the bulk of which was performed in the 1980s, uncovered an entirely new mechanism for how blood vessels in the body relax and widen. It led to the development of the anti-impotence drug Viagra and potential new approaches for understanding and treating other diseases.

The Nobel Assembly of the Karolinska Institute in Stockholm, which presented the prize, said that the identification of a biological role for NO was surprising for several reasons. Nitric oxide was known mainly as a harmful air pollutant, released

Louis J. Ignarro (far left), Robert F. Furchgott (left), and Ferid Murad (below) shared the 1998 Nobel Prize for Physiology or Medicine.

into the atmosphere from automobile engines and other combustion sources. In addition, it was a simple molecule, very different from the complex neurotransmitters and other signaling molecules that regulate many biological events. No other known gas acts as a signaling molecule in the body.

Nitric oxide's role began to emerge in the 1970s and '80s. In 1977 Murad, then at the University of Virginia, showed that nitroglycerin and several related heart drugs induce the formation of NO and that the colorless, odorless gas acts to increase the diameter of blood vessels in the body. Murad was born on Sept. 14, 1936, in Whiting, Ind., and received his M.D. and Ph.D. degrees from Western Reserve University (later Case Western Reserve University), Cleveland, Ohio, in 1965. Murad was also cited by the committee for work that he accomplished at Stanford University in the 1980s and later at Abbott Laboratories in Illinois.

Around 1980 Furchgott, in an ingenious experiment, demonstrated that cells in the endothelium, or inner lining, of blood vessels produce an unknown signaling molecule. The molecule, which he named endothelium-derived relaxing factor (EDRF), signals smooth muscle cells in blood vessel walls to relax, dilating the vessels. Furchgott was born on June 4, 1916, in

Charleston, S.C. In 1940 he earned a Ph.D. in biochemistry from Northwestern University, Evanston, Ill., and he joined SUNY-Brooklyn's Department of Pharmacology in 1956.

The Nobel Committee cited Ignarro for "a brilliant series of analyses" that demonstrated that EDRF was nitric oxide. Ignarro's research, conducted in 1986, was done independently of Furchgott's own work to identify EDRF. It was the first discovery that a gas could act as a signaling molecule in a living organism. Ignarro, who was born on May 31, 1941, in Brooklyn, gained a Ph.D. in pharmacology from the University of Minnesota. Before making his significant discovery at UCLA, he was professor of pharmacology (1979–85) at Tulane University's School of Medicine, New Orleans.

Furchgott and Ignarro first announced their findings at a scientific conference in 1986, triggering an international boom in research on nitric oxide. Scientists later showed that NO is manufactured by many different kinds of cells in the body and has

a role in regulating a variety of body functions. The Nobel Assembly said that the scientists' research was key to the development of the highly successful drug Viagra, which acts to increase NO's effect in penile blood vessels. Researchers expected that other medical applications of knowledge about NO would come in treating heart disease, shock, and cancer. Tests that analyze production of NO also could improve the diagnosis of lung diseases such as asthma and intestinal disorders such as colitis.

The Nobel Assembly cited one irony about the award. When Alfred Nobel, inventor of dynamite, became ill with heart disease, his physicians advised him to take

nitroglycerin. Dynamite consists of nitroglycerin absorbed in a material called kieselguhr, which makes nitroglycerin less likely to explode accidentally. Nobel, however, refused, unable to understand how the explosive could relieve chest pain. It took science 100 years to find the answer in NO, the Assembly said.

—Michael Woods

OBITUARIES

Barton, Sir Derek Harold Richard
Sept. 8, 1918—March 16, 1998

British chemist Sir Derek Barton altered the landscape of modern chemistry by originating the fields of conformational analysis and stereochemistry. He showed how differences in the spatial structure, or conformation, of molecules relate to differences in their reactivity and how the differences can be calculated by analyzing the conformation of the molecules. In 1950 Barton presented a theory that described organic molecules as having preferred three-dimensional forms that determine their chemical properties, a revolutionary concept that soon became a basic principle of modern chemistry. For this he was awarded the 1969 Nobel Prize for

Sir Derek Barton

Gamma Liaison International

Chemistry, along with Odd Hassel of Norway, who had earlier shown how chemically identical molecules can have different conformations. Barton left the family carpentry business to study chemistry at Imperial College of Science and Technology, University of London (B.S., 1940; Ph.D., 1942). After wartime service in military intelligence, he returned to Imperial College to teach physical chemistry, publishing calculations of the preferred three-dimensional shape of organic molecules. While a visiting professor (1949–50) at Harvard University, he presented a landmark four-page paper on conformational analysis, *The Conformation of the Steroid Nucleus* (1950), which explained the unusual reaction rates of steroids and related isomers. His findings won quick acceptance and were soon in-

corporated into basic science curricula. He returned to London as a reader at Birkbeck College (1950–55), where he uncovered the properties of phenol oxidative coupling and investigated how poppies produce morphine. During his career he also examined new chemical reactions and syntheses, experimenting with santonin, aldosterone, sulfur, photochemistry, fluorination, penicillin, and free radicals. After a brief stint at the University of Glasgow, Scot. (1955–57), he returned (1957) to Imperial College as chemistry chairman and remained there until 1978, when he became director of the Institute for the Chemistry of Natural Substances, Gil-sur-Yvette, France. In 1986 he joined the faculty at Texas A&M University, and at the time of his death, he was working on the oxidation of saturated hydrocarbons. Barton, who was knighted in 1972, was the author of more than 1,000 scientific papers, owner of many patents, mentor to hundreds of students, and a valued scientific consultant.

Cormack, Allan MacLeod
Feb. 23, 1924—May 7, 1998

South African-born American physicist Allan Cormack formulated the mathematical algorithms that made possible the development of the cross-sectional X-ray imaging process known as computerized axial tomography (CAT) scanning, for which he was awarded a share of the 1979 Nobel Prize for Physiology or Medicine. A lecturer in physics at the University of Cape Town, Cormack was hired for a part-time job at Cape Town's Groote Schuur Hospital in 1955 because of a regulation requiring that trained physicists calculate radiation doses for cancer therapy, even though he had no medical training and knew nothing about medical diagnostics. Cormack observed the inadequacies of X-ray technology, whose imprecise images made diagnosis haphazard. He determined that much greater precision could be achieved by taking many X-ray images of the same body part from different perspectives and then integrating the data to produce a single image. Recognizing that the problem was fundamentally mathematical, Cormack published the results of his work in two papers in 1963 and 1964, documenting a technique that represented a vast improvement over conventional X-ray imaging methods and permitted a much more precise differentiation of soft tissues. Cormack never attempted to build a working tomographic scanner that would demonstrate the technique he had formulated, and his papers attracted little notice. His work was reproduced independently in the early 1970s by the British engineer Godfrey Newbold Hounsfield, whose CAT scanning machine gained worldwide attention, and with whom Cormack shared the Nobel Prize. After his tenure (1950–56) at the University of Cape Town, Cormack held a one-year research fellowship at Harvard University, then moved to Tufts University, Medford, Mass., where he remained until his retirement in 1980, studying the interaction of subatomic particles and refining the mathematics of tomographic imaging methods. Cormack became a member of the American Academy of Arts and Sciences in 1980.

Costa, Lúcio
Feb. 27, 1902—June 13, 1998

Brazilian architect Lúcio Costa was the creator of the master plan for Brasília, the

capital of Brazil, and helped to establish the modern architectural aesthetic in the country. Six years after graduating (1924) with a degree in architecture from the National School of Fine Arts in Rio de Janeiro, Costa was appointed director of his alma mater. Although his tenure was brief—lasting only a year—he introduced young Brazilian architects to the Modernist style, especially the Functionalism espoused by Swiss architect and urban planner Le Corbusier. In 1939 Costa invited Le Corbusier to consult with him on the design of the Ministry of Education and Health Building in Rio de Janeiro. Costa also collaborated on that project with one of his students, Oscar Niemeyer, and the pair worked together again in 1939 to design the Brazilian Pavilion for the New York World's Fair. Costa completed several noteworthy projects on his own over the next decade, among them the award-winning Eduardo Guinle Apartments (1948–54) in Rio de Janeiro. In 1957 he won an international competition with his futuristic design of Brasília, which replaced Rio de Janeiro as the government center, and asked Niemeyer to design many of the city's major buildings. The undertaking was part of Pres. Juscelino Kubitschek's campaign to encourage Brazilian development, and Brasília, which had been an arid savanna, was constructed in only four years. The realization of Costa's plan was often likened to an airplane with a central axis for government and public buildings and wings on either side for the residential districts. Some critics, however, viewed Brasília as too sterile in character. Costa, who spent the final years of his life in Rio de Janeiro, collected and published his letters,

sketches, and writings in the book *Lúcio Costa: registro de uma vivência* (1995), his last major project.

Douglas, Marjory Stoneman
April 7, 1890—May 14, 1998

American author and environmentalist Marjory Douglas helped dispel the centuries-long revulsion that many had for the Everglades wilderness in southern Florida through her writings and environmental activism. In 1915, when Douglas arrived in southern Florida, the young Wellesley College graduate first encountered those negative attitudes, views that had little changed since the first Europeans set eyes on the region in the 16th century. In her influential 1947 book, *The Everglades: River of Grass,* she wrote of the beauty and the environmental usefulness of what had been described as "a series of vast, mi-

Marjory Douglas

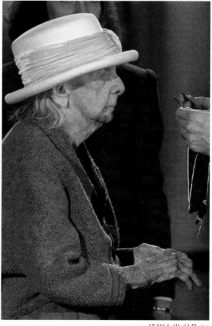

AP/Wide World Photos

asmic swamps, poisonous lagoons, huge dismal marshes without outlet, a rotting, shallow, inland sea, or labyrinths of dark trees hung and looped about with snakes and dripping mosses, malignant with tropical fevers and malarias, evil to the white man." Since its publication, *The Everglades* has been continuously in print. Before her death at age 108, Douglas witnessed a reversal of these attitudes, largely brought about by her own work. The daughter of the founding editor of the *Miami Herald,* Douglas wrote books and magazine articles with the intention of changing public perceptions of the attractiveness of the Everglades and of its ecological function as a vast recharge zone for southern Florida's freshwater supplies. Not content to watch the battle for the future of the Everglades from the sidelines, Douglas was a leading member of the committee that lobbied for the establishment of Everglades National Park in the 1940s. In 1969, to fight a proposal to build a jetport in the park, she helped to found Friends of the Everglades, a conservation group now numbering some 5,000 members. In the 1970s, when developers and farmers threatened to drain 622 sq km (240 sq mi) of the Everglades, an unflappable Douglas, dressed in her signature straw hat and formal string of pearls, defended the Everglades before a hostile audience. Almost deaf and already in her 80s, she boldly prefaced her remarks by urging the crowd to "boo louder." The recipient of numerous honors, Douglas was referred to as Mother Nature by Pres. Bill Clinton during a 1993 White House ceremony in which her work on behalf of the Everglades was honored with the Medal of Freedom.

Goldhaber, Gertrude Scharff
July 14, 1911—Feb. 2, 1998

German-born American physicist Gertrude Goldhaber was a prominent researcher who showed that spontaneous nuclear fission produces neutron emissions. She also was coauthor of a study confirming that beta particles are electrons and was active in increasing the participation of women in the sciences. Under the guidance of physicist Walther Gerlach, she earned a Ph.D. (1935) from the University of Munich at a time when Jews throughout Germany were being persecuted by the Nazis. She soon left the country, working until 1939 as a research associate in London, where she married physicist Maurice Goldhaber. In 1942, following the couple's transatlantic move to the University of Illinois at Urbana-Champaign, she made a discovery that was kept secret until after World War II—neutrons, she determined, are emitted during nuclear fission. In 1948 both Goldhaber and her husband were hired by Brookhaven National Laboratory, New York; Goldhaber was the first woman with a Ph.D. to work at the research center. Also in 1948 she and her husband confirmed, with experiments centered on the Pauli exclusion principle, that beta particles, or beta rays, are equivalent to emitted electrons. Among her other contributions was an examination (published in 1953) of even-even nuclei that provided evidence for the existence of electron shell structure in excited nuclear states. She also verified (1957) the concept of K-forbiddenness in long-lived nuclear isomers (K-isomerism), and researched the variable moment of inertia (VMI) model. In 1947 Goldhaber was elected a fellow of the American Physical Society, and in 1972 she became the third female physicist to gain election to the National Academy of Sciences. In 1979 she cofounded Brookhaven Women in Science; she also served on the American Physical Society's committee on woman physicists and on a similar committee of the National Research Council (1978–83).

Hitchings, George Herbert
April 18, 1905—Feb. 27, 1998

American pharmacologist George Hitchings was a medical research pioneer who was awarded the Nobel Prize for Physiology or Medicine in 1988 for the development of important disease-fighting drugs. He

George Hitchings

shared the prize with colleague Gertrude B. Elion and with Sir James W. Black. Hitchings made great strides in the fields of chemotherapeutics and immunology, and his drug discoveries brought him international repute and secured the success of his employer, Burroughs Wellcome Co. (now part of Glaxo Wellcome PLC). He graduated cum laude from the University of Washington (B.A., 1927; M.A., 1928) and earned his Ph.D. in biochemistry (1933) from Harvard University, where he taught until 1939, when he transferred to Western Reserve University (now Case Western Reserve University), Cleveland, Ohio. In 1942 Hitchings founded the biochemical department at the American laboratories of Burroughs Wellcome in Tuckahoe, N.Y. (In the late 1960s the company moved to Research Triangle Park in North Carolina.) He was joined in 1944 by Elion, who first worked as his assistant before becoming his research partner. Their discovery of cancer-fighting drugs led in turn to the development of important immunosuppressants. Much of this success could be attributed to their unique methodology, which eschewed the prevailing tactics of trial and error and pointedly examined the biochemical differences between the development of normal cells and diseased cells. The investigation of purines and pyrimidines, the nucleotide bases of DNA, revealed that compounds could be introduced to stop the spread of the cancer, bacteria, or virus by tricking the pathogen (disease-causing agent) into believing that the compound was necessary for replication; once the compound was metabolized, however, it would in fact suppress the growth of the diseased cell. Among the valuable drugs Hitchings and Elion helped create to treat diseases were pyrimethamine (Darapin) for malaria, 6-mercaptopurine (6MP) for leukemia, azathioprine (Imuran) for rheumatoid arthritis and to facilitate organ transplants, trimethorpim (Septra) for urinary and res-

piratory tract infections, acyclovir for viral herpes, and azidothymidine (AZT) for AIDS. Hitchings, who later headed charitable organizations, wrote or co-wrote more than 300 scientific papers.

Hodgkin, Sir Alan Lloyd
Feb. 5, 1914—Dec. 20, 1998

British physiologist Sir Alan Hodgkin shared (along with his countryman Sir Andrew Huxley and Australian scientist Sir John Eccles) the 1963 Nobel Prize for Physiology or Medicine for the discovery of the chemical processes involved in nerve conduction. After graduating (1936) from Trinity College, Cambridge, he worked (1937–38) at the Rockefeller Institute in New York City and spent some time at the Woods Hole (Mass.) Marine Biological Laboratory. It was there that he first dissected squid nerve fibers, structures that, owing to their comparatively large size, were ideally suited to his research. Because of his expertise in physics and mathematics, the British government called upon him to work on the development of airborne radar during World War II. In 1945 he joined the faculty at Cambridge. The central focus of his studies was the biomedical process by which nerve impulses travel along individual fibers. With Huxley, he elucidated the complementary roles of sodium and potassium ions in the transmission of nerve impulses, work for which they received the Nobel Prize. Hodgkin was elected a fellow of the Royal Society in 1948 and served as the society's president from 1970 to 1975. He held the posts of master of Trinity College (1974–84) and chancellor of the University of Leicester (1971–84). Among his many awards and honors were the

Royal Medal (1958) and the Copley Medal (1985). He was knighted in 1972. In addition to his scientific papers, Hodgkin wrote an autobiography, *Chance & Design: Reminiscences of Science in Peace and War* (1992).

Holub, Miroslav
Sept. 23, 1923—July 14, 1998

Czech writer and immunologist Miroslav Holub conducted advanced research in immunology with over 150 papers on the subject and was noted at home and in the West for his poetry, which was often infused with scientific imagery and vocabulary. During World War II Holub was conscripted to work on the railroad. After the war he earned (1953) a medical degree from Charles University in Prague and then worked as an immunologist at the Microbiology Institute of the Czechoslovak Academy of Sciences. In 1958 he was awarded a Ph.D. for the development of, and work with, "nude mice" as immunological test animals for various diseases. In 1958 Holub finished his first book of poems, *Denní služba* ("Day Shift"), and *Selected Poems,* his first volume in English, was published in 1967. From 1970 to 1980 his politically charged poetry was banned from publication in his homeland by the communist regime, and many of his works were published first in English. Other well-known titles include *Ačkoli* (1969; "Although"), *Notes of a Clay Pigeon* (1977), *Sagitální řez* (1980; "Sagittal Section"), *Sindrom mizející plíce* (1990; "Vanishing Lung Syndrome"), and *Poems Before and After* (1990), all of which featured subtle and surreal humor. In addition to his poetry and scientific papers, Holub wrote essays, notably the collection

Shedding Life: Disease, Politics and Other Human Conditions (1998). His works have been translated into 37 languages.

Kendall, Henry Way
Dec. 9, 1926—Feb. 15, 1999

American nuclear physicist Henry Kendall shared (with Jerome Isaac Friedman and Richard E. Taylor) the 1990 Nobel Prize for Physics for experiments confirming the existence of the subatomic particles known as quarks, the presence of which had been independently postulated in 1964 by Murray Gell-Mann and George Zweig. After attending (1945–46) the U.S. Merchant Marine Academy, he graduated (B.A., 1950) from Amherst (Mass.) College and then dealt with electromagnetic interactions while pursuing his thesis at the Massachusetts Institute of Technology (MIT; Ph.D., 1955). After joining the research faculty at Stanford University under the tutelage of 1961 Nobel prizewinner Robert Hofstadter, he met Friedman and Taylor, and the three began their collaboration. In 1967, using the newly constructed Stanford Linear Accelerator Center and the east-coast facilities of MIT (where Kendall was made a full professor), they made pioneering measurements of highly inelastic electron scattering—that is, examination of the process of energy loss from "targets" of liquid hydrogen and deuterium, which were bombarded by electron beams. The way that the electrons scattered from the targets' constituent protons and neutrons confirmed that the latter particles were composed of still smaller entities—quarks. Their experiments contradicted prevailing theories of subatomic structure and instigated a wide-ranging program of theoretical and experimental

Henry Kendall

work that produced the constituent quark model and hence the development, in 1973, of the theory of Quantum Chromodynamics (QCD), which discussed quarks, hadrons, and their strong interactions. In combination with the electroweak theory, the QCD generated the standard model of particle physics. In 1969 Kendall helped found the Union of Concerned Scientists (UCS), a group charged with questioning the roles of technologies wrought by modern science, especially those related to defense systems (e.g., the "Star Wars" and B2 ["Stealth"] bomber programs) and environmental issues such as the enhanced greenhouse effect. He became chairman of the UCS in 1973. In addition to his scientific and philanthropic interests, Kendall nurtured an adventuresome spirit, taking part in mountaineering expeditions to the Himalayas, the Arctic, and the Andes Mountains. He died while on an underwater photography session at Wakulla Springs State Park, Fla., where he was assisting a diving team from *National Geographic* magazine. Kendall received the Leo Szilard Award (of the American Physical Society) in 1981, the Bertrand Russell Society Award in 1982, and the Panofsky Prize in 1989.

Norris, Kenneth Stafford
Aug. 11, 1924—Aug. 16, 1998

American naturalist Kenneth Norris conducted pioneering research on marine mammals, especially dolphins, and in the course of his studies created a new science. His interest in dolphins' sound-processing abilities led to work that verified the animals' use of echolocation, a measurement of the time between a dolphin's click sound and the click's echo that allows the dolphin to determine distance, direction, size, shape, and texture and thus "see." Norris was educated at the University of California, Los Angeles (UCLA; M.A., 1951), and the Scripps Institution of Oceanography, La Jolla, Calif. (Ph.D., 1959). He served as the founding curator at Marineland of the Pacific from 1953 until he returned to UCLA in 1959 to research desert reptiles and teach herpetology. Recognizing the value that protecting natural habitats had for teaching and research, in 1965 he helped found the University of California's Natural Reserve System, an accomplishment of which he was especially proud. Norris maintained his interest in marine life, however, and in 1968 became the founding scientific director of the Oceanic Institute in Hawaii, where he served before joining the faculty of the University of California, Santa Cruz, as a professor of natural history in 1972. He also became director of the university's Center for Coastal Marine Studies (now the Institute of Marine Sciences), a post he held until 1975, and in 1977–79 he was chairman of the environmental studies department. He went on to found the Environmental Field Program and serve as its coordinator. He retired from the university in 1990. Norris helped bring to public attention the danger that tuna-fishing nets held for dolphins and, while acting as an adviser to the U.S. Marine Mammal Commission, helped write the Marine Mammal Protection Act of 1972. He also wrote a number of books, one of which, *Dolphin Days: The Life and Times*

of the Spinner Dolphin (1991), in 1992 gained him the John Burroughs Medal.

Ohain, Hans Joachim Pabst von
Dec. 14, 1911—March 13, 1998

German aeronautical engineer Hans Ohain designed the HeS3b, the turbojet engine that powered the experimental first jet aircraft, the He178, on its historic maiden flight on Aug. 27, 1939, near the German port city of Rostock. Ohain conceived his

Hans Ohain

AP/Wide World Photos

theory of jet propulsion in 1933 while pursuing a doctorate in physics at the University of Göttingen. After graduating in 1935, he was recommended by the university to the German aircraft manufacturer Ernst Heinkel. Ohain joined Heinkel's firm in 1936, and by September 1937 he had built a factory-tested demon-

stration engine. Shortly afterward, Ohain directed the construction of the HeS3b, the first fully operational centrifugal-flow turbojet engine. Although the development of this technology did not pique the interest of the German High Command during World War II, it revolutionized postwar transportation and defense. After the war Ohain was recruited by the U.S. Air Force, and he became the chief scientist at Wright Patterson Air Force Base in Dayton, Ohio. After retiring in 1979, he served as a consultant to the University of Dayton Research Institute. Ohain, however, was not credited with being the first to invent the jet engine. Great Britain's Sir Frank Whittle registered a patent for the turbojet engine in 1930, though he did not perform a flight test until 1941. In 1991 Ohain (along with Whittle) was honored by the U.S. National Academy of Engineering with the Charles Stark Draper Prize as a pioneer of the jet age.

Postel, Jonathan Bruce
Aug. 6, 1943—Oct. 16, 1998

American computer scientist Jonathan Postel was lauded for his work as a creator and manager of the Internet. In the late 1960s, when correspondence was sent via "snail mail" rather than E-mail and no one had ever heard of a Web site, Postel was a graduate student at the University of California, Los Angeles, and was working to develop the ARPANET (Advanced Research Projects Agency Network), a forerunner of the Internet designed for use by the U.S. Department of Defense. During its development Postel took on some of the administrative functions of this system, and later of the Internet, a responsibility he continued for some three decades. He formed and served as director of the Internet Assigned Numbers Authority, which was responsible for, among other duties, allocating numerical addresses (IP numbers) and turning those into simpler written addresses (*i.e.,* <www.eb.com>). Postel's behind-the-scenes influence over the Internet was made more visible in early 1998 when, during a test, he redirected some of the Internet's directory-information computers to his own system. The Internet grew rapidly in the 1990s, and there was concern about its lack of regulation. Shortly before his death Postel submitted a proposal for review by the U.S. government for the acceptance of the Internet Corporation for Assigned Names and Numbers, an international nonprofit organization that would oversee the Internet. At the time of his death, Postel was also director of the computer networks division of the University of Southern California Information Sciences Institute.

Reiche, Maria
May 15, 1903—June 8, 1998

German-born Peruvian mathematician and archaeologist Maria Reiche was the self-appointed keeper of the Nazca Lines, a series of Peruvian ground drawings more than 1,000 years old. For five decades the "Lady of the Lines," as she was known, studied and protected the 60 km (35 mi) of desert near Nazca in southern Peru that served as the blackboard for etchings of animals and geometric patterns. Scratched into the ground and preserved by a lack of wind and rain, the figures are hundreds of feet in length and only fully recognizable from the air. Reiche, who emigrated to Peru in 1932 to escape the political situa-

Maria Reiche

(Above) Alejandro Belaguer/AP/Wide World Photos; (below) AP/Wide World Photos

tion in Germany, became fascinated with the mysterious lines after visiting the site in 1941. By 1946 she had moved to the desert and begun mapping and measuring the figures. Her work, the first serious study of the lines, led to the publication of

The Mystery on the Desert (1949), in which she concluded that they represented an astronomical calendar; later experts, however, have suggested a ceremonial or community-building purpose. Reiche also funded several research projects and, as the region became a major tourist attraction, hired security guards to protect the drawings. UNESCO declared the Nazca Lines a World Heritage site in 1995 and in 1998 awarded Reiche a special medal for her work.

Reines, Frederick
March 16, 1918—Aug. 26, 1998

American physicist Frederick Reines was awarded the 1995 Nobel Prize for Physics for his detection in 1956 of neutrinos. The existence of these elusive subatomic particles, which have no electric charge and little, if any, mass, had been postulated by Wolfgang Pauli in the early 1930s but remained unproven until Reines and Clyde L. Cowan, Jr., used massive tanks of a water solution of cadmium chloride to observe signs of hydrogen nuclei being struck by the neutrinos from a nearby nu-

Frederick Reines (center)

clear reactor. While a science undergraduate at Stevens Institute of Technology, Hoboken, N.J., Reines also took voice lessons at the Metropolitan Opera in New York City. He eventually chose science over opera and received a B.S. (1939) and M.A. (1941) from Stevens and a Ph.D. (1944) from New York University. In later years Reines, a baritone, performed with the Cleveland (Ohio) Symphony Orchestra, and he could often be heard singing opera while working in the laboratory. Recruited to the Manhattan Project team at Los Alamos, N.M., after graduation, he also worked on atomic tests in the Marshall Islands after World War II. After finding the neutrino, Reines led pioneering research projects in neutrino astronomy and in 1959 became head of the physics department at Case Institute of Technology (now Case Western Reserve University) in Cleveland. In 1966 he was made the founding dean of physical science at the University of California, Irvine, where he worked until his retirement in 1988.

Rodbell, Martin
Dec. 1, 1925—Dec. 7, 1998

American biochemist Martin Rodbell was corecipient (with Alfred G. Gilman) of the 1994 Nobel Prize for Physiology or Medicine for discovering that certain proteins—the so-called G proteins—play a crucial role in cell communication. The son of a grocer, Rodbell set out to fulfill his father's dream that he become a doctor, but he soon found that a career in the biological sciences was his true calling. After service in the Pacific as a U.S. Navy radio operator, which interrupted his undergraduate education, he earned a B.A. (1949) from Johns Hopkins University,

Martin Rodbell

Baltimore, Md., and a Ph.D. (1954) in biochemistry from the University of Washington. As a researcher at the National Institutes of Health in Bethesda, Md., for nearly four decades, Rodbell investigated the effects of hormones on cells, especially fat cells. It was in the 1960s, after hearing a lecture by another future Nobel laureate, Earl W. Sutherland, Jr., about the latter's studies of the signaling action of hormones, that Rodbell began to elucidate the process of signal transduction—that is, how chemical messages from outside a cell are transmitted across the cell membrane to the interior. He showed that previously unknown molecules, which proved to be proteins, function in relaying chemical signals from the exterior to the interior. Because these proteins are activated by the energy-rich molecules guanosine diphosphate (GDP) and guanosine triphosphate (GTP), they were designated

G proteins by Gilman and his associates. From 1985 until his retirement in 1994, Rodbell continued his work on signal transduction at the National Institute of Environmental Health Sciences, Research Triangle Park, N.C.

Shima, Hideo
May 20, 1901—March 18/19, 1998

Japanese engineer Hideo Shima designed and supervised the construction of the world's first high-speed train. Shima, the son of a prominent railway engineer, graduated from Tokyo Imperial University in 1925. He joined the then state-run Japanese National Railways to design steam locomotives. By 1948 he had worked his way up to head of the rolling stock department, but he resigned three years later after taking responsibility for a fire at Yokohama station that killed more than 100 people. He worked for a time at Sumimoto Metal Industries but was asked by the president of the national railways to return as chief engineer. He soon began designs for the Shinkansen ("new trunk line"), a 515-km (320-mi)-long high-speed train line between Tokyo and Osaka. Shima oversaw the project until 1963, when he was forced to resign owing to escalating production costs. (The mostly straight tracks required construction of 3,000 bridges and 67 tunnels.) The project was completed just in time for the 1964 Summer Olympic Games in Tokyo, but Shima was not invited to the opening ceremony. The Shinkansen was the world's first train to reach top speeds above 209 km/h (130 mph). This bullet train, named after its aerodynamically shaped head, featured wide-gauge tracks, air suspension, and individually motorized cars instead of a sole front engine. Because the tracks were not shared with other trains, safety and punctuality were unprecedented. Despite the costs, Shinkansen rapidly expanded in the following years, and the train became a symbol of Japan's postwar economic prowess. After his resignation Shima continued to advise railway officials, especially on safety issues. In 1969 he began a new career as head of the National Space Development Agency. That same year he became the first non-Westerner to receive the James Watt International Medal of Great Britain's Institution of Mechanical Engineers. In Japan he was awarded the Order of Cultural Merit in 1994.

Spock, Benjamin
May 2, 1903—March 15, 1998

American pediatrician Benjamin Spock was the most influential child-care authority of the 20th century. His book *Baby and Child Care* sold over 50 million copies worldwide and was translated into 42 languages. Spock attended Yale University, where he rowed on a crew team that won an Olympic gold medal in 1924. He graduated (1929) from medical school at Columbia University, New York City, and following his internship and residency, he entered (1933) private practice in New York City and taught pediatrics at Cornell University, Ithaca, N.Y. After service in the U.S. Navy during World War II, Spock accepted a teaching post at the University of Minnesota; he also taught at the University of Pittsburgh, Pa., and at Case Western Reserve University, Cleveland, Ohio. The first edition of his most famous work, *The Common Sense Book of Baby and Child Care,* was published in 1946. In his work

Benjamin Spock

Spock eschewed the strict discipline and emotional reserve promoted by other child-care experts, advising instead that parents allow their children to develop in an atmosphere of understanding and love. Although Spock was accused by some of having fostered the permissiveness and self-indulgence of the 1960s and '70s, his views were nevertheless regarded as mainstream by the time of his death. In addition to his status as a pediatrician, Spock became a leading figure in the anti-Vietnam War movement and was arrested several times for his participation in demonstrations. In 1972 he ran for the U.S. presidency as a candidate of the People's Party, a coalition of left-wing groups. Spock continued to engage in leftist activism in the 1980s, mainly protesting against nuclear weapons.

Villas Boas, Cláudio
1916—March 1, 1998

Brazilian anthropologist Cláudio Villas Boas was an activist who dedicated his life to the search for and protection of the country's indigenous people as their lands were taken over and developed. He and his brother Orlando aided in the creation of the Xingu National Park reservation in 1961 and the National Indian Foundation six years later. The Villas Boas brothers' interest in isolated tribes was whetted by tales they heard from their father, who had encountered such groups on trips to the backlands. In 1943 they took part in an expedition into unexplored areas of the Amazon basin, and they realized the health and cultural consequences that exploitation of these areas could have on their inhabitants. Villas Boas and his brother spent nearly two decades in their ultimately successful attempt to persuade the government to protect the indigenous tribes by providing them with a reserve. Later, however, feeling that the individuality of the tribes had been endangered, they came to doubt whether their work had been of value. Nonetheless, because of the two brothers' efforts, the indigenous people were given an opportunity to survive as a culture, recover in number, and perhaps eventually re-create their societies.

Weese, Harry Mohr
June 30, 1915—Oct. 29, 1998

American architect Harry Weese designed the subway system in Washington, D.C., considered one of the most remarkable public-works projects of the 20th century, and played a prominent role in the planning and architecture of Chicago. Following graduation (B.A., 1938) from the Massachusetts Institute of Technology, Weese studied city planning under Eliel Saarinen at the Cranbrook Academy of Art, Bloomfield Hills, Mich. Though Weese cofounded an architectural firm in 1941, his career was interrupted by World War II service in the navy. Two years after his discharge (1945), Weese opened his own Chicago-based firm and soon began shaping the city's skyline. He was one of the first major architects to foster historic preservation and renovated numerous landmarks, including Adler and Sullivan's Auditorium Theatre and the Field Museum of Natural History. In addition, he created designs for such buildings as the Metropolitan Corrections Center, a concrete tower whose irregularly spaced slit windows made it resemble a computer punch card, and helped redesign the city's lakefront. Rather than revealing a trademark style, Weese's work reflected his attention to setting, historical relations, and functional requirements. His design style was best evidenced in Washington's 160-km (100-mi) subway system, which, with spectacular concrete vaults and rippling lights at each station, had both awed and delighted commuters since its opening in 1976. Weese's other works include the Arena Stage theatre in Washington, D.C., which featured the pioneering use of functional elements, such as lighting apparatus and catwalks as aesthetic features, and the Time and Life Building in Chicago.

Weil, André
May 6, 1906—Aug. 6, 1998

French mathematician André Weil greatly influenced the course of mathematical research in the 20th century, most notably with his conjectures, in which he formulated the foundations of modern algebraic geometry. Weil developed an interest in numbers at an early age. He earned a Ph.D. (1928) from the University of Paris and accepted his first academic position as professor of mathematics (1930–32) at the Aligarh Muslim University in India. He then moved to the University of Strasbourg, France, and there (1933–40) Weil and a number of French mathematicians formed Nicolas Bourbaki, a group somewhat mischievously named after an imaginary Russian general. The Bourbaki group took on the responsibility of synthesizing the content of all major areas of mathematics, work that was published as a series of encyclopedic volumes called *Éléments d'histoire des mathématiques*. At the outbreak of World War II, Weil, a conscientious objector, fled to Finland to avoid the draft. He was sent back to France, however, and spent about six months in a French prison, a dangerous place for the son of Jewish parents and the brother of the mystic philosopher and French Resistance activist Simone Weil. While imprisoned, Weil formulated the Riemann hypothesis, which was named for a German mathematician and became a fundamental element of number theory. To secure his release, he joined the French army but later managed to move to the United States, where he taught at Swarthmore and Haverford colleges in Pennsylvania. In 1945 Weil accepted a position at the University of São Paulo, Brazil, and in 1947 returned to the U.S. to serve (1947–58) on the faculty at the University of Chicago. From 1958 until his retirement in 1976, Weil taught at the Institute for Advanced Study, Princeton, N.J. In 1994 he was awarded the Kyoto Prize in Basic Science from the Inamori Foundation of Kyoto, Japan, for his lifelong contribution to mathematics.

West, Louis Jolyon
Oct. 6, 1924—Jan. 2, 1999

American psychiatrist Louis West specialized in the study and treatment of extreme human behavior and its effects on those who were its targets. Among those he treated were prisoners of war who had been brainwashed, abused children, and kidnap victims, and he was sometimes called upon to testify as an expert witness in court cases in which the mental state of a defendant was germane to the case. When Jack Ruby, who had killed John F. Kennedy's assassin, Lee Harvey Oswald, was due to be sentenced, West was instrumental in persuading the court not to give him the death penalty. He also attempted to gain pretrial treatment for Patricia Hearst after she was kidnapped and induced to engage in criminal activity, but his recommendation was ignored. West earned his medical degree from the University of Minnesota, did his psychiatric residency at New York Hospital–Cornell Medical Center, and at age 29 was made chairman of the University of Oklahoma School of Medicine's psychiatry department. In 1969 he left that post to be chairman of psychiatry and head of the Neuropsychiatric Institute at the University of California, Los Angeles, where he remained until he retired in 1989. West took part in civil rights activities in the 1950s and '60s, helping the leaders of lunch-counter sit-ins, and he participated in anti-apartheid activities in South Africa. His research in the 1950s included a notable study in which a disc jockey who broadcast live for 200 hours straight suffered temporary physical and mental ill effects. The powerful effects of sleep deprivation were again revealed when a panel on which West served investigated the circumstances that had led 36 of 59 American airmen captured during the Korean War to confess to war crimes or substantiate the charges made against them. Prolonged, chronic loss of sleep was found to have been key to the airmen's personality changes. West, an advocate of nonviolence, was for many years a leader of a group of doctors attempting to have the death penalty abolished, and he was among the first to demonstrate scientifically that successful child rearing does not require the infliction of painful punishment. In the early 1970s, he put forth a proposal to create a center for studying interpersonal violence, but it met with failure because of protests generated by descriptions of controversial behavior-modification methods, including brain surgery, that the center might employ.

Zoll, Paul Maurice
July 15, 1911—Jan. 5, 1999

American cardiologist and medical researcher Paul Zoll conducted pioneering research that led to the development of the cardiac defibrillator, improved pacemakers, and continuous heart-rhythm monitoring devices. Following his graduation from Harvard College (B.A., 1932) and Harvard Medical School (M.D., 1936), Zoll was made a research fellow (1939) in cardiology at Beth Israel Hospital, Boston, working under physicians Monroe Schlesinger and Herman Blumgart. During World War II, he was stationed in Great Britain as a U.S. Army physician. In that capacity, he observed numerous open-heart surgeries performed by Dwight Harken, and he noted with interest the manner in which the heart responded reflexively to the slightest touch. After the war, he became involved in attempts to regulate the heartbeat and treat myocardial infarctions (heart attacks). At the time, emergency cardiac resuscitation involved cutting open a patient's chest and squeezing the heart by hand. Zoll experimented with closed-chest electrical cardiac stimulation, and in 1952 he restarted the hearts of two patients at Beth Israel Hospital. Researchers worldwide were soon racing to enhance defibrillator designs, which later became standard issue in emergency rooms, ambulances, and airplanes. Acceptance from within the medical community was not universal or immediate, however; many questioned whether such "artificial" methods were ethical if not altogether blasphemous. Zoll's efforts were later concentrated on improving external cardiac pacemakers, which were massive, inefficient machines that often caused great pain to their users. His new designs were the forerunners of the permanent, miniaturized pacemakers that are now implanted in hundreds of thousands of patients each year. Zoll also worked to improve electrocardiographic monitoring devices. In the 1980s he founded the Zoll Medical Corp., which developed and marketed new defibrillator designs. Despite his numerous contributions to medical technology, Zoll received limited recognition until 1973, when he was awarded the Albert Lasker Clinical Medical Research Award.

RECENT BOOKS OF SCIENCE

The following list encompasses 75 recent books published in English in 1998, except where otherwise noted, that have been judged significant contributions to learning in their respective areas of science. Each citation includes a few lines of commentary to indicate the tenor of the work, and seven especially notable books are discussed at greater length. The citations are organized by broad subject area, using the appropriate parts of *Encyclopædia Britannica*'s Propædia as an outline.

Matter and Energy

James P. Harbison and Robert E. Nahory, *Lasers: Harnessing the Atom's Light,* an account of laser technology's growing number of uses, including precision measurements at cosmic distances, communications, and repair of living tissues.

Bernard Pullman, *The Atom in the History of Human Thought,* a panoramic intellectual history of the quest for the atom, originating with the Greek philosphers 2,500 years ago and climaxed by the first direct visual proof of the atom itself in the last decade.

John Emsley, *Molecules at an Exhibition: Portraits of Intriguing Materials in Everyday Life,* verbal sketches of important molecular materials, from the indispensable (phosphates, polystyrene) to the lethal (sarin, heroin).

Hans Christian von Baeyer, *Maxwell's Demon: Why Warmth Disperses and Time Passes,* a discussion of molecular behavior and whether mathematician James Clerk Maxwell's imaginary demon could change that behavior, thereby violating the laws of thermodynamics.

Armand Delsemme, *Our Cosmic Origins: From the Big Bang to the Emergence of Life and Intelligence,* a history of the universe and current views on the evolution of life on Earth.

Clifford A. Pickover, *Time: A Traveller's Guide,* an examination of the potentialities of time travel, based on concepts of modern physics and philosophy related to Albert Einstein's theories.

Henning Genz, *Nothingness: The Science of Empty Space* (1999), a synthesis of quantum mechanics and philosophy from early Greek thought to Einstein and Heisenberg, concluding with the

physicist-author's own view of interstellar "empty" space.

David H. Levy, *Comets: Creators and Destroyers,* an account of comets, their behavior, and their contribution to the origin of life on Earth, by the co-discoverer of the comet whose collision with Jupiter in 1994 was a major astronomical event.

Noel M. Swerdlow, *The Babylonian Theory of the Planets,* a history of mathematical astronomy beginning in the 8th century BC with the Babylonians' systematic observations of heavenly bodies, the first empirical study of the stars and constellations.

Alan Boss, *Looking for Earths: The Race to Find New Solar Systems,* a review of

---

Copenhagen
by Michael Frayn

In his two-act play, Michael Frayn dramatizes the intellectual, political, and spiritual fallout that hits the international scientific community as it scrambles to make a self-sustaining nuclear chain reaction and usher in the atomic age in the 1930s and '40s. Three of the principal personalities of that feverish era reminisce from beyond the grave and speculate about what alternative paths they might have taken that would have led to a less dark and frightening outcome for the human race than the production and detonation of nuclear bombs. Frayn plunges his audience into the ferment that underlay and finally eroded scientific collegiality. Giants of theoretical quantum mechanics found themselves hopelessly enmeshed in the nontheoretical world of war and politics by 1941.

Renowned Danish-Jewish physicist Niels Bohr, his wife and confidante, Margrethe, and Werner Heisenberg, the German enfant terrible of theoretical physics who was once Bohr's assistant and erstwhile friend, revisit their shared past, with all its ambivalences. In the process, they conduct the audience through the basic workings of quantum physics and the uncertainty principle. Each of them, in grappling with his or her version of reality, rearranges and even distorts facts and recollections. From their vantage point beyond life, they conclude that ambiguity and uncertainty represent humankind's last best hope for the future.

the players and politics involved in the visual exploration of deep space from 1968 to 1997.

The Earth

E.C. Pielou, *Fresh Water,* a natural history of water, discussing rivers, ponds, lakes, underground aquifers, and wetlands, and water's propensity for destructive action when it is channeled, dammed, or otherwise restrained.

Kerry Sieh and Simon Le Vay, *The Earth in Turmoil: Earthquakes, Volcanoes, and Their Impact on Humankind,* a study of the dynamics and history of earthquakes and volcanoes in different geographic regions of the U.S., illustrating various types of earth slippage and movement.

Pat Shipman, *Taking Wing: Archaeopteryx and the Evolution of Bird Flight,* an evolutionary study of the mechanics of bird flight, based on seven known fossil specimens of archaeopteryx.

Simon Conway Morris, *The Crucible of Creation: The Burgess Shale and the*

Rise of Animals, a description of some of the multitudes of 520-million-year-old soft-bodied marine fossils exposed in a shale outcropping, visualizing the behavior, habitat, and means of locomotion of the animals represented in the rocks.

Life on Earth

Niles Eldredge, *The Pattern of Evolution* (1999), a history and discussion of evolution, arguing that economic activities among organisms may affect their evolution as significantly as reproductive activities.

Richard Fortey, *Life: A Natural History of the First Four Billion Years of Life on Earth,* a comprehensive look at Earth's multitudes of living organisms as they developed, flourished, and vanished, linking geologic and astrophysical events to the fortunes of life on the planet.

Mark McMenamin, *The Garden of Ediacara: Discovering the First Complex Life,* a study of Earth's first multicellular organisms that existed in a prepredator "Eden" more than 600 million years ago.

Manny Rubio, *Rattlesnake: Portrait of a Predator,* a detailed account, with numerous color photographs, of the often misunderstood reptile whose 80 species and subspecies are found only in the Western Hemisphere.

Martin Wells, *Civilization and the Limpet,* a collection of essays by a marine zoologist who describes ocean-dwelling creatures from whales and sharks to limpets and octopuses and marvels at their infinitely varied modes of coping with life in the sea.

Adele E. Clarke, *Disciplining Reproduction: Modernity, American Life Sciences, and the Problems of Sex,* a history of repro-

ductive sciences, examining biology as engineering in humans and other animals.

Douglas W. Mock and Geoffrey A. Parker, *The Evolution of Sibling Rivlary* (1997), a study of the competition for survival among avian, plant, and mammalian siblings and the influence of natural selection on the success of one offspring at the expense of the rest.

Michael J. Denton, *Nature's Destiny: How the Laws of Biology Reveal Purpose in the Universe,* an argument that, for life to exist, the cosmos had to be designed precisely as it is, a seamless whole whose highest purpose is to support the presence of humankind.

Tyler Volk, *Gaia's Body: Toward a Physiology of Earth,* a meditation on the emerging field of "earth physiology," a view of Earth as a total living, breathing system from molecules to a Gaian system of the cosmos.

Michael Allin, *Zarafa: A Giraffe's True Story from Deep in Africa to the Heart of Paris,* the 3,200-km (2,000-mile) odyssey of a gift giraffe, concluding

Leonardo's Mountain of Clams and the Diet of Worms: Essays on Natural History
by Stephen Jay Gould

In his eighth volume of collected essays, humanist and evolutionary biologist Stephen Jay Gould explores a broad range of topics drawn from such fields as archaeology (prehistoric cave paintings), paleontology (Leonardo da Vinci's "mountain of clams"), exploration (Columbus's Bahamian clam), technology (the "Temeraire"), biology (a crab parasite's life cycle), and religious history (the Diet of Worms and the Defenestration of Prague). Charles Darwin's theory of natural selection is the organizing principle around which these essays revolve.

Gould illustrates adaptive triumphs and failures in nature, using as examples the evolutionary success of the giraffe's long neck and extinctions such as the dodo and the blue antelope. He meditates on the global implications that the loss of diversity entails and on the expanding role human beings are playing in the lottery of species survival. He marvels that the field of evolutionary biology itself continues to evolve. Molecular biology has unequivocally connected *Homo sapiens* to the entire universe of living creatures. Shared genetic material far exceeds the few segments that belong to humankind alone, and Gould celebrates this evidence of our belongingness throughout the book.

with her 885-km (550-mi) walk from Marseille, France, to Paris, where she became a beloved symbol of developing 19th-century enthusiasm for science.

Michael B.A. Oldstone, *Viruses, Plagues, and History,* an insight into the workings of viruses, with accounts of triumphs over such killers as smallpox, and a discussion of challenges posed by newly emerging viruses.

Evan Eisenberg, *The Ecology of Eden,* an analysis of the tension between wilderness and civilization, drawing on modern personalities and biblical and Middle Eastern traditions in the search for resolution.

Frank R. Wilson, *The Hand: How Its Use Shapes the Brain, Language, and Human Culture,* a meditation on that engineering marvel and first tool, the human hand, and its deeply reciprocal relationship to language, emotion, and cognition.

Steven Vogel, *Cats' Paws and Catapults: Mechanical Worlds of Nature and People,* a look at the first engineer, nature, whose designs in aerodynamics, submersibles, and kinetics inspire the scientific field of biomechanics.

Human Life

Christopher Wills, *Children of Prometheus: The Accelerating Pace of Human Evolution,* an argument that, over and above natural selection, medicine, technology, and other human interventions are accelerating the pace of evolution in *Homo sapiens.*

Ben Bova, *Immortality: How Science Is Extending Your Life Span—and Changing the World,* a research-based argument that immortality may be within the grasp of humankind, speculating on the impact that such an eventuality would have on public health, the economy, and political institutions.

Nicholas J. Wade, *A Natural History of Vision,* an account of the history and physiology of vision from the time of the Greek philosophers up to the 1830s.

Susan Scott and Christopher J. Duncan, *Human Demography and Disease,* a study relating population cycles to waves of disease, using 17th- and 18th-century northern England as the prototype and employing computer technology to digest and interpret statistics.

Nina Rattner Gelbart, *The King's Midwife: A History and Mystery of Madame du Coudray,* a biography of the determined and controversial 18th-century French midwife who received a royal commission to instruct provincial women in up-to-date birthing practices.

Denise Dellarosa Cummins and Colin Allen (eds.), *The Evolution of Mind,* a Darwinian approach to understanding the human mind, asserting that it is a product of evolutionary processes.

Tor Nørretranders, *The User Illusion: Cutting Consciousness Down to Size,* a meditation on the phenomenon of human consciousness, its biological and evolutionary background, its relationship to the cosmic and the subatomic, and its personal and political ramifications.

James H. Austin, *Zen and the Brain: Toward an Understanding of Meditation and Consciousness,* a discussion of the anatomy, chemistry, and physiology of the human brain and consciousness, examining the power of Zen Buddhism to assist consciousness in subduing the egocentric self.

The Bends: Compressed Air in the History of Science, Diving, and Engineering
by John L. Phillips

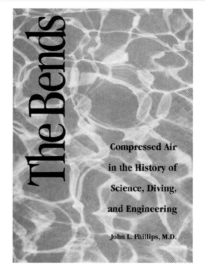

Phillips points out that the bends—also known as decompression sickness—is a human invention. It did not exist until the 19th century, when use of compressed air allowed miners, sandhogs, and bridge builders to stay underground and dig the mine shafts, tunnels, and bridge caissons that were essential underpinnings for growing cities. Phillips describes the collaborative efforts of physicians, scientists, and engineers to understand the bends, eliminate its causes, and treat its excruciating and often fatal symptoms.

In the late 20th century, research at the molecular level and refined methods of recompression and staged decompression are saving more scuba divers, airplane pilots, and others and have dramatically reduced crippling compression-related disabilities. Advances in compressed-air technology and changes in the mixture of gases have led to innovative uses in the treatment of burns and other wounds. The next development, Phillips predicts, may finally eradicate or at least sharply diminish the nightmare of the bends; "liquid breathing," an adaptation of the human in-utero mechanism, would circumvent the need for pressurized air and its attendant problems, thereby increasing the organism's range in environments that are currently beyond human physiological limits.

Human Society

Timothy Lenoir (ed.), *Instituting Science: The Cultural Production of Scientific Disciplines* (1997), a history of universities and other institutions that have formed, influenced, and sustained such sciences as medicine and engineering.

Mark Hertsgaard, *Earth Odyssey: Around the World in Search of Our Environmental Future,* a journalist's evaluation of the future of the human species in light of ecological fragility and spreading poverty, based on his travels through countries on five continents, observing living conditions and sampling local opinions.

Art

Caroline A. Jones and Peter Galison (eds.), *Picturing Science, Producing Art,* essays exploring the border between science and art, asserting that the two were not separated until the rise of 19th-century anatomists and industrialists.

David Lloyd Jones, *Architecture and the Environment: Bioclimatic Building Design,* an examination of new structures and complexes that exemplify the principles of bioclimatic architecture.

G. Malcolm Lewis (ed.), *Cartographic Encounters: Perspectives on Native American Mapmaking and Map Use,* a history of pre- and postcontact maps made by Native Americans both for themselves and for nonnative explorers of the wildernesses of North and Central America.

Technology

Stephen L. Sass, *The Substance of Civilization: Materials and Human History from the Stone Age to the Age of Silicon,* a history of civilization based on the materials used to fashion tools for making the artifacts and constructs that are civilization's hallmark.

Sandor Nagyszalanczy, *The Art of Fine Tools,* photographs and descriptions of antique hand tools, arranged according to function, that reaffirm the enduring marriage of beauty to utility.

David Ewing Duncan, *Calendar: Humanity's Epic Struggle to Determine a True and Accurate Year,* a history of the efforts, from Cro-Magnon eagle bones to the atomic clock's cesium atoms, to obtain an accurate method of measuring and using time.

Gerard L'E. Turner, *Scientific Instruments 1500–1900: An Introduction,* a historical survey of a broad range of scientific instruments, including optical, navigational, medical, and calculating devices and "philosophical instruments" that demonstrated various scientific principles.

William S. Ellis, *Glass: From the First Mirror to Fiber Optics, the Story of the*

419

Substance That Changed the World, an account of glass, whose molecular structure is still incompletely understood, with a summary of its 5,000-year history and of its numerous applications from art to fiber optics.

Thomas P. Hughes, *Rescuing Prometheus,* case studies of four major projects that led to innovations in management and systems engineering and affirmed the importance of government and military participation in industrial technology.

Ray Kurzweil, *The Age of Spiritual Machines: When Computers Exceed Human Intelligence* (1999), a vision of the future in which computer intelligence will surpass its fabricators and the automaton as companion, teacher, and even lover will blur the human-machine boundary.

Victor K. McElheny, *Insisting on the Impossible: The Life of Edwin Land, Inventor of Instant Photography,* a biography of the inventor of instant photog-

raphy, whose interest in optics and polarized light made him an important resource for World War II reconnaissance

TechGnosis: Myth, Magic, + Mysticism in the Age of Information
by Erik Davis

Presenting both an optimistic evaluation of information and communication technology and a warning about the power it wields over global politics, medicine, the sciences, culture, and the human psyche, Erik Davis interprets the worlds of virtual reality, cyberspace, and the Internet for the inquisitive layperson. He explores the myth and mystery as well as the mathematical science that are part and parcel of this technological revolution. He likens the technology of communication to its patron god Hermes, famous as both messenger and trickster, and he cautions the techno-enthusiast to keep in mind the difference between knowledge and information.

When writing, the first technology, appeared on cave walls thousands of years ago, it influenced the shape of human consciousness and the way people understood reality. Now reality has be-

come Web-shaped, with all the unforeseen interconnections that such a construct implies. The hypnotic virtuosity of cyberworlds, the living fantasy of virtual reality, and the Internet—with its unruly babble of opinion, hoax, rumor, insight, and commerce—are revolutionizing human culture and psychology.

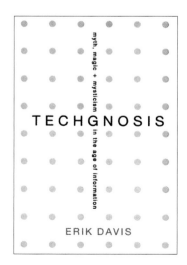

Davis asserts that the technological leap they represent may be giving birth to the first organic machine.

This New Ocean: The Story of the First Space Age
by William E. Burrows

Burrows traces the development of rocketry from the earliest devices that humans hurled against gravity to the series of space-exploration programs conducted by the U.S. and the Soviet Union following the Soviets' launch of Sputnik 1 in 1957. Unprecedented access to previously classified documents and interviews with participants in the U.S. space program enable Burrows to show how the technoscientific aspect of the race to space opened deep space to human study but also exposed the entire planet to the spying sensors of instantaneous satellite communication and imagery.

Although Cold War competition drove both superpowers to rush their complex and sometimes ill-prepared vehicles into space, the race became an incentive to scientific progress. Both nations cynically underplayed the catastrophes, misjudgments, and appalling failures that haunted their space programs, however. The push to enter the second space age by colonizing other planets and space will proceed, Burrows predicts, although its cost may preclude full international scientific participation.

photography and other intelligence matters.

Gary Kinder, *Ship of Gold in the Deep Blue Sea,* an account of the deep-sea recovery of a 19th-century gold-laden ship by a persistent and resourceful engineer-historian.

Religion

Lorraine Daston and Katharine Park, *Wonders and the Order of Nature, 1150–1750,* a history of the period when curiosity separated itself from wonder and empirical scientific investigation developed to explain comets, monstrous births, and similar exotica.

Marcelo Gleiser, *The Dancing Universe: From Creation Myths to the Big Bang* (1997), a book on how mythology, religion, and science have explained the origins of the universe, describing myths of creation and the search for common ground between science and faith.

Alister E. McGrath, *The Foundations of Dialogue in Science & Religion,* an inquiry into the relationship between Christian theology and the natural sciences, examining their use of critical realism to interpret the external world.

Lawrence Principe, *The Aspiring Adept: Robert Boyle and His Alchemical Quest,* a study based on a recently transcribed text fragment linking Boyle's alchemical thinking to theology and angelic visitations.

The Branches of Knowledge

Keith Devlin, *Life by the Numbers,* a tour through forms, functions, and applications of mathematics, from patterns in nature to economic and statistical analysis and forecasting.

The Children of Noah: Jewish Seafaring in Ancient Times
by Raphael Patai

In spite of Noah, builder and navigator of the Ark, the ancient Jews have not been regarded as a maritime people. Raphael Patai has marshaled an impressive body of evidence, however, that reveals the Jews of antiquity as accomplished sailors, shipbuilders, oarsmen, fishermen, and naval warriors.

Drawing from Old and New Testament sources, ancient Jewish legal tractates and commentaries, and historian Flavius Josephus's 1st-century AD work *War of the Jews*, Patai paints a vivid picture of maritime life among the Jews of antiquity. The terrors of storms at sea and the challenge of reconciling the strictures of Jewish law with managing a sailing ship on the Sabbath tested both the piety of the sailors and the ingenuity of the rabbinic commentators and sages. Many seaports on the shores of the Mediterranean and on Lake Tiberias (Sea of Galilee) were fishing centers and had Jewish populations. The well-preserved remains of a vessel found in Lake Tiberias in 1986 that dates from the beginning of the Christian era has given new credence to the biblical accounts and commentaries and has removed them from the realm of myth and legend.

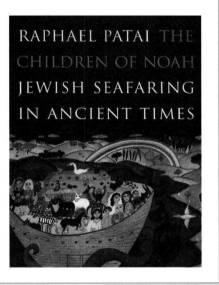

Richard Dawkins, *Unweaving the Rainbow: Science, Delusion, and the Appetite for Wonder,* a work that praises the poetic sense of wonder inherent in science and marvels at the human organism as a walking archive that embodies the history of its own paleolithic past.

Michel Morange (trans. Matthew Cobb), *A History of Molecular Biology,* an account of the development of genetic engineering, its connection to concepts drawn from molecular biology, and its indebtedness to biochemistry and genetics.

Jeremy Rifkin, *The Biotech Century: Harnessing the Gene and Remaking the World,* an evaluation of the potential benefits and hazards of the biotechnology revolution, whose value to the world is seen against the danger of domination by national or corporate self-interest.

Jon Turney, *Frankenstein's Footsteps: Science, Genetics and Popular Culture,* a history of stories that describe somewhat ambivalently what scientists do, speculating that cloning and DNA re-

The Archaeology of Human Bones
by Simon Mays

Mays, a human skeletal biologist, describes how archaeologists use evidence gleaned from the study of ancient human bones to reconstruct much about the life—and death—of some of Earth's early humans. What was life like for prehistoric people? What did they eat? What diseases afflicted them? How old were they when they died? Answers to these and other questions can be found through the study of early burial sites. Specialists in paleopathology and biology can determine from bones and teeth the age, sex, and height of early humans and can also gather evidence about family life and social practices from these ancient remains. Mays points out that the position and arrangement of bones in burial sites is one factor that indicates whether a body was cremated, embalmed, or simply put in the ground.

Radiocarbon dating and skull and bone measurements have helped archaeologists determine whether the anatom-

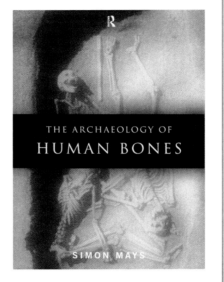

ical differences among these early humans are the result of the mingling of immigrant and native populations or are evolutionary or genetic developments. Both the microscope and the naked eye can disclose the marks of disease and injury and can sometimes even reveal the cause of death. Mays's reading and interpretation of what is written in ancient human bones and teeth help to shed light on the engrossing and enduring mystery of the human past.

search will inspire a growing rush of narratives about scientific "mischief."

Cathy Luchetti, *Medicine Women: The Story of Early-American Women Doctors,* a history of female physicians from their origins as midwives in colonial times to their establishment and acceptance as frontier doctors in the 19th century.

Douglas Starr, *Blood: An Epic History of Medicine and Commerce,* a history

of the magical, humanitarian, religious, medical, and commercial uses of blood.

C. James Goodwin, *A History of Modern Psychology* (1999), the evolution of psychology from its beginnings in 17th-century European philosophy to current developments in brain physiology, with chapter summaries and excerpts from numerous primary sources.

Noretta Koertge (ed.), *A House Built on Sand: Exposing Postmodernist Myths About Science,* collected essays on the value of cultural and social studies of science.

Michael Blay (trans. M.B. DeBevoise), *Reasoning with the Infinite: From the Closed World to the Mathematical Universe,* a view of mathematics as the language of science, reason, and the universe, explaining how calculus and the concept of infinity made celestial motions intelligible.

K.C. Cole, *The Universe and the Teacup: The Mathematics of Truth and Beauty,* a characterization of mathematics as a human creation, a way of thinking, and a way to attain truth, revealing how the work of Emmy Noether and Albert Einstein synthesized truth and beauty.

Paul Hoffman, *The Man Who Loved Only Numbers: The Odd Story of Paul Erdös and the Search for Mathematical Truth,* an admiring biography of one of the 20th century's most formidable mathematicians, an itinerant genius who never got the hang of tying his shoelaces or managing his money.

Edward O. Wilson, *Consilience: The Unity of Knowledge,* an argument that a united system of knowledge founded on basic natural laws governs the organization of the world and enables humans, building on the foundation of already-known fundamental principles, to investigate the unknown.

Wayne Biddle, *A Field Guide to the Invisible,* an omnium-gatherum whose organizing principle is invisibility to the naked eye.

—Jean S. Gottlieb

CONTRIBUTORS TO THE SCIENCE YEAR IN REVIEW

Richard A. Anthes
Earth Sciences: Atmospheric Sciences. President, University Corporation for Atmospheric Research, Boulder, Colo.

George F. Bertsch
Physics: Nuclear Physics. Professor of Physics, University of Washington, Seattle.

William A. Blanpied
Science Policy. Senior International Analyst, National Science Foundation, Washington, D.C.

Harold Borko
Electronics and Information Sciences: Computer Systems and Services. Professor Emeritus, University of California, Los Angeles.

John M. Bowen
Medical Sciences: Veterinary Medicine. Professor and Associate Dean Emeritus, College of Veterinary Medicine, University of Georgia.

Paul J. Campbell
Mathematics. Professor of Mathematics and Computer Science, Beloit (Wis.) College; Visiting Professor, University of Augsburg, Ger.

David L. Carlson
Anthropology. Associate Professor of Anthropology, Texas A & M University at College Station.

Kim Alan Chapman
Environment: Issues and Policy. Science Writer, Department of Conservation Biology, University of Minnesota.

David E. Collins
Materials Science and Engineering: Polymers. Graduate Research Assistant, School of Materials Engineering, Purdue University, West Lafayette, Ind.

Michael A. Covington
Electronics and Information Sciences: Electronics. Associate Director, Artificial Intelligence Center, University of Georgia, Athens.

Dave Dooling
Space Exploration. Owner, D^2 Associates, Huntsville, Ala.

Rolfe Erickson
Earth Sciences: Geology and Geochemistry. Professor of Geology, Sonoma State University, Rohnert Park, Calif.

David E. Farrell
Physics: Condensed-Matter Physics. Professor of Physics, Case Western Reserve University, Cleveland, Ohio.

Jean S. Gottlieb
Recent Books of Science. Freelance Writer and Editor; Historian of Science and Medicine; Bibliographer.

Robert Haselkorn
Life Sciences: Molecular Biology and Genetics. F.L. Pritzker Distinguished Service Professor, Department of Molecular Genetics and Cell Biology, University of Chicago.

Charles King Hoyt
Architectural and Civil Engineering. Principal, Charles King Hoyt Architect; Fellow, American Institute of Architects.

Matthew J. James
Earth Sciences: Paleontology. Paleontologist, Professor of Geology, Sonoma State University, Rohnert Park, Calif.

Lawrence W. Jones
Physics: Elementary-Particle Physics. Professor, Department of Physics, University of Michigan, Ann Arbor.

John Patrick Jordan
Food and Agriculture: Agriculture (in part). Director, Southern Regional Research Center, USDA-ARS, New Orleans.

Ronald H. Kaitchuck
Astronomy. Professor of Physics and Astronomy, Ball State University, Muncie, Ind.

Allan P. Katz
Materials Science and Engineering: Ceramics. Acting Chief, Ceramics Development and Materials Behavior Branch, Air Force Research Laboratory, Materials and Manufacturing Directorate, Wright-Patterson Air Force Base, Ohio.

George B. Kauffman
Chemistry: Applied Chemistry. Professor of Chemistry, California State University at Fresno.

Rebecca Kolberg
Medical Sciences: General Medicine. Editorial Supervisor, "Healthweek," PBS.

Matthew John M. Krane
Materials Science and Engineering: Metals. Assistant Professor of Materials Engineering, Purdue University, West Lafayette, Ind.

Patricia Brazeel Lewis
Food and Agriculture: Agriculture (in part). Public Relations Consultant, New Jersey Agricultural Experiment Station, Rutgers University, New Brunswick, N.J.

Charles Lydeard
Life Sciences: Zoology. Associate Professor of Biology, University of Alabama at Tuscaloosa.

John M. Mason
Transportation. Associate Dean of Graduate Studies and Research, College of Engineering, Pennsylvania State University.

Richard Monastersky
Earth Sciences: Oceanography. Earth Science Editor, *Science News,* Washington, D.C.

Charles S. Mueller
Earth Sciences: Geophysics. Geophysicist, U.S. Geological Survey, Golden, Colo.

Michael J. Pelczar, Jr.
Life Sciences: Botany (in part). Professor Emeritus and Emeritus Vice President for Graduate Studies and Research, University of Maryland, College Park.

Rita M. Pelczar
Life Sciences: Botany (in part). Horticulturalist.

Christopher Peterson
Psychology (in part). Professor of Psychology, University of Michigan, Ann Arbor.

Stuart L. Pimm
Life Sciences: Ecology. Professor of Ecology, University of Tennessee at Knoxville.

Marla Reicks
Food and Agriculture: Nutrition. Associate Professor, Department of Food Science and Nutrition, University of Minnesota at Minneapolis.

John Rhea
Defense Research. Washington Bureau Chief, *Military & Aerospace Electronics.*

C. Paul Robinson
Energy (in part). President and Laboratories Director, Sandia National Laboratories, Albuquerque, N.M.

Martin E.P. Seligman
Psychology (in part). Professor of Psychology, University of Pennsylvania; Past President, American Psychological Association.

Lawrence J. Shimkets
Life Sciences: Microbiology. Professor and Head of Microbiology, University of Georgia.

Ron Sims
Medical Sciences: Dentistry. Special Collections Librarian and Catalog Librarian, Galter Health Sciences Library, Northwestern University Dental and Medical Schools, Chicago.

Leslie Smith
Earth Sciences: Hydrology. Professor of Earth and Ocean Sciences, University of British Columbia.

Michael B. Smith
Chemistry: Organic Chemistry (in part). Professor, Department of Chemistry, University of Connecticut.

Ben P. Stein
Physics: Atomic, Molecular, and Optical Physics. Science Writer, American Institute of Physics, College Park, Md.

Robert E. Stoffels
Electronics and Information Sciences: Telecommunications Systems. Consultant, St. Petersburg, Fla.

Bud Ward
Environment: Environmental Technology. Executive Director, Environmental Health Center, National Safety Council, Washington, D.C.

Philip R. Watson
Chemistry: Physical Chemistry. Professor, Department of Chemistry, Oregon State University.

Stephanie A. Weiss
Electronics and Information Sciences: Photonics and Optical Technology. Executive Editor, *Photonics Spectra.*

James D. Wilde
Archaeology. Archaeologist, Headquarters, Air Force Center for Environmental Excellence, Brooks Air Force Base, San Antonio, Texas.

Charles H. Winter
Chemistry: Inorganic Chemistry. Professor, Department of Chemistry, Wayne State University, Detroit.

Alexander Wolfe
Electronics and Information Sciences: Computers and Computer Science. Managing Editor, Computers and Communications, *EE Times.*

Joan B. Woodard
Energy (in part). Vice President, Energy, Environment, and Information Technology Division, Sandia National Laboratories, Albuquerque, N.M.

Michael Woods
Chemistry: Organic Chemistry (in part); *Scientists of the Year: Nobel Prizes.* Science Editor, Washington Bureau, *Toledo* (Ohio) *Blade* and *Pittsburgh* (Pa.) *Post Gazette.*

INDEX

This is a three-year cumulative index. Index entries for review articles in this and previous editions of the *Yearbook of Science and the Future* are set in boldface type, *e.g.,* **Astronomy.** Feature articles appear under the article title and are identified as such. Entries to other subjects are set in lightface type, *e.g.,* radiation. Additional information on any of these subjects is identified with a subheading and indented under the entry heading. Subheadings in quotes refer to the feature articles on that topic. The numbers following headings and subheadings indicate the year (boldface) of the edition and the page number (lightface) on which the information appears. The abbreviation "*il.*" indicates an illustration.

Astronomy 00–233; **99**–250; **98**–252
 Galileo **00**–27
 gamma-ray bursts **99**–393
 "In the Realm of the Giant" **98**–28

All entry headings are alphabetized word by word. Hyphenated words and words separated by dashes or slashes are treated as two words. When one word differs from another only by the presence of additional characters at the end, the shorter precedes the longer. In inverted names, the words following the comma are considered only after the preceding part of the name has been alphabetized. Names beginning with "Mc" and "Mac" are alphabetized as "Mac"; "St." is alphabetized as "Saint." Examples:

 Lake
 Lake, Simon
 Lake Placid
 Lakeland

replication / Seilacher

replication, bacterial DNA **00**–326
reporter protein **99**–333
reporting: *see* media; news reporting
repression (psychol.) **99**–377
reproduction **00**–217, 349
bacteria **99**–331
dinosaurs **00**–272
environmental pollution effect **98**–112
general medicine **99**–350
population genetics **00**–320, *il.*
zoology **00**–330, *ils.* 330, 331
see also birth control; pregnancy
Reproductive Biology Associates (Atlanta, Ga., U.S.) **99**–351
Republican Party (pol. party, U.S.)
U.S. science policy **98**–381
repulsive force (astronomical) **00**–238
requirements model **00**–99
Rescher, Nicholas **00**–128
research and development **98**–233
bad science **00**–28
benefits **00**–37
bioremediation **98**–124
defense research, United States **99**–268; **98**–269
dentistry **99**–357
energy **99**–306
future **00**–128
information systems **99**–301; **98**–299
international science policy **99**–378; **98**–375
medical sciences **99**–350
nutrition **99**–321
obesity **98**–317
oceanography **99**–286
psychology **98**–372
science policy **00**–376
synchrotron radiation **98**–93
technological innovations **98**–78
reserves: *see* nature reserves
reservoir, Maya people **00**–20, *il.*
resistance to antibiotics **99**–332
respect, Japan **00**–187
response regulator, genome sequencing **99**–337
Retallack, Gregory **98**–289
reverse transcriptase, AIDS research **98**–261
reward (behavior), psychology **98**–370
Rezaei, Mohammad **00**–246
rf radiation: *see* radio-frequency radiation
Rhapsody (operating system), Macintosh computers **98**–294
rhenium, carbon chains **98**–260
rhenium-C_5H_{10} compound **00**–242
rhesus monkey, sleep patterns **98**–48, *il.*
rhinoceros, poaching **00**–65, *il.* 66
Rhizoctonia sp. (fungi) **00**–315
Rhizoium sp. (bacterium) **00**–315
rhizosphere, *or* root zone, phytoremediation **98**–131
rhodium, fluorocarbon solvents **99**–257
ribonucleic acid: *see* RNA
rice, global trade **00**–305
"Rice to Feed the Hungry" (feature article) **98**–170
Richards, Paul **98**–281
Richardson, Robert C. **98**–400, *il.* 401
Rickettsia prowazekii (bacterium) **00**–323, *il.* 324
ridge push, plate tectonics **98**–278
Right Livelihood Awards **00**–301; **99**–314
RIKEN: *see* Physical and Chemical Research, Institute of
ring system, Jupiter **00**–234, *il.*
ring-laser gyroscope, optics technology **99**–294
Rio Treaty of 1992 **00**–148
Rischel, Christian **99**–262
Rise Technology Co. (U.S.) **00**–283
ritonavir, *or* Norvir, AIDS treatment **98**–261, 343
river floodplain, floodwater source **99**–281
Rivera, Robert **00**–306
rivers and streams
arsenic concentrations **00**–266
civil engineering **00**–232
"Going with the Flow" (feature article) **99**–27
pollution, GPS technology **00**–88
probability model **98**–283
wild rivers **99**–329
RMSEL: *see* Robotic Manufacturing Science and Engineering Laboratory
RNA, *or* ribonucleic acid, molecular biology **99**–334; **98**–327
roads and highways
civil engineering **00**–232; **98**–251
GPS technology **00**–86, *il.*
transportation **00**–396; **99**–399; **98**–393, 398
Robbins algebra **98**–339
Robert Englekirk Consulting Structural Engineers (U.S. co.) **99**–246
Roberts, Paul **98**–281
Robertson, Leslie E. **99**–249
pedestrian bridge **99**–249, *il.*
Robida, Albert **98**–60, *il.* 62
Robinson, Gregory H. **99**–258
Robotic Manufacturing Science and Engineering Laboratory, *or* RMSEL (Albuquerque, N.Mex., U.S.), robotic research and development **98**–154
robotics, *or* robots
Disney creations **00**–101
future applications **00**–135
research and development **98**–153
spacecraft **99**–389
"Robots on the Move" (feature article) **98**–153
rock art **98**–244
Rocket Rod (Disney attraction), computer modeling **00**–100
rockets and rocketry
Apollo Applications **00**–46, 47, *il.* 46
futures research **98**–68
International Space Station **00**–52, 55
launch vehicles **00**–392, *il.*
rockfall (geol.) **98**–280
"rockoon" (launch vehicle, U.S.) **00**–393
Rockwell, Norman **00**–286
Rockwell International Corp. (U.S.), corporate acquisition **98**–269
Rodale Institute, organic farming **00**–306, *il.* 307
Rodbell, Martin (obit.) **00**–412
Rodriguez-Iturbe, Ignacio **00**–267
Roman Catholic Church, scientific heresy **00**–27
Roman people
dentistry **00**–353, *il.*
lead pollution **00**–259
Röntgen, Wilhelm Conrad **98**–89
Roosevelt, Anna **98**–246
root canal (dentistry) **98**–351
root zone: *see* rhizosphere
Rosenberg, Karen R., "The Secret Life of Neanderthals" **98**–135
Rosenberg, Nathan, "The Perils of Technological Forecasting" **98**–73
Roslin Institute (Scotland) **99**–317, 350
Rosman, Kevin J. **00**–259
Rossi, Aldo (obit.) **99**–413
Roswell (N.Mex., U.S.), alien conspiracy **98**–236
RotaShield (vaccine) **00**–347
rotavirus **00**–347
Rothman, Daniel H. **98**–288
"Roton" (spacecraft) **00**–392
rotor-shaped molecules: *see* molecular rotors
roundworm, *or Caenorhabditis elegans*, gene sequencing **00**–215, 329, 331, *il.* 332
Rousse, Antoine **99**–262
Rowley, Janet **00**–351
Roy, S.K. **00**–311
Royal Society of Chemistry (U.K.)
electronic database **99**–301
Industrial Innovation Team Award **00**–250
Royal Society of London, Leeuwenhoek papers **00**–196
RSN: *see* Russian Scientific News
RSP: *see* Reference Service Press
Ruapehu, Mt. (volcano, N.Z.) **98**–280
Ruderman, Malvin A. **00**–236
Rudolph, Paul (obit.) **99**–413
ruins, Maya people **00**–10, *il.*
Russell, R.M. **00**–312
Russia
food and agriculture **98**–312
fusion energy **00**–213
public lands **00**–148
radio navigation systems **00**–80
research funding **99**–380; **98**–375
RSN database **00**–288
satellite technology **99**–395; **98**–272
space program **00**–42, 51, 383, *il.* 50
exploration **99**–386; **98**–384
launch vehicles **00**–393
satellites **00**–90, 391
Russian Foundation for Basic Research **99**–380
Russian Scientific News, *or* RSN (database) **00**–288
Rutgers University (New Jersey, U.S.) **98**–313
ruthenium compounds **00**–240, 248
ruthenium-H_2 compounds **00**–240
Rüttgers, Jürgen **99**–379, *il.*
Rydberg state **98**–360

S

Sabloff, Jeremy A. **00**–16, 22
Saccharomyces cerevisiae: see yeast
Sacks, F.M. **00**–311
sacred lotus, *or* Nelumbo nucifera, botany **98**–318, *il.*
sacrifice: *see* human sacrifice
SAE: *see* Automotive Engineers, Society of
safety: *see* accident and safety
safety razor technology **00**–123
Sagan, Carl Edward **00**–28, 37; **99**–255
Gould's editorial **99**–386
obituary **98**–415
SAGE: *see* Selected Archives of Georgia Tech and Emory
Sager, Ruth (obit.) **99**–414
Sahagún, Father Bernardino de **00**–162, *il.*
Sahara Desert, paleontology **00**–272, *il.* 271
sailing, celestial navigation **00**–78, *ils.* 78, 79
"Saint-François" (ship) **98**–245
Salam, Abdus (obit.) **98**–416, *il.*
salinity, extremophiles **98**–17
Salisbury, Lord (Britain) **00**–179, *il.*
salt, solar power **00**–293
salt bridge **98**–19
Salt Lake City (Utah, U.S.), transportation system **00**–395, 399
Salt River (U.S.), arsenic contamination **00**–266
"Salyut" space stations **00**–48
Sambucus: see elder pith
San Antonio (Texas, U.S.), transportation system **00**–394
San Diego (Calif., U.S.), endangered species preservation **99**–313
San Francisco Bay, bridge **00**–232, 396
Sandia National Laboratories, *or* SNL, microelectromechanical systems **00**–297, *il.*
solar power plant **00**–293
U.S. science policy **98**–70, *il.*
sandstone **98**–102
geologic sciences **00**–258
paleontology **00**–271
Sandved, Kjell B., "Wonders on the Wing" **98**–186
sanitation systems
global warming effects **00**–167
Walt Disney Company **00**–109, *il.* 110
saquinavir, *or* Invirase, AIDS treatment **98**–261
Sarnoff, David **00**–127; **98**–83
Saskatchewan walls **00**–304
satellite imagery **00**–390
archaeology **00**–18, 20, *il.* 18
atmospheric sciences **00**–256
oceanography **00**–269
"Satellite Probatoire d'Observation de la Terre," *or* SPOT (France) **00**–390
Satellites and satellite systems 00–390
atmospheric sciences **99**–274
cost and longevity **00**–61
defense research **99**–270; **98**–272
Global Navigation Satellite System **00**–90, 91, 258
GPS: *see* Global Positioning System
imagery: *see* satellite imagery
lunar effects **00**–386
microgravity **00**–58
oceanography **99**–285
original launch **00**–45
space exploration **99**–394; **98**–385, 389
technological innovations **98**–85
telecommunications **00**–91, 290, *il.* 291; **99**–303; **98**–302
Tracking and Data Relay System **00**–55
see also space probes; individual satellites by name
Sato, Hazuhiko **00**–243
Saturn
astronomy **00**–234
space exploration **98**–389
space probe **00**–388
Saturn 5 (rocket) **00**–46, *il.*
spending cuts **00**–47
Saul, Frank **00**–23
Saul, Julie **00**–23
sauropod dinosaurs **00**–272
saw palmetto extract **00**–310
SBC Communications, *or* Southwestern Bell (U.S. co.) **99**–302
scandium trifluoromethane sulfonate **00**–244
Scannapieco, Frank **00**–352
scanning technology **00**–276
scanning tunneling microscope, *or* STM **00**–245
molecular pencil **00**–369, *il.* 368
SCATS: *see* Sydney Coordinated Adaptive Traffic System
scatterometer, weather information gathering **98**–273
Schaie, K. Warner **98**–371
Schele, Linda **00**–21
Schistosoma mansoni (parasitic worm) **00**–301
Schmidt, Brian **00**–237
Schneewind, Olaf **99**–333
Schneider, Glenn **00**–235
Schneider, Mycle **99**–314
scholarly journal, electronic information **98**–300
Scholes, Myron S. **99**–347
schools
telephones **00**–186, *il.* 187
see also education
Schools Adopt Monuments (Eur. educ. project) **98**–299
Schopf, William **98**–288
Schorah, C.J. **00**–312
Schramm, David Norman (obit.) **99**–414
Schreger lines (ivory) **00**–73, *il.*
Schriever Air Force Base **00**–82
Schrock, Richard R. **00**–244
Schultz, P.H. **00**–258
Schwarz, Norman **00**–373
Schwarzschild, Martin (obit.) **99**–414
Schweigart, Joseph A. **00**–232
science
"Bad Science" (feature article) **00**–26
future technologies: *see* millennium projections
see also scientific method
"Science, Jews, and Secular Culture: Studies in Mid-Twentieth-Century American Intellectual History" (Hollinger) **98**–238
"Science: The Endless Frontier" **00**–305, 381
"Science" (U.S. journal), environmental issues **99**–313
"Science and Engineering Indicators-1996" (U.S. report) **98**–383
Science and Technology Basic Plan, Japanese research **99**–380; **98**–376
Science and Technology Initiative, *or* STI, defense research **99**–269
Science and Technology Policy, Office of, *or* OSTP **00**–380, 382
"Science Behind the Magic: Research and Development at Disney, The" (feature article) **00**–92
science fiction, accuracy **00**–30, *il.*
"Science for the Soldier: The U.S. Army's Natick Labs" (feature article) **99**–167
"Science on Trial: The Clash of Medical Evidence and the Law in the Breast Implant Case" (Angell) **98**–238
Science overview 00–212; **99**–231; **98**–233
Science policy 00–376; **99**–378; **98**–375
see also United States science policy
science quiz **00**–38
Science Watch, Inc., pro-science voting **98**–381
Scientific Investigation of Claims of the Paranormal, Committee for the **98**–237
scientific method
critical thinking **00**–28
industrial ecology **00**–155
Scientists of the year 00–401; **99**–403; **98**–399
Sci-Fi Channel (TV), scientific accuracy **00**–34
S-class asteroid, "Galileo" project **98**–31
Scott, Foresman & Co. (U.S.) **99**–300
Scott, John M. **99**–323
Scott, Matthew **00**–348, *il.*
Scotti, James V. **00**–233
Scottish Office, Web site **00**–287
scrap iron, recycled **00**–338, *il.*
scrap metal **99**–344
scrapie test **00**–354, *il.* 355
screw-barrel microscope **00**–198
Scripps Institution of Oceanography, earliest life **98**–288
sculpture, ancient Maya **00**–15, *ils.* 11, 21
SDTV: *see* standard-definition television
sea crossings, archaeology **00**–226
sea ice, Antarctic decline **99**–284
Sea Launch system (U.S.) **00**–392, *il.*; **99**–396
sea level
geologic sciences **98**–276
carbon dating **99**–277
rate increase **98**–287
sea lion, environmental pollution **98**–115, *il.* 118
"Sea Squirt" (robotic vessel) **98**–160
seabed mining **99**–285
seaborgium, *or* Sg, chemical nomenclature dispute **98**–366
seafloor: *see* ocean floor
seal, pollution effect **98**–119
sealant, dentistry **99**–358
"Sealed Corridor" (r.r. safety project) **99**–400
sea-surface temperature
effect on rivers **98**–283, *il.*
El Niño **99**–283
Seattle (Washington, U.S.)
landscape architecture **99**–247
transportation system **00**–394
Sea-Viewing Wide Field-of-View Sensor, *or* SeaWifs, satellite technology **99**–395
seawater, biochemical reactions **98**–258
SeaWifs: *see* Sea-Viewing Wide Field-of-View Sensor
secondhand smoke **99**–354
security, voting systems **00**–122
sedimentary rock
geologic sciences **00**–258
paleontology **00**–271
sedimentation, *or* deposition
geologic sciences **98**–276
mass-extinction theory **99**–276
river hydrology **00**–266
see also sandstone
SED-Sat-1 (satellite, U.S.) **00**–391
Seed, Richard **99**–233, 350
Seidel, Günter **00**–244
Seilacher, Adolf **00**–271

ILLUSTRATION ACKNOWLEDGMENTS

17 Chris Higgins/Proof Positive/Farrowlyne Associates, Inc.
36, 39 Precision Graphics
42–43 Chris Higgins/Proof Positive/Farrowlyne Associates, Inc.
56–57 Precision Graphics. *Source:* NASA
62–63 Tom Curry/Conrad Represents
73 Dartmouth Publishing, Inc. Inset art by Precision Graphics. *Source:* NFWFL (National Fish and Wildlife Forensics Laboratory)
81, 82, 83 (top, bottom), 84 Precision Graphics
83 (top) *Source:* The Aerospace Corporation

84 *Source:* Smithsonian Institution
130–131, 137–141, 143 Geoff Smith/Scott Hull Associates Inc.
152 Dartmouth Publishing, Inc. *Source:* Intergovernmental Panel on Climate Change
154, 155, 158 Dartmouth Publishing, Inc.
244 Sandra McMahon/McMahon Medical Art
239 (top, bottom), 244–245, 246 (left, right) Dartmouth Publishing, Inc.
261 Dartmouth Publishing, Inc. *Source:* *Geotimes,* August 1998, Shaopeng Huang and Henry Pollack
320 Ortelius Design

322, 323 Sandra McMahon/McMahon Medical Art
328 Precision Graphics
339 Dartmouth Publishing, Inc. *Source:* http://www.guenthernet.com/holo/physics.html
341 Chris Higgins/Proof Positive/Farrowlyne Associates, Inc.
342 *Source: Science News,* vol. 154, August 24, 1998
366 Dartmouth Publishing, Inc. *Source: Science,* vol. 277, July 11, 1997
367 Dartmouth Publishing, Inc.